G000055637

THE IRISH FOOD GUIDE

The Irish Food Guide

JOHN McKENNA & SALLY McKENNA

WITH CAROLINE BYRNE

Estragon Press

FIRST PUBLISHED IN 2012

BY ESTRAGON PRESS

DURRUS

COUNTY CORK

ISBN 978-1-906927-12-7

PRINTED IN SPAIN BY GRAPHYCEMS

• Front cover photos: top left, Barron's Bakery, Cappoquin; top right and middle left, Avoca, Rathcoole; middle right and bottom, Ard Bia, Galway. Ard Bia photos by www.jamesfennell.com

WRITTEN BY JOHN McKENNA

Dublin chapter written by

CAROLINE BYRNE

with contributions from our editors

Contributing editors

EAMON BARRETT

WILLIAM BARRY

CAROLINE BYRNE

AOIFE COX

CLAIRE GOODWILLIE

CONNIE McKENNA

JOE McNAMEE

LESLIE WILLIAMS

Publisher

SALLY McKENNA

Copy editor: JUDITH CASEY

EDITORIAL ASSISTANTS: EVE CLANCY, MEGAN CLANCY

Web: FLUIDEDGE.IE

Apps: DAVORKA NALETILIC & GARY QUINN

For

COLM CONYNGHAM

THE AUTHORS WOULD LIKE TO THANK

Grainne Byrne, Sile Ginnane & Conor Cahill,

George Lane, Frank McKevitt, Edwina Murray,

Ernie Whalley, Sam and PJ McKenna,

Hugh Stancliffe, John Masterson, Mary Tallent,

Chris Carroll, Paul Neilan and all the team

at Gill & MacMillan

How to Use This Book

The Irish Food Guide is arranged alphabetically, by county so it begins with County Carlow, which is followed by County Cavan, and so on.

Within the counties the towns are once again listed alphabetically.

Northern Ireland is listed at the end of the book as a separate entity. Note that this is a sterling currency area, though the euro is often accepted, particularly in the border areas.

Many of the places featured in this book are only open during the summer season, which means that they can be closed for any given length of time between October and March. Many others change their opening times during winter. It is always advisable to check the website or telephone in advance if you are using this book in the countryside, out of season.

Finally, we greatly appreciate receiving e-mails with suggestions and criticisms from readers, and would like to thank those who have written in the past, whose opinions are of enormous assistance to us when considering which people, places and products finally make it into this book.

Send feedback to:

www.guides.ie

Introduction

"This is a book about good food". That was how we began the introduction to the very first *Irish Food Guide*, written and published back in 1989. This tenth edition is no different: once again, this is a book about good food.

• Happily, the number of people producing this good food throughout Ireland has grown exponentially. The 1989 *Irish Food Guide* had 250 pages of the good stuff, whilst this tenth edition has more than 700 pages of the good stuff. Whatever way you look at it, Irish food artisanship has triumphed, and this book is the proof – the delicious proof – of the triumph.

• After all the work of researching and writing a book as large as this, one of the great pleasures is to dissect the trends that lie underneath the myriad entries. In 2012, the most dynamic trends seem to us to be occurring in three exciting strands.

• First of all, craft brewing has hit the country like a tornado. From way up north to way down south, Ireland's craft brewers have found an appreciative audience for their wonderful ales, stouts and beers. The speed with which new beers have found a market is virtually unparalleled in our experience. Ireland, it seems, was thirsty. Who knew?

• Another dynamo has been the growth in artisans rearing rare-breed pork – the Irish Grazer is back in the ascendant, and good pork and bacon is more plentiful than ever.

• The third whirlwind has been in the field of sourdough bread baking. Sourdough is the high-wire act of baking, and it is heartening to see dedicated, devoted bakers allying themselves to this complex and passionate profession.

• But sourdoughs, ales and pigs are merely the new tips of a now-mighty movement of artisans in Ireland. There are many new producers in this book who have become involved with food having lost their jobs in the mainstream commercial marketplace as Ireland's economy melted away. Other entries have been in the Irish Food Guide ever since that first edition, way back in 1989. Today, speciality food is the most successful part of our national economy. Food is what we do, brilliantly. We are, indeed, Ireland: The Food Island.

• The significant aspect of this success story is the fact that the artisans have triumphed largely on their own. Stubborn, creative and imaginative, they display all the merits of individually-produced and locally-made food. Whilst mainstream farming in Ireland remains a problem zone – what are we to do about the middle farms? the price of milk? the price of beef? – artisans are out there in the markets, having the craic, making a living, delighting their customers, getting better and better every year. The future is theirs.

John and Sally McKenna
Durrus, County Cork 2012

County Carlow 21

Bagenalstown 21; Ballon 22; Borris 23; Carlow 23; Clonegal 24; Fenagh 25; Leighlinbridge 25; St Mullins 26; Tullow 26

County Cavan 27

Belturbet 27; Blacklion 27; Cavan 28; Cloverhill 29; Cootehill 29; Killeshandra 30; Stradone 30

County Clare 31

Ballina 31; Ballynacally 31; Ballyvaughan 32; Bunratty 34; Carrigaholt 35; Carron 35; Cratloe 36; Doolin 36; Doonbeg 38; Ennis 39; Ennistymon 42; Fanore 43; Inagh 43; Kilfenora 44; Kilkee 44; Kilkishen 46; Killaloe 46; Kilnaboy 47; Kilrush 47; Lahinch 48; Liscannor 49; Lisdoonvarna 50; Mount Shannon 51; New Quay 52; Quilty 53; Tuamgraney 53

County Cork 54

Cork City Centre 54; Ballincollig 76; Ballygarvan 77; Ballypheane 77; Blackrock 78; Blarney 79; Carrigaline 79; Cork City Centre 54; Cork City suburbs 76; Crosshaven 80; Douglas 81; Rochestown 82; North Cork 83; Ballyhoura 83; Ballyvourney 83; Blarney 83; Buttevant 84; Castlelyons 85; Castletownroche 85; Charleville 85; Coolea 86; Fermoy 86; Kanturk 87; Kilavullen 88; Macroom 89; Mallow 89; Mitchelstown 91; Newmarket 92; Ovens 93; Rathcormac 93; Watergrasshill 94; Whitechurch 94; East Cork 95;Aghada 95; Ballincurrig 95; Ballycotton 95; Carrigtwohill 96; Castlemartyr 97; Cloyne 97; Cobh 98; Ladysbridge 99; Midleton 99; Shanagarry 103; Youghal 106; West Cork 108; The Peninsulas (Beara, Schull, Sheep's Head) 108; Adrigole 108; Ahakista 108; Ardgroom 108; Ballydehob 109; Bantry 110; Cahermore 116; Castletownbere 117; Durrus 118; Eyeries 120; Garinish 121; Schull 122; The West 125; Ballinadee 125; Ballineen 126;

Ballinhassig 126; Ballinspittle 126; Ballyherkin 128; Baltimore 128; Bandon 129; Belgooly 132; Castletownshend 132; Clonakilty 133; Connonagh 137; Crookhaven 137; Drimoleague 138; Dunmanway 139; Enniskeane 140; Glandore 141; Goleen 141; Gougane Barra 142; Inishannon 142; Kilbrittain 142; Kinsale 143; Riverstick 147; Rosscarbery 147; Skibbereen 148; Timoleague 153; Union Hall 154

County Donegal 155

Ardara 155; Bridgend 155; Buncrana 156; Burtonport 157; Carndonagh 158; Culdaff 158; Clonmany 159; Donegal 159; Dunfanaghy 162; Dunkineely 163; Fahan 163; Glenties 164; Glenveagh 164; Greencastle 165; Letterkenny 165; Malin Head 166; Mountcharles 166; Moville 167; Ramelton 167; Raphoe 167; Rathmullan 168

County Dublin 172

Dublin City Centre 172; North Dublin 233; Dublin 3: (Clontarf, Fairview, North Strand) 233; Dublin 5: (Raheny) 236; Dublin 7: (Smithfield, Stoneybatter) 238; Dublin 9: (Drumcondra, Glasnevin) 243; Dublin 11: (Finglas, Glasnevin) 244; Dublin 15: (Ballycoolin) 246 North County Dublin 247; Howth 247; Lusk 252; Malahide 253; Naul 254; Oldtown 255; Portmarnock 255; Skerries 256; Swords 257; The Ward 258; South Dublin 259; Dublin 4: (Ballsbridge, Donnybrook, Sandymount) 259; Dublin 6: (Ranelagh, Rathmines, Rathgar, Terenure) 269; Dublin 8: (Harold's Cross, Liberties, Crumlin, Portobello, Rialto) 282; Dublin 12 & 14: (Churchtown, Dundrum, Rathfarnham) 287; Dublin 18: (Foxrock, Sandyford, Stepaside) 289; South County Dublin 292; Blackrock 292; Dalkey 293; Dun Laoghaire 296; Glasthule 299; Goatstown 300; Killiney 300; Leopardstown 301; Monkstown 301; Mount Merrion 303; Newcastle 304; Rathcoole 304; Stillorgan 305; Tallaght 306

County Galway 315

Galway City 315; Galway County 336; Aran Islands 336; Athenry 338; Ballinafad 339; Ballinasloe 340; Ballyconneely 341; Bearna 341; Claregalway 343; Clarinbridge 343; Cleggan 344; Clifden 344; Corrandulla 347; Furbo 347; Gort 348; Inis Meáin 336; Inis Mór 336; Inis Oirr 337; Kilcolgan 349; Kinvara 349; Leenane 350; Letterfrack 351; Loughrea 352; Moycullen 352; Oranmore 354; Oughterard 355; Recess 356; Roscahill 356; Rossaveal 356; Roundstone 357; Salthill 357; Spiddal 359

County Kerry 360

Annascaul 360; Ballinskelligs 360; Ballybunion 361; Blackwater 362; Bonane 362; Caherdaniel 362; Cahersiveen 363; Castlecove 366; Castlegregory 366; Castlemaine 367; Cromane 368; Dingle 368; Kenmare 374; Killarney 380; Killorglin 385; Listowel 387; Milltown 388; Portmagee 389; Sneem 390; Tralee 390; Tuosist 393; Valentia 394

County Kildare 395

Allenwood 395; Athy 395; Ballymore Eustace 396; Ballysax 397; Carbury 397; Castledermot 398; Clane 398; Kilcullen 398; Kildare 400; Maynooth 401; Naas 402; Newbridge 405

County Kilkenny 406

Bennettsbridge 406; Callan 406; Castlecomer 406; Cramer's Grove 407; Cuffesgrange 407; Gathabawn 408; Gowran 409; Graiguenamanagh 409; Inistioge 410; Kilkenny 411; Kilmacow 417; Lavistown 417; Piltown 418; Shellumsrath 419; Stoneyford 419; Thomastown 420; Tullaroan 422; Urlingford 423

Contents

County Laois 424

Abbeyleix 424; Ballacolla 425; Ballickmoyler 425
Ballyfin 425; Killenard 426; Mountrath 426; Portlaoise 427; Rathdowney 428; Stradbally 428

County Leitrim 430

Carrick-on-Shannon 430; Dromahair 431; Dromod 432; Drumshanbo 432; Jamestown 433; Kinlough 433; Rossinver 434

County Limerick 435

Adare 435; Annacotty 436; Ballingarry 437; Drumcollogher 438; Hospital 439; Kilcornan 439; Killonan 440; Limerick City 440; Newcastle West 452

County Longford 453

Aughnacliffe 453; Longford 453

County Louth 456

Annagassan 456; Ardee 456; Blackrock 457; Carlingford Peninsula 457; Castlebellingham 460; Drogheda 460; Dundalk 463; Dunleer 465; Termonfeckin 465

County Mayo 466

Achill 466; Ballina 468; Ballycastle 471; Castlebar 471; Claremorris 473; Cong 473; Louisburgh 474; Mulranny 474; Newport 475; Westport 476

County Meath 483

Ashbourne 483; Athboy 485; Ballivor 485; Carnaross 485; Kells 487; Laytown 489; Navan 489; Ratoath 490; Slane 491; Stamullen 492; Tara 493

County Monaghan 495

Ballybay 495; Carrickmacross 495; Clones 496; Clontibret 496; Emyvale 496

County Offaly 498

Ballinahown 498; Banagher 498; Birr 498; Cloghan 500; Coolnagrower 501; Killeigh 501; Portarlington 501; Tullamore 502

County Roscommon 504

Athlone 504; Boyle 504; Castlemine 504; Roscommon 505

County Sligo 508

Ballymote 508; Castlebaldwin 508; Collooney 508; Grange 509; Rathlee 509; Riverstown 510; Sligo 510; Strandhill 515

County Tipperary 516

Ballymacarbry 516; Borrisokane 516; Cahir 517; Carrick-on-Suir 518; Cashel 519; Clogheen 521; Clonmel 522; Cloughjordan 525; Emly 527; Fethard 527; Golden 527; Kilgarvan Quay 528; Lorragh 529; Nenagh 529; Roscrea 534; Templemore 534; Terryglass 535; Thurles 535; Tipperary Town 538

County Waterford 539

Ardmore 539; Ballyduff 540; Ballymacarbry 540; Butlerstown 541; Cappoquin 541; Dungarvan 543; Dunhill 546; Dunmore East 547; Fenor 548 Ferrybank 549; Kilmacthomas 549; Knockanore 550; Lemybrien 550; Lismore 551; Portlaw 552; Tramore 552; Waterford 553

County Westmeath 562

Athlone 562; Colinstown 563; Glasson 564; Kilbeggan 565; Mullingar 565

County Wexford 569

Arthurstown 569; Bridgestown 569; Broadway 569; Bunclody 570; Carne 570; Duncannon 571; Enniscorthy 571; Ferns 573; Gorey 574; Kerlogue 575; Kilmore Quay 576; New Ross 577; Rosslare 578; Saltmills 579; Wexford 579; Yoletown 581

Contents

County Wicklow 583

Arklow 583; Ashford 584; Aughrim 585; Baltinglass 586; Blessigton 586; Bray 587; Delgany 590; Donard 590; Enniskerry 591; Glenealy 592; Greystones 592; Kilcoole 596; Kilmacanogue 596; Kiltegan 597; Kilternan 598; Macreddin 598; Newcastle 600; Newtownmountkennedy 601; Rathdrum 601; Roundwood 602; Tullow 602; Wicklow 603

Northern Ireland 606

Belfast 606; Country Antrim 626; Annaghmore 626; Ballyclare 626; Ballymena 627; Ballyrobert 628; Bushmills 628; Galgorm 629; Glenarm 630; Glengormley 630; Lisburn 630; Portrush 632; County Armagh 633; Armagh 633; Craigavon 633; Forkhill 634; Lurgan 634; Portadown 635; Tandragee 636. County Down 638; Annalong 638; Ardglass638; Ballynahinch 639; Banbridge 639; Bangor 640; Comber 643; Crossgar 644; Donaghadee 644; Downpatrick 646; Dromara 647; Dromore 647; Dundrum 648; Greyabbey 649; Groomsport 650; Helen's Bay 650; Hillsborough 651; Holywood 652; Kearney 655; Kilkeel 655; Killinchy 656; Killyleagh 657; Kircubbin 658; Lisbane 658; Moira 659; Newcastle 659; Newry 660; Newtownards 660; Portaferry 662; Saintfield 663; Strangford 663; Warrenpoint 664 County Fermanagh 665; Derrygonnelly 665; Derrylin 665; Enniskillen 666; Irvinestown 667; Lisbellaw 667; Lisnaskea 668 County Londonderry 669; Ballykelly 669; Castledawson 669; Claudy 669; Coleraine 670; Desertmartin 671; Limavady 671; Londonderry 673; Maghera 676; Magherafelt 676; Portstewart 677 County Tyrone 678; Donaghmore 678; Dungannon 678; Fivemiletown 679; Moygashel 679; Omagh 680; Strabane 680

County Carlow

Bagenalstown

Brewery

● Carlow Brewing Company

The story of the CBC is one of the great success stories of Irish speciality food. When Seamus and Eamon O'Hara first set up their company in 1996, getting the first brew out in 1998, the omens were inauspicious for a little craft brewery in rural Ireland. Fifteen years on, they have triumphed against all the odds, simply by doing what they do as superbly as they do it, and then by gradually upscaling, steadily adding new brews – there are now five in total – and always minding the quality. Their scale today, their export success, is almost phantasmagoric: can this huge operation be real?! But real it is, as real as the beers – Curim, O'Hara's Stout; Pale Ale, Leann Follain, Irish Red – all of them delicious, refreshing, and distinct. Keep your eyes peeled for their seasonal brews, when the holiday seasons roll around. (Seamus & Eamon O'Hara, Muine Bheag Business Park, Royal Oak Road, Bagenalstown ☎ 059-972 0509 info@ carlowbrewing. com www. carlowbrewing. com)

Country House

● Kilgraney House

Bryan Leech and Martin Marley are artists of the country life. Kilgraney is their canvas, and they adorn it with the colour of Seurat and the confidence of Matisse. It is one of the great country houses, and Bryan and Martin make it better every year, their stewardship of the house and grounds seeing them planting orchards, creating galleries, harvesting honey, cooking delicious food, fashioning the most glorious space and ambience, creating a place where country living is simply an art. (Bryan Leech & Martin Marley, Bagenalstown ☎ 059-977 5283 info@kilgraneyhouse.com www. kilgraneyhouse.com – Open Mar-Nov, Wed-Sun)

Country House

● Lorum Old Rectory

Bobbie Smith's handsome 19th-century rectory is the very essence of the venerable Irish county house – formal; imposing; grand; polished; manorial. But its formality is offset by Mrs Smith's grace and warmth as an hostess, and the combination is utterly winning. (Bobbie Smith, Bagenalstown ☎ 059-977 5282 bobbie@lorum.com www.lorum.com – Open 1 Feb-30 Nov)

Ballon

Free Range Eggs

● Ballon Free Range Eggs

Mary and Pat's happy hens produce the eggs that are the choice of all the smart cooks in Carlow.
(Mary Gittens, Ballon ☎ 086-169 8691)

Coffee Shop

● The Forge Craft & Coffee Shop

Set just a step down from the road, Mary Jordan's pretty, stone-built coffee shop has been a vital fixture for more than a decade. It's genial, and genuine, and a most welcoming place for simple, calming cooking, using ingredients that are sourced as close to home as you can imagine – Carlow chicken; Ballon beef; Kilbride crumble – proper unpretentious food that has been made with care. A real little sweetie. (Mary Jordan, Kilbride Cross, Ballon ☎ 059-915 9939 theforgekilbride@gmail.com – Open 9.30am-5.30pm Mon-Sun)

made in Carlow

O'Hara's Stout

Fruits & Preserves

● Malone Fruit Farm

Tom and Elizabeth's strawberry business has multiplied from two acres to 12 acres, and in addition to soft fruits they make a lovely range of preserves, available in good local shops, at their own farm shop, and at the Saturday Carlow market. (Tom & Elizabeth Malone, Closh, Ballon ☎ 086-847 2765 malonefruitfarm@eircom.net)

Borris

Hotel

● Step House Hotel

The Step House has a touch of Ballymaloe, a touch of Brooks Hotel, a touch of Ballynahinch Castle. People are very chilled when eating and drinking and staying here, enjoying the vibe, the rooms, the bar and dining area with its clubby informality. The Step House feels just right, it feels in the right place, and there is no pretentiousness. And Alan Foley's cooking is superb. Here is a chef who uses brilliant local artisan foods and knows just what to do with them, so his food is clamorous with flavour and shows classy execution. Mr Foley is shaping up to be one of the stars of the decade and we are looking forward to seeing the development of a dynamic chef. (James & Cait Cody, Main Street, Borris ☎ 059-977 3209 www. stephousehotel.ie – Open all year)

Carlow

Farmers' Market

● Carlow Farmers' Market

The good food folk of County Carlow congregate each week in the Potato Market to offer superb hand-made cheeses, great local meats, super sweet baking, local organic vegetables and all the good things the county has to offer. It's a lovely market – clubby, intimate, lively, fun – with more than a dozen stalls manned by darlin' people. CFM is what you do on a Saturday morning. (Potato Market, beside Hadden's Car Park. Sat 9am-2pm)

Deli and Café

● Hennessy's Fine Food Store

"Trisha's Magic Twists!" Now isn't that the very ingredient you want to see used in a classy, packed-to-the-rafters shop and café like Hennessy's? A twist of magic, Carlow magic. Brilliant. Trish and Michael have all the good stuff here, to buy in the shop, and to eat upstairs, and it's an ace space, with just the right twist of magic. (Michael & Trish Hennessy, 26 Dublin Street, Carlow ☎ 059-913 2849 trishhennessy@eircom.net – Open 8.30am-4pm Mon-Sat, 7pm-9pm Fri & Sat)

Café Bar

● Lennon's @ VISUAL

To a beautiful room in the beautiful Visual, Sinead and Ross Byrne, and chef Gail Johnson, have brought the most beautiful food. They have sourced their ingredients with fastidious determination, and have set themselvs the task of presenting these ingredients with Zen-like sympathy and simplicity. Meyler's natural smoked haddock in a smokie. O'Hara's beer batter with fresh cod. Ox tongue from Nolan's of Kilcullen for a salad. Lavistown sausages with champ and onion gravy. Brennan's fillet steak with Irishman whiskey and garlic sauce. Wild Wicklow venison with ale and mustard. Coolattin cheddar rarebit with Brennan's smoked bacon and Llewellyn's cider balsamic. This is as smart as cooking gets, and the intelligence is at work everywhere, from breakfast through to the hip, sharp wine list. Artful and inspiring. (Sinead & Ross Byrne, Carlow College, Carlow ☎ 059-913 1575 ✉ lennonscafebar@eircom.net – Open for food day-time. Early evening dinner Thurs & Fri. Kitchen closed Sunday & bank holidays)

Ginger Beer

● Sullivan's Traditional Irish Ginger Beer

As with many once-ubiquitous things, ginger beer has effectively vanished from our lives, and our consciousness. So the appearance of the handsome bottles of Sullivan's ginger beer is something to celebrate, for the beer is a wonderfully refreshing tonic, a great pick-me-up, and a balm for the health. Ace. (Paddy Sullivan, IT Carlow, Kilkenny Road ☎ 059-917 5220 ✉ paddy.sullivansgingerbeer@hotmail.com 🖱 www.sullivansgingerbeer.com)

Clonegal

Restaurant

● Sha Roe Bistro

Henry and Stephanie's modest and impressive restaurant, Sha Roe, proves that what is vital in order to succeed is to sympathetically cook good food that you appreciate and understand, and to sign it with your own signature style. That's what they do in Sha Roe. Mr Stone likes to riff on favourite ideas – a pork and chorizo burger, or a pheasant and apple burger, or Asian ideas such as noodles with crab or prawns with coconut. But whatever the ingredient or the style, everything is consistent, and quietly wonderful. (Henry Stone, Main Street, Clonegal ☎ 053-937 5636 ✉ sha-roebistro@hotmail.com – Open 7pm-9.30pm Wed-Sat, 12.30pm-3.30pm Sun)

Fenagh

Farmhouse Cheese

● Carlow Cheese

Elizabeth Bradley's cheese is one of those seductive, modest, local cheeses that improve your life hugely when you first get a taste of those sweet, herbaceous lactic notes. As with so many farmhouse cheeses, Ms Bradley's cheese has diverted from the original edam-style into something unique. We like it best when it is aged about 6 or 7 months, when the purity of the milk seems to enjoy a second life, but it's also a delight when fresh and young. There are a variety of flavoured versions also, and Elizabeth sells them all at the Saturday Carlow market. (Elizabeth Bradley, Ballybrommell, Fenagh ☎ 087-6124452 ✉ e.bradley@o2.ie)

Free Range Chickens

● Carlow Foods Limited

We eat Carlow chickens all the time here at McKennas' Guide Central. Bertram and Celine produce healthy, beautiful birds, fowl that cook beautifully, and eat even better than they cook. The Carlow birds are sumptuous with flavour, the sure sign of proper breeding and care. Carlow Foods is a model Irish food company, and just one taste of this fantastic chicken will hook you for life. (Bertram & Celine Salter, Kilkea, Fenagh, Carlow ☎ 059-972 7851 ✉ info@carlowfoods.com 🖱 www. carlowfoods.ie)

Leighlinbridge

Café & Garden Centre

● Rachel's Garden Café

The funky Rachel's Café, at the enormous Arboretum garden centre, has attracted a lot of attention on account of its exotic urinals. In time, we have no doubt that consultant Neil Shirt's menus in this stylish space will be the thing that will win attention. Mr Shirt has a terrific CV, and just the right sort of sensibility to turn Rachel's into an Avoca for the Carlow-Kilkenny crowd. (Neil Shirt, Kilkenny Road, Leighlinbridge ☎ 059-972 1558 sales@arboretum.ie www.arboretum.ie – Open 9am-5.30pm Mon-Sat, 11am-6pm Sun)

St Mullins

Café & Cottages

● Mullicháin Café

St Mullins is celebrated for its ancient beauty, so whether you come here by car to spend a week in one of Martin and Emer's cottages, formerly the forge and coach house of this old Grain Store, arrive by foot on the towpath from Graiguenamanagh or paddle up the Barrow in your kayak, the Mullicháin Café is your destination for coffee, soups, brown bread and smoked salmon. Sit outside, and feel the peace of this gorgeous idyll. (Martin & Emer O'Brien, St Mullins ☎ 051-424 440 info@oldgrainstorecottages.ie www. oldgrainstorecottages.ie – 11am-6pm Tue-Sun during high season. Check off season and bank holidays.)

Tullow

Chocolates

● The Chocolate Garden

Jim and Mary Healy's chocolate adventure land is a place where you can enjoy getting stuck into a chocolate workshop, then enjoy anything from an almost bewildering array of chocolates – Kilbeggan whiskey truffles! Rocky Road! Chocolate waffles! – and organic ice creams. The craftsmanship and creativity are only brilliant. (Jim & Mary Healy, Rath, Tullow ☎ 059-648 1999 info@chocolategarden.ie www.chocolategarden.ie)

Butcher's Shop

● Laz Murphy

Murphy's is a local legend. Laz and his family sell the best stock of the best local farmers, and they sell it with skill and confidence, dedicated charcutiers who enrich the lives of all who shop here. (Laz Murphy, Church Street, Tullow ☎ 059-915 1316 jimmurphy12@eircom.net – Open 8am-6pm Mon-Sat)

County Cavan

Belturbet

Farmhouse Cheese

● Corleggy Farmhouse Cheese

"A most distinctive, beautiful cheese" was how we described Silke Cropp's Corleggy, way back in 1989 in our first ever Food Guide. Almost twenty five years later, Ms Cropp's ground-breaking cheese remains distinctive, and beautiful, and has been joined by Creeny, made with sheep's milk, Drumlin, made with cow's milk, and Quivvy, a fresh cheese. There is also a cheesemaking summer school, where students learn how to fashion artisan cheeses under Ms Cropp's patient supervision. Silke Cropp is the very personification of the artisan as artist, her cheeses an offspring of her creativity, her work a testament to her life as an agrarian, a philosopher of the land who makes distinctive, beautiful things. (Silke Cropp, Belturbet ☎ 049-952 2930 corleggy@eircom.net www.corleggy.com)

Blacklion

Restaurant with Rooms

● MacNean House & Restaurant

Neven Maguire is in that rare, exalted position achieved by very few chefs: he has his name above the title. MacNean House & Restaurant is – properly – "Neven Maguire's MacNean House & Restaurant." He is the most famous Irish chef of his generation and he is deservingly famous. Not just because of his cooking, which is a whirlwind of pleasure, but because he is famously modest, famously curious, famously nice. And it is worthwhile to remember two things about Maguire: he is a great team player, and always orchestrates a great crew who love working alongside him. And, he has known tough times. Before the fame, the acclaim, before the name above the title, there were years of hard times and hard work up here in little Blacklion. Maguire hasn't forgotten that, and that is why he is the people's chef. (Neven & Amelda Maguire, Blacklion ☎ 071-985 3022 info@macnean-restaurant.com www.macneanrestaurant.com – Open 6.30pm-9.30pm Wed-Sat, 7pm-8.30pm Sun, 12.30pm & 3.30pm Sun)

Cavan

Duck and Geese Farm

● Thornhill Ducks

Ken Moffit's ducks and geese are the preferred choice of scores of restaurateurs throughout Ireland, their quality always impeccable. Mr Moffit's neighbour, Neven Maguire, showcases the duck and geese in triumphant County Cavan culinary splendour in the MacNean House. (Kenneth Moffit, Thornhill, Blacklion ☎ 071-985 3044 ✉ thornhillfarm@eircom.net www. thornhillduck.com)

Cavan

Butcher

● Barry John Crowe

Barry John's fame as a butcher is spreading: you can now find some of his signature sausages retailed by supermarkets, and we are sure this is just the first step towards a national reputation by a gifted, hard-working charcutier who is one of the leading young butchers of his generation. Those sausages are rather special, but then so is everything this dynamic young man offers for sale. (BJ Crowe, 2 Connolly Street, Cavan ☎ 049-436 2671 – Open 8am-6pm, till 7pm on Fri barryjohnsausages@eircom.net)

Farmers' Market

● Cavan Farmers' Market

The Egg Market on Friday morning is the place to be for Fred's fish, James' fruit and veg, Silke's cheese, nice things from Cherrybank Farm, Marian Mansell, Therese MacSeain, Moran's Homestore, Pepper Pot Pantry and the indispensable Irish Organic Meats from Declan and Deirdre amongst many other sparkling talents. (Egg Market, Cavan Fri 10am-2pm)

Restaurant

● The Oak Room

In a smart upstairs room to which they moved in mid-2010, Norbert Neylon shows one and all what a skillful, sophisticated cook he is. The menus in The Oak Room are eclectic, simply because the chef can pull off whatever he fancies cooking – lamb samosa; confit of Silverhill duck; Thai-style fish cakes; Chateaubriand; Eton Mess; warm chocolate fondant. Mr Neylon has great fluency and dexterity through his dishes, so his pastas are good, his meat cookery is good, the food for children is good, and the desire to achieve their best is evident in every plate. Good value menus early in the evening are very attractive. (Norbert Neylon, 32 Main Street, Cavan ☎ 049-437 1414 info@theoakroom.ie www.theoakroom.ie – Open Dinner 5.30pm-9.30pm Tue-Sat, 5pm-9pm Sun)

Cloverhill

Restaurant with Rooms

● Olde Post Inn

"Seventy five percent of what I cook now comes from within a 10-mile range of the restaurant," Gearoid Lynch told a Eurotoques award ceremony in late 2011. Mr Lynch's statement is one of the great chicken-and-egg stories: are the producers there because of The Olde Post, or is The Olde Post there because of the producers? We suspect it is the former: Mr Lynch has created an aureola of suppliers because he has fashioned such a brilliant restaurant with rooms, a destination overseen with assured poise by Tara McCann. Together, they have shown that building a restaurant with a great reputation also builds a thriving local economy, and they have also shown that a restaurant and an economy together build a culture. (Gearoid Lynch & Tara McCann, Cloverhill, Butler's Bridge ☎ 047-55555 gearoidlynch@eircom.net www.theoldepostinn.com – Open 6pm-9pm Tue-Thur, 6pm-9.30pm Fri & Sat, 12.30pm-2.30pm 5.30pm-8.30pm Sun)

Cootehill

Deli

● O'Leary's

Three generations of O'Learys have baked and cooked in Niall O'Leary's Cootehill delicatessen. Hand-made foods, excellent breads, good service, lovely wines and a calm, engaged atmosphere, where past and present seem to intermingle, explain why they have thrived for eighty years. And do check out those old LP records. (Niall O'Leary, 14 Bridge Street, Cootehill ☎ 049-555 2142 - Open 9am-6.30pm Mon-Sat)

Killeshandra

Boxty

● Drummully Boxty

Paul's boxty is a seasonal product, made around hallowe'en and sold locally in small supermarkets. His speciality is dumpling boxty, so if you are in Cavan around the hallowe'en season keep an eagle eye out for a genuine rarity. (Paul Farrelly, Drummully, Killeshandra ☎ 049-433 4626)

Organic Meat

● Irish Organic Meats

Declan and Deirdre are a dynamic duo, working five markets per week in addition to box deliveries and a monthly delivery to Dublin. Their organic chickens are raised by the wonderful Margaret McDonnell, their organic pork is from Felix Croppe in Cavan (we knew him as a boy...), the beef is tasty breeds such as angus and shorthorn from farmers like Gerry Fitzsimons, and the lamb comes from farmers like Rory Anderson of Boyle. A brilliant venture, so keep an eye out for their smart IOM vans. (Declan & Deirdre McCarthy, Burren, Killeshandra ☎ 049-433 3915 www.irishorganicmeats.com irishorganicmeats@gmail.com)

Stradone

Chocolate Shop

● Aine Handmade Chocolates

Ann Rudden is one of those mighty women who wins awards, all of the time. Numerous Taste awards, Enterprise awards, business awards, you name it, she's got it. She is a consummate professional with a superlative array of chocolate bars and boxes created for the Aine portfolio. The design, execution and appearance are purest luxury brand deluxe, exactly the way good chocolate should be made and sold. (Ann Rudden, Stradone Village ☎ 049-4323744 info@aineschocolates.com www.chocolates.ie)

County Clare

Ballina

Restaurant

● The Cherry Tree

Harry McKeogh learnt his craft with Johnny Cooke, and the inspiration of that fine cooks shows in his style. He inclines to sweetness: scallops, peas, crab, quail, asparagus; he knows how to cook a killer sirloin steak; and his risotti and pasta dishes shown aplomb and colourful confidence. He works with the seasons, and knows when enough is enough, knows when the sweetness of his ingredients is piqued. Experience has given him a sprezzatura rigour as he is finishing a dish in this handsome room beside the river in Killaloe. So, you might find those asparagus and peas together in a risotto with roast corn-fed chicken; barbary duck will have a bitter counterpoint of endive sweetened with some honey, and his classic dishes of Tipperary sirloin or rack of Limerick lamb show a chef who isn't interested in re-inventing the wheel, just making sure it runs smoothly. (Harry McKeogh, Lakeside, Ballina, Killaloe ☎ 061-375688 🖱 www.cherrytreerestaurant.ie – Open 6pm-10pm Tue-Sat, 12.30pm-3pm Sun)

Ballynacally

Farmhouse Cheese

● Bluebell Falls Goat's Cheese

Paul Keane takes the nomenclature for his cheeses from the constellations – Cygnus; Pegasus; Orion; Delphinus – but the fresh, flinty flavours of the Bluebell cheeses are right down to earth and even when young these goat's milk cheeses are agrestic, fulsome. 200 Saanen and Toggenburg goats are milked, and we reckon the flora of bluebells in this bluebell-bedecked area – we have never seen so many bluebells anywhere – gifts that floral note in combination with grasses from good, ancient pastures. (Paul Keane, Ballynacally ☎ 065-683 8024 📫 bluebellfalls@gmail.com 🖱 www.bluebellfalls.ie)

Ballyvaughan

Farmhouse Cheese and other produce

● Aillwee Cave

Everything about Aillwee Cave is superbly managed. The design, the structure of the tours, the charm of the staff, the good food in the café, the hawk walk and birds of prey area and, of course, their rather special shop. You shop here for their own Burren gold cheese, but over the years their range has increased exponentially, so now you come for the cheeses, and the fudge, and the ice cream and much more. An enlivening, vital experience. (Ben Johnson, Ballyvaughan ☎ 065-707 7036 info@aillweecave.ie www.aillweecave.ie – Open 10am-5pm Mon-Sun. By appt Nov & Dec)

Clare

Cafe

● An Fear Gorta

"I don't think I've ever seen anything like it!" said Eamon Barrett when he walked into Jane O'Donoghue's tea rooms and spied the amazing display of sweet delights set out on the big table in this chaste and lovely room. Cakes with fruit, chocolate, coffee, cheese, caramel, toffee – you name it. If the baking is fantastic, the service matches it step by step, making for one of the great Ballyvaughan destinations. That is Stephen Spielberg over there, isn't it? Yeah, thought so. (Jane O'Donoghue, Pier Road, Ballyvaughan ☎ 065-707 7023 www.tearoomsballyvaughan.com – Open 11am-5.30pm Mon-Sun. Closed Tue & Wed off season. Closed Nov-March)

Farmers' Market

● Ballyvaughan Farmers' Market

They call themselves the BFM, the girls and guys who make and grow the lovely things that are for sale in Ballyvaughan on Saturday mornings. So, armed with your Food Guide, come along to the BFM and meet Chris and Finola and Liz and Mary and Maureen and Peter and Roshan and Tracey and Claire and Deborah. They will make your life better.

Keep an eye on the website for special markets at Harvest Time, and, of course, Christmas.

(St John's Hall car park, Saturday 10am www.ballyvaughanfarmersmarket.ie)

Shop, Café and Hampers

● Burren Fine Food & Wine

Don't miss Cathleen's roadside operation as you climb or descend Corkscrew Hill. Not only is the cooking really fine, but service is gracious and sincere. So, a pizza for you, some lemon drizzle cake for me and are we happy? More than. Quite lovely. (Cathleen Connole, Corkscrew Hill Road, Ballyvaughan ☎ 065-707 7046 info@burrenwine.ie www.burrenwine.ie – food served 11am-5pm, May-Sept)

B&B

● Drumcreehy House

Bernadette and Armin Grefkes run a very pretty and very popular B&B, just a few miles out of Ballyvaughan on the Galway road. Mrs Grefkes has a very precise and exact aesthetic which is evident in every aspect of the house: she does things well and she does things right. (Bernadette & Armin Grefkes, Ballyvaughan ☎ 065-7077377 info@drumcreehyhouse.com www.drumcreehyhouse.com)

Accommodation & Restaurant

● Gregan's Castle Hotel

Everything in Simon and Freddy's extraordinary Gregan's Castle seems to float with the ease and grace of a note of music moving through air. The setting; the architecture; the design; the aesthetic; David Hurley's inspired cooking; the welcome, all conjoin to make for one of the greatest experiences in Irish hospitality, and there are times here when you can feel you are in a work of art, rather than simply staying at an hotel. Freddy's design plays an enormous part in creating this effect, for here is a house – so rare in Ireland! – where every object and every objet is in exactly the right place. Mr Hurley worked his way to the top job in the kitchen, which means his food had the maturity and mellifluity it needed right from day one, and he will surely be one of the cooks of the decade. Some cooks foreground themselves in their cooking, but Mr Hurley effectively disappears into his cooking: the food takes over completely. As a key element of the tone-poem aesthetic of Gregan's Castle, it is hard to imagine cooking that could be more appropriate, or more sublime. (Simon Haden, Ballyvaughan ☎ 065-707 7005 stay@gregans.ie www.gregans.ie – Open 16 March-27 Nov)

Italian Restaurant

● L'Arco

The Quinn family offer good cottage accommodation in Ballyvaughan, and also run the fine craft shop, in addition to their L'Arco restaurant, which specialises in Italian cooking. L'Arco is a solid, mid-market destination, with all of Italy's greatest culinary hits on offer, and it's a place that is good for families and offers good value. (George Quinn, Main Street, Ballyvaughan ☎ 065-708 3900 www.burrenrestaurant.com – Open Thur-Sun, from 6pm)

Bar

● O'Lochlainn's Bar

O'Lochlainn's is one of the most beautiful bars in Ireland. Intimate, zen-like, handsome, and with a jaw-dropping selection of whiskeys, it is probably the Irish pub we would most like to be locked into. Time stands still from the second you walk through the narrow green doors. (Peter O'Lochlainn, Ballyvaughan ☎ 065-707 7006 drink@irishwhiskeybar.com www.irishwhiskeybar.com)

made in Clare

Mount Callan Cheddar

Bunratty

Cookery School

● Bunratty Cookery School

Donnagh has taken her highly-regarded cookery school to a new location in 2012, and the school now overlooks the Bunratty Folk Park. Is that a deer just out that window? Yes, it probably is. The school now boasts a hands-on classroom, a dining space and a separate demonstration kitchen, and this is a skilled and professional operation. (Donnagh Gregson, Bunratty House, Bunratty ☎ 061-466000 www.bunrattycookeryschool.ie info@bunrattycookeryschool.ie)

Carrigaholt

Restaurant & Bar

● The Long Dock

Pub owners who are despairing of how to invigorate traditional Irish pubs should drive to Carrigaholt to see how Tony and Imelda Lynch have made The Dock into a destination address for good food and good times. The Lynchs make it look simple – have a handsome, well-turned-out flower-bedecked exterior, a comfy, traditional interior that feels like a proper pub, a warm welcome, a promising blackboard list of fresh fish, and some solid-sender favourites like bacon and cabbage and liver and bacon. Critically, Tony knows how to handle his fish - simply and respectfully – so that everything tastes not just as good as it can, but also tastes of itself: lemon sole with brown butter; their classic chowder; crab tart; steamed mussels; herb-crusted cod. A model example of what a coastal pub could, should, and can be. (Tony Lynch, Carrigaholt ☎ 065-905 8106 🖱 www.thelongdock.com – Food served 11am-9pm Thur-Sun, and Mon-Wed during high season).

Clare

Fishmonger

● Sea Lyons Seafood Sales

Sea Lyons have a factory shop in Carrigaholt, and the company runs fish vans throughout Clare, Limerick and Kerry. There is also a home delivery service for those in their catchment area. The quality of the fish on offer speaks of Gearoid Lyons' 27 years working with seafood. (Gearoid Lyons, Carrigaholt ☎ 065-905 8222 📫 info@sealyons.ie 🖱 www.sealyons.ie)

Carron

Café & Perfumery

● The Burren Perfumery

Sadie Chowan isn't from the Burren but, when she arrived here, "I just thought: I've come home, that's it". Today, no one articulates the aesthetic of home – the Burren – better than this formidable woman, and the Burren Perfumery is one of the glories of the county. Everything here – perfumery, herb garden, tea rooms –

has a calm and holistic aesthetic that – to be perfectly honest – simply blows us away. Ms Chowan is an artist of the natural world, and it is a privilige to be able to enter her domain. (Sadie Chowan, Carron ☎ 065-708 9102 burrenperfumery@eircom.net www.burrenperfumery.com – Perfumery open all year. Tea rooms open May-Sept, 11am-5pm Mon-Sun)

local knowledge

Burren Perfumery

As well as their excellent coffee shop, make sure to visit the Perfumery in Carron. Watch as they make their creams, balms, soaps, oils, salts and botanicals, then saunter slowly in their atmospheric, aromatic garden.

Clare

Cratloe

Farmhouse Cheese

● Cratloe Hills Sheep's Cheese

Cratloe has become a cult cheese in recent years, thanks largely to the superb flavours – and the versatility – of the mature Cratloe Gold cheese. It will happily take the place of Parmiggiano Reggiano in your larder, and shares the same adaptablity and suitability when cooked. But it's also a great cheeseboard cheese. Denis Cotter of Café Paradiso in Cork uses it to make a sublime nettle gnocchi, so off you go and get those nettles.(Sean & Deirdre Fitzgerald, Cratloe ☎ 061-357185 cratloehillscheese@eircom.net www.cratloehillscheese.com)

Doolin

Preserves

● The Clare Jam Company

As defining a part of the county as the Cliffs of Moher or Willie Clancy, the Clare Jam Company is an archetypal artisan company, its distinctiveness due to the diligence and vivid creativity of David and Vera. Beautiful jams, traditionally made, and the views from the shop will take your breath away. (David & Vera Muir, Lough North, Doolin ☎ 065-707 4778 vera@clarejam.ie)

Restaurant & Guesthouse

● Cullinan's Restaurant & Guest House

James and Carol Cullinan's restaurant with rooms in the centre of Doolin is a peachy destination. Whilst the rooms are compact, floor-to-ceiling glass walls have the effect of making them seem huge. Bedrooms and public rooms enjoy superlative housekeeping, so Cullinan's gleams. James Cullinan's cooking relies on classic principles, allied to good sourcing of his ingredients. It's a template that has served him unshakably, whilst keeping his food up to date in dishes such as sea bream with smoked salmon and spring onion risotto, or marinated Burren lamb with a spring roll filled with confit shank of lamb, and in good puddings like baked caramel cheesecake. Excellent breakfasts will set you up for that promising day ahead. (James & Carol Cullinan, Doolin ☎ 065-707 4183 ✉ info@cullinansdoolin.com 🖱 www.cullinansdoolin. com – Open mid Feb-mid Dec)

Clare

Bakery

● Fabiola's Patisserie & Café

Fabiola Tombo's patisserie is only excellent. Ms Tombo worked just up the road at the great Gregan's Castle as a pastry chef before setting out her stall in Doolin in 2011, and her baking made an instant splash with locals. Most of the baking is sweet, and expert, such as her great hazelnut sponge with chocolate ganache, but savoury local foods do sneak deliciously into muffins with St Tola goat's cheese and spring onions. Not to be missed. (Fabiola Tombo, Ballyvoe, Doolin ☎ 086-660 2582 ✉ fabshaminus@hotmail.fr – Open 10.30am-6pm Fri-Sun with longer hours high season)

Restaurant

● Roadford House

Frank Sheedy cooked a Burren Slow Food menu at the Clare SF festival, and it showcased how this cook works with his local foods. With St Tola goat's cheese, he served a pistachio and honey fritter. He made a confit of pork belly, crisped it and matched it with an apple purée. With Lisdoonvarna smoked salmon, there was simply pickled cucumber. With Burren lamb, he made a spring roll with the confit shoulder, while halibut was served with a lemongrass and ginger infusion, and baked with crabmeat. He sent everyone home singing with a stunning dark chocolate truffle cake, with a marinated strawberry and mint compote and a hazelnut parfait, showing that he is as fine a pastry chef as you can get. A lovely exhibition of his skills and temperament. (Frankie Sheedy, Doolin ☎ 065-707 5050 ✉ roadfordhouse@eircom.net 🖱 www.roadfordrestaurant.com – Open 6pm-9pm Mon-Sun. Check off season. Closed Nov-Mar)

made in Clare

Burren Smokehouse

Doonbeg

Restaurant

● The Long Room at Doonbeg Lodge

We don't do golf courses in the *McKennas' Guides*, but one must make exceptions. Just as Shanks in Bangor used to grace these pages, so we must applaud Wade Murphy's cooking in the glam, grand The Lodge, a big hotel and golf course that may be overblown for some tastes, but which is nevertheless stylishly executed. Mr Murphy is a fine cook, a chef widely admired by his peers, and the Lodge is worth the trip even without a bag of clubs in the boot of the car. (Wade Murphy, Doonbeg Golf Club, Doonbeg ☎ 065 9055600 ✉ info@doonbeglodge.com 🖱 www.doonbeglodge.com)

Gastro Pub

● Morrissey's Pub

Hugh Morrissey has transformed this lovely pub from a traditional Irish bar into a svelte restaurant with rooms, yet he has managed to keep the graceful ambience of the old place, where four generations of the Morrissey family have plied their trade. The cooking is modern and informal – chicken Caesar salad; Angus beef burger; salmon and cod fish cake; home-made scampi with tar-tare sauce – food that you can relax with. That relaxed air is the signature of Morrissey's, a destination that enjoys a youthful, laid-back sang-froid. (Hugh McNally, Doonbeg ☎ 065-905 5304 ✉ hughmcnally@hotmail.com 🖱 www.morrisseysdoonbeg.com – Open 12.30pm-3pm, 6pm-9pm Mon-Sun)

Ennis

Artisan Bakery

● Carrie's Cakes

Caroline Gardiner's bakery got a groovy makeover and a lot of good advice after Feargal Quinn featured the bakery on his Retail Therapy TV show. Ms Gardiner has added a café space and sandwiches featuring her own breads alongside the bakery offer – yes, you do need a slice of that mint Aero cheesecake – so all bodes well for this brave venture. (Caroline Gardiner, 3 Salthouse Lane, Ennis ☎ 065-689 1306 ✉ carriescakes@live.ie – Open 9am-6pm Mon-Sat)

Clare

Chocolatier

● Chocolate Here

Gillian O'Leary is one of those brilliant artisans who have been liberated by the recession, and tumbled into the world of speciality food. In her case, it is the production of superb chocolate bars, in white, milk and dark chocolate, wonka bars, and the most beautiful chocolate lollipops. This is superb work, so snap them up at Ennis and Limerick markets and you can order online, where you can also read Gillian's superb blog. (Gillian O'Leary, Caherbannagh, Fountain, Ennis ☎ 086-832 8799 www.chocolatehere.ie)

Farmers' Market

● Ennis Farmers' Market

There is so much good stuff at the Ennis market: Kim Robert's Scotch eggs; Eva's pork sausages; Michael Seymour's fabulous organic meats; Peter and Kath's eggs; Caroline's veg and herbs; Anne's apple tarts; Dominic's cabbages; Danny's tomatoes; Gillian's chocolates; Dave's cheeses (especially the County Clare ones, some of them extremely rare); Peter's pies; Jean's cookies; Marese's flowers, and on and on. It's only brilliant, a market that distills the Banner County creativity in the most delightful way. (Upper Market Street, Ennis, Friday 8am-2pm www.ennisfarmersmarket.com)

Shop & Café

● Ennis Gourmet Store

The EGS is a vital destination in the town as wine shop, deli and bistro. Anne and David have been doing the good thing for many years, and their expertise fires their enduring enthusiasm. (Anne Leyden & David Lasblaye, 1 Barrack Street, Ennis ☎ 065-684 3314 ✉ hampers@ennisgourmet.com 🖱 www.ennisgourmet.com – Open 10am-7pm Sun-Thur, 10am-9pm on Thur & Fri)

Café

● Food Heaven

What do queues mean in a restaurant? Pete Wells of the *New York Times* reckons they have three meanings. They show a place is democratic: everyone waits. They are a signal of freshness: cooking takes time. They are an endorsement: if people are queueing, the wait is worth it. So, as you wait in the queue at Food Heaven, you will have time to ponder these three truisms. Is Noirin Furey's café democratic? Indeed it is – table sharing is a must. Is the food fresh? For sure: just smell that brown bread. Is the wait worth it? Are all these people stupid! No sir! Ms Furey and her team do good, straight-ahead, tasty food – goat's cheese and tomato omelette; quiche lorraine; club tripledecker; chocolate biscuit slice – and everyone knows the wait is worth it. (Noirin Furey, 21 Market Street, Ennis ☎ 065-682 2722 ✉ n_furey@yahoo.ie – Open 8.30am-6pm Mon-Sat)

Clare

local knowledge

Scattery Island

Scattery Island is an island at the mouth of the River Shannon. An ecclesiastical centre, the island has a history of battles and invasions, from Vikings, to the Tudors, to the Spanish Armada. Now uninhabited, it makes a great spot for a picnic. Boat trips depart from Kilrush Marina during the summer season.

Butcher

● Derek Molloy

Derek Molloy has won just about all the trophies, awards and prizes a butcher can win. He has been garlanded for both his traditional and speciality sausages in regional and national competitions, the sort of accolade that puts him at the top of the craft butcher world. But whatever you buy from Mr Molloy's two stores will be characterised by expert sourcing, preparation, balance and finesse, the hallmarks of an expert charcutier and butcher. (Derek Molloy, Abbey Street, Ennis ☎ 065-682 3296 – Open 9am-6pm Mon-Sat and Roslevan Shopping Centre, Tulla Road, Ennis ☎ 065-686 8350 molloybutchers@eircom.net – Open 9am-7pm Mon-Fri, 9am-6pm Sat)

Hotel

● The Old Ground Hotel

The Old Ground is a genteel market town hotel. The style may be modern, but the hospitality, the gentility, is ageless: they look after you. Their latest initiative to make guests comfortable and happy is the provision of some nifty bicycles, so you can *wheee!* around Ennis. The bikes join a reading library, plenty of historical sites on your doorstep, beaches, good food and a fine welcome as reasons to visit one more time, here in Ennis. (Allen Flynn, O'Connell St, Ennis ☎ 065-682 8127 reservations@oldgroundhotel.ie www.oldgroundhotel.com – Open all year)

Clare

Wholefood Shop

● Open Sesame

Sally Smith's shop is a pioneer, flying the flag for whole-foods and local foods since the 1980's. With their sister store in Gort, the Open Sesame ethos flourishes, thanks to great service and vital products. (Sally Smith, 35 Parnell St, Ennis ☎ 065-682 1480 opensesame@eircom.net www.opensesame.ie – Open 9am-6pm Mon-Sat)

Fishmonger

● Rene Cusack

Paul Cusack is the great intellect of Irish seafood. They should put this man on the telly, if they want to encourage people to eat more fish and shellfish. He's a fantastic analyst of retail in general, and of fish retail in particular, and this Ennis store is one of four essential Cusack stores spread throughout the country. (Paul Cusack, Market Street, Ennis ☎ 065-689 2712 – Open 10am-6pm Mon-Tue, 9am-6pm Wed-Sat)

Restaurant

● The Town Hall Café

Once *the* Town Hall in Ennis, this lovely high-ceilinged

café is now home to the restaurant of the adjacent Old Ground Hotel. Recommended are the cakes and the seafood dishes. (Allen Flynn, O'Connell Street, Ennis ☎ 065-682 8127 www.flynnhotels.com – Open 10am-noon for coffee, noon-5pm lunch, 6pm-10pm dinner)

Wine

● The Wine Buff

In a new location from the original, Chris Primo runs the Ennis outpost of the respected Wine Buff franchise. (Chris Primo, 8 Merchant's Square, Ennis ☎ 065-684 2082 www.thewinebuff.com)

Ennistymon

Farmers' Market

● Ennistymon Farmers' Market

Good meats from Doolin farm, sausages from Eva, chocolate from Gillian, veg from Rathlir Farm, line-caught fish and much, much more on Saturday morning, from 10am at the Art Gallery.

Farmhouse Cheese

● Mount Callan Cheddar

When we had the good luck to taste a 21-month-old Mount Callan a few years back, we described it as "one of the great elemental cheeses", and so it is. At that age, Lucy and Michael Hayes' cheese shows notes of both sweet silage and sherry in its bouquet, a summation of two extraordinary types of fermentation. This is Mrs Hayes gift as a cheesemaker: she presents the elemental elements of the raw milk from Montbeliard cows pastured on summer grass in a way that is rearranged or – if you want to be experiential about it – deconstructed. It is a mighty achievement, a reconfiguration of nature in one of the great Irish farmhouse cheeses. (Lucy Hayes, Drinagh, Ennistymon ☎ 065-707 2008 mtcallancheese@eircom.net)

Bakery

● Unglert's Bakery

Mr Unglert's Bakery precedes the days of part-baked bread. This small selection of loaves is hand-made and when it sells out, it sells out. The store also sells various other consumables, all great for making a picnic. (Mr Unglert, Ennistymon ☎ 065-707 1217 – Open 9am-6pm Tue-Sat)

Fanore

Restaurant

● Vasco

Ross and Karen have wandered the world, and they bring that experience and those influences back home to Fanore and to the menu at Vasco: Burren lamb in a Tangier sauce; braised Burren kid goat pie; beef massaman curry; smoked mackerel and rocket tart; Fanore wild garlic pesto and walnut pasta bake; carrot and walnut cake. The value is good, the room is colourful and funky, and the left-field vibe is pure County Clare. (Ross & Karen Quinn, Fanore ☎ 065-707 6020 www.vasco.ie Open 10.30am-11pm Mon-Sun June-Sept, check their winter hours on their website)

Inagh

Farmhouse Cheese

● Inagh Farmhouse Cheeses

St Tola is part of the culture. Everyone knows Siobhan ni Ghairbhith's superlative organic goat's milk cheeses to be a cornerstone of the culinary culture, a position they have occupied ever since the cheeses were first made more than 25 years ago. But during her dozen years at the helm of the enterprise of minding, milking and making cheese from a herd of almost three hundred goats, Ms ni Ghairbhith has taken St Tola to a more elemental part of the food culture. She acquired organic status, she has won every significant award for cheese making, and she has expanded the range of cheeses, from the best-known St Tola goat's log to fresh crottins, soft cheese, aged cheeses and flavoured cheeses. All of this has happened thanks to a profound vision of working with the land, understanding its potential, and its goodness. Ms ni Ghairbhith is a philosopher of food, her philosophy expressed in the most elementally delicious way: she brings forth goodness, and shares it with us. (Siobhan ni Ghairbhith, Inagh ☎ 065-683 6633 info@st-tola.ie www.st-tola.ie)

local knowledge

Irish Seed Savers

The Irish Seed Savers Association is based in Scarriff, with a team of 16 staff and many more volunteers. The objective of the ISSA is the conservation of Ireland's plant resources and they work to preserve heritage varieties that are suitable for Ireland's growing conditions. You can visit the Centre, where they run courses and are open for viewing their Seed Gardens, Orchards and Woodlands. You can subscribe to them through www.irishseedsavers.ie

Kilfenora

Free Range Pork

● Burren Free Range Pork

We love Eva's happy, healthy pork, especially her plump, herby sausages, pure prongs of goodness that call out for white beans and mustard. 82% pork meat: now, that's a sausage. Get them at the farm and at Ennis, Ennistymon and Kilrush markets. (Stephen & Eva Hegarty, Kilfenora ☎ 065-708 8931 www.burrenfreerangepork.com)

Kilkee

Restaurant

● Murphy Blacks

Cillian and Mary are somehow managing to bi-locate between Murphy Blacks and The Buttermarket, in Kilrush, where they cook during the day. The couple share an ability to source smartly from their locality, and Ms Redmond then gracefully cooks what they have sourced. The fish and shellfish dishes are the best bet in Kilkee, managing to be both logical and lush – monkfish scampi; gratin of hake; plaice cannelloni; scallops with mussels and clams – but there are smart, modern carnivorous choices also. (Cillian Murphy & Mary Redmond, The Square, Kilkee ☎ 065-905 6854 – Open Dinner. Weekends only off season)

Bistro and Shop

● The Pantry Shop & Bakery

Imelda's café and bakery can seem to be the very epicentre of Kilkee on a busy summer day, with everyone in the town calling in to eat breakfast, buy breads and cakes, sit around over a lazy lunch or read the paper over a cup of coffee. We suspect that many Kilkee holidaymakers, in particular, are in and out of The Pantry several times a day, starting with a berry dazzler and a wee Irish in the morning, then a coronation chicken salad for lunch, and a nice cup of tea and a slice of carrot cake as evening draws towards us. Vital. (Imelda Bourke, O'Curry Street, Kilkee ☎ 065-905 6576 info@thepantrykilkee.com www.thepantrykilkee.com)

Hotel

● Stella Maris Hotel

Stella Maris is another of those fine, sweet, ageless family-run hotels that survive so well in Clare, and which suit the character of the county so snugly. (The Haugh family, Kilkee ☎ 065-905 6455 info@stellamarishotel.com www.stellamarishotel.com – Open all year)

Hotel

● The Strand

Caroline Byrne really enjoyed Johnny and Caroline Redmond's cooking and hospitality in The Strand. "Lovely food, and a stunning view of the bay", says Caroline. That lovely food is modest and true – Carrigaholt crab claws; Parmesan chicken; Donegal silver salmon; chocolate cola cake. Six nice rooms upstairs are advising you that it's okay to have another digestif. (Johnny & Caroline Redmond, Kilkee ☎ 065-9056177 info@thestrandkilkee.com www.thestrandkilkee.com – Open 5.30pm-10pm Mon-Sun)

Artisan Bakery

● West Clare Artisan Bread

Eoin MacEntee has spells at the Ballymaloe school, the Dublin Bakery College and UCC's Speciality Food Production school under his belt, so he is a learned baker and relish maker, and his breads are stars at the various markets here that Eoin sells throughout County Clare. Lovely baking, vital breads. (Eoin MacEntee, The Ferneries, West End, Kilkee ☎ 087-989 2671 eoin@westclareartisan.com www.westclareartisan.com)

Kilkishen

Bakery

● Sunflower Bakery

The name tells you what you need to know. Vi and Pat's baking brings the sun into your life. The breads and cakes of Sunflower Bakery seem packed with an elemental goodness. Pat bakes the breads – rye sourdough; farmhouse white; walnut and cinnamon breadsticks amongst many others – whilst Vi is the cake maker and pastry chef – leek, potato and cheddar pasties; Provençal tarts; blueberry cake with cream cheese topping. They make their own puff pastry, grow their own vegetables, herbs and fruits, and bring the business of baking back to its fundamental elements: pure ingredients, shaped by skill, care and time into things that sustain and delight us. You can find the Sunflower Bakery products in the Saturday Milk Market, Limerick, the Thursday Tulla market, and the Graney Health Food store in Scarrif. (Vi Russell, Cappalaheen, Kilkishen ☎ 061-367924 macmcmanus@eircom.net)

Clare

local knowledge

Burren Beef and Lamb

Lamb and beef reared in the Burren benefits from a unique Burren grass-based diet distinctive of its upland limestone terrain. There is today a positive awareness of this special landscape, and farmers and producers are actively involved in conservation with strict self-imposed codes of practice. There is a huge pride Burren food that starts on the farm, and ends at the butcher's counter or in the local restaurants.

Killaloe

Deli and Seafood Bar

● Gravitas

Only Mark Anderson would dare to reinvent "fish & chips". As a chef, Mr Anderson has always had an abstract way of looking at things, so his fish & chips are rebirthed as roasted scallops with a fried malt vinegar mayonnaise, purple potato crisps and pea purée. Gravitas indeed! Mr Anderson is a fine talent, and has fashioned a choice deli, fish shop and seafood bar here in Killaloe. There are only 18 seats, so get there early for Mark's tapas and his always innovative and sincere cooking. (Mark Anderson, Bridge St, Killaoe ☎ 061-622 618 ✉ gravitas@live.ie – 10am-6pm Tue-Sat, 11am-3pm Sun)

Farmers' Market

● Killaloe Farmers' Market

The Sunday market at Killaloe is heading towards a decade of service to the community, and has gradually grown to embrace more than twenty stalls, offering the best of the county. See you there at Between The Waters. (Sunday 11am-3pm)

Kilnaboy

B&B

● Fergus View

Mary Kelleher's handsome house has been a staple of the Bridgstone Guides ever since we first started writing books back in the late 1980's. The house is as high, wide and handsome today as it ever was, a quintessential part of County Clare, and one of the great Irish hostesses. (Mary Kelleher, Kilnaboy, Corofin ☎ 065-683 7606 ✉ deckell@indigo.ie 🖱 www.fergusview.com – Open mid March-Nov)

Kilrush

Café

● The Buttermarket Cafe

First we take Kilkee, then we take Kilrush. Having made a great success of Murphy Blacks, their evening time restaurant in Kilkee, Cillian and Mary have opened a daytime destination in Kilrush. "Everything is cooked by me, and we are using local suppliers", says Mary, so that bap with St Tola goat's cheese and roasted red pepper is from Considine's bakery, and that is Brigitta Curtin's smoked salmon from Lisdoonvarna on Mary's brown bread. Lovely savoury baking, excellent soups and good drinks – they serve Fixx coffee – and smashing value characterise a model example of how to cook and serve good, simple, soulful food. (Cillian Murphy & Mary Redmond, Burton Street, Kilrush ☎ 065-905 6853 – Open 9.30am-5pm Mon-Sat)

Farmers' Market

● Kilrush Farmers' Market

Hand-baked breads, hand-harvested veg, hand-made chocolates, hand-fed chickens, and hand-crafted chat and cheer from the happy stallholders in Kilrush makes for a lovely time every Thursday morning. (Town Square, Thursday 9am-2pm)

Café

● The Potter's Hand

Aisling Hamilton's pretty, arty café is a local hero, and the other local heroes turn up for a big bowl of "Would you look at that" soup, and maybe some cottage pie with nice organic salad leaves or an open sandwich on Flynn's soda bread. The Potter's exudes community spirit, so visitors mustn't miss it. (Aisling Hamilton, Vandeleur Street, Kilrush ☎ 086 8804946 ✉ info@thepottershand.ie – Open 9am-6pm Mon-Tue, Thur-Sat, 9am-9pm Wed, 2pm-5pm Sun)

Lahinch

Farmhouse Cheese

● Kilshanny Cheese

A fixture of the *McKennas' Guides* since we began to write way back in the late 1980's, Kilshanny is one of the original west coast cheeses, a subtle, long-flavoured gouda-style cheese that delivers huge satisfaction within its milky, fudgy compass of tastes. You will find it in all the local markets and some of the best local shops, and it's a delight. (Peter Nibbering, Derry House, Lahinch ☎ 065-707 1228)

Guesthouse

● Moy House

Moy House is the real deal. It's handsome, it's distinctive, it's singular. It's a house that unwinds its charms slowly, a quiet, seductive destination that soon captivates you. Eamon Barrett found that: 'Initially I wasn't sure I liked it. But the more time I spent there, reading, looking out to the rough sea, helping myself to Power's 12-year-old whiskey from the honesty bar, the more I liked it. In the evening, there were slippers and candles lighting. We had our own turf fire in the room, for goodness sake! At breakfast the next morning there was truly superb service and an excellent breakfast of scrambled egg with mushroom accompanied by really good brown bread. Staff were excellent - again that all-important welcome from Brid - and nothing we asked for was too much trouble.' (Brid O'Meara, Lahinch ☎ 065-708 2800 moyhouse@eircom.net www.moyhouse.com – Open Feb-Dec)

Clare

Guesthouse

● Vaughan Lodge

Multi-millionaire Chip O'Hare stayed at Vaughan Lodge as part of a golfing trip with a bunch of similarly affluent buddies during summer 2011. Kathy Sheridan, of *The Irish Times,* asked Chip what he reckoned of Michael and Maria Vaughan's work: 'Vaughan Lodge was excellent', wrote Chip. 'Obviously new and neat and clean. Superb food and service was cordial and first rate. Michael was a great host and hard worker. We had a dinner there on our last night with the guys from Lahinch and it was lovely.' Well, that's the million-dollar American market taken care of for the foreseeable future. Michael and Maria are consummate professionals, which makes Vaughan's a wonderful place to stay and to eat. (Michael & Maria Vaughan, Ennistymon Road, Lahinch ☎ 065-708 1111 info@vaughanlodge.ie www.vaughanlodge.ie – Open Apr-Oct)

Liscannor

Restaurant with Rooms

● Vaughan's Anchor Inn

'Proper prawn cocktail made with Irish langoustines and iceberg lettuce'. Wow! That's fighting talk, isn't it? And proof of the seriousness that Denis Vaughan brings to his craft in this dynamic restaurant with rooms with rustic bar in pretty Liscannor. Mr Vaughan does things proper, and whilst he is ambitious, his ambition is not to be famous – he isn't – but just to do his best. So, book a room, have an aperitif in the bar, then settle in for some serious fish and shellfish cookery – Liscannor mackerel with smoked hen's egg and truffle butter; fruits de mer for two people with lobster, king crab, shrimp, langoustines, crab claws, mussels, white clams, palourdes, crab meat and winkles; butter-poached lobster with asparagus, peas and samphire.(Denis Vaughan, Main Street, Liscannor ☎ 065-708 1548 www.vaughans.ie – Open 12.30pm-9pm Mon-Sun. Bar food daily, dinner in restaurant)

Lisdoonvarna

Smokehouse

● The Burren Smokehouse

There is a wildness in both Brigitta and Peter Curtin, the sense of a pair who are happy to improvise, happy to see what can be achieved, what can be made with what you have. Mrs Curtin's Swedish background, her youth on a farm where one "preserved cleverly", as she says, explains the expertise of their fish smoking: their fish get exactly what they need, and no more. The aim is to make the most perfect fish product, the thing that speaks of itself, and so discipline lies at the heart of the Burren Smokehouse, but also a sense of fun, and a search for pleasure and the good things. It is one of the great destinations in the West, and one of the great European smokehouses. (Birgitta Curtin, Kincora Road, Lisdoonvarna ☎ 065-707 4432 www.burrensmokehouse.ie – Open 9.30am-5pm May-Aug, more limited hours off season)

Pub

● The Roadside Tavern

Peter Curtin's pub is a west coast classic, and the arrival of his own beers, which Peter created and began brewing in 2011, has made a great pub even greater. The Burren Brewery, as the micro-brewery is called, offers three beers: Burren Gold, a lager; Burren Red, a sweet ale, and Burren Black, a stout. A pint of Burren red and some Burren Smokehouse salmon: now you're talking! The Roadside Tavern is atmospheric, quaint, and quintessentially County Clare. (Peter Curtin, Kincora Road, Lisdoonvarna ☎ 065-707 4084 roadsidetavern@gmail.com www.roadsidetavern.ie)

Hotel

● Sheedy's

Sheedy's is one of those discreet, modest, family-run hotels that once expressed the hospitality culture of Ireland. Happily, that meticulous, subtle and charming culture of Irish hospitality lives on in this family hotel, thanks to Martina Sheedy's polite, quiet service, and John Sheedy's utterly delicious cooking. Everything is done by hand, from the handcrafted work of their local suppliers to the hands-on care of the kitchen. 'All dishes are cooked fresh to order', it says at the foot of their dinner menu, and that cooked-to-order care extends to breakfast, every part of which is cooked individually and served by the team. Simple it may be, but its heart is the heart of hospitality, the essence of Irish generosity. (Martina & John Sheedy, Lisdoonvarna ☎ 065-707 4026 ✉ info@sheedys.com 🖰 www.sheedys.com)

Clare

Restaurant with Rooms

● Wild Honey Inn

'The Wild Honey Inn confounds your expectations by placing really stellar cooking at the centre of its USP', says Eamon Barrett. 'The exterior is certainly pleasant, but gives no clue that the food served inside will be anything other than standard fare. But standard fare it ain't: a starter of gravadlax is really good, that lovely clean taste that comes from delicately cured fish is just perfect, especially when served with some really good brown bread. A rare rib-eye steak with twice-cooked chips is served with salsa verde, again perfect cooking. Service throughout is understated and genuine and a real sense of care permeates.' At breakfast, you can even get an omelette Arnold Bennett, one of the great treats in the West. The Wild Honey is ace. (Aidan McGrath, Kincora Road, Lisdoonvarna ☎ 065-707 4300 ✉ info@wildhoneyinn.com 🖰 www.wildhoneyinn.com – mid Feb-end Dec, with restricted hours off season)

Mount Shannon

Café

● An Cupàn Caifè

Mount Shannon is delectably pretty and the lake area around it is ever-so-slightly magical. Dagmar's café nestles charmingly into this zone, the cooking is honest and tasty – shank of lamb with mirepoix of root vegetables; vegetable strudel with herb sauce; chicken with mushroom sauce; Kavanagh's fillet steak. Delightful. (Dagmar Hilty, Main Street, Mountshannon ☎ 087-294 3620 dhilty@eircom.net www.ancupan.ie – Open 6pm-9pm Wed-Sun, 1pm-5pm Sun)

New Quay

Clare

Ice Cream and Ice Cream Parlour

● Linnalla Ice Cream

Wild lavender and garlic ice cream, anyone? Sounds bizarre, dosn't it? But someone did ask Roger and Brid Fahy to make them an ice cream with these flavours once, so these guys are genuinely up for any challenge. Certainly, they have seized the challenge of becoming artisan ice cream makers with gusto, expanding their range, creating new flavours, opening a shop in New Quay (which you have to visit), and winning deserved acclaim. Their signature style – away from the lavender and garlic – is one of subtlety: they let the milk and the flavours speak. (Brid & Roger Fahy, New Quay ☎ 065-707 8167 info@linnallaicecream.ie www.linnallaicecream.ie – 11am-7pm seven days during high season, noon-5pm and more limited hours off season)

Country House

● Mount Vernon

'Mount Vernon is a house of true beauty', says Connie McKenna. One of its secrets is that it shows the importance of travel, as everywhere you look an artefact collected from Asia, Africa, South America, or elsewhere is to be found in exactly the right place within the room. Yet it's not cluttered, it's almost as if all the ornaments ran into the house and chose their own space. The food is simply delightful: fish broth with prawns, lemon and dill nourishes the soul. Halibut, juicy to the bone and well cooked, with new potatoes and colourful, well-cooked vegetables is what simple, honest, home cooking is about. Mount Vernon fits beautifully with the wild Flaggy Shore – Ally and Mark have made a special place here. (Ally Raftery & Mark Helmore, Flaggy Shore, New Quay ☎ 065-707 8126 info@mountvernon.ie www.mountvernon.ie – Open 1 April-31 Oct, or by arrangement)

Wine Bar & Gallery

● The Russell Gallery

We are big fans of the lovely Italian wines Stefania Russell imports from her native Italy – look out for the Pugnitello, a grape variety that dates back to Etruscan times – along with coffees and organic leaf teas and fresh scones and smoked salmon and antipasto plates, in the aesthetic comfort of Stefania and Andy's delightful gallery, in gorgeous New Quay. Mrs Russell selects her featured artists well, and Mr Russell's raku pottery is sublime. (Stefania & Andy Russell, New Quay ☎ 065-7078185 🖱 www.russellgallery.net)

Clare

Quilty

Seaweed

● Spanish Point Sea Vegetables

"Hand harvested, hand packed", says Gerard Talty, explaining the stunning quality of the Spanish Point sea vegetables. Mr Talty might have also pointed out that four generations of the family have harvested vegetables from the sea, so experience and knowing discrimination play their part. These are outstanding products, benchmark examples of each variety, all beautifully packaged, and there is no easier nor better way to get vital, mineral-rich sea vegetables into your diet. (Gerard Talty, Quilty ☎ 087-0922555 🖱 www.spanishpointseaveg.ie)

Tuamgraney

Chocolatier

● Wilde's Chocolates

The Wilde of Patricia Farrell's chocolate company is, of course, darling Oscar, who could resist anything but temptation. Ms Farrell's exceptional chocolates are well-named: they are Wildean flights of chocolate fancy, sublimely colourful, trenchantly satisfying, witty and fun. Oscar once wrote: "The only difference between a caprice and a life-long passion is that the caprice lasts a little longer". Patricia seems to us to have turned her life-long passion for chocolate into the most exquisite series of chocolate caprices, with the only problem being that these caprices don't last half long enough. (Patricia Farrell, Tuamgraney ☎ 061-922080 🖱 www.wildeirishchocolates.com)

County Cork

CORK CITY CENTRE

Bar & Beer shop

● Abbot's Ale House

Abbot's is the kind of bar and beer shop that Corkonians miss when they move away from the city, because you only find places like this in Cork. Downstairs has a mind-blowing assortment of hundreds of beers, upstairs is friendly, easygoing, and staffed by people who know their beers. If there is a howling gale outside, and you really want a Howling Gale inside, then head to Abbot's. (17 Devonshire Street, Cork ☎ 021-450 7116)

Bakery

● Arbutus Bread

Declan Ryan enriches the culture. His breads make life better, in every way, in every sense. He isn't a young man, but he exudes a young man's hunger, and he has a young man's energy and a kid's inquisitiveness. In a parochial country, he has always been internationalist – he worked with the Troisgros brothers at their height, and Elizabeth David's writing struck him like a lightning rod. He has stayed true to those faiths – modernism, and classicism – and married them to his own Cork culture. He is as singular as his breads, and his breads are as singular as it gets, every loaf articulating and exemplifying the culture behind the staff of life. (Declan Ryan, Unit 2B, Mayfield Industrial Estate, Mayfield, Cork ☎ 021-450 5820 info@arbutusbread.com www.arbutusbread.com)

Tea

● L'Attitude 51

Beverley and Emma's L'Attitude 51 is a very easy room to settle in, its pastel shades smudged by the cascades of light that pour in the windows. The large blackboard list of wines adds to the temptation to sit back, order some chowder, then a game pie with its superb pastry and a green salad, and let the afternoon do what it will as you ponder L'Attitude's transgressive personality: is it a pub?

A wine bar? A wine café? All and none of the above, really, just a lovely location for good times. (Beverley Matthews, Emma Lagrande, 1 Union Quay, Cork ☎ 021-239 0219 info@latitude51.ie www.latitude51.ie – Food served 10am-10pm)

Tea

● Barry's Tea

Barry's Tea is commercially successful, yet quality driven. It's large-scale in terms of Irish food businesses, yet remains family owned. In truth, Barry's is something of a paradox, but we only wish more food companies could work so well, and be so comfortable, with the paradoxes of making profits yet staying at the cutting-edge, of being controlled by the family who created the company, and yet being endlessly dynamic in terms of creativity and innovation. Barry's are the Avoca of tea blending; hip, smart, cool, essential. Could we imagine life without their Earl Grey and Classic tea blends? We certainly could not. (Tommy Barry, Kinsale Road, Cork ☎ 021-491 5000 info@barrystea.ie www.barrystea.ie)

Asian Foods

● Mr Bell's

There are two Mr Bell's in the English Market, one concentrating on products from the Mediterranean, the other focusing on foods from Asia. Both are essential, charismatic and fun, and somehow Mr Bell always manages to have even the most arcane item you need, whether it's a good curry sauce, or some Chinese noodles. (Driss Belmajoub, The English Market, Cork ☎ 021-488 5333 – Mr Bell's produce is available in gourmet stores throughout Cork)

Craft Beer Pub

● Bier Haus

Dave O'Leary's hipster pub has by far the largest draught beer selection in the county, with at least two guest taps to ensure that there is always something different on offer. Mr O'Leary manages to balance the beers on offer cleverly, with local brews alongside good imports. Bierhaus is a good lively location on a Friday or Saturday night, and a nice place to hang out and quietly sip tasty Irish craft beer any day of the week. (Dave O'Leary, Pope's Quay, Cork ☎ 021-455 1648 info@thebierhauscork.com www.thebierhauscork.com)

Drinks Shop

● Bradley's

Bradley's is where you go to find that hard-to-find Irish craft ale, or to track down that rare-and-obscure Irish farm cider along with good artisan foods. It's an essential address in the city, a place that satisfies the demands of the most demanding. A warning: browsing Michael Creedon's huge selection of brilliant bottles – Irish craft beers; ports, specialist whiskeys, wines from all over the world – may consume an inordinate amount of your time. Time well spent. (Michael Creedon, 81-82 North Main Street, Cork ☎ 021-427 0845 bradleysofflicence@wordpress.com)

Cookware Shop & Cookery Classes

● Brennan & Co

Good gear, and good cookery classes that show you how to use all that good gear, are the twin drivers of Denis and Mark's vital shop. Believe it or not, but Brennan's actually dates as far back as 1872, when the firm was established on Tuckey Street. What has made the firm so long-lived? Integrity. And, of course, charm. (Denis Collins & Mark Ivers, 7 Oliver Plunkett Street, Cork ☎ 021-427 8283 shop@cookshop.ie www.cookshop.ie – Open 9am-5.30pm Mon-Sat)

Butcher

● Bresnan & Son

Bresnan's was the first stall to be established in the English Market and, to be honest, they do business today just the way they have always done it. Grass-fed meats from their own farm are prepared and sold with skill and deep, deep knowledge, not to mention with modesty and decorum. Fantastic. (Michael Bresnan, 13/14 Grand Parade Market, Cork ☎ 021-427 1119 – Open 9am-6pm Mon-Sat)

Café

● Brew

Anne and Elmarie celebrate five years at the counter in Brew, in 2012, five happy years of making and selling excellent, tasty, unpretentious food for the good folk of Cork. The girls exemplify the sharing-and-caring ethos that defines Cork city, and they do it via food that one can simply never tire of, cooking from the Land of Goodness: beef and vegetable stew; cherry tomato and goat's cheese tart; a raspberry scone and a good cup of tea to start the day; a warm brownie and a good coffee to bring delight to the afternoon. Precious. (Anne Dempsey & Elmarie Mulcahy, 21 Paul Street ☎ 021-427 4729 – Open 9am-5.30pm Mon-Sat)

Wine Merchant

● Bubble Brothers

It seems extraordinary that it is 15 years since Billy Forrester first set up Bubble Brothers, with a little portfolio of fine fizzes from France that Mr Forrester proved adept at selling to Irish people. Today, BB has two shops in Cork, sells online and services lots more good shops with its excellent range, which has grown well beyond fizz. The Brothers have prospered because they are witty, smart, affable and fun, and so are their wines. They get the fun side of wine culture, the craic of wine culture, without getting serious, and that's a mighty gift. (Billy Forrester, Wine Depot, Marina Commercial Park, Centre Park Road, Cork ☎ 021-484 5198. English market shop ☎ 021-425 4641 info@bubblebrothers.com www.bubblebrothers.com – Open 11am-6pm at Commercial Park, Market open Mon-Sat 10.30am-5.30pm)

Cork Central

Café

● Café Gusto

Only in Cork: in Café Gusto's Washington Street branch, they serve Cicchetti. What? Yep, Venetian tapas, pretty bites of tasty delight, using Ardsallagh goat's cheese with piquillo peppers, or fried padron peppers, or tortilla. Meantime over on Lapp's Quay in the café Gusto on the Boardwalk, you can sit outside with a meatball, spinach and provolone wrap and watch the dolphins in the River Lee, or cheer on the exhausted kayakers in the Ocean to City race. And you might ask: where am I? Venice? San Sebastian? San Francisco? No. Cork, boy. Only in Cork. (Marianne Delaney & Denis O'Mullane, 3 Washington Street, ☎ 021-425 4446 & The Boardwalk, Lapp's Quay, 021-422 4099 www.cafegusto.com – Open 8am-5pm Mon-Wed, 8am-10pm Thur-Sat, Washington Street, Daytime only Lapp's Quay)

Vegetarian Restaurant with Rooms

● Café Paradiso

Here is Connie McKenna on dinner in Denis Cotter's legendary Café Paradiso. Take it away, Connie: 'The first night, I ordered a tantalizing dish of sweet chili-glazed panfried tofu with Asian greens in a coconut and lemon grass broth, soba noodles and a gingered aduki bean wonton. Now, this dish met the standards of how a good Asian dish should be: comforting, spicy and well balanced. The warm lemon grass broth soaked the tofu, the chili spices set it on fire, every mouthful seemed to have a different flavour. On Wednesday evening, I happily ordered the feta, pistachio and couscous cake with sweet and hot pepper jam, wilted greens, spiced chickpeas and coriander yogurt. There's so many things you can do with couscous. It's one of those dishes that acts like a charismatic person. It makes friends with any food and fits into any dish. It had made friends with sweet, spicy, savoury and tangy.' Café Paradiso: it's food to make friends with. (Denis Cotter, Geraldine O'Toole, Lancaster Quay, Cork ☎ 021-427 7939 www.cafeparadiso.ie – Open 5pm-10pm Tue-Sat, noon-3pm Fri & Sat)

Artisan Chocolates

● The Chocolate Shop

You could almost miss Niall and Rosemary's chocolate shop in the English Market. Like a bar of good chocolate, it's petite, perfectly formed, and with every inch crammed with tasty treats. Those chocolate treats come from all over the world and from all over the world of chocolate, so you can get a Skelligs 71% and a Cluizel 67% Gracinda, and even that great Cork icon, a Hadji Bey box of Turkish delights. Online ordering is swift and fun: the hard part is knowing when to stop. (Niall & Rosemary Daly, English Market, Cork ☎ 021-425 4448 info@chocolate.ie www.chocolate.ie – Open 9am-5.30pm Mon-Sat)

Market

● The Coal Quay Market

God love us, but isn't it all smart and neat now on Coal Quay. No cars. Nice walkways. Nice, coloured walkways! A culinary catwalk! We'll have to get dressed up now on Saturday morning to go shopping, it's so smart! Look out for exciting newcomers such as Caroline & Kate's ● **Slice of Pie** (☎ 086 843 1930 www.sliceofpieirl.com). Their beautiful shortcrust creations have powered their way into the hearts of pie lovers in double quick time. A haute couture market, that's Coal Quay. (Coal Quay, Saturdays 9am-4.30pm Contact Caroline Robinson ☎ 021-733 0178)

Coffee Shop

● Coffee Central

Is there anything nicer than pulling up a stool at Mary Rose's Coffee Central, ordering a cup of tea or a single estate espresso, and taking five minutes to watch the world go by in the English Market? It's Les Deux Magots for Cork. There isn't anything nicer. Mary Rose's family has traded in the market for more than fifty years, so Ms Daly is pure market royalty. (Mary Rose Daly, The English Market, Cork ☎ 021-427 1999 – Open 8.30am-5.30pm Mon-Sat)

local knowledge

Drisheen

Drisheen is a blood pudding that is better known for its pungent aroma than its fairly mild taste. It is still sold in one shop in the Cork market, O'Reilly & Sons, and is sometimes served traditionally cooked with tripe, in the Farmgate Café in the same market. Its bicycle tube appearance, fierce smell and greyish colour gives this product limited appeal, but Cork people are proud to have this quaint food still sold in the county.

Coffee Roaster & Coffee Shop

● Cork Coffee Roasters

You need to be a character to get ahead in Cork's food culture. No wonder John Gowan fitted in so easily when he set up Cork Coffee Roasters, just a few years ago now. Mr Gowan has been a deep-sea trawlerman, a Seattle coffee-head, and much more besides. So, he has that sang froid that you need for Cork, in spades. He roasts beautiful coffees, and makes superb cups of coffee from them. And he has eclectic, left-field tastes, so his coffee vans and his shop on Bridge Street are little art treasures in and of themselves. A character, for sure. (John & Anna Gowan, 2 Bridge Street ☎ 087-776 6322 johngowan@gmail.com www.corkcoffee.com – Open 7.30am-6.30pm Mon-Fri, 8am-6.30pm Sat, 9am-5pm Sun)

Restaurant

● Crawford Gallery Café

The thing about the Crawford Café – an outpost of the Allen family's Ballymaloe House – is that they know how to choose well. Their smoked haddock risotto will use undyed haddock from Pat O'Connell in the English Market. They use Tom Clancy's amazing east Cork chicken to make their linguini with shredded roast chicken. Fish comes from Ballycotton, along with their eggs. Everything is wisely chosen, and then treated with respect, and trusting sympathy. The result is utter deliciousness, simple deliciousness, profound deliciousness. Jean Manning runs the room superbly, and we just wonder when her portrait will be hanging on the walls upstairs. (Jean Manning, Emmet Place, Cork ☎ 021-427 4415 – Open 9.30am-4pm Mon-Sat)

Cork Central

Wine Warehouse

● Curious Wines

Michael Kane has moved from Bandon to the Kinsale Road roundabout, to a fine big wine warehouse that lets you while away aeons of time as you peruse the cases of nice things Mr Kane and his crew have culled from around the world. Curious is a really switched-on company, and they are curious and ambitious, real players in the game. Their website is amongst the best, and with free delivery it's a breeze to get good wines straight to your door. (Michael Kane, Unit 36, Kinsale Road Commercial Centre, Kinsale Road, Cork ☎ 021-432 0233 curious@curiouswines.ie www.curiouswines.ie – Open 10.30am-6pm Mon-Sat)

Butcher

● Tom Durcan

When An Bord Bia had their big promotion of Irish artisan food in Selfridge's in London in early 2012, Tom Durcan's iconic Cork spiced beef was there with all the other trailblazers. The beef picked up two competition awards in 2011 alone, but the perseverance that creates the quality of Mr Durcan's spiced beef is evident in everything he makes, and in the care he takes in presenting his meats: this is one of the most handsome stalls in the market. Mighty sausages, too. (Tom Durcan, The English Market, Cork ☎ 021-427 9141 info@tomdurcanmeats.ie www.tomdurcanmeats.ie – Open 8am-5.30pm Mon-Sat)

Restaurant

● Electric

Joe McNamee likes Electric because it "appeals successfully to a wide cross-section of the dining public". For Caroline Hennessy, "there's something for everyone". Kevin O'Regan has brilliantly managed to navigate this balancing act, so Caroline will walk a country mile for the bavette with duck egg bearnaise, whilst Joe finds the fried tripe with chorizo, chickpeas and kale gets his mojo working. There are lots of bright sparks in Electric, working hard to make sure everyone is happy, and it's a great room with top drawer service. (Kevin O'Regan, 41 South Mall, Cork ☎ 021-422 2990 ✉ info@Electric-Cork.com 🖱 www.ElectricCork.com – Open 5.30pm-10pm Mon-Wed, 12.30pm-10pm Thur-Sat, noon-9pm Sun)

Cork Central

local knowledge

The English Market

Many of the stalls in the English Market are dealt with in this book in separate entries. The following are some of the other outstanding traders who make up Ireland's best food market:

● **K. Noonan Pork & Bacon**, for all those delicious fiddly bits of the pig from Kathleen Noonan's stall (☎ 087-297 1895) ● **P. Coughlan**, for superb meats from Paul Murphy's family-run stall, now into its fifth generation (☎ 021-427 2068) ● **Stephen Landon**, for traditional pork and bacon cuts. ● **The Alternative Bread Company** for fine traditional Cork loaves as well as international breads (☎ 021-489 7787) ● **The Meat Centre** for good mutton, a meat as rare as hen's teeth (☎ 021-427 7085) ● **Fruit Boost**, for a clean fruit hit in a glass (☎ 021-435 8467) ● **The Sandwich Stall**, for funky, imaginative sandwiches and salads which zing with freshness ● **Superfruit**, for super fruit (☎ 021-427 5721) ● **William Martin** for good fresh fish from a market veteran ● **Frank Hederman**, city outpost of the mighty Cobh fishsmoker ● **Café Anraith**, for nice baking as gaeilge from Caroline Murphy (☎ 021-422 6017) ● **Ballycotton Seafood**, the city outpost of the Midleton seafood masters (☎ 021-464 6522)

Chocolates

● Eve's Chocolate Shop

Eve St Leger has been making Cork's favourite chocolates for almost two decades now, believe it or not. Our teenage children have been reared on the Metre Chocolate – there is no other bar of chocolate to make a child wide-eyed with wonder as this metre-long bar – along with the golden crunch, whilst their parents have eaten so many Corkies that they must at some point – surely! – be given the freedom of the city. Ms St Leger is a patient perfectionist, but her technical skills never blind her to the magic of chocolate. She is alive to the magic, and that makes Eve's Chocolates special. (Eve St Leger, College Commercial Park, Magazine Road, Cork ☎ 021-434 7781 info@evechocolates.ie www.evechocolates.ie – Open 9.30am-6pm Mon-Fri, 9.30am-1pm Saturday plus extra hours for holidays)

Cork Central

Sweets

● Exchange Toffee Works

Hand-made sweets. Consider that. Consider what it means, in a world of industrialised candy. Sweeties made by the hands of two masters, Dan and Tony. Hand poured. Hand coloured. Hand cut. Hand bagged. So, next time you are sucking on one of these magical Shandon sweeties, just consider all that craft, all that history – Dan's father started the business back in 1928 – all that culture. Magic. (Dan & Tony Linehan, 37a John Redmond Street, Mulgrave Road, Cork ☎ 021-450 7791 shandonsweets@yahoo.co.uk – Open 9am-6pm Mon-Fri)

Restaurant

● The Farmgate Café

Kay Harte never rests. Her latest project at the iconic Farmgate, upstairs in the English Market, is to forge stronger links with the catering school in CIT, the better that the students can understand the relationship between customer and cook and supplier. And no one understands that relationship better than Ms Harte, who uses the produce of the Market to cook for the people who come to the market. It's all so logical, and it's all so good, a dignified, maternal cuisine that mainlines you straight to the source of the food. Inspiring. (Kay Harte, English Market, Princes Street, Cork ☎ 021-427 8134 farmgatecafe@yahoo.ie www.farmgate.ie – Open 8:30am-5pm Mon-Sat)

local knowledge

Cork Butter Museum

Cork's Butter Museum tells the story of Ireland's most important food export: butter. At one time, Cork's Butter Exchange was the largest butter market in the world, and butter has always occupied a central role in Ireland's culture, alongside its central role in Ireland's food culture. So, find out all about the butter roads, steal a look at the thousand-year-old butter keg, and learn how to preserve butter in a bog. ● http://corkbutter.museum

Pizza

● Fast Al's

Cork Central

Alan Goulding is taking over Cork city, and that is a very good thing. The newest Fast Al's is on College Road, and for the first time it offers full pizzas. So, if you were debating whether you wanted to go to college in Galway, Dublin, or Cork, it's now decided: Cork has Fast Al's, close to UCC, the Crawford and CIT, and Dublin and Galway don't. A million CAO forms just got rewritten. The FA's team make superb pizza, and they do it all the time: we have never had a bad slice in twelve years of buying at Al's. Fast Al's: Pizza with a college education. (Alan Goulding, 3 Paradise Place, 2 Pembroke Street, College Road ☎ 087-609 9544 fastals@gmail.com www.fastals.ie – The three Al's are open 10am-late Mon-Sat, 2pm-late Sun)

Brew Pub

● Franciscan Well Brew Pub

A former monastery with a holy well: now, isn't that the ideal spot for a classic Irish artisan brewery and brewpub? The Franciscan Well was amongst the first wave of Irish craft brewers, and remains one of the few who survived. That they now enjoy veteran status amongst the new craft brewers is only right: the FW team has trailblazed in every way, and set a template for others to follow. Their beers are stonkingly fine, with five beers as the core range – Rebel Red; Rebel Lager; Shandon Stout; Blarney Blonde, and Friar Weiss. Other seasonal and special beers are just pure delights:

Bellringer Winter Warmer for the chilly nights; Purgatory Pale Ale for summer, and Shandon Century Stout which takes stout back to the days of yore by using special hops and a higher concentration of flavour and character. Brilliant. (Shane Long, 14b North Mall, Cork ☎ 021-439 3434 info@franciscanwellbrewery.com www.franciscanwellbrewery.com – Open 3pm-11.30pm Mon-Wed, 3pm-midnight Thur, 3pm-12.30am Fri & Sat, 4pm-11pm Sun)

B&B

● Garnish House

Consider this: we were chatting to Hansi Lucey in Garnish House one bright summer's morning in late summer 2011, when Hansi suddenly said, in that disarming, sing-song Cork accent: 'You know, but we are having our best ever year in business.' We put her right straight away: if Garnish was having its best-ever year, it was because Hansi Lucey never stops trying to get better, and every one of her team is right there with her, trying to be their best also. It makes for one of the great Cork destinations, a place of consummate care and hospitality, a place where the breakfasts are the stuff of legend – a place where they look after you. (Hansi Lucey, Western Road, Cork ☎ 021-427 5111 info@garnish.ie www.garnish.ie – Open all year)

Restaurant

● Gourmet Burger Bistro

They use organic lamb and beef and free-range chicken in GBB, so they are setting new standards in the boutique, bespoke burger stakes. They do lots of smart riffing on the accompaniments, and the room is simple and lean. A few Irish craft beers on the menu would be nice. (Michael Condon, 8 Bridge Street, Cork ☎ 021-450 5404 michaelccondon@gmail.com www.gourmetburgerbistro.ie – Open noon-10pm Tue-Sat, 2pm-9pm Sun)

Restaurant

● Greene's

Fred Desormeaux is a really fine cook, and you can enjoy some really fine cooking in Greene's. He likes to riff on classic French creations – seabass with pesto beurre blanc; goat's cheese fritter with beetroot purée; cassoulet with parsley crust; pistachio crème anglaise. Value for money is good, and there is great potential in Greene's. (Richard Evans, 48 McCurtain Street, Cork ☎ 021-455 2279 ✉ greenes@isaacs.ie 🖱 www.greenesrestaurant.com – Open 12.30pm-2.30pm Tue-Fri, 6pm-11pm Mon-Thur, 6pm-11.30pm Fri & Sat)

Restaurant

● Les Gourmandises

Pat Kiely cooks very, very good food, bringing a meticulous technique to bear on the best ingredients Cork has to offer. In the modern style, he likes to separate out the elements of his dishes and arrange them painterly-style on dark slates, but, as Joe McNamee points out, he does this in a "no nonsense style". At heart, he remains a classical cook, even referring to their cuisine as "Fine French Dining", though it is more Michel Bras than Fernand Point. Mrs Kiely has sommelier's skills to match her husband's culinary skills, and it makes for a potent pairing. (Patrick & Soizic Kelly, 17 Cook Street, Cork ☎ 021-425 1959 ✉ info@lesgourmandises.ie 🖱 www.lesgourmandises.ie – Open 6pm-9.30pm Tue-Thur, 6pm-10pm Fri & Sat, Sun 12.30pm-3pm)

Patisserie

● Heaven's Cake

Joe and Barbra make smashing cakes, and they bring to them a professional élan and stylishness that is all-too-lacking in Irish patisserie. Just one bite of that chocolate mousse cake, or that lemon curd tart, and you will have the sugar rush from heaven. (Joe & Barbra Hegarty, English Market, Cork ☎ 087-206 3008 ☎ 021-422 2775 🖱 www.heavenscake.ie – Open Mon-Sat 9am-5.30pm)

Café

● House Café

House is cool, quirky, friendly and food-driven and Owen O'Reilly is putting together some nice food here. Elderflower cured salmon, beetroot gnocchi, farmhouse cheese panini and good coffees. It all happens in the lobby of the Opera House. (Owen O'Reilly, Cork Opera House, Emmet Place ☎ 021-490 5277 ✉ housecafecork@gmail.com – Open 10am-6pm)

Café

● Iago

In 2013, Sean and Josephine will celebrate 20 years of Iago in the English Market. Along the way, the character of the stall has morphed and shifted, but whatever guise Iago has adopted – sandwich bar; wine bar; cheese retailer; pasta maker – has always been superb, characterised by meticulous standards and quiet professional service. When they made sandwiches, they were the best. Today, when they make pasta, their pasta is the best. The cheese selection is superlative, the charcuterie is moreish, and Cork needs 20 more years of Iago. (Sean Calder-Potts, English Market, Cork ☎ 021-427 7047 ✉ iago@eircom.net – Open 9.30am-5pm Mon-Sat)

Café

● Idaho Café

Idaho is just the coolest place, run by the coolest people, Richard and Mairead. Cool they may be, but they are also modest and calm, which means they have the perfect DNA to be restaurateurs. This little tardis of a room is always packed – not least with McKenna children who time their visits to Cork based on whether they will have breakfast or lunch here. The food is simple, soulful and executed with stunning efficiency, as it has been ever since they opened more than a decade ago. The TLC that anoints everything in Idaho makes every customer feel very special indeed. Magic. (Richard & Mairead Jacob, 19 Caroline Street, Cork ☎ 021-427 6376 – Open 8.30am-5pm Mon-Thu, 8.30am-6pm Fri & Sat)

Cork Central

Restaurant

● Isaac's

In May 1992, Michael Ryan and Canice Sharkey opened Isaac's Restaurant in an old furniture removal building, out of which they had fashioned a most beautiful dining room. If you get it right at the start, you don't have to change it, and Ryan and Sharkey got it right – with design, with cooking – and they haven't had to change it. That's how you earn classic status. John McKenna's last visit showed all the virtues of Isaac's in full colour: lovely tomato and basil soup; fantastic seared beef salad with French fried onions and a delicious horseradish mayo; a great prune and almond tart; then a perfect espresso. Twenty years of getting it right, that's Isaac's. (Canice Sharkey, 48 MacCurtain Street, Cork ☎ 021-450 3805 ✉ isaacs@iol.ie 🖱 www.isaacsrestaurant.ie– Open 10am-2.30pm, 6pm-10pm Mon-Sat, 6pm-9.30pm Sun)

Restaurant

● Italee Caffe Italiano

"The real deal", is how Joe McNamee describes Italee. "Nice minimalist decor; good simple Italian food and no nonsense". Step in the door and you step into Tuscany by the River Lee, with gorgeous mellifulous accents. Early days as yet for evening time service, which is still finding its feet. The daytime offer is spot on. (Michele Monaco, Gabriele Pacchera, Oliver Plunkett Street, Cork ☎ 021-422 6006 🖱 www.italee.ie – Open 8am-6pm Mon-Thu, 8am-9pm Fri & Sat)

Restaurant

● Jacques

"Still love the challenge", says Jacque Barry. Ms Barry and her sister, Eithne, sure do love the challenge, as they now run not just their legendary Jacque's restaurant, but also do the terrific food across town in The Woodford. In Jacques, the cooking is logical and lovely: mackerel with beetroot and horseradish cream; lamb salad with Knockalara cheese; quail with sprouting broccoli and Gubbeen chorizo, Irish cheeses with handmade biscuits and drunken figs. Lovely room, and great value for money. (Jacqueline & Eithne Barry, 9a Phoenix Street, Cork ☎ 021-427 7387 📫 jacquesrestaurant@eircom.net 🖱 www.jacquesrestaurant.ie – Open 6pm-10pm Mon-Sat)

Cork Central

Cafe & Wholefood Store

● Jam @ Hanley's

Miserable? Depressed? At your wits' end? Here is the solution: go into James Mulchrone's Jam café and bakery at Hanley's – a big garden centre place with smashing staff – and the girls in Jam will have you smiling in seconds. We do not know of any place that has better staff – period. These girls are so friendly, so caring, that they make our heart sing, and that's before we have even had anything to eat.Life enhancing. (James Mulchrone, Hanley's of Cork, Frankfield Road, Ballycurreen, Cork ☎ 021-432 3018 📫 info@jam.ie 🖱 www.jam.ie – Open 9am-5.30pm Mon-Sat, noon-5.30pm Sun)

Nuts

● Just Nuts

Fiona Buckley used to be a lawyer and, like other lapsed and recovering lawyers before her – Robert Parker,

Jacqueline Friedrich, John McKenna, to name just three – she has found her way into the world of food. Just Nuts is a really smart idea, for a simple reason: most of the nuts sold commercially aren't any good. But Ms Buckley's are very good – sweet spiced nuts with cinnamon and nutmeg; New York nuts with rosemary and cayenne; almendras fritas, are some of the ingenious and spirited flavours. We just want a bag of each, and a bottle of Sauvignon Blanc, please. (Fiona Buckley, Fairview Park, Military Hill, Cork ☎ 087-2430519 thejustnutscompany@gmail.com www.thejustnutscompany.com – available in shops and markets throughout Cork)

Chipper

● Jackie Lennox Restaurant

Jackie Lennox's legendary chipper tied for first place when *The Irish Times* conducted a reader survey of the Best Chips in Ireland. "It beats anything Dublin and Galway have to offer" Fióna Ní Gháibhín said about Lennox's, a reply which is, when you think about it, a very Cork reply. Lennox's is worthy of its status: they do proper food, properly, both on the Bandon Road and in Ballincollig. Sure, what would Dublin and Galway know about fish and chips? (Brian Lennox, 137 Bandon Road, Cork ☎ 021-431 6118 – Open noon-1.30am Mon-Sun. Also in Ballincollig ☎ 021-487 4668 Open noon-late Mon-Fri, 2pm-late Sat-Sun)

Cork Central

Restaurant

● Lancaster Lodge

People are very comfortable in Lancaster Lodge. The breakfasts are correct and good – pancakes with bacon and maple syrup; creamed scrambled egg with smoked salmon; a choice of omelettes; the Full Irish. It's breakfast's Greatest Hits, and it's all very nicely done, much better done than one might expect at the keen prices Lancaster charges. The location is ace, service is good, the place gleams with good housekeeping, it's a good call. (Robert White, Lancaster Quay, Western Road, Cork ☎ 021-427 1049 info@lancasterlodge.com www.lancasterlodge.com – Open all year)

Restaurant

● Liberty Grill

"The Liberty does a great job at being a diner," says Joe McNamee. We know just what Joe means: lip-smacking, tasty, unpretentious food, and good service and good value, is what you should expect from a diner, and the Liberty does that. But it's also a stylish diner, and a nice place to relax in the evening as you share some pan-zanella, then enjoy that classic crab burger, or maybe john dory with salsa verde with a bottle of Longueville House cider. They work hard in the Liberty, and they have that Steve Jobs thing: they keep on tweaking, tweaking, make it better, make it better. (Marianne Delaney & Denis O'Mullane, 32 Washington Street, Cork ☎ 021-427 1049 dine@libertygrill.ie www.libertygrill.ie – Open 8am-9pm Mon-Thurs, 8am-10pm Fri & Sat)

Coffee Roasters

● Maher's Coffee

John and Mary Mackey have steered the good ship that is Maher's coffee for more than two decades now, charting their way through a business that has become all too treacherously fashionable. They continue to serve customers in their cute, sweet little shop on Oliver Plunkett Street, and have successfully built the wholesale side of the business throughout the province. (John & Mary Mackey, 25 Oliver Plunkett Street, Cork ☎ 021-427 0008 info@maherspurecoffee.ie www.maherspurecoffee.ie – Open 9.30am-5.30pm Mon-Sat)

Farmers' Market

● Mahon Point Farmers' Market

Mahon Point is unique. What Rupert Hugh-Jones and the producers have created here – in the most unlikely location – is a success story on a phenomenal level. For a start, Mahon is actually two markets. In the morning, there are shoppers, on the hunt for the best foods in the county of every hue and cry, including newcomers like – ● **Gan Gluten** (Clare O'Brien ☎ 086 233 9519); ● **Treat Petite** (☎ 086-241 5513 www.treatpetite.ie). And then, from noon onwards, the eaters arrive to feast on some of the best cooking in the county, and suddenly Mahon is a place to feast, al fresco. By 2.30pm, it's all over, and the market vanishes into thin air. The waiting list to get a stall here is longer than the River Lee. Mahon is the benchmark others imitate, but no one else has the mix and magic of this amazing market. (Rupert Hugh-Jones, Thursdays, 10am-2pm ☎ 021-464 6601 rupert@rupertsfarm.com www.mahon-pointfarmersmarket.com)

Restaurant

● Nash 19

September 30th, 2011, and Claire Nash and the team at Nash 19 celebrated 19 years of Nash 19. Typical of Ms Nash, she had reserved a place of honour at the celebration for Myrtle Allen of Ballymaloe House: her mentor, her inspiration. But, with twenty years in the bag, Ms Nash herself is a mentor, an inspiration. She has built her business organically, patiently, adding in the superb food shop to complement the restaurant, opening up on Saturdays lest the people of Cork have nowhere to eat, sourcing her ingredients for the kitchen with meticulous care, always assisted by her brilliant lieutenant, Mairéad O'Brien. The two of them are shining stars amongst the mighty food mavens of Cork. (Claire Nash, 19 Princes Street, Cork ☎ 021-427 0880 info@nash19.com www.nash19.com – Open 7.30am-4.30pm Mon-Sat (4pm closed Sat)

Cork Central

Wholefood shop, bakery and café

● The Natural Foods Bakery

Back in 1989, working on our first book, one of the first places we visited in Cork city was Natural Foods, on Paul Street. We bought beautiful breads and the amazing cherry buns – which were famous even then – and we thought we had found heaven. Which, of course, we had, for a bakery that makes the staff of life both wholesome and beautiful is a place that makes slices of heaven. More than 20 years on, and Natural Foods, minded by Orla, Ellie and Roddy, is still baking foods for the gods. Their vision of good food is rock solid: proper soups – nettle; celeriac with lemon; mushroom with black and white pepper – fine breads; proper pies; clean and fresh salads; artisan meats. These guys do the food that salves your soul. (Ellie & Orla O'Byrne & Roddy Henderson, 26 Paul Street, Cork ☎ 021-427 7244 orlaobyrne@yahoo.com www.thenaturalfoodsbakery.com – Open 9am-6pm Mon-Fri, 10am-6pm Sat, noon-6pm Sun)

Chocolates

● O'Conaill Chocolates

The brilliant Gillian from Chocolate Here has written that O'Conaill's make the best hot chocolate, a sentiment echoed by many other chocoholics. But Casey and his team do much more than just hot chocolate – there are also great bars, great coffees, and they are stalwarts of the best Cork markets: just join the queue. You can also get a fix of terrific sweetness at their bakery and coffee dock on Princes Street. (Casey O'Conaill, 16 French Church Street, Cork ☎ 021-437 3407, 13 Princes Street)

Fishmonger

● Kay O'Connell Fishmongers

So, what did Pat O'Connell say to Queen Elizabeth of England that had her chortling with laughter, an event that created the most memorable image of the monarch's trip to Ireland? What Made Liz Laugh? Well, we do know what Pat said, but it wouldn't be fair to Mr O'Connell to tell you what the joke was, so you will have to make a trip to the massive O'Connell's fish stall in the English Market, and ask Pat himself. Whilst you are there, just marvel at the unbelievable display of pristine fish which the O'Connell family display and sell every day, a selection unmatched anywhere else in Ireland. And enjoy the craic and the banter, again ummatched anywhere else, in our experience. O'Connell's, purveyors of fish, and humour, to monarchs and the man in the street. (Pat & Paul O'Connell, The English Market, Cork ☎ 021-427 6380 freshfish1@eircom.net www.koconnellsfish.com – Open 8am-5.30pm Mon-Sat)

Butcher

● O'Mahony's Butchers

"O'Mahony's have opened up a whole new world in terms of butchery", says Joe McNamee. "I really rate the place". What Eoin O'Mahony has done to give himself a USP is to offer Continental cuts – onglet; bavette, and so on, for his customers. In addition, he will age a fine T-bone, and source any manner of offal you request, so this is a very customer-focused destination, especially if you are on the hunt for a goose skirt or a butcher's piece. (Eoin O'Mahony, English Market, Cork ☎ 021-427 0254 – Open 9am-5.30pm Mon-Sat)

Butcher

● O'Flynn's

"I have that cut of lamb you like", says John O'Flynn to Sally McKenna one Thursday morning in Cork. Now: is that service, or what? O'Flynn's butcher's shop is a Cork legend, because John and Simon's concept of service is based on remembering what your customer likes, and anticipating what your customer might like. So, in addition to that lap of lamb, Sally also bought a rib of beef, on the bone, aged for 6 weeks. It was beef ice cream, it was beef chocolate, it was the best piece of beef the McKennas had ever eaten. The day you first walk through the doors of O'Flynn's on Marlborough Street is the day your life just got better. (Simon & Patrick O'Flynn, 36 Marlborough Street, Cork ☎ 021-427 5685 – Open 9am-5pm Mon-Thur, 8am-5pm Fri, 8am-4pm Sat)

made in Cork
Maher's Coffee

Sausages

● O'Flynn's Gourmet Sausage Grill

Cork Central

O'Flynn's gourmet sausages are recognisable by their smart packaging and full on flavour. You can buy them in the Cork Market, and at various summer festivals. They have also now opened a sausage grill on Winthrop Street, and this is good short-order cooking with carefully sourced ingredients, most of which come from the English Market. Expect sangwiches, burgers, mash and hot potatoes, all with sausages, of course. (Declan O'Flynn, Winthrop Street, Cork & The English Market, Cork ☎ 021-427 4422 declan@oflynnsgourmetsausageco.ie www.oflynnsofcork.ie – Open 9am-6pm Mon-Sat, 10am-6pm Sun)

General Stores

● O'Keeffe's Artisan Food Store

"Providing people with local products from their own back yard", is how Donal O'Keeffe describes his family's ambitions for their Montenotte food store. That sounds simple, but the simplicity of the O'Keeffe's philosophy cannot be overstated: thinking local, eating local, saving the planet. The shop, we think should really be called The Tardis: how can so much of the great artisan foods of Cork city and county be crammed in to what is an extremely modest space? Turn every corner, scan every shelf, and the great food icons of Cork are sitting there waiting for you, a blissful bounty. "Remaining independent gave us the opportunity to be unique", says Donal, and the charm of the staff congratulates the character of the shop. (Donal O'Keeffe, St Luke's Cross, Cork ☎ 021-450 2010 info@okeeffes-shop.ie www.okeeffes-shop.ie – Open 7.30am-10pm Mon-Sun)

Delicatessen

● On The Pig's Back

Are you strong enough, as you find yourself buying lovely things at On The Pig's Back, to resist having a slice of onion tart, or a piece of their lush pizzas? If so, you are made of sterner, more self-denying stuff, than us. We can't resist the aromas, the delectable sticky, savoury tastes, just as we can't resist the cheeses, charcuterie, breads and all the moreish, delightful things that Isabelle and her team place before us. And if you can't make it to the city centre, there is a second fantastic store in Douglas, adjacent to the South Ring Road. (Isabelle Sheridan, The English Market, Cork ☎ 021-427 0232 info@onthepigsback.ie www.onthepigsback.ie – Open 8am-5.30pm Mon-Sat)

local knowledge

Spiced Beef

Cork's coastal position and its natural harbour means this thriving port always traded in salt and spices. This may explain why Spiced Beef is so much associated with this city. Salted beef shipped from Cork became a valuable commodity in Europe and in the colonies beyond, and this was always a prized food. Spiced beef is a refinement of the Irish salted, or corned beef, and it is a food that became associated with Christmas. It's traditionally served hot, with cabbage and mashed potatoes.

Tripe and Drisheen & Sausages

● A O'Reilly & Sons

As they head towards a century of service to the people of Cork, O'Reilly's have gotten revolutionary. How else to explain that a shop that sold tripe and drisheen, and only tripe and drisheen, should choose a couple of years back to also start selling speciality sausages. Revolutionary! Radical! Unprecedented! So now, you come here for your pungent drisheen, your flouncy tripe, and your sausages. (Donagh O'Reilly, The English Market, Cork ☎ 087-677 6848 dtoreilly@eircom.net – Open 9.30am-5.30pm Mon-Sat)

Greengrocer

● Organic Garden & Paradise Garden

We love everything about the Garden, but best of all are the cool, calm staff who serve you all the goodies they have grown, collected and collated. How do they make such a tiny space seem so bounteous? We don't know, but it is surely a form of magic. (Donal O'Callaghan, The English Market, Cork ☎ 021-487 5958 bohrdt@gmail.com – Open 9am-5.45pm Mon-Sat)

Wholefood Shop and Self Service Restaurant

● The Quay Co-Op

The Quay is "The biggest and best health food shop", says Joe McNamee, with, of course, a rock-steady vegetarian café on the first. Always a pleasure, whether it's your third visit or your third decade coming here. (24 Sullivans Quay, Cork, ☎ 021-431 7026 quaycoop@eircom.net www.quaycoop.com – Restaurant open 10am-9pm Mon-Sat, noon-9pm Sun, Shop open 9am-6pm Mon-Sat)

Olives and Sandwiches

● The Real Olive Company

Like the Hewlett Packard garage, or Steve Jobs and Steve Wozniak at the Homebrew Computer Club, the English Market is where it all began for the Real Olive Co. Toby Simmonds took a stall in a market that was going nowhere fast, and started selling stuff Irish people didn't eat. The rest is history. The Cork instigator remains the only fixed point for the ROC, but they cover every other inch of the country – on Saturdays alone, they are at 10 other markets around the country. Mr Simmonds is now making sublime dairy products with buffalo milk, and don't miss their superb sandwiches. (Jenny-Rose Clarke, The English Market, Cork ☎ 021-427 0842 info@therealoliveco.com www.therealoliveco.com – Open 8.30am-5.30pm Mon-Sat)

Gastro Pub

● Sober Lane

"It's a great pub and I really think their food should be talked about", says William Barry. William's faves are the Sober Lane pizzas – Clonakilty pudding with onions and apples; Sober Lane Special with ham, pepperoni and chilli – but there are lots of other tasty things, from barbecue wings to steak sandwich. Witty and fun, and they even do beer pong. (Ernest Cantillon, 5 Sullivan's Quay, Cork ☎ 021-467 7212 party@soberlane.com www.soberlane.com – Open pub hours, lunch and dinner served)

Restaurant

● Star Anise

Star Anise is delightful. A delightful space with delightful food, it's often referred to as "Cork's best-kept secret", which is surprising since it has enjoyed a decade of success here on Bridge Street. Recently, SA seems to have really stepped up a gear, and the cooking is punchy and up-front: swordfish with orzo and saffron aioli; Ardrahan and courgette pithivier; Tom Durcan's fillet steak with smoked Gubbeen; chicken Caesar salad with crispy egg. The staff are super welcoming, and it's a delight. (Virginie Sarrazin, 4 Bridge Street, Cork ☎ 021-455 1635 staranise@eircom.net www.staranise.ie – Open noon-2.30pm Thu-Fri, 6pm-10pm Tue-Sat)

Cork Central

Restaurant

● Gulpd @ Triskel Arts Centre

"A left-field insouciance masking an obsessive's care and attention to detail", is how Joe McNamee rates the team in the uber-cool Gulpd Café. (Triskel Arts Centre, Tobin St, Cork ☎ 01-427 2022 – Open 9.30am-11.30pm Mon-Thur, 9.30am-12.30am Fri-Sat, 2pm-11pm Sun)

Soup and Sandwich Bar

● Wildways

For more than a decade now – Maura Roche opened her café back in 2000 – Wildways has shown the benefits of organic food and the pleasures of a visionary venture that marries goodness with simplicity. The sandwiches read like something you might find almost anywhere – egg mayo and ham; salmon with cucumber; chicken and herb stuffing; prawns and marie rose – and yet the care in preparation and attention to detail in sourcing means that the Wildways sarnies are a million miles from the forecourt and the supermarket deli. Ms Roche has an unfailing eye for flavour and for precision, and no one makes a better soup 'n' sambo combo. (Maura Roche, 21 Princes Street, Cork ☎ 021-427 2199 info@wildways.net www.wildways.net – Open 7.45am-5pm Mon-Fri, 8.30am-4pm Sat)

Gastro Pub

● The Woodford

"Great food in relaxed and friendly surroundings", is how Caroline Hennessy describes the swish, smart operation that is The Woodford. The team from Jacques restaurant under the gaze of Jacque Barry bring well-sourced and sustainable foods from Cork and make lovely things with them – leek, blue cheese and caramelised onion tart; hot blaa with spicy meatballs; Irish stew; "the best roast ham salad you've ever had", says Caroline, who also strongly advises you "don't miss the opportunity to feast on the pear and chocolate tart". Let us feast. (Jacque Barry, Daunt Square, Cork ☎ 021-425 3931 info@thewoodford.ie www.thewoodford.ie – Open noon-4pm Mon-Sat, 5pm-8.30pm Tue-Sat)

Wine Warehouse

● The Wine Buff

Cork Central

Now relocated into the centre of the city, the Wine Buff offers excellent wines at excellent prices. Their range from in and around Bordeaux is particularly interesting. (Darragh Collins, 78 Oliver Plunkett Street, Cork ☎ 021-425 1668 cork@thewinebuff.com www.thewinebuff.com – Open Mon-Tue 11.30am-7pm, Wed-Sat 10.30am-7pm closed Sun)

CORK CITY SUBURBS

Ballincollig

Butcher

● Michael O'Crualaoi

Ballincollig is the original of the quartet of O Crualaoi stores, and has been transformed today into a deli, take-away and hot food bar, with the butcher's shop at the rere. Michael O Crualaoi's team are amongst the very best – helpful, knowledgeable, fun, hard-working, and from the simplest things – their fine sausage rolls – to the complex things – their prepared meats and prepared meals – they get it right. (Michael O'Crualaoi, Ballincollig ☎ 021-487 1205 info@ocrualaoi.com www.ocrualaoi.com – Open 7am-6.30pm Mon-Thu, 7am-7pm Fri, 7am-6pm Sat. Also at 46 Patrick Street, Fermoy (☎ 025-49100), Wilton Shopping Centre, Cork (☎ 021-434 4004), Main Street, Carrigaline (☎ 021-437 6716)

Pie Maker

Úna's Pies

Úna Martin's pies have become a phenomenon. Switching from a career as a town planner, Ms Martin has shown that she can plan a pie better than almost anyone. Her riffs on classic ingredients – mince and onion, steak and Murphy's, chicken and chorizo, spinach and ricotta – are gee whiz! with flavour and the most perfect pastry. Ms Martin has quickly garnered acres of editorial coverage, the food festival awards, the groovy packaging, and, all in all, Úna's has become nothing less than a pi-enomenon. (Úna Martin, Unit 4, Innishmore Ind Estate, Ballincollig ☎ 087-285 9957 unaspies@gmail.com)

Ballygarvan

Garden Centre Café & Shop

The Pavilion

The symbiotic relationship between a good garden centre and a tasty café is explored and exploited in this delightful hillside location, where leafy lunches and herby soups are served alongside signature oilcloths for the table, and pots for that herbaceous border. (Charlie O'Leary, The Pavilion, Myrtle Hill, Ballygarvan ☎ 021-488 8134 info@thepavilion.ie www.thepavilion.ie – Open day time, lunch available from noon)

Ballyphehane

Fish & Chip Shop

C.F Lennox

Linda Hegarty has a simple explanation for the success of Lennox's, a chipper established almost sixty years ago: "I feel that even though take aways are not posh food, they can do very good food if they know what they are doing, don't change it, and offer consistency." That's exactly what Ms Hegarty and her crew do both here at Tory Top Road, and in their second branch in Midleton. Lovely pies, great chips, super battered fish. Who needs posh when you can have unpretentious and good. (Linda Hegarty, Tory Top Road, Ballyphehane lindahegartyschull@hotmail.com – Open noon-11pm Also at 81 Main Street, Midleton ☎ 021-463 9678 – Open noon-12.30am Mon-Wed, noon-1am Thur, noon-3am Fri-Sat)

Blackrock

Farmers' Market

● Blackrock Village Farmers' Market

Sociably held in and around the Natural Foods Bakery, Blackrock is a fun Sunday outing, a spiritual retreat for food lovers. It's a lovely mix of food to graze on, food to purchase, and crafts and plants and craic. And the sun always shines. Really. (Blackrock, ☎ 087 245 1096 – Open Sunday 10am-2pm)

made in Cork

Arbutus Bread

Cork Central

Restaurant

● The Castle Restaurant

On Caroline Hennessy's last visit to The Castle, "Shreds of the sweetest, twice-cooked ham hock lifted my salad above the ordinary". Excellent, but: wait for it! "The Husband's (jealously guarded) fish and chips won the most-enviable-dish award in our corner, inspiring a neighbouring table to call for the lunch menu." There is a nice global vibe to the food in the café – hake with saffron couscous, lamb and aubergine stew with flatbreads – and whilst some dishes may miss the target, on form the Castle will have you arguing about who gets the most-enviable-dish award. (Jerry O'Sullivan, Blackrock Castle, Castle Road, Blackrock ☎ 021-4357911 info@castlecafe.ie www.castlecafe.ie – Open 9.30am-5pm Mon, 9.30am-9pm Tue-Sat, 10am-6pm Sun)

Farmers' Market

● Natural Foods Bakery

Natural Foods is one of the city's best-known food brands, and they are movers and shakers on Paul Street in the city as well as Farmers' Markets and here, in Blackrock, where the bakery is based. The soups are great, the pies are great, the breads are great, the sweet things are great. And the staff are great. But you knew that. (Orla O'Byrne, Pier Head, Blackrock ☎ 021 4614555 orlaobyrne@yahoo.com www.thenaturalfoodsbakery.com – Open daytime)

Blarney

Guesthouse

● Ashlee Lodge

Anne and John O'Leary describe Ashlee as a four-star private hotel, but one of the secrets of their house is the fact that it doesn't feel anything like a conventional hotel, and it doesn't look like an hotel, though it does enjoy hotel levels of decor and comfort. But what no other comparable four-star hotel could offer is the incomparable service that this dedicated couple practice. Above all, there is the constant presence of Anne and John themselves, as they prove themselves masters of the art of hospitality in each and every detail of Ashlee. (Anne & John O'Leary, Tower, Blarney ☎ 021-438 5346 ✉ info@ashleelodge.com 🖱 www.ashleelodge.com)

Gastro Pub

● Blair's Inn

Blair's Inn is the real thing, says Joe McNamee. It has "the kind of ambience advertising creatives trade souls with the devil to recreate, but there's simply no substitute for the real thing". The cooking is real, too: Cromane mussels with white wine and garlic; tian of O Crualaoi's corned beef and cabbage; duck with potato and herb stuffing; a good Angus steak. The wine list is excellent, as are the craft beers, and how marvellous to see a thriving Irish country pub, doing the good thing everywhichway. (Duncan & Richard Blair, Cloghroe, Blarney ☎ 021-438 1470 ✉ blairs@eircom.net 🖱 www.blairsinn.ie – Food served in bar 12.30pm-3.45pm, 4pm-9pm. Restaurant opens at 6pm)

Carrigaline

Country Market

● Carrigaline Country Market

Carrigaline has always been one of the outstanding country markets. Just watch out for those sharp elbows as you wade into the crush for the last bag of meringues. (Carrigaline GAA Pavilion, Fridays 9.30am)

Farmhouse Cheese

● Carrigaline Farmhouse Cheese

Pat O'Farrell knows his land. Under the grass his

Friesian cows happily graze on there is limestone, and limestone makes for sweet grass and sweet milk. This gives Carrigaline its fudgy, open flavours, the hint of hazelnut and honeycomb, the delicacy. Pat and Anne then simply capture and mature these inherent flavours, and bundle them up in the little orbs of Carrigaline. And, what's more, they even make fine biscuits to partner your cheese. (Pat & Anne O'Farrell, The Rock, Carrigaline ☎ 021-437 2856 www.carrigalinecheese.com)

Gluten-free Bakery

● Delicious

Denise and Michael O'Callaghan's gluten-free cakes and breads have been featuring in telly adverts, bringing them fame, and a wider audience for their superb baking. Their range has expanded to comprise a full complement of fine breads, cakes, buns, seasonal and celebration cakes and some frozen products, and they are life-savers for anyone who follows a gluten-free diet. (Denise O'Callaghan, Unit 6, Carrigaline Industrial Park, Carrigaline ☎ 021 491 9538 info@delicious.ie www.delicious.ie)

Cork Central

Wine Importer

● Karwig's Wines

Joe Karwig is one of the great personalities of the Irish wine world, and he runs a great wine shop in Carrigaline. There are more than 800 wines here, carefully selected from round the world. Joe likes to discover symmetries and stories with the wines he sells, so do ask about his selection of Rieslings, and about the wines they sell with an Irish connection. (Joe Karwig, Kilnagleary, Carrigaline ☎ 021-437 2864 www.karwigwines.ie – Open to visitors 9.30am-5.30pm Mon-Fri, 11am-6pm Sat)

Crosshaven

Gastro Pub

● Cronin's Pub & Mad Fish Restaurant

Denis Cronin and his crew tick all the boxes down here in Crosshaven. They cook great grub, most especially great seafood. They serve excellent drinks. They create the cosiest ambience imaginable. They look after you, properly. Cronin's is unpretentious and real, a template for how every bar in Ireland could and should be a great destination for eating and drinking and having a great old time. 'Some damn fine cooking', wrote Caroline Hennessy. Some damn fine everything in Mad Fish, we reckon. (The Cronin family, Cronin's Pub, Crosshaven ☎ 021-4831829 www.croninspub.com – Mad Fish Restaurant open 6pm-9pm Thur-Sat, Cronin's serves food noon-2.45pm Mon-Fri, noon-3.30pm Sat, 1pm-4.30pm Sun)

Farmers' Market

● Crosshaven Farmers' Market

The market takes place in front of Cronin's pub and look out for stalarts like Tom and Carol from Earth Angel organics, Mags Curtin's lovely Milis baking, the Cronin's cheese stall, fresh fish, lovely breads, hot sausages, Italian foods, and lots of great Cork crafts. (Village Square, Crosshaven, Saturday 10am-2pm)

Cork Central

Douglas

Butcher

● Liam Bresnan

The meat aristocrats of the English Market also man this fine shop in Douglas. (Liam Bresnan, Douglas Village Shopping Centre ☎ 021-489 1109 www.bresnans.ie – Open Mon-Sat 8am-6pm)

Farmers' Market

● Douglas Farmers' Market

Three local markets have combined to create the new Douglas Market, and the line up features some market luminaries – Golden Bean; Una's Pies; Woodside pork; Badger & Dodo; Arbutus breads – with some of the most exciting newcomers – Just Nuts; Martin O'Leary's Beara lamb; Crepe-a-Lolo; Stephen Joyce's fish; Ballyhoura Mushrooms. There is a great vibe, good music, lots of kids, good times, fab food. (Douglas Court Shopping Centre Park, Saturdays 10am-2pm)

Traiteur

● Billy Mackesy's Douglas Village Foods

A tiny traiteur crammed with nice cooked foods, both sweet and savoury. (Billy Mackesy, 1 Tramway Terrace, Douglas ☎ 021-489 0060 – Open 8am-6.30pm Mon-Fri, 8am-4.30pm Sat)

Fish and Chips

● KC's Fish & Son & Sons

KC's is the wittiest place to eat in Ireland. Wes Crawford and his team – KC and Son and Sons: you call it family, they call it nepotism – put the fun into eating, for they see humour, puns, drollness, laughs and jocularity in everything. The graphics are a hoot. The website is a scream. And queueing in the little shop is a treat in itself, for there is so much to be amused by. But, as well as being funny, they are people who care about what they cook and serve, so this is proper food: lovely fresh fish; ace pork belly bbq; the classic meat pattie; the chicken curry; the pig in spuds. Laugh? Once inside this tardis of good food, you will. (Wes Crawford, Douglas, Cork ☎ 021-436 1418 ✉ info@kcandco.ie 🖱 www.kcandco.ie – Open 12.30pm-2pm Wed-Fri, 5pm-12.30am Sun-Wed, 5pm-1.30am Thu-Sat)

Delicatessen and Café

● On The Pig's Back

A beautiful, groovy store café is home to the Cork icon's unbeatable mix of delicious things to eat and drink. (Isabelle Sheridan, St Patrick's Woollen Mills, West Douglas Street, Douglas ☎ 021-461 7841 🖱 www.onthepigsback.ie – Open 9.30am-5pm Mon-Sat, open till 5.30pm Fri & Sat)

Rochestown

Delicatessen

● Cinnamon Cottage

Carole and Kieran will soon be celebrating 20 years of doing the delicious thing on Rochestown Road, a major birthday which is worthy of a major celebration. Cinnamon is the quintessential traiteur: a beautifully curated mix of smartly sourced foods and wines, and delicious home-cooked foods that can suit any and every occasion. Best of all, Carol and Kieran have kept everything at CC fresh, lively, rejuvenated and inspiring, they make each day like the first day of opening, and there is a spring in their step and a zest in their work. Lucky customers get all the benefits of their tireless dedication. (Carol Murphy & Kieran Corcoran, Monastery Road, Rochestown ☎ 021-489 4922 ✉ cinnamon@eircom.net 🖱 www.cinnamoncottage.ie – Open 9.30am-6pm Tue-Thur, 9.30am-6.45pm Fri, 9.30am-5.30pm Sat, noon-5.30pm Sun)

Ballyhoura

Mushrooms

● Ballyhoura Mountain Mushrooms

Lucy Deegan and Mark Cribbin make a shiitake mushroom soup that would secure the fate of nations. Up here in the hills of North Cork, up in Ballyhoura, they grow mushrooms and demonstrate, in the most dynamic and creative way, just what you can do with them. Nice fresh oysters and shiitakes; beautiful mushroom powders; mighty pâtés; delicious cep oils; terrific mushroom pestos. And that mushroom soup: dark, lingering, beefy, intense, silky, umami. The country is gone to the dogs, you say? Taste this. See? It isn't gone to the dogs just yet. (Lucy Deegan & Mark Cribbin, Ballyhoura ☎ 086-8100808 ✉ ballyhouramushrooms@gmail.com 🖱 www.ballyhouramushrooms.ie)

Ballyvourney

Preserves

● Folláin

Peadar and Mairin are heading towards thirty years of production of the superb Follain preserves, jams, and relishes. During that time, they have simply gotten better and better, producing one benchmark product after another. It's unfair, of course, to just pick one product, but for us the tomato relish is particularly brilliant, particularly useful, and is a classic demonstration of the Follain virtues of restrained exuberance and dedicated culinary consistency. (Peadar & Mairín O'Lionáird, Ballyvourney ☎ 026-45288 🖱 www.follain.ie)

Blarney

Tea Rooms and Restaurant

● Blarney Woollen Mills

There is a rather handsomely renovated restaurant and food shop – The Mill – here at Blarney Woollen Mills, in between the woollen shop and the hotel. Sinead

Doran and her team are ambitious, and you get the sense of someone who sees the potential to create an Avoca-meets-Fallon & Byrne here in Blarney, and who is determined to get there. The room is quite lovely and we are looking forward to seeing Ms Doran turn this great space into a don't-miss! destination. (Sinead Doran, Blarney ☎ 021- 438 5011 retail@blarney.com www.blarneywoollenmillshotel.com – Open 9.30am-6pm Mon-Sun)

Tea Rooms and Cupcake Bakery

● Miss Katie's Tea Rooms

Kay Weldon opened this pretty retro-styled room as a showcase for her well-known cupcakes, which are a sweet, riotous blast of colour at the Douglas Market. Proper tea, delicate tea cups, tiered cupcake stands, all make for the life well lived. Well, for the duration of tea and cake anyhow. (Kay Weldon, Blarney ☎ 087-235 9046 cupcakesbykatie@eircom.net – Open 11am-7pm Tue-Sun)

Cork North

Buttevant

Fish Smokehouse

● Old Millbank Smokehouse

Geraldine Bass is best known for her luscious organic smoked salmon, but when you see all her products arrayed on Thursday morning at the Mahon Market, you realise that Ms Bass's expertise extends to every element of the piscine parlour. Her fish pâtés are superb; her fish cakes are superb; her smoked trout is superb. Everything is characterised by subtlety, delicacy and a defining restraint, everything is defined by superlative eating quality and organoleptic delight. (Geraldine Bass, Willow Pond, Buttevant ☎ 022-23299 bass3@indigo.ie)

local knowledge

North Cork Milk

The pastures in North Cork are responsible for the wealth of farmhouse cheeses in this region. The milk here is the best in the country, so look out for local milk from the local creamery.

Castlelyons

Country House

● Ballyvolane House

What did Justin Green learn from his mum, the great Merrie Green? "Seasonality, growing your own, humour, and the love of nature", he says. Could anyone be better fitted out for the business of running a country house, and being a first-class restaurateur, than to have imbibed those attributes? No way. His mum gave Mr Green all the skills he needs to run both Ballyvolane House, where he succeeded his parents in 2004, the house itself having first opened to guests twenty years before. Ballyvolane is one of the great Irish country houses, because it offers one of the great Irish country house experiences: it is experiential, in the most profound way, because it lets you into the elements of the country, and the country life. Anyone planning their nuptials, by the way, should take a look at the amazing wedding venue that Ballyvolane offers. (Justin & Jenny Green, Castlelyons, Fermoy ☎ 025-36349 info@ballyvolanehouse.ie www.ballyvolanehouse.ie – Open all year)

Cork North

Castletownroche

Preserves

● Heaven Preserved

Marilyn Cassey grew up "preserving everything that the garden yielded", and a lifetime's experience of stirring pots of jams, marmalades and chutneys reveals itself in every jar of her Heaven Preserved relishes. She manages to capture the essence of the ingredient she is working with, and then to get just the right balance, whether it's a fig and lemon marmalade, a tart raspberry jam, a fine onion marmalade. Best of all, the "home made feel" Mrs Cassey aims to capture is there in every jar. (Marilyn Cassey, Wallstown Castle, Wallstown, Castletownroche ☎ 086-373 1898 www.heavenpreserved.com)

Charleville

Farmhouse Cheese

● Clonmore Goat's Cheese

If you want to explain the richness and balance of the Biggane family's Clonmore goat's cheese and their

Shandrum cow's milk cheese, then look first at the grass. Their goats and cows eat from the Golden Vale itself, the ruminant equivalent of being born with a silver spoon in your mouth. Tom, Lena and their son, William, then carefully craft both Clonmore and Shandrum, working seasonally, working sympathetically with their animals. The result is two cheeses that impress as pure expressions of milk: cheeses that are not so much made, as born. (Tom, Lena & William Biggane, Clonmore, Newtown, Charleville ☎ 063-70490)

Coolea

Farmhouse Cheese

● Coolea Farmhouse Cheese

Cork North

The Willems family have been making Coolea for almost 35 years now, so they are amongst the pioneers of the artisan cheese movement, and the history of their cheese has much to teach us about farmhouse cheese. Originally made by Dick Willems using raw milk from their own herd, it is today made by Dicky Willems, Dick's son, using pasteurised milk from Dan Lynch's nearby farm. Ostensibly, everything has changed, and yet Coolea has not changed. If anything, the mature cheeses one can buy today represent a pinnacle of achievement, of excellence, for the family. In recent years they have focused intently on the maturation of the cheeses, which brings the organoleptic qualities ever more into focus: the caramel note, the apricot note, the Parmesan-like flintyness and sweetness. Coolea is the cheese that cried out to be made, here in the Múscrai Gaeltacht, and whilst circumstances change, the cheese endures. (Dick & Sinead Willems, Coolea ☎ 026-45204 info@cooleacheese.com. www.cooleacheese.com)

Fermoy

Artisan Coffee Roaster

● Badger & Dodo

"There are a thousand compounds in coffee", says Brock Lewin of Badger & Dodo, and Mr Lewin is on the hunt to articulate them. The Mzuzu Geisha from Malawi has "berries and citrus fruit, mango, papaya and peach". The Brazilian Daterra Estate Bruzzi has "caramel and marzipan with distinctively chocolate aftertaste." Mr

Lewin marries precise barista skills to his roastery talent, and he will sometimes opt for a well-roasted finish: if you like big New World shirazes, then these are the beans for you. If you find those wines too fulsome, seek out the delicate fruit-and-spice roasts. Look out for their van at markets and festivals. (Brock Lewin, Fermoy ☎ 087-053 2660 info@badgeranddodo.ie www.badgeranddodo.ie)

Farmhouse Cheese

● Fermoy Natural Cheeses

They are patient people, Frank and Gudrun. They don't so much make cheeses as compose cheeses, and sometimes the compositional gestation can be very long indeed: Frank reckons there is two years of tweaking and testing behind any new cheese they produce. But if the gestation is lengthy, their creativity never falters. In the last ten years, they have brought six cheeses into the artisan marketplace, all of them wonderfully successful themes and variations on classic mountain cheese archetypes. The Fermoy cheeses are amongst the finest in Ireland. (Gudrun & Frank Shinnick, Strawhall, Fermoy ☎ 025-31310 gudrun1@eircom.net)

Café

● O Crualaoi Butchers

The ultra-cool Fermoy branch of the O Crualaoi group is one of four stores in Cork, the others being the original shop in Ballincollig, along with Wilton and Carrigaline. The shops are innovative, customer-orientated, and distinguished by brilliant staff who are charm itself. The Fermoy store adds in a café to the mix of butcher's shop and deli, and it's a key destination. (Michael O Crualaoi, 46-48 Patrick Street, Fermoy ☎ 025-49100 www.ocrualaoi.com – Open 8am-7pm Mon-Fri, 8am-6.30pm Sat, 11am-3pm Sun)

Kanturk

Farmhouse Cheese and Milk

● Ardrahan Farmhouse Cheese

It is quite amazing to read the descriptions that people reach for to describe the broad, refulgent taste of Mary Burns' Ardrahan cheese. Bacon. Farmyard straw. Mushrooms. Citrus notes. Flowers. Meaty. Zesty.

Buttery. Earthy. Smoke. Put them all together and they point to one conclusion: Ardrahan is umami. It offers that panorama of tastes that characterise soy sauce, Parmesan, tomatoes, cooked ham, meat and other foods that have a savoury taste built on glutamate. But its USP is that there is no other cheese quite like Ardrahan, despite the fact that it is, ostensibly, similar to many other Irish semi-soft, washed-rind cheeses. The Burns family have always poured body and soul into making their cheese, and we reckon that this passion explains the mighty explosion of goodness found in every wheel of the cheese. (Mary & Gerald Burns, Ardrahan, Kanturk ☎ 029-78099 ✉ ardrahancheese@gmail.com 🖱 www.ardrahancheese.ie)

Butcher

● Jack McCarthy

Cork North

In recent years, Jack and Tim McCarthy have blazed across the Irish artisan firmament like nobody else. McCarthys fed the Queen of England, successfully invaded and conquered French culinary culture, re-invented Christmas – you have to try their Xmas (black) pudding – were crowned as Local Food Heroes by public acclamation, amongst a flush of other awards. And yet, amidst the ferment, Jack and Tim still found time to produce the most imaginative, singular range of meat and charcuterie you could imagine. Jack and Tim are the alchemists of our age, magician butchers whose every piece of meat brings magic to your table. (Jack & Tim McCarthy, Main Street, Kanturk ☎ 029-50178 ✉ info@jackmccarthy.ie 🖱 www.jackmccarthy.ie – Open 8.30am-6pm Mon-Sat)

Kilavullen

Market

● Kilavullen Farmers' Market

Kilavullen market has been doing the good thing for a decade now. Held in a great big polytunnel – with a smart new floor! – it's a supremely social space, with everything from cupcakes to crafts for sale. Kilavullen is one of our favourite markets, a unique fusion of farmers' market and country market that is quite unlike any other. (Nano Nagle Centre, Sat 10.30am-1pm fortnightly, details from ☎ 022-26470 🖱 www.kilavullenfarmersmarket.com)

Macroom

Oatmeal

● Macroom Oatmeal

Newer artisan oatmeals are beginning to arrive in Ireland, but Donal Creedon's Macroom Oatmeal remains the most individual and the most bespoke of all the Irish porridges. Cook it right, and Macroom offers you magic for breakfast – especially if you have it with cream and sugar in Ballymaloe House. Donal also makes a splendidly agrestic wholemeal flour that will put a mighty oomph! into your breadbaking. (Donal Creedon, Kanturk ☎ 026-41800 ✉ macroomoatmealmills@eircom.net)

Oatmeal

● Toonsbridge Dairy

Toby Simmonds and Johnny Lynch make mozzarella so good, so fresh, so true, that when you give it to Italian friends, they disdain it. Of course they do, for how can you admit that one of the cornerstones of one of the world's greatest cuisines can be made with such expertise in a wee, old dairy at Toonsbridge, near to Macroom. Sacrilegious to Italians, sublime to the rest of us, Toonsbridge mozzarella is going to conquer the world. The mozzarella is joined by terrific soft cheeses and a wonderful ricotta. (John Lynch & Toby Simmonds, Toonsbridge, Macroom ☎ 026-41471)

Mallow

Country House

● Longueville House

There is a voracious element of the pastoral in William O'Callaghan's cooking, a sense that he wants a super-sensory overload of the natural world in his dishes. Partly, this is because of his good fortune in having the fruits of Longueville's 500 lush acres to feed his kitchen - everything from fish to pork to apple brandy to cider, all their own, all characterised by true provenance, the Longueville terroir. But it is just as much on account of the fact that he is a true countryman: an expert mushroom hunter; a grower; an orchard keeper; a fish smoker, and his culinary skills take all these ingredients and transform them into a multitude of delightful things for his guests. He tries to bottle the pastoral, does O'Callaghan, he is after its essence. (William & Aisling O'Callaghan, Mallow ☎ 022-47156 ✉ info@longueville-house.ie 🖱 www.longuevillehouse.ie – Open Dinner & Lunch for groups)

Country House

● Luceys The Good Food Shop

Ian Lucey is the 5th generation to run Mallow's Good Food Shop, continuing a tradition that goes right back to 1880. The combination of farm and shop gives the family a particular USP, for the farm is only 5 miles from the shop, and provides lots of their vegetables and fruit, as well as allowing them to keep their own stock for the butchery business. Over the last decade, Ian has expanded the deli and catering side of the business, so Lucey's is today a one-stop-solution-shop, whatever your needs. (Ian Lucey, Mallow ☎ 022 21130 ✉ info@luceysgoodfood.com 🖱 www.luceysgoodfood.com 8.30am-6pm Mon-Sat)

Cork North

Country House Hotel

● Springfort Hall

Springfort Hall is upping its game, says Joe McNamee. And with Bryan McCarthy in the kitchen, they have a cook with "the lightest of touches, a dollop of patience, and a sense of adventure". His signature 12-hour feather blade of beef, with swede purée, leek croquette, truffle and beetroot, is a classic, and Caroline Hennessy is another fan of Mr McCarthy's ambition and drive. Simple, clean accommodation means Springfort is fast becoming a hot North Cork destination. (Paul Walsh, Bryan McCarthy, Mallow 🔔 022-21278 ✉ stay@springfort-hall.com 🖱 www.springfort-hall.com)

Shop

● Springfort Hall Shop and Cafe

"A great asset to the town", John McKenna noted in his wee notebook after a stop off to enjoy coffee and cake in the Springfort shop. Along with the foods to eat in, including nice sarnies made with Twomey's Bakery bread, there are choice things to take away, along with good jars and boxes of treats on the shelves. (Bryan McCarthy, Main Street, Mallow ☎ 022-43779 ✉ stay@springfort-hall.com 🖱 www.springfort-hall.com – Open 9am-5.30pm Mon-Sat)

Mitchelstown

Accommodation

● Ballinwillin House

Blimey, but it all seems to be happening at Ballinwillin, all the time, all at once. "Deer are calving at the moment and calves are dancing around the fields. Wild boar and Irish grazer sows are all having their bonhams. Nine newborn piglets on the farm this week. Very busy time on the farm saving hay. Ballinwillin milk being churned into butter, yogurt and cheese." And all the while, Pat is farming and conducting school tours and organising food festivals and minding their 46-hectare wine estate in Hungary. And Miriam is using the foods from the farm for her "one-pot wonders" for guests who stay in their beautiful rooms. Phew! (Pat & Miriam Mulcahy, Mitchelstown ☎ 086 256 1478 ✉ ballinwillinhouse@gmail.com 🖱 www.ballinwillinhouse.com)

Cork North

Brewery

● Eight Degrees Brewing

Scott Baigent and Cameron Wallace, partners in Cork's 8 Degrees Brewing Co, always knew what they wanted to do when they set up their 8 Degrees Brewery. "We were very clear about what we were looking for", they say. And that was? "A modern Irish identity". Mr Baigent is a Kiwi, Mr Wallace an Aussie, and their outlier status has proffered them a different version of Irishness, one that is savvy, discriminating, fun. One that is modern, in a word. And that modern Irish person will, of course, be drinking an 8 Degrees Beer: Howling Gale Ale; Sunburnt Irish Red; Knockmealdown Porter, beautiful, modern drinks, brewed with precision, verve and skill. That Knockmealdown porter, for instance, will assuredly knock you down: it is one of the great modern Irish creations, and a first encounter recalls that time you first tried O'Hara's Stout fifteen years ago. It's as creamy as raw milk and as hoppy as heaven. Welcome to Modern Ireland: it never tasted better. (Cameron Wallace & Scott Baigent, Unit 3, Coolnanave Ind Park, Dublin Road, Mitchelstown ☎ 025-84933 ✉ cam@eightdegrees.ie 🖱 www.eightdegrees.ie)

made in Cork

Toonsbridge Mozzarella

Delicatessen & Cafe

● O'Callaghan's

It's going on twenty five years now since Pat and Mary opened the doors of O'Callaghan's, and gave the town a destination for hungry souls in search of sublime sustenance. Over the years, the café has grown, but the central tenet of O'Callaghan's – fresh food made by care and made by hand – hasn't altered an iota. We know there is a bypass around Mitchelstown, but you should bypass the bypass and stop here on Cork Street. (Mary & Pat O'Callaghan, 19 Lr Cork Street, Mitchelstown ☎ 025-24657 ✉ ocalhansdeli@eircom.net 🖱 www.ocallaghans.ie – Open 8.30am-5.30pm Mon-Fri, 8.30am-5pm Sat)

made in Cork

McCarthy's Black Pudding

Cork North

Newmarket

Organic Meats

● Knockatullera Farm

There is a video on Youtube of John Forde ploughing with a pair of big happy horses on his demonstration farm at Knockatullera, and it would do your heart good to watch it. The calmness and savvy of the horses is simply amazing, as amazing as the speed with which John and the team get the job done. It's a signifier of how far John and Olive have gone in their farming and food production: they have taken the process right back to the fundamentals, and it is one of the reasons why their Knockatullera meat is so amazing. (Olive & John Forde, Newmarket, ☎ 029-60079 ✉ oliveforde@gmail.com)

Garden Centre, Tea Room

● The Secret Garden

What a pretty tea rooms Brian and Sarah have here in The Secret Garden, one of those cultish Cork garden centres that has so much more than just plants. "Who could resist?", asks Caroline Hennessy, "Especially since the tea comes in proper pots with china cups and real homebaking. My first taste of Christmas mince pies was here in October and I had to be held back from buying pots of the deliciously rich mincemeat there and then. The garden centre is the only place I managed to find a long-sought-for quince tree. Definitely worth a detour". Even if you do not know a begonia from a brassica, the aesthetic of the garden, and a cup of good tea in a good tea cup, is sufficient reason to make that detour. (Brian Paterson, Aghaneenagh, Newmarket ☎ 029-60084 info@thesecretgardener.com www.thesecretgardener.com – Open 10am-6pm Tue-Sat, 1pm-6pm Sun)

Ovens

Orchard

● Mealagulla Orchard

James Scannell's farm in Killumney/Ovens, north west of Cork city, has been in the family for generations, and his fruit is a welcome throwback to the days when apples actually tasted of something. He sells them from great big wooden crates at farmers' markets along with Bramley cookers, tart apple cider vinegar and a nice crisp apple juice, all local, no imports. When there are no more Irish apples, James takes a break and waits for the new season. His Elstars are the stuff of legend. Don't miss them at County Cork markets. (James & Shannon Scannell, Knockane, Ovens ☎ 086-267 4825 jnscannell@gmail.com www.mealagulla.ie)

Cork North

made in Cork

Howling Gale Ale

Rathcormac

Country House

● Ballinterry House

Right from the moment you pick up the 'phone, Ann O'Sullivan puts you at your ease. "Nothing phases Ann", says Caroline Hennessy, "and after seeing what an enormous labour-of-love restoration she and Michael Garvey have done on this gracious Queen Anne house, you can understand why". Good food matches the comfort, and Ballinterry is renovated, renewed and so very relaxing. A hot new destination. (Michael Garvey & Ann O'Sullivan, Rathcormac, Fermoy ☎ 025-87835 ballinterryhouse@yahoo.co.uk)

Watergrasshill

Traiteur

● Taste A Memory

We were there when Anne Bradfield sold the first TAM pie at the Bandon Market in 2006. Now, you will find these fantastic pies, pasties and dinners in more than thirty shops in County Cork and as far afield as Limerick, Kilkenny and Dublin. The secret of their success is the balance of ruddiness and finesse, like domestic savoury baking, but done by a patissier. We would scarcely think of going on a picnic without a warm beef, or a spicy bean, pasty, wrapped up nice and warm in the centre of the basket. (Anne Bradfield, Rolls House, Watergrasshill ☎ 086-868 2201 ✉ anne@tasteamemory.ie 🖱 www.tasteamemory.ie)

made in Cork

Coolea Farmhouse Cheese

Whitechurch

Farmhouse Cheese

● Hegarty's Farmhouse Cheddar

Dan and John Hegarty's sublime Whitechurch cheddar is the go-to cheese for many of Ireland's leading cooks. If you want power and poise added to a dish that needs cheese, if you want that cheese soufflé to have depth as well as lightness, if you want that bacon jam and cheese sandwich to sing for its supper, then the Hegarty brothers have just what you need. That's the beauty of the cheese: slow maturation for 12 months gives it an enormous depth of flavour, with extra flavour notes appearing out of nowhere to surprise you – a hint of pineapple, a hint of hazelnut, a hint of barley, a hint of umami. An icon in the making. (Dan & John Hegarty, Ballinvarrig, Whitechurch ☎ 021-488 4238)

Aghada

Pizzas

● Volcano Pizzas

"It is the huge dollop of imagination slathered all over the top that can make his daily specials a treat" says Joe McNamee. (Simon Mould, Aghada ☎ 086-793 0062 simon@volcano.ie www.volcano.ie)

Ballincurrig

Free-range Pork

● Woodside Farm

Pork people talk in awed terms about Noirin and Martin's Woodside Farm pork. "They make the best pork sausages you can buy", says one Dublin pork man who knows his stuff. What makes Woodside so good? Easy: Saddleback and Gloucester porkers who lead the life of Reilly, fed on turnips, the nutritional powerhouse that is kale, fresh grass, and rolled wheat. How could they be other than brilliant? You will find the Woodside pork and bacon at the Midleton, Mahon and Douglas markets. It will change your life. (Noirin & Martin Conroy, Oldcourt, Ballincurrig ☎ 087- 276 7206 info@woodsidefarm.ie www.woodsidefarm.ie)

Ballycotton

Fre-range Poultry

● Ballycotton Free-Range Poultry

"Tom Clancy's birds have meat in places other birds don't even have places", says Joe McNamee. And yet Mr Clancy himself would be the very last to tell you of the superlative quality of his Ballycotton birds, such is his beguiling modesty. His chickens, geese, turkeys and ducks do the talking, and they are beyond good: come November, and every one of his turkeys and geese will already be sold for the Xmas meal for smart folk who know the finest birds when they try them. So, look out for the ice cream fridge and the plaster of paris goose at Cork markets. Brilliant. (Tom & Jacinta Clancy, Church Road, Ballycotton ☎ 086-308 9431)

Cookery School

● Rory O'Connell

Rory O'Connell has an aesthetic. There is a very distinct 'Rory O'Connell' style to his cooking – Clodagh McKenna, who has worked alongside him in the kitchen, uses terms such as "elegant", "clean", and "pure", to describe how Mr O'Connell sees and executes a dish. Skye Gyngell has described a dinner cooked by Mr O'Connell as "one of the most truly delicious meals of my life". Now, that's praise. (Rory O'Connell, Snugsboro, Ballybraher, Ballycotton ☎ 086-851 6917 rory@rgoconnell.com www.rgoconnell.com)

Day Boat Fish Delivery Service

● Love Fish

Brenda and Tadhg O'Riordan catch and deliver the freshest fish imaginable, from inshore boats, and they deservedly picked up a Eurotoques award for their work. (Tadhg & Brenda O'Riordan, Ballycotton ☎ 086-170 4085)

Cork
East

Potato Grower

● Willie Scannell's Ballycotton Potatoes

Willie is a potato grower, and a legend. He's one of the stalwarts of the Midleton market, where he sells his balls-of-flour potatoes. The salt-washed clifftop hills of Ballycotton are his stomping ground, and that terroir makes for the most grandiloquent tubers. (Willie Scannell, Ballytrasna, Ballycotton ☎ 021-464 692)

Carrigtwohill

Farmhouse Cheese

● Ardsallagh Goats' Cheese

Jane Murphy and her family personify the artisan calling, a way of working that works when you get close to nature, close to your animals, close to the products you produce, and close to the customers whose lives you improve because your foods are so good. Buy some Ardsallagh goat's cheese, milk or yogurt, and you are buying a small part of this family's philosophy, their work practices, their commonality with nature, their creativity. And some folk think it's just a goat's cheese. Frankly, my dears, it is life itself. (Jane Murphy, Woodstock, Carrigtwohill ☎ 021-488 2336 jane@ardsallaghgoats.com www.ardsallaghgoats.com)

Vegetables and Plants

● Ballintubber Farm

In the last Food Guide, we mentioned how we had bought one of Dave and Siobhan's turnips, brought it home from Mahon Market, cooked it, and had been blown away by its quality, its flavour. This time, it's cauliflower. When we bought the cauliflower, Dave gave us a fascinating spiel about the methods needed to grow them properly – plenty of manure, plenty of manure. Sam and PJ McKenna listened transfixed – this is true – to what Dave had to say. We brought the cauli home, cooked it, and it blew us away, again. Ballintubber Farm: magic, thanks to plenty of manure. (Dave & Siobhan Barry, Carrigtwohill ☎ 021-488 3034/086-823 8187)

made in Cork

Ardsallagh Goats' Cheese

Castlemartyr

Greengrocer and Takeaway

● The Village Greengrocer & Foodhall

There is a very busy traiteur counter here in the Village Greengrocer, with a busy lunchtime and take-away trade, and the shop has lots of nice things to pile into your basket. (Sean & Dorothy Walsh, Main Street, Castlemartyr ☎ 021-466 7655 thevillagegreengrocer@eircom.net – Open 7.30am-7pm Mon-Fri, 7.30am-6pm Sat)

Cloyne

Farmhouse Cheese & Farmshop

● Castlemary Farm

Olive and John Hallahan have created one of the newest farmhouse cheeses – Cloyne Goat's Cheese – here in Castlemary, making both a fresh and an aged goat's cheese. And they have had the smarts to create a new farm shop from which to sell it, along with goats' milk, goat meat, jams, eggs and yogurts, and more. We need farmers selling their foods in their own farm shops, so let's see more shops like Castlemary. (Olive & John Hallahan, Castlemary, Cloyne ☎ 087-797 7203 – Open Saturday 10am-4pm)

Honey

● Lisanley Honey

We love Lisanley honey. It's so floral, so clean, such a patient and powerful addition to the morning's porridge, or drizzled over some good yogurt. It is goodness personified, and every spoonful of Samuel's honey gets you up close and personal with nature itself. (Samuel Kingston, Cloyne ☎ 021-465 2627)

made in Cork

Green Saffron

Cork East

Cobh

Fish Smokehouse

● Belvelly Smokehouse

We have described Frank Hederman of Belvelly Smokehouse as "The Mozart of smoke", for his culinary signature with his smoked fish is lithe, impish, unpredictable, wildly creative. His favoured wood for smoking fish is beech, not oak. The great naturalist, Richard Mabey, writes that the beech has an "intriguing eccentricity... They don't conform to the image of the 'good' tree". That wildness, that rascal nature, suits Hederman's approach: he doesn't want a blanket of smoke on his fish: he wants a suspicion of smoke, a conspiracy of its elements, its ethereality. He is a child of the 60's – just – and credits Myrtle Allen as the primary influence on his work. But he has adapted Mrs Allen's vision to his own template, for his culinary aesthetic is all and entirely his own: he has a poet's judgement, and judgement is all. (Frank & Caroline Hederman, Belvelly, Cobh ☎ 021- 481 1089 shipping@frankhederman.com www.frankhederman.com)

Farmers' Market

● Cobh Farmers' Market

Friday morning, 10am, and when the market is held on the seafront during the summer months, it is truly special. (Friday, 10am, Seafront, Cobh)

Organic Prepared Foods

● Just Food

We buy Just Foods soups, salads, pestos, and pâtés in our local supermarket, and we love the way in which Deirdre Hilliard has gotten her delicious, organic, handmade, benchmark products into so many shops. It's a classic example of guerilla tactics, for Deirdre started off at a market stall in Midleton, and has steadily grown the company, all the while remaining true to their ethos: organic, and handmade. So, Just Foods are in URRU and Ardkeen, and in Supervalu and Dunnes, and they belong in both. (Deirdre & Kevin Hilliard, Rushbrooke Commercial Park, Cobh ☎ 021-481 5516 ☝ www.justfood.ie)

Guest Accommodation

● Knockeven House

Pam and John run the most comfortable, elegant house here in Cobh, a benchmark address for great hospitality and one of the best breakfasts you can find. (Pam & John Mulhaire, Rushbrooke, Cobh ☎ 021-481 1778 ✉ info@knockevenhouse.com ☝ www.knockevenhouse.com)

Ladysbridge

Organic Farm & Brewery

● Rupert's Farm

In addition to his pivotal work orchestrating Farmers' Markets in and around Cork, Rupert Hugh-Jones also finds time to grow very fine organic vegetables and leaves. Plans for a craft brewery are in train, moving steadily forward. (Rupert & Lydia Hugh-Jones, Kilcreden, Upper Ladysbridge ✉ info@rupertsfarm.com ☝ www.rupertsfarm.com)

Midleton

Organic Chickens

● Dan Ahern Organic Chickens

Dan Ahern is best known for his organic hubbard chickens, but his Angus beef is as fine as his birds, and his eggs are gorgeous, and his turkeys and geese are ace. Quietly and meticulously, Dan does the good thing, and these birds will come a revelation the first time you cook them, so full of flavour, so satisfying, and such good value for money. (Dan Ahern, Ballysimon, Midleton ☎ 021-463 1058/086-165 9258)

Fishmonger

● Ballycotton Seafood

Having their own boats and their own processing plant means that the fish the Walsh family sell in Midleton, and in the English Market, is top notch. If you are pressed for cooking time, their range of prepared fish dishes is notably excellent. (The Walsh family, 46 Main Street, Midleton ☎ 021-461 3122 info@ballycotton.ie www.ballycottonseafood.ie)

Butcher

● Crowley's Craft Butchers

Cork East

Jim Crowley is one of those dynamic, competitive butchers, one of those guys who haul in the competition medals and the awards certificates for the prepared meats and meat products, a butcher whose shop and staff are utterly customer-focused. It's an excellent shop, with everything you could need on offer. (Jim Crowley, Mill Road, Midleton ☎ 021-461 3542 www.crowleyscraftbutcher.com – Open 8am-6pm Mon-Sat)

local knowledge

Irish Whiskey

Midleton is the modern home of Irish distilling, and the huge Irish Distillers' plant here both produces an exhilarating range of Irish whiskeys, and gives visitors a chance to understand the nuances and magic imparted by traditional distilling methods. Whiskey is made from barley, malt, grain, water and yeast. But what makes many Irish whiskeys distinct is the triple distillation in copper pot stills.

It is this technique, along with the absence of peat smoking when the malt is being dried, that gives the Midleton whiskeys their smooth, rounded and slightly sweet character.

www.tours.jamesonwhiskey.com

Delicatessen and Restaurant

● The Farmgate

Marog O Brien will celebrate thirty years of the Farmgate next year, a remarkable achievement by one of the great Cork restaurateurs. Throughout that period, Ms O Brien has never stopped developing, innovating, improving, refining an aesthetic that is grounded in a philosophy of "honest simplicity". There is so much potency in the use of those two words, and honest simplicity shines through the dishes cooked by Ms O'Brien and her daughter, Sally: mackerel with hollandaise and chive cream; duck with sage and onion; rack of Kerry lamb; brill with salsa verde. Both the restaurant and the shop are particularly delightful places, exuding comfort and hospitality, the ether and actuality of cooking. (Marog & Sally O'Brien, Coolbawn, Midleton ☎ 021-463 2771 restaurant@farmate.ie www.farmgate.ie – Open 9am-5pm Tues-Sat, 6.30pm-9.30pm Thur-Sat)

Cork East

Farmers' Market

● Midleton Farmers' Market

Midleton is one of the finest Farmers' Markets in Ireland. We were here on the first Saturday the market began, at the dawn of the new millennium, and its development and improvement and expansion has been an utter delight. It's a stand-out market for a simple reason: every producer is a benchmark producer, so everything you buy – apple juice; fish; carrots; cakes; pork; cheese; pâté; pizza, you name it – is as good as it gets. The setting is sylvan and sympathetic, and every Saturday we shop here we spend an absolute fortune. (John Potter Cogan jpotcog@eircom.net or contact through www.midletonfarmersmarket.com – Open Sat 9am-1pm)

Butcher

● Frank Murphy

"One of the most remarkable people I've met in a very long time" is how the great Ella McSweeney described Frank Murphy. Ms McSweeney also spoke of the compassion with which butchers like Mr Murphy approach their animals when they deal with them in their abattoir. So, in Murphy's, you get local meat from local farms dealt with in their own abattoir close to the shop. You cannot get a better system for producing meat than this, and Frank and his dad, Dan, have done the good thing every day for sixty years, and there is 200 years of selling meat behind the whole superb operation. All Irish, all good, and as good as it gets. (Frank Murphy, 79 Main Street, Midleton ☎ 021-463 1557 www.murphybutchersmidleton.com – Open 9am-6pm Mon-Sat)

Restaurant

● The Pantry

Gordon and Alison's Pantry combines an interesting food store, which has lots of good things from Katie's chocolates to Justnuts to Karmine apple juice, with a café – offering breakfasts, sandwiches and daily specials – and a bakery. So, whether it's an apple tart or a Malteser cheesecake to go, boiled eggs with soldiers for breakfast or a seafood pie for lunch, or a packet of Cork Coffee Roasters brew, it's all here. (Gordon & Alison Callinan, Distillery Walk, Midleton ☎ 021-463 3335 – Open Mon-Sat 8.30am-6.30pm)

Restaurant

● Sage

"I believe Sage to be currently one of the best restaurants in the country", says Joe McNamee. "Kevin Aherne is quite a special chef. He has an extraordinary palate for one so young and his fundamental techniques are flawless. He is also rather puritanical in his outlook, which means his devotion to local produce is utterly genuine." On a recent trip, Joe enjoyed hake and chorizo fishcakes; organic smoked salmon with beetroot fritters; twice-cooked duck with dauphine potatoes; chicken supreme with brussels sprouts, all of it perfect. Mr Aherne also specialises in both market menus – everything sourced from the Midleton market – and his 12-mile menus, which feature classics like James Stafford's corned beef and cabbage or Woodside Farm pork shoulder and colcannon, all of the dishes filtered through the chef's enigmatic and creative prism. A young man we are all going to be hearing a great deal about. (Kevin Aherne, 8 The Courtyard, Main Street, Midleton ☎ 021-463 9682 info@sagerestaurant.ie www.sagerestaurant.ie – Open from 10am, food served noon-3pm Tue-Sat, 9am-3pm Sun, 5.30pm-9pm Thu, Fri & Sat)

Wholefood Shop

● Well & Good

You only need to steal a glance at her Facebook page to see what a smart, cultured, vital person Jill Bell is. And that intelligence, culture and vitality is put to the service of her customers in one of Midleton's essential shops. Ms Bell has been doing the good thing since 1997 now, and she is one of the mighty food mavens of County Cork. (Jill Bell, Broderick Street, Midleton ☎ 021-463 3499 – Open 9.30am-6pm Mon-Sat)

Shanagarry

Cookery School

● Ballymaloe Cookery School & Gardens

Two factors have helped Darina Allen to make the Ballymaloe School a global brand. First, she brought the awesome energy of the O'Connell family of Cullahill to Ballymaloe. Secondly, in Ballymaloe she found a culture that allowed her to contribute her own philosophy slowly, patiently, painstakingly. She discovered things about which she could be certain: how to grow things, how to cook things, how to weave an aesthetic in a life, and how to find a politics that was not just parish pump. Her involvement with the Slow Food movement showed her that what the Ballymaloe School is about is actually an international culture, a global politics that calls for decency and fairness. She has a power, expressed most recently through her formidable large-scale cookery books, and she can galvanise people, and change their lives for the better. And she makes it fun, not least at the Saturday pizza sessions at the cookery school, where scores of food lovers turn up for Philip's pizzas: see you there. (Darina & Tim Allen, Shanagarry ☎ 021-464 6785 info@cookingisfun.ie www.cookingisfun.ie)

Cork East

Relish

● Ballymaloe Relish

Yasmin Hyde and the Ballymaloe Relish crew got it right, right from the start: the original Ballymaloe Country Relish is one of the modern Irish food icons, a steadfast standby in every larder. Over the years the company has developed patiently and organically, waiting until every new product is just right before it lands on the shelves. Ourselves, we wouldn't dream of a wrap without the sweet hot hit of the Jalapeno Pepper Relish in particular. (Yasmin Hyde, Courtstown Park, Little Island ☎ 021-435 4810 www.ballymaloecountryrelish.ie)

Restaurant and Country House

● Ballymaloe House

The power of Ballymaloe House lies in two things. Firstly, Myrtle Allen has always understood better than anyone what makes a food special: purity; locality; provenance. Secondly, she has never flinched from practising and expressing that belief in the intrinsic goodness and valour of food, ever since they opened their doors in 1964. Empires have fallen around her feet, bright stars have fizzled out, societies and cultures have changed, but she has not. She has stood her ground, time and again, her message unwavering. And so, in Ballymaloe it is always 1964, and time for a dinner of local foods - Ballycotton fish; Cloyne beef; garden gooseberries; Milleens cheese from down the Beara peninsula. Her power is such that her status as the most important person in Irish food is completely unchallenged. We would go further than this, however: Myrtle Allen is the most important person to have practised and expressed an individual culture in the history of the Irish state, and that is why Ballymaloe is so important. (Myrtle Allen, Shanagarry ☎ 021-46 2531 info@ballymaloe.com www.ballymaloe.com – Restaurant Open 7pm-9.30pm Mon-Sat, 7.30pm-8.30pm Sun)

Kitchen Shop and Café

● Ballymaloe Shop & Café

Wendy Whelan runs a great shop, a place where everything is covetable, where everything has been chosen because it fits so well with everything else. But, in addition to the shop, Mrs Whelan also runs a café – the Café at the end of the Shop – that is a superb exemplar of the Ballymaloe ethos: simple food, cooked with lovin' care, served with grace and an utter lack of pretension, a place to enjoy quiet moments of perfection. In the last Food Guide, we singled out the baked cheesecake prepared in the Café at the End of the Shop. This time, it has to be the chocolate and raspberry tart. Perfect beyond belief, the tart showed why these ingredients belong together, and yet it took their natural affinities even higher, into a perfect synthesis that defined what great cooking is. Perfect. There is some lovely Friday evening cooking also: small plates of cured meats; chicken cannelloni with spinach and wild garlic; albondigas with Woodside Farm pork; spider crab cocktail. (Wendy Whelan, Ballymaloe House, Shanagarry ☎ 021-465 2032 www.ballymaloe.ie – Open Day-time Mon-Sun)

Smoked Salmon

● Casey's Smokehouse

Bill Casey's enduring style with his excellent smoked fish is a deft lightness and a subtle aromaticism, thank to judicious use of both oak and beech wood. (Bill Casey, Shanagarry ☎ 021-464 6955 ✉ smokiec@gofree.indigo.ie)

Coffee Roaster

● Golden Bean

Mark Kingston is regarded by many coffee lovers as the best roaster in the business, and a man whose barista skills mean he can serve those roasts at their optimum. His style is one that captures essences: ethereal flavour notes, textures and temperatures are captured, and you have a cup of coffee for the gods. (Mark Kingston, An Tigin Beag, Ballymaloe, Shanagarry ☎ 086-836 6325)

Cork East

Spice Mixes

● Green Saffron

Steadily, surely, inexorably, Arun Kapil is becoming a figure in the popular consciousness. The awards, the media profiles are piling up and, any minute now, we will be able to say that Mr Kapil is, indeed, famous. Proper order. He is a dynamic, creative, hard-working guy who has transformed people's perception and respect for Indian food, and he has done it the hard way: selling and cooking at busy Farmers' Markets, patiently introducing the complexities and culture of Asian food to the Irish. What The Real Olive Co did for olives and the Med, Green Saffron has done for Indian cooking. (Arun Kapil, Unit 16, Knockgriffin, Midleton ☎ 021-463 7960 ✉ eatwell@greensaffron.com 🖱 www.greensaffron.com)

Pig Roasts

● Wildside Catering

Does anyone dare get married these days without booking Ted Berner and his Wildside team to do the catering? We're pretty sure that all the cool cats have to have a Wildside pig roasting on a spit at their nuptials, its crackling carved into complex hieroglyphic patterns by these artists of the porky arts. Wildside do the coolest grub, in the coolest way. So, as soon as you have made the proposal, be sure to book that pig. (Ted Berner, Shanagarry ☎ 086-868 1863 ✉ ted@wildsidecatering.ie 🖱 www.wildsidecatering.ie)

Youghal

Restaurant and Guesthouse

● Aherne's

There is almost 90 years of family history and experience at work in Aherne's, a stylish hotel with both a restaurant and with food served in their popular bar. David Fitzgibbon's speciality in the restaurant is seafood cooking, which he delivers with classic élan. (The Fitzgibbon family, 163 North Main Street, Youghal ☎ 024-92424 ahernes@eircom.net www.ahernes.com – Open all year except Christmas. Bar open noon-10pm, Restaurant open 6.30pm-9.30pm)

Mobile Rotisserie

● Annie's Roasts

Good free-range birds from East Ferry and a garlic-brown sugar and secret ingredient marinade give Annie Murphy's roasted birds a real zing. Her tidy trailer is fast becoming a Cork market fixture. One taste and you'll know why. (Annie Murphy, Knockmonlea, Youghal ☎ 086-305 9664 annie@anniesroasts.ie www.anniesroasts.ie)

Cork East

Traiteur and Caterer

● Le Gourmet

M. Bernard runs a valuable catering service and traiteur, tucked away down the mall in Youghal. Good breads and baking underscore a tasty offer on every front. (Jean-François Bernard, 5 River Gate Mall, Youghal ☎ 024 20000 legourmet@eircom.net – Open 9am-6pm Mon-Sat)

local knowledge

Saturday Pizzas

Residents of East Cork turn up in vast numbers to the Ballymaloe Cookery School on Saturday afternoons (12.30pm-4pm) to eat woodfired pizza, made by Philip Dennhardt using produce from their farm and garden.

Country House

● Newtown House

Caroline Hennessy has described Newtown House as "a retreat from the hurly burly of life", and capturing that elusive feeling and delivering it explains why guests are so devoted to Georgie and Michael Penruddock's beautiful house. Newtown enjoys a pretty breathtaking location, on the edge of the Blackwater estuary and directly across from the town of Youghal, so even just arriving here inspires the feeling of escape. (Georgie & Michael Penruddock, Kinsalebeg, Youghal ☎ 024-94304 info@stayatnewtown.com www.stayatnewtown.com)

Fishmonger

● Yawl Bay Seafoods

David Browne is a smart innovator. He has already made a classy double act with his smoked salmon and smoked haddock, both star brands, and the company sells fine fresh fish from its factory shop. But his latest innovation, cooked crab meat with an extended shelf-life of two weeks, is really out there. The smart bit is the fact that the quality of the crab is ace: the extended shelf-life hasn't impacted on quality at all. This took a lot of time to get right – 9 months of trials, believe it or not. So, respect to Dr Susan Steele and John Fagan of BIM who worked with the dynamic Mr Browne. And you don't even have to be in east Cork to get the crab meat: just get your plastic and get on line. (David Browne, Foxhole Industrial Estate, Youghal ☎ 024-92290 yawlbay@indigo.ie www.yawlbayseafood.ie – Open 9am-5pm Mon-Fri, 10am-2pm Sat, closed for lunch Mon-Thur)

WEST CORK

THE PENINSULAS – BEARA, SCHULL & SHEEP'S HEAD

Adrigole

Shop

● Peg's Shop

Maureen Sullivan runs a lovely shop here in Peg's. Like the best Beara stores, it's friendly, atmospheric and fun, with lots of tasty things to eat and good bottles of wine. (Maureen Sullivan, Adrigole, ☎ 027-60007 – Open from 8.30am Mon-Sun, closed between 2pm-6pm Sun)

Cork West

Ahakista

Café and Art Gallery

● The Heron Gallery and Café

The Heron Gallery is one of West Cork's hidden gems, thanks to the wonderful artwork of Amabel Langrish whose distinctive, ocean-inspired prints are becoming increasingly visible throughout the country. If the art is simple, elegant, fun and approachable, then so is the food served in the cafe. Light wholesome lunches, cakes and bakes, all served in a beautiful space. (Amabel Langrish, Rossnacaheragh, Ahakista ☎ 027-67278 www.herongallery.net)

Ardgroom

Pub

● Harrington's Post Office

Noraleen's store is one of those places that seems to sit at the centre of the community, at the centre of the peninsula, at the centre of the universe. Harrington's is a defining place, in the way that great general stores used to be. So, come here to enjoy a coffee in the café in the morning or a sandwich at lunchtime, sit outside at a table in the summer sunshine, then choose a nice bottle of wine to bring home for dinner. Harrington's is an axis of good things, the centre of the universe brought down to the Beara. (Noraleen ni Urdall, Ardgroom ☎ 027-74003 ardgroompostoffice@eircom.net – Open 8am-8pm Mon-Sun, open till 9pm during summer)

Ballydehob

Italian Restaurant and Pizzeria

● Antonio's

Antonio's is one of the busiest restaurants in West Cork: its charismatic mix of good Italian food and good pizzas a winning formula, whether you want to just grab a pizza to go, or else settle in for a fun dinner. Their signature pasta dishes are really fine, and an evening here is always great theatre as well as great fun. (Antonio & Julie Pisani, Main Street, Ballydehob ☎ 028-37139 antonioristorante@gmail.com – Open 9am-9pm Mon-Sat, noon-5pm Sun in summer, 9am-5pm Mon-Sat in winter)

Wholefoood Shop and Café

● Hudson's

The artisan producers of West Cork beat a path to Hudson's with their produce once the season gets underway, closely followed by Gillian Hudson's devoted customers who want to get their hands on all that lovely produce. The combination of a fine bakery, a wholefood store, a vegetable shop and a fine café makes for a one-stop-oasis of good things, and it makes for one of the key West Cork addresses. (Gillian Hudson, Main Street, Ballydehob ☎ 028-37565 www.hudsonswholefood.com – Open 9.30am-6pm Mon-Sat)

Free-range Ducks

● Skeaghanore Ducks

We eat the Skeaghanore duck legs in red wine and black olive stews. We roast the duck breast with Chinese spices. We mix the duck wings with chickpeas for a satisfying braise. We skewer the duck livers and grill them. And for a Sunday dinner treat, we roast the Skeaghanore ducks whole. I guess that makes us devoted users of Eugene and Helena's beautuful birds. So, what do you do with your Skeaghanore duck? (Eugene & Helena Hickey, Skeaghanore, Ballydehob ☎ 028-37428 skeaghanoreduck@eircom.net www.skeaghanoreduck.ie)

Deli Café

West Cork Gourmet Store

Joanne has created a clever and enduring concept in this tiny space. Food is prepared behind a large display of charcuterie and salads; chairs are dotted around underneath shelves of oriental and Irish produce, and there is a tiny garden out back. WCGS is a place for lunch, and the occasional summer dinner, with lovely wines and good things to eat. (Joanne Cassidy, Staball Hill, Ballydehob ☎ 028-25991 ✉ ydissacj@yahoo.ie – Open 9.30am-6pm Mon-Sat. Open dinner Thur-Sat during summer evenings)

Bantry

Cork West

Cookware Shop

Bantry Cookware Company

Andrew and Maria's BCC is where we get our meat probes, our Kilner jars, our must-have kitchen gear, and they even sharpen our knives for us, and do it brilliantly. A great shop. (Andrew & Maria Campbell, Bridge Street, Bantry ☎ 027-55651 ✉ info@cookware.ie 🖱 www.cookware.ie – Open 10am-6pm Mon-Sat)

Farmers' Market

Bantry Friday Market

The Bantry Market is our local stomping ground on Fridays, the place where we meander from stall to stall doing the week's food shopping. The food content of the market has now expanded, and has crossed the street and taken up residence in part of the square, with space for newcomers who are surely and steadily expanding the weekly delights of this lovely market. The enlarged market on the first Friday in the month is one of the best markets in Ireland, with everything for sale. So, if you need a donkey, or some West Cork ricotta, this is where you will find it. (Bantry Town Centre, Fridays)

Fishmonger

Central Fish Market

After a busy day working on this book, we cooked some haddock bought from the Central Fish market for our dinner. We did it the Martin Shanahan way – dusted in seasoned flour, fried in rapeseed oil – and it was as perfect as a piece of haddock could be, and made for a perfect dinner. So simple, so good, so our thanks to Colman and the crew in the CFM. (Colman Keohane, New Street, Bantry ☎ 027-53714 ✉ centralfishmarket@eircom.net – Open 9am-6pm Tue-Fri, Sat 10am-5pm, Mon 9.30am-5.30pm)

Restaurant

● The Fish Kitchen

They cook nice fresh fish in the FK, a bustling little room upstairs from the fish shop in the centre of town. There are choices other than fish – a 10oz sirloin is on the evening menu, and there is a steak and scallops offer – but fish is the signature style here: grilled cod; battered haddock; tagine of monkfish. Nice cooking, great service from Ann-Marie, and extremely good value for money adds up to a really smart choice. (Diarmuid & Ann-Marie Murphy, New Street, Bantry ☎ 027-56651 ✉ thefishkitchen@gmail.com 🖱 www.thefishkitchen.ie – Open noon-4pm, 5.30pm-9pm Tue-Sat)

Cork West

Organic Growing Supplies

● Fruit Hill Farm

Manfred's covetable gardening tools and seeds, and Eddie's pitch-perfect organic vegetables, are the yin and yang of the essential Fruit Hill Farm. Ever fallen in love with a trowel? You will here. Mrs Wandel's vegetables are sold locally during the summer season and they are definingly fine.(Manfred & Eddie Wandel, Bantry ☎ 027-50710 🖱 www.fruithillfarm.com)

local knowledge

Hand-Crafted Knives

Bantry in West Cork boasts not one, but two cutlers: Pat Mulcahy and Rory Conner. Both men are masters of this arcane, delightful and absorbing art, and their knives are things of beauty to treasure forever.

● www.roryconnerknives.com
● www.knifecraft.biz

Skeaghanore Ducks

Local Shop

● Manning's Emporium

Who would have thought that Manning's Emporium could be so wonderfully rejuvenated at this stage of its existence? The touchpaper was lit by the arrival of Val's niece, Laura, and her husband Andrew Heath into the business and their enthusiasm seems to have sprinkled the whole place with some magic dust. More than just an emporium for the finest locally sourced food in the area, Manning's is now a super cool café - it might be the only place in West Cork serving a Flat White – and just try those raspberry cupcakes or scones – the food is delicious. The genius touch is the addition of a sherry bar, right at the front of the shop. It's hard to imagine anything more enjoyable than sitting at that little bar with a glass of chilled fino sherry, some local cheese or cured meats, listening to the genial and venerable Val chatting away to customers and so visibly enjoying his work. (Laura Manning, Andrew Heath, Val Manning, Ballylickey, Bantry ☎ 027-50456 ✉ lauramanning@gmail.com 🖱 www.manningsemporium.ie – Open 9am-6.30pm Mon-Sat, 9am-5pm Sun)

Organic Farm & Willow Baskets and Structures

● Maughnasily Organic Farm

Martin and Yvonne run the most gorgeous farm, produce beautiful food – kid meat, for instance, which is rare as anything, fantastic eggs, great vegetables and organic meat – and are basket makers extraordinaire. Their vision of the pastoral life is intensely practical, and endearing, and don't miss their stall at the Bantry Market. (Martin & Yvonne O'Flynn, Maughnasily, Kealkill, Bantry ☎ 027-66111)

Restaurant

● O'Connor's Seafood Restaurant

Pat Kiely was once head chef in O'Connor's. Today, as owner, he has brought some nice signature touches to the menu: mussels in three styles – white wine and cream; garlic and herb breadcrumb; coconut curry.

Oysters 3 ways – with stout and walnuts; Rockefeller; baked with garlic and herbs. Fish and chips two ways – smoked haddock and cod in beer batter, and southern-fried goujons of hake. Fish is the way to go, though there are, of course, carnivorous choices. (Pat Kiely, The Square, Bantry ☎ 027-50221/51094 ✉ eat@oconnorsbantry.com 🖰 www.oconnorseafood.com – Open 12.30pm-3pm Mon-Fri & Sun, 5.30pm-9.30pm Mon-Sun)

local knowledge

Spelling Bee

Children need to experience food in the most tactile way, and the best way for them to do this is to tend to beehives. Seriously. So, first of all get a copy of Tim Rowe's *Bees, Hives, Honey! Beekeeping For Children*, **written and published in Bantry 🖰 www.rosebeehives.com**

Cork West

Wholefood Shop and Bakery

● Organico

In Organico, both shop and next-door restaurant, Rachel and Hannah Dare have created a pair of spaces where time seems to stand still. If it is still, then what time is it? It's that time when you were young, when you knew who you were, and where you wanted to go. Organico is like a portal into your own back pages. It's rare to be able to achieve this, especially in what is ostensibly a wholefood shop. But Organico is different, and it is more than just a wholefood shop and fine bakery. It's a slice of West Cork culture. (Hannah & Rachel Dare, 2 Glengarriff Road, Bantry ☎ 027-51391 🖰 www.organico.ie – Open 9.30am-6pm Mon-Sat)

Café

● Organico Café

If you thought Organico was exclusively a vegetarian café, think again. Rachel Dare and her team now serve some non-vegetarian dishes, and it would be more accurate now to describe Organico as a local café: ie a place serving local, West Cork foods. The cooking is imaginative, inventive and clean, the room is languorous and social. (Rachel Dare, 2 Glengarriff Road, Bantry ☎ 027-55905 🖰 www.organico.ie – Open 10am-5pm Mon-Sat)

Nursery

Peppermint Farm

Doris sells her beautiful herbs on Friday mornings in Bantry, and her range is extraordinary – more than 300 varieties of culinary, medicinal and fragrant herbs, many of which she uses to make an excellent range of teas. The herb plants and the teas are both available to buy online. (Doris Hoffman, Toughraheen, Bantry ☎ 028-31869 www.peppermintfarm.com)

Restaurant

Pizza Base

Maartin's pizzas are amongst the best we know. Pizza Base is well-named, for the crusts here are just right – crisp, firm, the tasty canvas supporting the cast of ingredients that Maartin lines up ready for their wood-fired finish. Any festival or fun event where Pizza Base arrives at is suddenly a better festival. (Maartin La Haye, Pearson's Bridge, Bantry ☎ 086-367 4360 pizzabaseireland@gmail.com www.pizzabase.ie)

Cork West

Beekeeper

Tim Rowe Rose Hives

Tim Rowe not only produces magnificent honey, he produces magnificent books about bees and honey. His second book, *Bees, Hives, Honey! Beekeeping For Children* is a little masterpiece, and should be part of the curriculum in every school in Ireland. When children know how to nurture and care for bees, they know how the world works. Every home should have a copy of this beautiful book, and every home should have a hive in the garden. Get started with a rose hive. (Tim Rowe, Ballylickey, Bantry ☎ 027-66472 www.rosebeehives.com)

Hotel

Sea View House Hotel

Kathleen O'Sullivan runs her hotel the old school way, with correct cooking, correct service, simple and correct design, eager and correct housekeeping. The pleasures to be derived from her didactic approach to running an hotel are myriad. This may be the old school way, but that means it is the good school way, and this sense of correctness explains why so many customers regard Sea View House as one of their favourite places to stay in Ireland. Your heart leaps with anticipation and delight every time you turn up the driveway. (Kathleen O'Sullivan, Ballylickey ☎ 027-50073 info@seaviewhousehotel.com www.seaviewhousehotel.com)

Goat's Cheese

● Saoirse Goat's Cheese

Sean OBriain's soft goat's cheeses are delicious and, in the way of the best West Cork traditions, they are extremely hard to find. Just as it can be difficult to track down Ardagh Castle cheese from Baltimore, or Sunview Goat's cheese from Kilmichael, or a West Cork blue cheese that turns up occasionally at the Bantry Market and which is completely mysterious, so the Saoirse cheeses need to be hunted down. They are worth the hunt, so keep an eye out for the little circular ash boxes. (Sean OBriain, Bantry ☎ 086-376 0851)

made in Cork

Irish Atlantic Sea Salt

Pub

● The Snug

The Snug isn't trendy. There are no craft brews (yet), no wraps or ciabatta (ever). What there are is nightlight candles lit at the bar, polished glasses, a proprietress who calls everybody "Pet", water with ice and lemon without having to order it, black uniformed staff, and more polishing of glasses. Sit up, and order plaice with mushroom sauce, a good cheese burger, sirloin and gravy, baked haddock, minute steak, and relish the amazing vegetables. Heartwarming, delicious and delightful. (Maurice & Colette O'Donovan, The Quay, Bantry ☎ 027-50057 – Food served 10am-8.45pm Mon-Sun)

Delicatessen

● The Stuffed Olive

"My favourite ever deli" is how the brilliant Sheila Kiely, author and blogger of gimmetherecipe, describes Trish and Marjorie's The Stuffed Olive. "I ogled the salad bar: I have never seen salad made to look more inviting." Indeed, Trish and Marjorie make everything look catwalk chic – cakes; salads; foods to go; their legendary sandwiches; the delectable foods on the shelves. Just brilliant. (Marjorie Kelly & Trish Messon, New Street, Bantry ☎ 027-55883 – Open 9am-6pm Mon-Sat)

Restaurant

● Willie Pa's

On Christmas Day evening 2011, having served Xmas dinner to 110 people, Willie Pa's was destroyed by a fire. It was big news in West Cork for a simple reason: WP's is the most popular restaurant in these parts, the sort of destination that serves 110 people even on Christmas Day. Happily, by Easter they were open once again, and instantly packed with happy West Cork punters. Christian Barcoe and his team know what their customers like and no one is more expert at delivering the good times every time. (Christian Barcoe & Helen O'Brien, Colomane Cross, Bantry ☎ 027-50392 – Open 6pm-9.30pm Fri-Sat, 12.30pm & 3pm, 6pm-8pm Sun, open for special bookings only mid-week)

Thai & Vietnamese Food to Go, Caterer

● Wok About

Henry Hegarty understands Thai food in a way few people in Ireland do. Wok About's cooking isn't afraid to be different, isn't afraid to be spicy, isn't afraid to be real. Mr Hegarty gets the flavours to sing and dance the way good street food should, and you can tell that Henry learnt his skills in Thailand, as well as Cambodia, Laos and Vietnam. Friday morning in Bantry is the time to get the chopsticks out, and any festival where Mr Hegarty sets up his tent suddenly gets a whole lot more interesting. (Henry Hegarty, Bantry ☎ 086-023 4788 henry@wokabout.ie www.wokabout.ie)

Cahermore

Goat's Cheese

● Irish Atlantic Sea Salt

After decades of devotion to Maldon salt, Michael and Aileen's Atlantic Sea Salt has won the prize as our go-to-salt for seasoning at the table. The crystals are harder and larger than Maldon, and the flavour is wonderfully clean and seasalty saline. We expect to see many imitators copying the brilliant innovation of IASS all around the coast of Ireland over the next few years. (Aileen & Michael O'Neill, Lickbarrahan, Cahermore, Beara ☎ 027-73222 michael@irishatlanticsalt.ie www.irishatlanticsalt.ie)

Castletownbere

Goat's Cheese

Angel Foods

The ginger chefs, as Donna and Angela call themselves, used to work as interior designers and architectural technicians, until cookies and baking took over their busy lives. They make ace cake mixes, simple to use, superb for introducing children to baking. Consider them your Kitchen Angels. (Donna Black & Angela Murray, Castletownbere info@angelfoods.ie www.angelfoods.ie)

Café

Copper Kettle

A modest space, specialising in enormous breakfasts. Lunch in the Copper Kettle is good too, with home-made crumble a recommended choice. The CK is much beloved of the strange and wonderful inhabitants of the Beara Peninsula, who come here to meet, drink coffee and read the Examiner. (Maria Lowney & Darren Lynch ☎ 027-71792 – 10am-5pm Mon-Sat)

Ice-cream parlour and Chocolate Shop

Issie's Handmade Chocolate Shop

The McKenna children can't return from a trip down the Beara without a visit to Issie's for chocolates, hot chocolate and ice creams. Isabel makes excellent chocolates, and the shop is pretty, and special. (Isabel O'Donovan, Derrymihan, Castletownbere ☎ 027-70348 www.issieshandmadechocolate.ie – Open 11am-6pm Fri-Sun)

Healthfood Store

Loop de Loop

Helena Murphy has recently taken the helm of this colourful community healthfood store and Fair Trade gift shop, where along with wholefoods on the shelves, there is a very tiny and pretty garden seating space for those lucky enough to get there first. (Helena Murphy, Bank Place, Castletownbere ☎ 027-70770)

Gallery Café

Mill Cove Gallery

The Mill Cove is one of the nicest places to take tea and eat superb cakes, and to linger over lunch, in

West Cork. John Goode brings the same fastidious eye to food as he does to art, ceramics and garden sculpture, and the Mill Cove is a true oasis, a place of heightened aesthetics, where every gaze finds something to delight, intrigue, and amuse the eye. A really unmissable destination. (John Goode, Mill Cove House, Castletownbere ☎ 027-70393 www.millcovegallery.com – Open 11am-6pm Mon-Sun, high season only. Open for bookings of 8-20 people mid and low season)

made in Cork

Durrus Farmhouse Cheese

Cork West

Bar

● McCarthy's Bar

As you sip a pint in the legendary McCarthy's Bar, make sure to ask Adrienne the story of her father, Aidan's, life. She will refer you to Aidan's book, which tells the incredible story of his wartime service. Once you open it, you won't be able to put it down. The McCarthys are special, and McCarthy's Bar is special. "It might just be the best pub in the world", wrote the late Pete McCarthy. Too right. (Adrienne McCarthy, The Square, Castletownbere ☎ 027-70014 adrimac22@yahoo.com - 11am-5pm Mon-Sat, 12.30pm-5pm Sun)

Delicateseen

● Taste

Sheila Power's shop is simply jammers with good things – brilliant breads, organic vegetables, coffee, cheeses, wholefoods, wines, whatever you might need or could need. Nice sandwiches and wraps too to take care of the hunger pangs. (Sheila Power, Bank Place, Castletownbere ☎ 027-71943 – Open Mon-Sat)

Durrus

Wine Importer

● Albatross Enterprise

Harro and Gisi bring in some nice wines from Germany and sell them in a pretty little wine store, just beside their house, just as you come into the village of Ahakista: look out for the sign. (Harro & Gisi Federsen, Ahakista, Durrus ☎ 027-67248)

Restaurant & Accommodation

Blair's Cove

Is Blair's Cove the most beautiful dining room in the country? No one will argue with you if you say "Yes!". It's a serene, elegant temple for dining in the most jaw-dropping location, jutting out into Dunmanus Bay. Ronald Klotzer is head chef, and continues the much-loved template of the large selection of starter dishes served from the centre of the room, and the selection of puddings and cheeses on the piano, with roasts and grills from the fire in between. There are very elegant rooms for those who wish to stay in his idyllic location. (Philippe & Sabine De Mey, Durrus ☎ 027-62913 mail@blairscove.ie www.blairscove.ie – Open 6.30pm-9pm)

Farmhouse Cheese

Durrus Farmhouse Cheese

The interesting thing about Jeffa Gill is that she is a woman who has spent almost 35 years as the creator of one of the best-known cheeses in Ireland, working to make her cheese as fine as it can be. In the process, she has made Durrus cheese world-famous. And yet she is, personally, self-effacing. Her cheese is foreground, but Ms Gill is background. The reality is that her personality is sublimated into her cheese: it speaks for her, it tells the story of her work, it can alter as her moods might alter. One day, the flavours in the paste are strawberries and green fruits. A few months later, it's mushrooms and damp woodland and umami steak. Most recently, the team have begun to produce Durrus Og, a smaller version of Durrus, and Dunmanus, an aged cheese which is matured for at least 3 months. Durrus cheese is a dance of flavours, and Ms Gill is the lead dancer. (Jeffa Gill, Coomkeen, Durrus ☎ 027-61100 info@durruscheese.com www.durruscheese.com)

Restaurant & Cookery School

Good Things Café & Cookery School

Good Things? By this stage, after nine years in existence during which time Carmel Somers's cooking has improved year-on-year, Good Things should really be called Best Things. Best Things Café! Each year the standard of food takes another step forward – simpler yet more quixotic, more personal yet more open to influence, more local yet with a fresh set of international influences. Combine these seemingly contradictory ingredients and you get a style of cooking like no other – Rebecca's potato omelette with aioil and seabeet; white pollock baked with potatoes and tomatoes; shoulder of lamb with prunes; Dunmanus Bay sea urchins with Gubbeen scrambled eggs and seaweed salad; Elizabeth David's Rhone beef with Ballydehob British queens. No one else makes food like this, informed by everything from Hannah Glasse to Alice Waters. (Carmel Somers, Durrus ☎ 027-61426 info@thegoodthingscafé.com www.thegoodthingscafe.com – Open 11.30am-4pm (lunch served from 12.30pm-3pm), 7pm-8.30pm Thu-Mon. Open Easter, bank hol weekends & from Jun-Sep)

Shop

● The Village Grocer & The Gateway

Eddie and Claire Ryan have added a relaxed, informal café and restaurant to their busy shop in the centre of Durrus village, and it's a lovely spot for morning coffee or a friendly dinner. (Edward & Claire Ryan, Durrus ☎ 027-61184 (shop) ☎ 027-61353 (restaurant) – Open 7am-10pm Mon-Sat, 8.30am-10pm Sun)

Cork West

Eyeries

Bistro & Deli

● Auntie May's

Is Eyeries the prettiest village in Ireland? Well, on our last couple of visits, we lucked out with sunshiney days, and the village, with its colourful houses and magnificent flowers, looked incredible. After a stroll, we went into Auntie May's and had delicious food, once inside the pretty stone-walled room, and once outside under the umbrellas as the wind whistled around us. The cooking is simple and true – excellent Santa Barbara fish stew; tasty burgers; properly-made sandwiches; nice smoked salmon. Then we drove to Dursey and took the cable car, and then we drove home past banks of vivid wild flowers, and we had the best time. (Ciannait Walker, Main Street, Eyeries ☎ 027-74477 – Open seasonally, lunch and dinner)

Farmhouse Cheese

● Milleens Farmhouse Cheese

Milleens Cheese is the Big Bang of Irish artisan foods.

Before Veronica and Norman Steele began making their cheese, starting with the milk of a one-horned cow called Brisket whose milk was originally transformed into cheddar-style cheeses, there were no distinctive, speciality Irish artisan foods that spoke of the place they were made in and the people who made them. Milleens was a new agricultural equation: A = EWC: Agriculture = Energy at the speed of West Cork. The Steeles brought the dairy farm tradition of Munster to modern Ireland. In doing so, they also enshrined a vital aspect of the West Cork way: "making a living making something that matters" as Norman Steele said. Today, Quinlan Steele makes this iconic cheese, the Big Bang cheese of Ireland. (Quinlan Steele, Eyeries, Beara ☎ 027-74079 ✉ milleens@eircom.net 🖱 www.milleenscheese.com)

Garinish

Take-away

● The Dursey Deli

There is a coffee trailer parked up at windy Malin Head, whilst Dursey has the Dursey Deli. Malin 'oop north, Dursey down south, both with places that do the good thing at the extremes of either end of the country. The Dursey Deli is essentially a chipper, but if you're lucky, there'll be fresh mackerel from Dursey's beautiful bay. Time your trip on the terrifying Dursey Cable car to coincide with lunch. (Marg ☎ 086-1799270, Open Easter to September)

Cork West

local knowledge

West Cork Sea Urchins

John Chamberlain exudes the air of an alchemist in his lair as he moves from vat to trough to basin and onwards into the Atlantic itself to secure the future of his beloved sea urchins. Chances are, if you are enjoying some scrambled egg with sea urchin, it's thanks to Mr Chamberlain's dedicated work.

● **Dunmanus Seafoods Ltd** (John Chamberlain, Dunmanus West, Goleen ☎ 028-35500/ 087 2335857)

Schull

Chocolates

● Casa Diego

Diego and his friends have been making some nice Spanish-accented food here at the top of Main Street. The lean rooms suit the simple elegance of the food, and it's a splendid place to feed children on good patatas bravas, paella, calamari, albondigas and their very good homemade croquettes. (Diego Maguez, Main Street, Schull ☎ 086-397 8364 🖰 www.casadiego.ie – Open 10am-10pm)

Cafée & Chocolatier

● The Courtyard

The Courtyard was for decades the very fulcrum of Schull's culinary culture and both residents and visitors will be hoping that Gwen and Claire will restore this lovely warren of rooms to its former glory. M Lasserre's splendiferous chocolates are for sale alongside teas, coffees, pastries and an evolving menu that is a work in progress as we write. How wonderful to see these lovely rooms freshly painted and freshly energised. Excellent wines have been sourced from Le Caveau in Kilkenny. (Gwendalle & Claire Lasserre, Main Street, Schull ☎ 087-317 1369 ✉ gwen@gwenschocolate.com 🖰 www.schullcourtyard.com)

Guesthouse

● Grove House

"Stayed in Grove House in Schull, which I absolutely love!", writes Eamon Barrett. That's a typical reaction to this lovely Colla Road address. Katarina Runske is a human dynamo, one of those people whose elemental energy is astounding to an outsider. How she does all she does we simply do not know, but she runs the house, the restaurant, the gallery and all else as if it is just an average day's work. With her smart young son, Nico, handling things in the kitchen, Ms Runske has moved Grove House centre stage in the hospitality culture of Schull. It's patrician, eccentric, 100% West Cork. (Katarina Runske, Colla Road, Schull ☎ 028-28067 ✉ info@grovehouseschull.com 🖰 www.grovehouseschull.com – Open for light lunches outside when the weather is good, and open for dinner to non residents if booked)

Farmhouse Cheese

● Gubbeen Farmhouse Cheese

Giana Ferguson came to West Cork, aged 24, and took a job "in a little village bar where potters, Buddhists, farmers, poets and fishermen found a great deal to say over a pint". She met and married Tom Ferguson, whose family had farmed the land at Gubbeen for generations, land that is rock and bog, but with clean air and wonderful pasture. Just the place to make a washed-rind, semi-soft cheese. Gubbeen debuted in 1979, and a couple of years later a smoked cheese was created. Gubbeen, today, is made where it was created. "Food has been our life work at Gubbeen", Giana Ferguson has said. Gubbeen Cheese is unique: a micro flora, Microbacterium Gubbeenense, is an element of the rind-washing process as the cheese matures, yards from where the cows are milked each day. The micro flora brings bloom and flavour to the cheese rind. You only find it here, on a farm at the edge of the Atlantic Ocean itself. (Tom & Giana Ferguson, Gubbeen, Schull ☎ 028-28231 ⌖ www.gubbeen.com)

Cork West

Smokehouse and Charcouterie

● Gubbeen Smokehouse

"There was the honour of rearing something, killing it, and making every part of it into something", Fingal Ferguson once said about his work. Honour. Honour amongst Charcutiers. Honour amongst Smokehouses. It's a most unusual language to hear in Ireland, mainly because it's so ancient – it sounds as if it belongs in a medieval Guild – and mainly because the rearing, slaughtering and processing of animals has become an industrialised practice, carried out away from the human eye, away from the honourable gaze. But Mr Ferguson's Gubbeen Smokehouse is different. He shows the respect and, in honouring his pigs, Mr Ferguson also honours his customers. The Gubbeen Smokehouse range are stellar artisan foods, kitchen essentials, menu stalwarts. (Fingal Ferguson, Gubbeen, Schull ☎ 028-27824 ✉ smokehouse@eircom.net ⌖ www.gubbeen.com)

Bar

● Hackett's Bar

Hackett's is the coolest bar, and it is cool in that cool-West Cork way: it's not self-conscious, and nor are the people who come here. It's just cool, cool. They make soups that would sustain the fate of nations, indeed these soups could secure the fate of entire continents, they are so complete, and delicious. Not to be missed. (Trudy Etchells, Main Street, Schull ☎ 028-28625 ✉ trudyetchells@eircom.net – Food served noon-3pm Mon-Sat, 7pm-9pm Fri & Sat)

Charcutier

● Frank Krawczyk's West Cork Charcuterie

Look out for Frank's wonderful charcuterie in the Schull Sunday market, where you can buy a sausage in a bap that beats them all. Quiet, expert, sincere, Frank is one of the pillars of the West Cork food scene. (Frank Krawczyk, The Barn, Dereenatra, Schull ☎ 028-28579 ✉ westcorksalamis@gmail.com)

Fishmonger, Restaurant & Exporter

● Normandy Ireland

The Restaurant is L'Escale – dining at the pier, fish and chips, pizza, crepes, ice cream. But the real gem here is The Fish Shop, on Main Street in Schull. Impeccably fresh fish is served in a crystal clean shop with some good cooked seafood dishes, like their wonderful chowder. (Xavier Legrix, The Pier, Schull ☎ 028-28599 – Restaurant open Jun-Aug, 10am-10pm)

Fish Stalls

● O'Driscoll's Fish

The O'Driscoll brothers and their team are heavyweight hitters at the Cork markets for their fresh Irish fish, filleted in front of your eyes. Just join the ever-present queue for excellent fish at excellent prices. They have also a smashing chipper van that tours the county, producing stunningly good fish and chips at fairs and festivals. (O'Driscoll family, Schull ☎ 028-27569 ✉ olischull@hotmail.com)

Guesthouse

● Paradise Creperie

This French-owned creperie is popular with the visitors who flock to picturesque Schull in the summertime. The real deal when it comes to crepes. You can sit out in their Courtyard out back when the sun shines. (Main Street, Schull ☎ 087-7437427 – Open from 9am, open seasonally)

Wholefood Shop

● Roaring Water Wholefood Shop

Roaring Water is something of an Aladdin's cave of wholesome goodies. There are locally-grown vegetables, supplied by gardeners, as well as all the wholefood essentials. (Lisa Davies, 47 Main Street, Schull ☎ 028-27834 – 9.30am-6pm Mon-Sat & Sun during the summer)

Farmers' Market

● Schull Market

Schull Market is one of the best of the West Cork markets, dominated at one end by the magnificent Gubbeen stall, and dotted with great food offerings that make for a great Sunday Lunch. (Pier Road, Sundays 10am-3pm)

local knowledge

The Ewe Gallery

The Ewe Gallery and Sculpture Garden is an experience that lives up to the description of a "spectacular oasis". The sculptures, created by Sheena Wood and her writer husband Kurt are humorous, telling and instructional, true spectacles. You will be amazed, you'll laugh, you'll cry. And at the end of it you can have tea in their little coffee shop. Not ever to be missed.

● www.theewe.com

WEST CORK

Ballinadee

Pub

● Glebe Country House

Gill Good runs a postcard-pretty house just on the edge of the village, and her reputation as a hostess is spreading quickly. Glebe is a lovely house, with stunning gardens, a place that pulls the West Cork magic together into a personal delight. (Gill Good, Ballinadee, Bandon ☎ 021-477 8294 info@glebecountryhouse.com www.glebecountryhouse.ie)

Ballineen

Café & Shop

● Toirtin @ River Lane Café

Susan Fehily is a magnificent baker, who supplies cakes to local West Cork delis. In Ballineen, the River Café is a charming space with real, rustic, vital cooking. (Susan & Tom Fehily, Bridge Street, Ballineen ☎ 023-884 7173 fehilyrobbins@eircom.net – Cafe open 9.30am-5pm, Shop open 9am-7pm)

Ballinhassig

Goat's Cheese

● Orchard Cottage Dairy

Barry Desmond tends to a herd of happy Nubian goats and utilises their milk to make some splendid fresh cheeses. The cheeses are mild and mellow, but show great character. Don't miss them at the Cork markets. (Barry Desmond, Rigsdale, Ballinhassig ☎ 086-303 7871)

Ballinspittle

Café

● Diva Boutique Bakery

The potato bread was still warm from the oven, and we didn't wait to get it home: sitting in the car in the little square in Ballinspittle, right outside Diva Boutique Bakery, we simply tore chunks off the loaf and scoffed them before even driving away. By the time we had reached Timoleague, half the big, beautiful loaf was gone. Now, that is what bread is. That is what bread can be. "Bread can be the *thing* you're eating, not a prelude to the meal, or an afterthought", writes Tamar Adler, and this was that bread: bread as the meal, the ultimate staff of life. Shannen Keane and her crew can do that sort of magic, they understand how to capture the magic of great baking, and not just with their signature breads: these guys can fire off some killer sweet baking too: true; finessed; earthy yet ethereal. Food for your inner angel, and an unmissable destination. (Shannen Keane, Ballinspittle ☎ 021-477 8465 diva.ballinspittle@gmail.com http://divaboutiquebakery.blogspot.com – Open 9.30am-5pm Thu-Sat, 11am-5pm Sun, longer high season)

Café

● Diva Café

Because everything had been perfect, we were almost reluctant to have coffee. It couldn't be as good as the homemade lemonade, as the stunning spicy lentil soup served with amazing Diva bread, as the Mexican tortilla which was the best we had ever eaten in Ireland. So, let's call it quits, we agreed, and just remember a perfect lunch in this brilliantly burlesque destination.
And then the waitress said: "But you have to have coffee!". So we did, because we couldn't let the poor girl down. And it was perfect. Perfect doesn't happen very often, you know, but Diva has cranked the dials to Perfect these days. (Shannen Keane, Ballinspittle ☎ 021-477 8465 ✉ diva.ballinspittle@gmail.com 🖱 http://divaboutiquebakery.blogspot.com – Open 9.30am-5pm, Thu-Sat, 11am-5pm Sun, with longer hours high season)

Cork West

Food Producer, Chef & Caterer

● Forage & Find

Kevin O'Connell is a chef, and a very good one at that. But away from the kitchen he forages, he finds, and he prepares, and his tonics and concoctions are very good indeed: meadowsweet and rhubarb cordial; sprouted chickpea hummus with sugar kelp; hawthorn jelly; Irish seaweed sprinkle. These are lovely, life-giving foods, so hunt them down at Farmers' Markets and in shops such as Diva. (Kevin O'Connell, Ballinspittle ☎ 085-757 6782 🖱 www.forageandfind.com – Open 8.30am-6pm Mon-Sat)

Butcher

● Lordan's Family Butcher

Donal Lordan is a quiet kind of bloke. He should be famous, for he is famously skilful, but he doesn't bother with that stuff, preferring instead to source and serve superb meats. His butchery skills put most Irish butchers to shame, for this man is an artist of the carcass. A friend once had some West Cork lamb butchered here and shared it with us, and the cuts were so elegantly finished that we admired every piece as a piece of the charcutier's art, before we cooked and ate them. Everything here is good. (Donal Lordan, Ballinspittle ☎ 021-477 8226 – Open 8.30am-6pm Mon-Sat)

Ballyherkin

Vegetarian B&B

● Gort na Nain

And for breakfast at Gort na Nain? Lucy's chestnut sausages, with a poached egg straight from the hens. Ah, the good life was never better than here. That's the thing about Lucy and Ultan's farmhouse B&B: everything looks simple, but everything is sheer class – the comfort of the farmhouse, the cheer of the hosts, the sublime nature of the food, with virtually all of it coming straight from Ultan's acclaimed organic farm. It's their own honey, their own eggs, their own chutneys, breads, pastas, the whole nine yards. Dinner is sublime, and breakfast is... a chestnut sausage with a freshly laid organic egg. (Lucy Stewart & Ultan Walsh, Ballyherkin. Nohoval ☎ 021-477 0647 ✉ lucy@gortnanain.com 🖱 www.gortnanain.com)

made in Cork

Gubbeen Bacon

Baltimore

Café & Gardens

● Glebe Gardens

Jean Perry explains it like this: 'We get our fish from the Fish Station in Skibbereen, our meats from Tom Walsh's butchers, and the vegetables we grow ourselves in the garden.' If you needed to know what you have to do to run a restaurant that will attract attention from the *McKennas' Guides*, then that is as succinct a summation as you can get. Of course, it helps that Ms Perry is also one of the great West Cork pioneers, a superlative grower, a serious thinker about food and creativity, and a person who can assemble a good family crew around herself and her husband, Peter, and daughters Tessa, Keziah and Jo-Jo. A summer's lunch in the courtyard, under blue skies, is just bliss. (Jean Perry, Glebe Gardens, Baltimore ☎ 028-882 0232 ✉ info@glebegardens.com 🖱 www.glebegardens.com. – Open Wed to Sunday, Easter to September)

Self-Catering Accommodation & honey

Inish Beg

The Boathouse at Inis Beg is one of the best known, and most beautiful, places to stay anywhere in Ireland. But even if you can't bag the Boathouse, all the houses on this brilliant getaway are cherishable. (Paul & Georgie Keane, Inish Beg, Baltimore ☎ 028-21745 bookings@inishbeg.com www.inishbeg.com)

Country House

Rolf's Country House

Rolf's really is a smashing place, whether you are down in Baltimore for the boating, or just wending your way pleasurably through the wonders of West Cork. Aside from the comfort, the charm and the spot-on cooking, it is the energy and humour of Johannes and Frederike – and they are witty, droll, animated people – that animates Rolf's and gives it both character and soulfulness, making it a place loved by travellers and, crucially, beloved by locals: Rolf's isn't just for tourists, the locals eat here. (Johannes & Frederike Haffner, Baltimore ☎ 028-20289 www.rolfscountryhouse.eu – Open 8am-11pm, noon-2.30pm, 6pm-9.30pm)

B&B

The Slipway

A pretty and winning B&B just across the road from the sea at beautiful Baltimore. (Wilmie Owen, The Cove, Baltimore ☎ 028-20134 theslipway@hotmail.com www.theslipway.com)

Bandon

Butcher

Asian Junction

Piers knows his way around fiery chillis and dipping sauces: a few bites of his spring rolls and your mouth will be delightfully on fire: the real thing! the real burn! Piers worked in Asia as a photographer and diving instructor, and wound up at the Chiang Mai cookery school. He has learnt well, so if you crave the flavours that blew you away when you were on holiday, then Asian Junction is your destination. (Piers Gourley-Diment, Bandon ☎ 085-722 0259 piersgourleydiment@gmail.com www.asianjunctioncatering.com)

Farmers' Market

● Bandon Farmers' Market

Look out for the bright yellow signs that lead you to the delights of a great West Cork market. (Old Market Yard, back of the New Spar, Saturday 9.30am-1.30pm)

Butcher

● Carey's Butchers

Martin Carey is one of the great butchers, and he runs one of the great butcher's shop. Standards are stellar in here, and everything from the chicken skewers, that the McKenna children adore, to the forerib of beef is as good as you will find. Outstanding. (Martin Carey, 82 South Main Street, Bandon ☎ 023-884 2107 mcarey-ie@yahoo.com – Open 7am-6.30pm Mon-Sat)

Cork West

Chocolate

● Katie's Real Chocolate

Katie Buckley was born to make chocolate, and she brings imagination and humour to the art. Her chocolates are great value, so at some time you must experience buying the chocolate where it is made, this bubbling boutique of cocoa-craft. Visit the cafe on the ring road, to sample the entire range, whilst enjoying a cup of good hot chocolate and a nice slice of chocolate cake. (Katie Buckley, Bandon ☎ 023-882 9659 katie@katiesrealchocolate.ie www.katiesrealchocolate.ie)

Butcher

● Maloney's Meat Centre

Dan Maloney is a local food hero in West Cork, respected for his knowledge, respected for the quality of his meats, respected for the excellent, sociable stndards of customer service you will enjoy here. (Dan Maloney, 25 Sth Main Street, Bandon ☎ 023-884 4206 dan.maloney@live.co.uk – Open 8am-6.30pm Mon-Sat)

Gastro Pub

● The Poacher's Inn

The Poacher's Inn is a feel-good place. The way everything sparkles and shines in the bar and the restaurant makes you feel good. The companionability of the staff makes you feel good. And Barry McLoughlin's cooking is a pure feel-good experience, largely thanks to the God-is-in-the-detail elements that he loves to add to his dishes. So, his chowder has a hit of star anise and the clean taste of fresh chives to round it off. His creamy salad dressing has the shine of tarragon. His lovely fish pie has tart, garlicky breadcrumbs to add texture and resonance. And, when he needs to play it straight, he leaves well alone, so Dan Maloney's striploin has champ, sautéed mushrooms and onions and pepper sauce, a Saturday-night classic. Modest, community-serving restaurants like the Poacher's Inn are a sheer delight.(Barry & Catherine McLoughlin, Clonakilty Road, Bandon ☎ 023-884 1159 ✉ McLaughlinbc@hotmail.com – Open for bar lunch Mon-Sat. Restaurant open Thur-Sat dinner & Sun lunch)

Organic Growers

● Eddie and Caroline Robinson

Eddie and Caroline are major players in the Coal Quay Market, and they are superlative organic growers. Their produce fairly bursts with natural energy, exuberance, vitality and the force of life itself. Fantastic. (Eddie & Caroline Robinson, Parkmore, Templemartin, Bandon ☎ 021-733 0178 ✉ carolinerobinson@eircom.net)

Cork West

Biscuits

● Seymour's of Cork

It seems that every time we walk into a good deli, there is a new Seymour's biscuit looking at us and saying: "Buy me!". And we do. Philip O'Connor is a whiz at devising new riffs for his shortbread biscuits, so when we saw Seymour's Little Bites in URRU, with raspberry and white chocolate, tempting us, tempting us, sure what could we do other than buy them? And we did. And they were delicious, like all the Seymour's range. You need these wonderful biscuits in your life. (Philip O'Connor, Cloughsimon Business Park, Bandon ☎ 086 330 9378 ✉ info@seymours.ie 🖱 www.seymours.ie)

Wholefood Shop

● An Tobairin

Mary Wedel is an erudite purveyor of all things wholesome in the treasure trove that is An Tobairin. Real goodness is on sale here in every shape and form, in a shop that is a model wholefood store in every way. (Mary Wedel, 79 South Main Street, Bandon ☎ 023-885 2985 ✉ well@antobairin.com 🖱 www.antobairin.com)

Delicatessen

● URRU

There is a rule in shopkeeping, which says that if you only stock stuff you like, then you will go bust quickly. Ruth Healy doesn't believe in that rule. URRU sells the stuff Ms Healy likes. The store is one of the most masterly examples of what we call "The Edit": like a painter working on a canvas, nothing superfluous must be allowed intrude into the exercise of capturing and evoking an aesthetic. And that, really, is the secret of URRU. It isn't truly a store, it isn't really a shop. It's an aesthetic, both in how it greets you and accommodates you, and in what you find when you get there. It's home. The ideal home. Ms Healy has brought innovation and cutting-edge thinking to her store, the frame for the products she loves. You will love them too. (Ruth Healy, The Mill, McSwiney Quay, Bandon ☎ 023-885 4731 ✉ info@urru.ie 🖱 www.urru.ie – Open Mon-Sat 9.30am-6.30pm)

Cork West

Belgooly

Restaurant

● Feirm Ur

John and Mary's organic dairy products are benchmark productions. Milk from their herd of 50 Friesians allows them to make the best buttermilk you can buy, but do look out also for their yogurt and for the fine kefir, the only example of this drink that we know to be made in Ireland. The Feirm Ur products can be found in good West Cork stores and delis. (John & Mary Cronin, Dúncronin, Coolcarron, Belgooly ☎ 087-1674011 ☎ 021-477 1657 ✉ feirmur@gmail.com)

Castletownshend

Gastropub

● Mary Ann's

A justly celebrated and very commodious bar and restaurant in lovely little Castletownshend. (Trish O'Mahony, Castletownshend ☎ 028-36146 ✉ mary-anns@eircom.net – Open noon-2.30pm, 6pm-9pm Mon-Sun. Closed Mon & Tues off season)

Smokery

● Woodcock Smokery

"Sally is a law unto herself", Richard Corrigan once remarked of Sally Barnes, creator of Castletownshend's Woodcock Smokery. Mr Corrigan was quite right, but Sally's Law is an unusual one. Instead of being written on unalterable tablets of stone, Sally's Law is an improvisation, a mix of organoleptic appreciation, common law, precedent, argument, dialectic, common sense, sensibility. Since she established the smokehouse in **1981**, every piece of fish she smokes – salmon, albacore tuna, mackerel, haddock; pollock; kippers – is treated according to its needs. "All we add are salt, smoke, skill, care, and lots of time", says Ms Barnes. That's the secret of Sally's Law. That's how you get the bliss. (Sally Barnes, Gortbrack, Castletownshend, ☎ 028- 36232 ✉ sally@woodcocksmokery.com 🖱 www.woodcocksmokery.com)

made in Cork

Milleens Farmhouse Cheese

Cork West

Clonakilty

Restaurant

● Costelloe's Malthouse

Irene Collins is now owner as well as chef in the eclectic and atmospheric Malthouse, and we are looking forward to seeing how this chef, with her instinctive devotion to West Cork artisan ingredients, drives forward one of 'Clon's iconic destinations. (Irene Collins, 30 Ashe Street, Clonakilty ☎ 023-8834355 www.malthousegranary.ie – Open 5pm-10pm Mon-Sun, closed Sun & Mon off season. Open lunch Fri & Sat high season)

Restaurant

● Deasy's Harbour Bar

'Carpet shell clams with belly pork and herb butter breadcrumbs.' Sounds simple, doesn't it? But Caitlin Ruth can make a dish with these simple ingredients and, as you pleasurably eat your way through its saline unctuousness, there is only one thought in your head: this is the best thing I have eaten all year! That's the sort of cook Ms Ruth is: she's a star, and we expect her to be recognised as such someday soon. Her regular customers appreciate her stellar cooking already, of course, and turn up for her crab cake and fish spring roll platter, or maybe some deep-fried calamari with chilli and mango dip, or just a lunchtime bowl of yellow courgette and mushroom soup. It's the individuality of her pairings that sets her apart, knowing that the belly pork with its sweetness will sing together with the salty clams, that the courgettes and mushrooms will be a Fred 'n' Ginger match. Caitlin Ruth is a West Cork star and she cooks in that instinctive, deep-rooted way that makes for real soul food. Deasy's is hot, and simply not to be missed. (Billy Blackwell, Ring Village, Clonakilty ☎ 023-883 5741 ✉ deasysrestaurant@hotmail.com – Open 6pm-9.30pm Wed-Sat, 1pm-3pm Sun)

Coffee Shop

● Hart's Coffee Shop

Aileen Hart runs one of the glories of Clon, a beautiful tea rooms with beautiful food that shines with care, sympathy and astuteness. Delightful. (Aileen Hart, Ashe Street, Clonakilty ☎ 023-883 5583 ✉ hartscoffeeshop@gmail.com – Open 10am-5.15pm Mon-Sat)

Restaurant

● Inchydoney Island Lodge & Spa

There is ambition in Inchydoney, and maybe the best way to see it is through this simple portal: in 2012, the student chef of the year competition was won by Shane Deane, an apprentice chef at Inchydoney, who has been working with head chef Adam Medcalfe for the last two years. That is the sort of attitude and ambition coursing through the corridors of this fine hotel, and one senses that they are only beginning: we are expecting truly great things from Des O'Dowd and his team. (Des O'Dowd, Clonakilty, West Cork ☎ 023-8833143 ✉ reservations@inchydoneyislandcom 🖱 www.inchydoneyisland.com)

Shop & Bakery

● Lettercollum Kitchen Project Shop

The best pastry. In the world. That's what Con, Karen, Bridget and the team make in Lettercollum. We would like to bathe in this pastry. We would like to be buried in this pastry. Failing this, please let us eat it for as long as we can humanly manage, for we know of no other pastry that makes us so happy. Con and Karen have always done the magic, right from way back when we started writing books. They make that magic today, with everything they cook. But it is the pastry that blesses their sausage rolls, pies, tarts, and pizzas that is sui generis. It is only given to very few people to do the magic, and they do it here, day after day. The shop itself is one of the nicest in Ireland, always full of little local surprises like the fine Inchydoney chocolate, which is as rare as hen's teeth. (Con McLoughlin & Karen Austin, 22 Connolly Street, Clonakilty ☎ 023-883 6938 info@lettercollum.ie www.lettercollum.ie – Open 10am-5pm Tue-Sat)

Fudge

● Mella's Fudge

Mella is a ledge. Almost single-handedly, she has made fudge into a funky, cutting-edge, hip, glam, must-have sweetie accessory, and created a band of customers who can only be described as fudgistas. Are you one of Mella's fudgistas? If not, then brother you are not where you need to be. Mella makes four flavours for you – vanilla; walnut; rum & raisin, and chocolate – so get started and get West Cork's hippest accoutrement into your life. (Mella McAuley, Lisavaird Co-Op, Clonakilty ☎ 086-159 5949 mella@mellasfudge.com www.mellasfudge.com)

Wholefood Shop

● The Olive Branch

A colourful and chock-a-block wholefood store in the funky Spiller's Lane enclave. The shop is particularly valuable for sourcing produce from West Cork organic growers. (Olive Finn, Andy Beaty, Mark Holland, Spiller's Lane, Clonakilty ☎ 023-883 5711 – Open 9.30am-6pm Mon-Sat)

Bar & Bistro

● Richy's Bar & Bistro

Richy's is ten years old, so happy birthday baby! Mr Virahsawmy has been making locals and visitors happy with modern, happy snappy cooking since day one and today the offers provides pretty much everything you could need: RCafé is the day-time location, there is a deli for takeaway foods which also offers a catering service, and Richy somehow manages to squeeze in cookery classes in addition to cooking for the restaurant. Phew!

(Richy Virahsawmy, 4 Wolfe Tone Street, Clonakilty ☎ 023-882 1852 richysbarandbistro@eirom.net www.richysbarandbistro.com – Open noon-3pm, 5pm-11pm Mon-Fri, 10am-11pm Sat-Sun)

Supermarket

● Scally's Supervalu

Want to amaze a bunch of Irish food bloggers? Draw them in from all around the country, then bring them to Eugene Scally's supermarket, and they will be blown away. Watch their jaws drop as they see a milk selection that has all the West Cork milks as well as Mossfield, Lullaby, and Ardsallagh. See the bloggers as they gawp in amazement at the award-winning fish counter. Register their astonishment as they see the superlative selection in every department: vegetables; breads; charcuterie; cheese; oils; dairy; meats; fish. All this, they say, and the best staff in the world, and no chi-chi prices. How does Eugene Scally do it? We're not sure. We're simply grateful. (Eugene Scally, Six Bridge, Clonakilty ☎ 023-883 3088 info@supervaluclon.ie www.supervaluclon.ie – Open 8.30am-9pm Mon-Fri, 8.30am-8pm Sat, 9am-6pm Sun)

made in Cork

Mella's Fudge

Butcher's Shop

● Edward Twomey

Colette Twomey's stewardship of the Clonakilty Black Pudding company over the last five years has been one of the most outstanding pieces of business management Ireland has seen. If Mrs Tomey had been running the country, rather than just her company, we would be on the pig's back as a nation. Instead, we are in the gutter, and she is up in the stars. She has deservedly won every business and culinary award going, but there is still a lot more to come from a woman who is so aware of the need for authenticity, honesty and creativity in business that she is that rarest thing: a shining star. Business is full of people who love to congratulate themselves. Mrs Twomey believes in congratulating her customers. She is a true entrepreneur. (Colette Twomey, 16 Pearse Street, Clonakilty ☎ 023-883 3365 www.clonakiltyblackpudding.ie – Open 9am-6pm Mon-Sat)

Connonagh

Craft Shop

● The Old Mill Stores

Claire and Tom have the most gorgeous homeware store, here, in the newly refurbished home of Ovne Stoves. In theory, you likely don't need any of the witty, colourful, fun things they sell. In reality, you need everything they sell, for your soul, for your aesthetic aspirations, for your inner artist. Even the clothes pegs are wow! (Claire Graham & Tom Keane, Gortroe, Leap 028 34917 theoldmillstores@gmail.com www.theoldmillstores.ie Tue-Sat 11am-6pm, Sun 2pm-6pm)

Crookhaven

Gastropub

● The Crookhaven Inn

Back in the day, we used the phrase "low-key magic" to describe what Emma and Freddy do in the Crookhaven Inn. And in the unchanging, comfortable way of this special inn, the phrase resounds louder then ever with every new season. They do lovely food and they don't make a fuss about it, and the signature dishes are resoundingly successful – braised lamb shank with rosemary mash; fish soup with aioli; rigatoni with roasted red pepper pesto and smoked chicken; monkfish wrapped in Gubbeen pancetta. Mrs Olsson is one of the great hostesses, but she lets the magic stay low-key, just the way we – and everyone else – likes it best. (Emma & Freddy Olsson, Crookhaven ☎ 028-35309 crookhaveninn@eircom.net www.crookhaveninn.com – Open 12.30pm-9pm Mon-Sun, check off season. Closed Oct-Easter)

Pub

● O'Sullivan's Bar

The O'Sullivan family's bar is as much a part of West Cork as pastel-painted villages and the Fastnet Rock. You come here to this unique bar to chill, to have excellent sandwiches and chowder, and to see who else has come here to have excellent sandwiches and chowder. You come here to feel away-from-it-all, and yet to feel at-the-centre-of-it-all. No, we don't know how Dermot and the team manage that duality, but they do, and they do it effortlessly. The family also run Nottages bar, run by Alison O'Sullivan, who offers some nice cooking in a cute, pretty space. (Dermot O'Sullivan, Crookhaven ☎ 028-35319 O'sullivans@crookhaven.ie www.osullivanscrookhaven.ie – Food served noon-7pm winter, noon-8.30pm summer)

made in Cork
Glenilen Dairy

Cork West

Drimoleague

Fish & Chips

● The Drimoleague Chipper

Hand-made chips, 100% beef burgers and local fresh fish make this chipper a destination. "We pride ourselves on being the best that we can be" says Patrick Keohane, which is pretty much a definition of the McKennas' manifesto, so you can't say fairer than that about a valuable local chipper. (Patrick Keohane, Main Street, Drimoleague ☎ 028-32625 patkeohane1@eircom.net – Open 5pm-11pm Mon-Thur, 5pm-11.30pm Fri-Sun)

Dairy

● Glenilen Dairy

Milk is a magic liquid. Alan and Valerie Kingston know that. They know something about its mystery, and its multiplicity. At Glenilen Farm, just outside Drimoleague, Mr and Mrs Kingston have spent fifteen years exploring not just the magic of milk, but also the maths of milk, as their milk has begotten butter, yogurt, cream, and so on. As a team, they represent the ideal union: he the dairy farmer whose family had milked cows on the banks of the River Ilen for generations, she the dairy science graduate with a spell working amidst nomadic people in Burkina Fasso, helping to transform milk into cheese to provide food during the dry season. "Alan and Valerie Kingston are people who are producing common things, uncommonly", Myrtle Allen once said of them. Exactly. (Alan & Valerie Kingston, Drimoleague ☎ 028-31179 val@glenilenfarm.com, alan@glenilenfarm.com www.glenilen.com)

Dunmanway

Bakery

● The Baking Emporium

Andreas's stall is a stalwart of many of the best West Cork markets, serving excellent breads and pastries. Mr Haubold has morphed and adapted his baking company with enviable skill over the years, going with the flow, finding his audience, enjoying it all. The BE is a quintessential West Cork enterprise. (Andreas Haubold, Dunmanway ☎ 023-884 5260 info@bakingemporiumltd.com www.bakingemporiumltd.com)

Quail Eggs

● Coturnix Quail

Brendan's terrific quail's eggs are the begining of every delicious summer salad, either popped straight from the jar and sliced, or else cooked gently by your good self as the beginning of that Scotch quail's egg recipe that has been thrumming in the back of your mind. Look for the Coturnix eggs in good delis and supermarkets. (Brendan Ross, Droumdrastil, Dunmanway ☎ 087-206 5067)

Cork West

made in Cork

Brown Envelope Seeds

Patisserie

● Patisserie Régale Cookies of Character

How do you make the best cheese biscuit in the world? Well, you get the great Richard Graham-Leigh of Patisserie Régale, working in collaboration with the brilliant Sheridan's Cheesemongers, to originate and bake it. You utilise Macroom Mills stoneground flour, from Donal Creedon, you use creamy Bandon Co-Op butter, and you use Cronin family farm buttermilk, from Riverstick, a most delicious, true buttermilk. The result was never going to be in doubt: the Sheridan's cheese biscuits are not just the greatest cheese biscuits in the world, they are a prime example of Irish artisan collaboration at its most ingenious and creative. Mr Graham-Leigh, when he isn't making the world's greatest cheese biscuits, also make superb cookies, and he has no peer as an artistic baker: an artist of the baking world. (Richard & Janet Graham-Leigh, Maulanimirish, Dunmanway ☎ 086-086 8183 jandrgrahamleigh@eircom.net www.regale.ie)

made in Cork

Gubbeen Farmhouse Cheese

Cork West

Enniskeane

Café & Garden Centre

● The Blue Geranium

Olive Brennan cooks mature, composed food in the bright, florid space of the Blue Geranium. Her touch is delicate and confident, whether she is offering comfort food such as Martin Carey's pork and leek sausages with mash, or a quiche with asparagus, spinach and Gubbeen cheese or her signature Ummera smoked salmon potato cakes. We love the fact that the café hosts art exhibitions, has musicians dropping in – a little Debussy in here is just the trick – but what we love best is the fact that this isn't a garden centre with a café: Hosford's is a cultural centre with a cultured café. That's the way things should be. (John Hosford & Olive Brennan, Cappa, Enniskeane ☎ 023-883 9159 john@hosfordsgardencentre.ie www.hosfordsgardencentre.ie – Open 10am-4.30pm Tue-Fri, 10am-5pm Sat, noon-5pm Sun)

Country House

● Kilcolman Rectory

There is a word – a superb Italian word coined by Baldassare Castiglione in his *The Book of the Courtier*, written in 1528 – for what Sarah Gornall achieves in the gorgeous Kilcolman Rectory, and the way in which she achieves it: sprezzatura. The nonchalance that conceals effort. The effort underscoring every detail in Kilcolman Rectory is huge – the cooking, the design, the garden, the aesthetic – but you'd never guess, because Ms Gornall seems to do it all effortlessly, and so you will tumble into the delights of Kilcolman, and not want to leave. (Sarah Gornall, Enniskeane ☎ 023-882 2913 info@kilcolmanrectory.com www.kilcolmanrectory.com)

Glandore

Gastro Pub

● Hayes' Bar

Simple, unpretentious and good, Declan and Ada Hayes' bar is where you eat in Glandore. Sitting outside in the summertime, under an umbrella, with a croque monsieur and a glass of one of Declan's good white wines (and you should drink wine here: Declan is a true advocate of good wine), or with a bowl of soup and a sandwich, you will experience true contentment. Inside, the bar is splendidly wayward and abstruse, as good pubs should be. Unique, and delightful. (Declan & Ada Hayes, Glandore ☎ 028-33214 ✉ dhayes@tinit.ie – Food served noon-5pm Mon-Sun. No credit cards. Open Jun-Sept)

local knowledge

Kayak Foraging

Atlantic Sea Kayaking is a small family company based in Castlehaven Bay in West Cork. One of the courses they host is a foraging trip, where you kayak for a day, stopping on a beach, fishing for mackerel and examining and identifying the local seaweed. Many of ASK's customers have never kayaked before, beginners are welcomed and all equipment is provided.

● www.atlanticseakayaking.com

Goleen

B&B

● Fortview House

"The archetype Irish B&B in all its wonder", says Eamon Barrett. "The MOST friendly welcome, the MOST impressive breakfast you will ever come across. A warren of comfortable rooms, and the most wonderful care. Probably the best B&B we have ever stayed in. Violet Connell is one of the nicest people you will ever meet and we loved every minute staying in this smashing house." No more need be said about wonderful Fortview. (Violet Connell, Gurtyowen, Toormore, Goleen ☎ 028-35324 ✉ fortviewhousegoleen@eircom.net 🖱 www.fortviewhousegoleen.com)

Gougane Barra

Hotel and Restaurant

● Gougane Barra Hotel

Neil and Katy's Gougane Barra Hotel is one of the nicest hotels in Ireland. We love the simplicity of the rooms, we love walking in the woods, and walking by the beautiful, peaceful lake and the church, and we love especially the Theatre by the Lake in summertime, when a evening of d 'n' d 'n' d – dinner and drama and duvet – is one of the best experiences you can enjoy in Ireland. Gougane Barra is priceless, just priceless, the expression of Irish hospitality at its simple, quiet best. (Neil & Katy Lucey, Gougane Barra, Macroom, ☎ 026-47069 ✉ gouganebarrahotel@eircom.net 🖱 www.gouganebarrahotel.com)

Inishannon

Food Store

● Rohu's Country Market

You will spot Tom's shop at the Cork end of Inishannon by the classic Aston Martin sports car parked at the entrance. Pass by the car and be prepared to be enchanted by one of the best new stores to have opened in Cork in recent years. It's funky and fun and the foods of every hue and cry are simply fantastic, and chosen with instinctual care. Must remember next time to ask Tom if the car is his. (Thomas Sewell, Main Street, Inishannon ☎ 087-923 7213 ✉ rohuscountrymarket@hot.mail.com – Open 10am-6pm Tue-Fri, noon-6pm Sat & Sun)

Kilbrittain

Guesthouse

● The Glen

The Glen is one of those places that seem to tap into our need and desire for nostalgia, so there is something fundamentally primal about this most beautiful house. You might have been reared in a deluxe Gorballs tenement, but when you step in the door of The Glen you will feel you not only belong here, you will feel you were somehow born here as well. Diana and Guy orchestrate the illusion with masterly hospitality. (Diana & Guy Scott, Kilbrittain ☎ 023-884 9862 ✉ info@glencountryhouse.com 🖱 www.glencountryhouse.com – Open Easter-Nov)

Kinsale

B&B

● Blindgate House

Maeve Coakley's Blindgate is a terrific base for staying, relaxing and exploring, enjoying all the best of Kinsale whilst just being far enough up the hill to ensure peace and quiet when the town is at full tilt, but also allowing you to head out both eastwards and westwards through County Cork to sample the incredible varieties of the county, both geographically and gastronomically. Breakfasts are just as stylish and fine as the design, setting you up for the perfect day. (Maeve Coakley, Blindgate, Kinsale ☎ 021-477 7858 ✉ info@blindgatehouse.com 🖱 www.blindgatehouse.com)

Cork West

Restaurant

● Crackpots

Carole Norman does it all, and more, at Crackpots. There is her ceramics workshop. There is an art gallery, whereby the restaurant space is also used to show new works. There is an apartment for guests who want to stay over, at the top of the house, and a B&B outside the town. There is an al fresco space outside for when the sun shines. There is a Friday night piano bar and there is, of course, the restaurant, where Sean Williams riffs confidently on classic dishes – scallops with saffron beurre blanc and crispy Parma ham; fillet of salmon with hollandaise and quail's egg; duck confit with red cabbage; aubergine strudel. Ms Norman is a mighty powerhouse for Kinsale. (Carole Norman, Cork Street, Kinsale ☎ 021-477 2847 ✉ crackpts@iol.ie 🖱 www.crackpots.ie – Open 6.30pm-9pm Tue-Sat, noon-2.30pm Sun (closed Mon-Wed off season)

Restaurant & Fishmonger

● Fishy Fishy Café

Martin Shanahan is the man of the moment, and Fishy Fishy Café is one of the most successful restaurants in the country. Fishy Fishy's success is worth analysing, and it has arisen because Mr Shanahan has deep roots in the Kinsale community. The fish and shellfish you enjoy in FF have come straight from day boats. So the stunning quality of that piece of gurnard, or those superb Dublin Bay prawns, is explained by a system that maximises quality, freshness and directness. The kitchen, then, never puts a foot wrong, sending out plate after plate of perfectly cooked food, served by charming, smiling staff. It's a brilliant operation, a sustainable, happy success story, and a vital destination. (Martin & Marie Shanahan, Crowley Quay, Kinsale ☎ 021-470 0415 ✉ info@fishyfishy.ie 🖱 www.fishyfishy.ie – Open mid Mar-mid Oct noon-9pm Tue-Sat, noon-4.30pm Sun-Mon)

Restaurant & Fishmonger

● Fishy Fishy Shop & Chippie

The original Fishy Fishy serves fantastic – fantastic! – fish and chips. (Martin & Marie Shanahan, The Guardwell, Kinsale ☎ 021-477 4453 🖱 www.fishyfishy.ie – Open, shop, 9.30am-5.30pm, chippie noon-4.30pm)

Farmers' Market

● Kinsale Farmers' Market

The Kinsale Market has suffered the indignity of being bussed to different locations around the town, but the development of Short Quay should grant it an ideal and permanent home. It's an excellent market, with lots of good choices for grazing and taking cooked food home as well as getting all the essential shopping. (Short Quay, Kinsale, Wednesday mornings)

Cafe & Shop

● The Lemon Leaf Café

It ws the lure of good Ariosa coffee that got us over the threshold into Tracy's pretty café, and whilst a good brew is reason to return, there is lots to enjoy in this bright, handsome space. As well as smart, informal food during the day, there is a good selection of artisan foods to buy. The enterprise has a clear debt to the clear-eyed and colourful Avoca style of food and design, and that's as good a place as any to start. (Tracy Keoghan, 70 Main Street, Kinsale ☎ 021-470 9792 ✉ info@lemonleafcafe.ie. 🖱 www.lemonleafcafe.ie – Open 8.30am-5pm Mon-Sat, 9.30am-5pm Sun. Brunch served Sunday till 2pm)

Restaurant

● Man Friday

Philip Horgan has run the good ship Man Friday for almost 35 years years now, one of the country's most enduring and long-lived restaurants. He has brought his audience across to Scilly night after night for good cooking, good service and good times. Like the best restaurateurs, he knows that the food has to match the mood, and that the mood should be upbeat and the food should be upbeat also. So, don't call it old-fashioned, just call it classic: crab gratin; stuffed mussels with breadcrumbs; deep-fried brie; sole on the bone; Kinsale seafood platter; fillet steak with cream, brandy and peppercorn sauce. Time marches on, but in Man Friday it is always Friday night. (Philip & Joss Horgan, Scilly, Kinsale ☎ 021-477 2260 🖱 www.manfridaykinsale.ie – Open 5pm-10.15pm Mon-Sat, 12.30pm-9.30pm Sun)

Wine Bar

● Max's Wine Bar

Max's has always enjoyed an archetypal restaurant ambience. Anne Marie and Olivier Queva describe Max's as "quaint" and "professional", and that is just right, though we must also add "unpretentious". Everything marries well in this delightful set of rooms: the food, which swerves towards seafood in summertime – langoustines with angel hair pasta; monkfish with cumin and beurre blanc – and then towards game in the autumn – pheasant with choucroute; venison with Brussels sprouts. The decor, with its artful bricolage style. And the service, which is calm, confident, and charming. (Anne-Marie & Olivier Queva, 48 Main Street, Kinsale ☎ 021-477 2443 🖱 www.maxs.ie – Open from 6pm Mon-Sat)

B&B

● Pier House

Is the Pier House a B&B, or a small boutique hotel? You will find it described as both but, truth be told, whatever you choose to call it, what you will remember most about Pier House is not the colourful design, or the luxury spec. What will linger in your memory will be the hospitality of Ann and Pat. Mrs Hegarty makes sure everyone is looked after, cooks lovely breakfasts and maintains a pristine house, and she does it all with charm and relish. (Ann & Pat Hegarty, Pier Road, Kinsale ☎ 021-477 4475 🖱 www.pierhousekinsale.com)

Delicatessen

● Quay Food Co

For pâtés and preserves, for cheeses and olives, for food gifts for others and treats for your good self, for a special lunchtime sambo or a rare blend of tea, The Quay is where you go in Kinsale. It's a pivotal part of the town's culinary culture, quietly doing the good thing for more than 15 years now, and serving the people with grace and knowledge. (David & Laura Peare, Market Quay, Kinsale ☎ 021-477 4000 quayfood@hotmail.com www.quayfood.com – Open 9.30am-5.30pm Mon-Sat, open till 6pm Sat during summer)

Cider

● Stonewell Irish Craft Cider

Cork West

Daniel Emerson uses apples sourced in Tipp, south Kilkenny and Waterford to get the characteristics he wants to enshrine in the Stonewell cider. The apples are pressed in season, then fermented, racked and aged, and a little fresh apple juice is used to modify the dryness before bottling. Don't confuse Stonewell with commercial Irish ciders: this is the real deal, and whilst it is sweeter than some other artisan ciders it drinks cleanly and crisply. (Daniel & Geraldine Emerson, Nohoval, Belgooly, Kinsale ☎ 086-869 1148 info@stonewellcider.com www.stonewellcider.com)

Restaurant

● Toddies @ The Bulman

Ten years of good cooking, in three different locations in and around Kinsale, has been the story for Pearse and Mary O'Sullivan and their much-loved Toddie's restaurant. Happily housed in the classic bar space of the Bulman, Mr O'Sullivan's cooking has probably never been better, pulling in all of his international influences: Trinidad-style crab gratin; Dublin Bay prawn soup with chilli, lemongrass and coriander; skewered chicken with wasabi coleslaw – and his solid-sender super hitters that come out of the classic textbook – char-grilled rib-eye with Parmesan mash and onion rings; lobster risotto; Oysterhaven mussels with smoked bacon. This is good, smart cooking from a chef with a true touch. (Pearse & Mary O'Sullivan, Summercove, Kinsale ☎ 021-477 7769 toddies@eircom.net www.toddies.ie – Open 6.30pm-10.30pm Tue-Sun, Mon-Sun high season. Closed Jan & Feb)

Riverstick

Restaurant

● Flynn's Kitchen

"The unifying factor at Iain Flynn's multiple award-winning market 'deli' is an astute palate", says Joe McNamee. Crucially Mr Flynn's judgement is "perfectly calibrated to know when the optimum balance has been achieved, and he has the nous to stop right there". This sensibility explains how Iain Flynn can produce such a broad range of deli foods, everything from the celebrated spinach and ricotta cannelloni to pâtés, preserves, prepared meals and soups, and yet manage such high standards and individual distinctiveness across the entire range. He sources with utter care, cooks with care, and it shows. (Iain Flynn, Riverstick ☎ 087-9048709 iainflynn@gmail.com www.flynnskitchen.ie)

Cork West

Rosscarbery

Free-range Pork & Sausages

● Caherbeg Free-Range Pork

Back in 2007, Rosscarbery Recipes black pudding, which had only been in production for 3 months, won a gold medal at the annual competition organised by Normandy's Confrerie des Chevaliers du Goute Boudin. Sending Irish black pudding to the home of boudin noir and bringing home a gold medal at your first attempt is the culinary equivalent of climbing Mount Everest without oxygen. But that accolade was simply a crowning achievement during a decade of success that has seen Avril and Willie Allshire's Rosscarbery pork acquire a stellar reputation. Beautiful pork products, and look out in particular for the Caherbeg pork sausages. (Avril & Willie Allshire, Caherbeg, Rosscarbery ☎ 023-884 8474 caher@caherbegfreerangepork.ie www.caherbegfreerangepork.ie)

Organics

● Devoy's Organic Farm

We like to tell a story about the Devoys to our kids. It's the one about how John Devoy wanted to travel to South Africa. So, he got on his bike, and he got there. Then he came home, on his bike. Their jaws – rightly

– drop in amazement. But for the Devoys, this sort of thing is standard. They make their world, and they don't need for it to be made easy. They are pioneer spirits, and powerful producers of superb organic produce. Their stall at the Skibbereen Market is one of our Meccas: we turn up, and show respect. (John & Sara Devoy, Rosscarbery ☎ 087-235 0900 jsdevoy@eircom.net www.devoysorganicfarm.com)

Restaurant

● O'Callaghan-Walshe

Can you believe that O'Callaghan-Walshe has been cooking happy food in the square in Rosscarbery for fully twenty years now? What Sean and Martina offer is great West Cork fish, but just as important as the food is the lugubrious, sanguine atmosphere of the room, a place where you come to chill out. Everything in O'C-W is underpinned by superlative fish and shellfish cooked with quiet élan, like their classics such as Roxanne's scampi or Dover sole on the bone. But the care evident in the fish is shown in everything they cook, so pay particular attention to the potatoes – especially the potatoes! – and the vegetables, the ice creams and the desserts. There is no other room quite like this one. (Sean Kearney, The Square, Rosscarbery ☎ 023-884 8125 funfish@indigo – Open 6.30pm-9.30pm Tue-Sun, Weekends only Oct-May)

Skibbereen

Café

● Apple Bettys Café

Celine Jackson and Liz Crowley are hard-working girls who run a calm café in the centre of the market town of Skibb. The food is simple, and sincere: quiches, paninis, wraps. It's clean and crisp, straightforward, honest food, and a lovely stop for breakfast or lunch. (Celine Jackson, The Square, Skibbereen ☎ 028-51833 applebettyscafe@gmail.com – Open 9am-5pm Mon-Sat)

Organic Seeds

● Brown Envelope Seeds

Where Madeleine McKeever lives, on Turk Head, down at the edge of Roaringwater Bay, the wind is always blowing. Always. It's easy to imagine a murmuration of seeds riding in the air, tossed and buffeted by the winds, on any given day. It's enough to make you want to cast a net high in the air to catch them. And that is what Madeleine McKeever does: she's the seed catcher. Ever since she produced the first Brown Envelope seed catalogue in 2004, the range has grown steadily, a cornucopia of nature's bounty: Painted Mountain corn; purple podded peas; touchon carrots; chop suey greens; crystal apple cucumbers; Newton wonder apples. Every little envelope of seeds saved by Ms McKeever and her partners, Ruth Bullough and Mike Sweeney, represents not just optimism for the future, but also a communion with nature. (Madeleine McKeever, Ardagh, Church Cross, Skibbereen ☎ 028-38184 ✉ madsmckeever@eircom.net 🖱 www.brownenvelopeseeds.com)

Supermarket

● Field's SuperValu Supermarket

John Field belongs amongst that pantheon of great food pioneers who have shaped modern Ireland: Myrtle Allen; Declan Ryan; Nick Price; Veronica Steele; Maura Foley; Denis Healy; Simon Pratt; John Field. His achievement as a retailer has been to build a bridge between supplier and customer, so that he has foods from the smallest allotment to the mightiest corporation, and then to offer the best foods he can find in as commodious a space as possible. Field's has accomplished all this, and much more, and it is one of the icons of Irish food. It's not just a shop, it's an aleph: a place from where you can view the entire food culture. (John Field, Main Street, Skibbereen ☎ 028-21400)

Bakery and Bread School

● The Firehouse

What do you get if you mix a corporate lawyer with a chef from Thornton's Restaurant? The answer is a baker. The road from lawyer, via Thornton's and the Thoughtful Bread Company in Bath to the Firehouse on beautiful Heir Island has been a winding road for Patrick Ryan, and one that has gifted him with the skills to magic sourdoughs, sodas and stone-baked pizzas. What could possibly be nicer than a one-day bread course that sees you setting off on the boat with your own bag of delicious breads. The Firehouse is a West Cork icon in the baking. (Patrick Ryan, Heir Island, Skibbereen ☎ 085-156 1984 ✉ info@thefirehouse.ie 🖱 www.thefirehouse.ie)

Fishmonger

● The Fish Station

The last time we bought fish in the Fish Station, there must have been a dozen people in the queue and, as we inched our way towards being served, the queue behind us grew and grew. That's the sure sign that someone is doing the good thing, and that is what they do here. Every piece of fish we have bought at the 'Station has not only been of superb quality, it has also been fantastic value. They are very focused on keeeping the supply chain as short as possible, and in offering fresh fish at the keenest prices. They get it right at every point. (Padraic O Donovan, Marsh Road, Skibbereen ☎ 028-21869 info@thefishstation.ie www.thefishstation.ie – Open 10am-3pm Mon-Fri, 10am-1pm Sat)

Cork West

Restaurant & Cookery Courses

● Island Cottage

John Desmond has become increasingly renowned as a painter, and a gallery exhibiting his work is adjacent to the cottage where he and Ellmary Fenton run their seasonal restaurant. The formula here remains unchanged: a set menu is served to the diners, who travel over on the ferry and walk up the boreen to the little cottage restaurant. The cooking is classical and pure – Mr Desmond cooked in France for many years and continues to act as a standard bearer for the legacy of Fernand Point. (John Desmond & Ellmary Fenton, Heir Island, Skibbereen ☎ 028-38102 www.islandcottage.com – Open Dinner Wed-Sat. No credit cards. Closed 15 Sept-15 June)

Restaurant

● Kalbo's Café

Siobhan O'Callaghan is one of the best cooks in West Cork, and one of the mighty culinary mavens who characterise County Cork's food culture. To illustrate how fine a cook she is, consider the simplest thing: boiled eggs and soldiers. In Kalbo's they raise this nursery food to the stars: perfect eggs, perfect hot soldiers, perfect presentation. You could not make it better. But then, that applies to everything Siobhan does, whether it's a chocolate brownie or a Friday night T-bone with fine garlic butter. Siobhan's husband, Anthony Boyle, grows organic produce for the menus. A West Cork star. (Siobhan O'Callaghan, 48 North Street, Skibbereen ☎ 028-21515 – Open 9am-6pm Mon-Thu, 9am-9pm Fri & Sat)

Restaurant

● Leslie's Diner

It doesn't look like much, does Leslie's Diner. And, truthfully, it really isn't an awful lot to write about, just a simple room, with nice staff, and simple food. But that simple food is good, and that is what counts, and that is what Leslie knows. (Leslie Salter, 5 Regal Estate, Skibbereen ☎ 028-40380)

Restaurant

● Liss Ard Estate

Friends of ours stayed at Liss Ard for several days during summer 2011 with their two kids. It is no exaggeration – truly, honestly – to say that they did not want to leave. For the kids, the house was an enchanted palace: out-of-scale, secretive, grand, Lewis Carroll meets Tim Burton by way of Enid Blyton. For the parents, the house was the West Cork country idyll writ large, a place of stunning beauty, both in the elegant, high tone house itself and in the magical gardens. Arthur Little understands and appreciates the magical space and place he runs here in Liss Ard, and he manages it with just the right tone – he is there when you need him, and he melts away when you just want to disappear into the magic of the house. (Arthur Little, Russagh, Skibbereen ☎ 028-40000 arthur@lissardestate.com
www.lissardestate.com)

Restaurant

● Riverside Café

A long, lovely room that looks out over the river gives the Riverside its name and its charm. The food at lunchtime is a smart mix of sandwiches, bruschettas and salads and it works really well. In the evening, clever cooking offers dishes such as a very fine quinoa risotto, but perhaps the room deserves a funkier kind of food at night to match the funky daytime offering. (Majella & Shane O'Neill, North Street, Skibbereen ☎ 028-40090 www.riversideskibbereen.ie – Open 9am-5pm Mon-Sat, 6pm-9.30pm Wed-Sat)

Farmers' Market

● Skibbereen Saturday Market

You wouldn't believe the amount of money John McKenna spends at the Skibb Saturday market. First of all, the kids have to have money to buy hot chocolates and breakfast at the Kalbo's stall. And Sally has to have money to go buy plants, trees, shrubs, crafts and whatnot. And then John has to do what a man's got to do: fill the bags at Gubbeen, Devoy's, Ardagh cheese, Pagan's bread, Mr Pettersen's raspberry sauce; Gik's olives, Sheila's fish, Anthony's veg, Knockeen honey, and on and on. He shops, almost 'til he drops. But he keeps going, at least until the money runs out. Penniless, he goes home and starts cooking. (Fairfield, Skibbereen, Saturdays 10am-2pm)

Restaurant

● Le Voyage

The Le Voyage crew snapped up the West Cork chowder prize at the Skibbereen festival, proof of the attention to detail and precision in execution that marks this atmospheric and engaging restaurant. (Marie Dooley, Christian Pozimksi, David Espagnat, 73 Bridge Street, Skibbereen ☎ 028-23112 ✉ info@levoyage.ie 🖱 www.levoyage.ie – Open noon-11pm Tue-Sat, noon-9pm Sun)

Cork West

Butcher

● Thomas Walshe Butchers

This is a great butcher's shop. Walshe's do the simple-but-difficult things – pork sausages; black pudding – as well as you can do them, and it's a cult address in the town for great meats, and lovely, darlin' service, and great chats with the other customers whilst the staff take care of your needs. (William Walshe, 67 Bridge Street, Skibbereen ☎ 028-21063)

Hotel & Restaurant

● The West Cork Hotel

Two blokes leading from the front, and inspiring the rest of their crew. That's the story of what is happening in The West Cork Hotel, as owner Tim Looney and manager Neil Grant pull this iconic address forward. It's hard to know which of these two guys works the hardest, but the net effect of their work has been to restore the status of this much-loved hotel. The West Cork feels like an hotel: it's where you eat, meet, drink, celebrate, debate, enjoy, relax. An hotel at the heart of the community, it's a very West Cork sort of hotel, and a key part of West Cork. (Neil Grant, Ilen Street, Skibbereen ☎ 028-21277 ✉ info@westcorkhotel.com 🖱 www.westcorkhotel.com)

Timoleague

Restaurant

● Dillon's Restaurant

"John and Julie Finn run one of the very nicest restaurants in West Cork", was how Jack Power, in *The Examiner,* summed up a Friday evening dinner in Dillon's, and it would be hard to beat that. It is a beautiful room – and there is an extra-pretty courtyard – and The Finns know how to make this room feel special. It's functional and pretty during the day, then the white tablecloths and candles come out for nighttime, and the room is as enchanting as John's cooking: chowder with coconut and coriander; duck confit with apple jelly; trio of West Cork lamb; hake with salsa verde; the great pear and almond tart with its seasonal fruit riffs using blackberries, blueberries and raspberries. The very nicest. (John & Julie Finn, Mill Street, Timoleague ☎ 023-884 6390 ✉ info@dillons.ie 🖱 www.dillons.ie – Open 11am-2.30pm, 6pm-9.30pm Thur-Sat, 12.30pm-2.30pm, 6pm-8pm Sun)

made in Cork
Woodcock Smokery

Smokehouse

● Ummera Smokehouse

Ummera is one of the destinations profiled in the fine new Bandon Food Trail, which includes many of the entries here and hereabout in this section. It is worth recording, however, that Ummera is the pioneer in this zone, a superlative fish smoker since the 1970's, with an international reputation second to no other Irish artisan producer. Mr Cresswell and his smoked foods created the culture into which so many talented newcomers have rushed, and they should be very grateful indeed, for Ummera showed how the alliance of quality, place, singularity and skill could create a niche market at the highest levels. Today, Ummera smoke gorgeous fish, bacon and chicken, and their smoked duck is one of the hippest gourmet items currently wowing! food lovers. (Anthony Cresswell, Inchybridge, Timoleague ☎ 023-884 6644/087-2027227 ✉ info@ummera.com 🖱 www.ummera.com)

Union Hall

Coffee Shop

● The Coffee Shop

"What a lovely place" is what everyone says as they exit this simple room. Breakfast and lunch are offered with all the details carefully observed. Bread is home-made, and Carol makes the best sandwiches. Cakes and scones are tempting. Soups are ambrosial. Some days it gets very busy here, especially when the Union Hall Women's Group crosses with the Atlantic Sea Kayaking visitors. This year the art and crafts side of the shop is increasing, and they actually sell quite a few paintings. A magical space. (Carol Noonan, Main Street, Union Hall ☎ 028-34444 – Open daily 9am-5pm, shorter hours off season)

Spirit

● Drombeg

Drombeg is the brainchild of three life-long friends, and is a low-alcohol brown spirit, with an alcohol content that is slightly more than half of whiskey – 22% as opposed to whiskey's standard 40%. They use oak during the maturation, giving the spirit a limber, clean taste that is very enjoyable. Pour it onto lots of ice for something delightful, and we can see talented mixologists having great fun concocting cocktails with Drombeg. (John O'Connell, Dennis McCarthy & Gerard McCarthy, Union Hall ☎ 028-34788 www.drombeg.org)

Fish Shop

● Glenmar Shellfish

We love to be in Glenmar Shellfish in the summertime, when there is a big queue. Being Union Hall, it is a big queue of folk from all over the world and, honestly, it is often hard to believe just how much people conform to their national stereotypes. Watch the next time you are here: it's a great entertainment. But, mind you, not as great an entertainment as the fish and shellfish, which are superlative: Glenmar is one of the great fish shops, and even the sight of the wet fish and shelfish will have you planning that fish feast. Brilliant. (Peter Deasy & Anthony Walsh, Main Street, Union Hall ☎ 028-33818 thefishshop@glenmarshellfish.com www.irish-prawns.com – Open daily, 9am-5pm, closed lunch 1pm-2pm, Sat 9am-1pm)

County Donegal

Ardara

Bar

● Nancy's Bar

How could you not love a traditional Donegal bar that describes its seafood chowder as "very fishy"! How cool is that? Well, cool is what Nancy's Bar is. It's been made famous by the hard work of the McHugh family, who have kept it the way it should be – a warren of cosy rooms – and just made it better with the passing of time. Nancy's is a member of the Donegal Good Food Taverns collective, a group who are committed to using local foods, and one of the best pub food initiatives of recent years. (The McHugh family, Front Street, Ardara ☎ 074-954 1187)

Café

● The West End Café

Charlie and Philomena's café is a legendary destination for their famous fish and chips, freshly cooked and a perfect demonstration of the fryer's art. But the menu offers much more besides, and the cooking is generous and real. The Whytes have provided a great service for almost twenty years now: more power to them. (Charlie & Philomena Whyte, Main Street, Ardara ☎ 074-954 1656 – Food served noon-9.30pm Mon-Sun, Easter-Sept)

Bridgend

Café & Takeaway

● Doherty's Café

Sheila Doherty has been baking her soda bread every morning in this cafe since she opened in 1974, perfect with some home-made jam. The chips are still chipped fresh, in-house, each morning, and the coffees are also well sourced. Sheila's sons Donal and Kevin are the forces behind Harry's restaurant, just a few doors down the street. (Sheila Doherty, Bridgend ☎ 074-938 6603 – Open 8.30am-8.30pm, takeaways close 9pm)

Restaurant & Bar

● Harry's Restaurant

Have any other restaurateur and chef become so famous so fast as Raymond Moran and Donal Doherty of Harry's? This pair put René Redzepi in the also-ran stages when it comes to acquiring rapid fame. Except, of course, Ray and Donal have actually been around for some time now, working away, perfecting the sourcing and polishing the dishes which are today the subject of so much acclaim and attention, and which have made Harry's one of the busiest restaurants in the country. Nevertheless, their ascent to national attention holds a lesson for many restaurateurs: Harry's works because it is a total restaurant, a media player as well as a culinary player, a provocateur as well as a crowd-pleaser, an agenda setter as much as a menu planner. The agenda, of course, is stunning Inishowen food from the peninsula, cooked with imagination and insight – the incredible dry-hung Donegal sirloin; Glebe Brethan rarebit with local mushrooms; Greencastle gurnard with chorizo cream; Bramley crumble with vanilla custard. Harry's is stunning, and it's one of the great contemporary Irish restaurants. (Donal & Kevin Doherty, Raymond Moran, Bonemaine, Bridgend, Donegal ☎ 074-936 8544 info@harrys.ie www.harrys.ie – Open 12.15pm-9pm Sun-Thur, 12.15pm-10pm Fri-Sat)

Buncrana

Bar & Restaurant

● The Beach House Bar & Restaurant

Claire McGowan is a great restaurateur, and The Beach House is a great restaurant. It is great because it feels right, because the food feels right, because the room seems to act almost like a tabula rasa: ready to be whatever you want it to be, whether that is a bowl of soup and a sandwich at lunchtime or a blow-out special with a bunch of friends on a Friday evening. We can explain this effect by saying simply that Ms McGowan's focus is entirely on her customers – she is one of the new generation of hosts who are transforming the traditional reputation of Donegal. Peter Cheesman's cooking is right on the money: a tasting plate of local crab; deep-fried St Tola's goat's cheese and beetroot ice cream; Greencastle cod with freshwater prawns;

Donegal fillet steak with red wine jus; Beach House snowball. The wine list is superb, service is understated and polite, and value for money is excellent. (Claire McGowan, Swilly Road, Buncrana ☎ 074-936 1050 🖱 www.thebeachhouse.ie – Open lunch from noon, dinner from 5pm Mon-Sun, more limited hours off season)

B&B

● Linsfort Castle

Alan and Brigeen's Linsfort Castle is a cult destination. "I reckon it's possibly the best base for a holiday in Inishowen", says Caroline Byrne. "For starters, Brigeen's gardens, while not only beautiful to walk through, produce fruit, vegetables, free-range eggs (from a clutch of Blackrock hens), and honey, all of which are served up to guests in the B&B. Inside the house, her talented eye is evident in every room, each individually and tastefully decorated, as is every nook of the house. In the old kitchen where breakfast is served every morning, an old fireplace replete with traditional hob and pots, and an old still-working wireless give a certain country elegance." Like everyone else, Caroline fell under the spell of this charming big house and its larger-than-life hosts. Alan and Brigeen are singular, modest and generous, and they look after you and cook delicious breakfasts and they introduce you to the riches of this glorious peninsula. Believe us, but you simply will not – will not! – want to leave Linsfort. (Alan Rooks, Buncrana ☎ 087-9677244/074-936 3148 ✉ booking@linsfortcastle.com 🖱 www.linsfortcastle.com)

Burtonport

Sea Vegetables

● Quality Sea Veg

Manus McGonagle was born to harvest sea vegetables and, to this birthright, he has allied an engineering degree, making Quality Sea Veg one of the most dynamic sea harvesters in Ireland. The packaging of the sea vegetables is superb, and the range of products offers everything from Atlantic spirulina, sea stock, sea salt and kelp, dulse crisps, dividing up the sea's gifts into sea herbs, sea vegetables and bath products. (Manus McGonagle, Cloughglass, Burtonport ☎ 074-954 2159 🖱 www.qualityseaveg.ie)

Carndonagh

Café

● Claire The Bakers

Claire's is a little husband-and-wife-run café in the SuperValu car park at Carndonagh. A great place to buy a picnic, or to stop by for coffee and a sandwich. Home-made cakes are their real speciality. (Claire & Aaron Gallagher, Unit 4, SuperValu, Carndonagh ☎ 074-937 3927 – Open 9.30am-5.30pm Mon-Fri, 10am-5.30pm Sat)

made in Donegal

Donegal Rapeseed Oil

Culdaff

Restaurant and Bar

● McGrory's

The Inishowen legend that is the mighty McGrory's powers on, with siblings Anne, John and Neil ladling out the hospitality as to the Donegal manner born. There is something that is so very generous about this trio as they go about their business: managing the bar, managing the restaurant and the rooms, managing the music and the gigs, so generous with their time, their energy, their knowledge and experience, that it animates the entire place. The music sessions held here are the stuff of legend, of course – Townes van Zandt live! – but McGrory's is special whether you can pick with a plectrum or pluck a pizzicato, or whether your speciality is listening to other people doing just that. Creating a destination address in such a remote, northerly place is an heroic act, but the McGrorys are wise people: they have developed slowly, organically, patiently, and they exude the culture of their area with delightful charm. (Anne, John & Neil McGrory, Culdaff ☎ 074-937 9104 info@mcgrorys.ie www.mcgrorys.ie – Food served in bar and restaurant Mon-Sun. Bar food served all year 12.30pm-8.30pm. Closed Mon-Wed Oct-Mar)

Clonmany

Country House & Restaurant

● The Glen House

When Fionn Davenport picked his favourite place to rest his head in the Northwest for the "Defining Ireland" series for Newstalk radio, the place he chose was Sonia McGonagle's The Glen House, in little Clonmany. We understand perfectly. The Glen is a beautiful house, superbly run by Sonia, with lovely rooms, with a spick and span tea room you can stop off in after a visit to the Glenevin waterfall next door, and a neat restaurant. It pushes all the buttons, therefore, and we can't think of anything nicer than a few days here spent walking on the beaches and on through the Urris Hills and the Mamore Gap, with the promise of dinner in The Glen to end a perfect day. Ah! (Sonia & Martin McGonagle, Straid, Clonmany ☎ 074-937 6745 ✉ glenhouse@gmail.com 🖱 www.glenhouse.ie)

Donegal

Coffee Shop and Mini Bakery

● Aroma Coffee Shop

Congratulations to Michael D. Higgins, President of Ireland. We used to share pages with him in *Hot Press* magazine, back in the day, and now he's in the big house: Wow! But, one big, looming question now lies ahead: how soon will President Higgins visit Aroma? Because Aroma is a Presidential fave: it has the seal of approval. President McAleese, a woman who knows good food, knew that Aroma was a place to which you made a detour, in order to get the brilliant breads and cakes baked by Tom, and to grab a spot of lunch cooked by Arturo. It's an astonishing incongruity, in many ways, the idea of the Presidential entourage turning off the road in order to take in this teeny-tiny little café-restaurant. But the President isn't the only person to detour here, for the food has a class and a personality that would make it stand out anywhere. Tom's breads have won gold medals at the Great Taste Awards, so Aroma may be a minnow, but it's a mighty minnow, able to take on and beat the big boys. (Tom Dooley, The Craft Village, Donegal Town ☎ 074-972 3222 – Open 9.30am-5.30pm Mon-Sat, lunch served noon-4pm, 7 days in high season)

Tearoom

● The Blueberry Tearoom

The Blueberry is a small, flower-bedecked room where Brian and Ruperta Gallagher takes care of everyone as if they were family and where tasty, clever food makes sure that everyone who visits comes back. The honesty and hard work of this couple is inspiring, and don't miss Ruperta's great puddings and desserts. (Brian & Ruperta Gallagher, Castle Street, ☎ 074-972 2933 ✉ birchill88@hotmail.com – Open 9am-7pm Mon-Sat)

Farmers' Market

● Donegal Farmers' Market

The third Saturday in each month is the time for the trestle tables and canopies to go up in the centre of town. (The Diamond, Donegal, 3rd Saturday 10am-2pm)

Butchers

● McGettigan's Butchers

It's not everyday that the Commanderie des Fins Goustiers du Duché d'Alencon decide that a little butcher's shop in Donegal makes the best sausage in Europe, so let's hear it for Ernan and Diarmuid McGettigan and their hickory and maple pork sausage, which earned the brothers a knighthood from the Normandy-based Commanderie. McGettigan's is synonymous with sausages – they have won the Craft Butchers' competition no fewer than five times – and with the most vividly creative sausage concoctions you could imagine, all two dozen varieties. So, pork, rhubarb and ginger? Beef & Guinness? Lamb, plum and rosemary? Pork, garlic and leek? Here's the thing to do: start at the top of the list, and work your way through it. Happy days! (Ernan & Diarmuid McGettigan, The Diamond, Donegal ☎ 074-972 1461)

Bar & Restaurant

● The Olde Castle Bar & Restaurant

Seoirse and Maeve O'Toole are pushing all the right buttons here in the Olde Castle, a beautifully restored bar and restaurant. As Caroline Byrne has pointed out, it's a place for visitors and locals – visitors can enjoy the good local seafoods that they expect to find in Donegal – Donegal Bay mussels, lobster, Mullaghmore crab, Greencastle haddock – as well as Irish stew and Wicklow venison pie and braised Sligo lamb shank. For locals who are more regular patrons, the menus offer smart, accessible cooking – triple club sandwich; cheddar cheese beef burger; Maeve's prawn salad. The Olde Castle is the star of the town, and they pull together service, value, style and substance into one hugely successful package. (Seoirse & Maeve O'Toole, ☎ 074-972 1262 www.oldecastlebar.com – Open for bar lunch noon-5pm, restaurant open 5pm-9.30pm)

Wholefood Shop

● Simple Simon Natural Foods

Simple Simon is one of Donegal's benchmark destinations, an essential place for wholefoods, salads and olives, coffee and breads, nice wholesome lunches, or just tea and a slice of cake upstairs. (Finbar Rock, The Diamond, Donegal ☎ 074-972 3690)

Butcher

● Eddie Walsh & Sons

From their farm at Rockhill to their shops in Donegal and Ballintra, the Walsh brothers have half-a-century of farming and butchering in their DNA. Their specialities are Aubrac beef, reared on their farm, and sausages, for which they have won prizes at national level, and which they produce in more than thirty amazing permutations. (Edmund, John & Liam Walsh, Main Street, Donegal Town ☎ 074-972 2595 info@eddiewalshbutchers.com www.eddiewalshbutchers.com)

local knowledge

Atlantic Seaweed

The Irish coastline is rich in seaweed, a product that has been harvested for centuries. There is an old Irish phrase – *práta, peaiste, feamainn* – potatoes, children, seaweed: the order of care for the woman in the house. Traditionally dulse, carrageen and nori (sleabhac) were harvested, though many more varieties are edible. Quality Sea Vegetables have begun to harvest pepper dulse – also known as "the truffle of the sea". Due to its amazing health properties and fabulous flavours, seaweed is a dynamic sector of the Irish artisan food market.

Dunfanaghy

Wholefoods & Wines

● The Green Man

Eileen and Neil draw in lots of interesting foods from near and far in this essential shop, everything from Dongal sea vegetables to Ainé's chocolates to Glastry Farm ice cream to wines from Richard in Letterkenny's Wine Buff to the brilliant Filligan's Preserves. Essential. (Eileen Gallagher & Neil Hougardy, Main Street, Dunfanaghy ☎ 074-910 0800 – Open 9.30am-6pm Mon-Sat, 10am-2pm Sun)

Restaurant and Accommodation

● The Mill Restaurant

It's such a quietly gracious place, The Mill, a quietly gracious place to visit, to eat in, and to stay in. In a food world filled with hype and hustle, it's just two people – Derek and Susan Alcorn – and their tight-knit crew doing what they do as well as they can, and doing it that way every night. The effect of their work is to create a place that seems uniquely relaxed, where customers are regulars, where the ambience, appositely enough, reminds us of a destination at the very opposite end of the country – Kelly's Resort Hotel in Rosslare. From north-north west to south-south east, hospitality and good food is a shared language, a shared experience. Derek Alcorn and his team have been cooking great food for more than a dozen years now, and their food is beyond fashion – lamb's liver salad with a whiskey prune dressing; risotto of baby clams with Greencastle halibut and Prosecco sauce; rack of Ballyare wild boar with white onion purée; chocolate delice with salted caramel and malted barley ice cream. The Mill is one of the dream escapes, 'oop North. (Derek & Susan Alcorn, Figart, Dunfanaghy ☎ 074-913 6985 info@themillrestaurant.com www.themillrestaurant.com – Open Easter-Halloween, Restaurant open 7pm-9pm Tue-Sun)

Café and Bistro

● Starfish Café and Bistro

Victoria Massey has the eye. Just take one look at the Starfish room and you see the work of someone who has an aesthetic compass working at full tilt: it's pure gorgeous, really bright and simple and invigorating. So, let's meet for hot pancakes with Marble Hill yogurt and Horn Head honey, or for a goat's cheese and local spinach tart, and let's meet and bring a bottle for one of their weekend bistro dinners – three starters, three main courses – with Ards Bay cockles and mussels and Greencastle hake and a nice Donegal steak.Pure stylish. (Victoria Massey, Main Street, Dunfanaghy ☎ 087-3299 7169 victoria.c.massey@gmail.com www.starfishcafeandbistro.com – Open 9.30am-5.30pm Mon-Sun. Evening Bistro open weekends and in summertime)

Dunkineely

Restaurant with Rooms

● Castle Murray House

The rooms in Castle Murray are simple and comfortable, the hospitality is genuine. "Peopled by warm, charming staff who made us welcome, made us laugh, and made us some truly excellent food", as a correspondent noted in a fine piece of analysis which explains how Castle Murray works: they make you welcome, they make you happy. The consistency of the cooking and the wealth of the hospitality explains why Castle Murray House has been in the *McKennas' Guides* ever since our first book, written back in 1991, and they have been helped by the fact that Remy Dupuy has been in the kitchen almost since the beginning, cooking house classics such as prawns and monkfish in garlic butter, tartare of Inver sea trout with blinis, or ravioli of Donegal crab. And, of course, we have been writing since the beginning that the views from the dining room are amongst the most captivating in the entire county. (Marguerite Howley, Dunkineely ☎ 074-973 7022 - info@castlemurray.com www.castlemurray.com – Restaurant open 6.30pm-9.30pm Mon-Sat; 1.30pm-3.30pm, 6.30pm-8.30pm Sun)

Fahan

Country House, Bar & Restaurant

● The Red Door

Sean Clifford has charge of the kitchens in The Red Door, having formerly been second chef at Harry's Restaurant in Bridgend. Already he has set about restoring and utilising their own walled garden, so we can expect exciting things to come in this beautiful waterside location. The house, which is a very popular wedding destination, also offers four rooms for guests staying overnight. (Sean Clifford, Fahan, Inishowen ☎ 074-936 0289 info@thereddoor.ie www.thereddoor.ie – Open noon-6pm Mon-Tue, noon-late Wed-Sun)

Glenties

Preserves

● Filligan's Preserves

Here's the thing about the brilliant Filligan's: Philip and Sarah aren't really business people. Realistically speaking, they are artists. And yet for fifteen years they have run one of the tidiest, most distinctive artisan businesses in Ireland. And, all the while, they have kept under the radar. They just work away, making beautiful things, and they don't bother with publicity or promotions. And yet their art is in their products, as well as their life. Perfect. (Sarah & Philip Moss, Tullyard, Glenties ☎ 074-955 1628 filligans@hotmail.com www.filligans.com)

Biodynamic Grower, Shop & Café

● Good Earth

Thomas and Lucia Becht have always known all about the good earth, in their role as leading bio-dynamic farmers, so it's fitting that this should be the name of their shop in the middle of Glenties. You can buy their own produce and their own meat, supplemented by imports of what they can't produce, and also enjoy some nice baking and cooking in the café. Visitors can still call to the farm on Sundays, and their popular box delivery system is thriving. (Thomas & Lucia Becht, Doorian, Glenties ☎ 074-955 1177/087-262 5590 donegalorganic@hotmail.com – Shop open 9am-6pm Mon-Sun)

Glenveagh

Restaurant

● Glenveagh Tearooms

If only every national park could offer the quality of food which Michelle Hunter and her team manage at the impossibly beautiful Glenveagh National Park. They are shining examples of taking the ordinary - salads, quiches, tray bakes – and making it special. What they do, they do so well. This is real food, food that shows care and skill, food that is simple and delicious. The self-service set-up is casual and informal so, before you visit, make sure to have a good walk in the estate while you try to spy an eagle, and build up an appetite for some soul-ful cooking in the café. Like many things of impossible beauty, Glenveagh has a sting in the tail: the local midges are keen to meet you, so have the insect repellent ready. (Michelle Hunter, Churchill, Letterkenny ☎ 074-913 7090 - info@glenveaghtearooms.com 🖱 www.glenveaghtearooms.com – Closed Sept-Easter)

Greencastle

Restaurant

● Kealy's Seafood Bar

Kealy's has always been a restaurant where seafood is treated with classical respect and classical restraint – haddock with a Stilton sauce; salmon with bear-naise sauce; john dory with anchovy butter; dover sole meuniere; lobster thermidor. These dishes are as unchanging, classic and confident as is Kealy's itself, one of the country's quintessential classic seafood restau-rants. If for some reason you don't want to try the fish, they source excellent Angus beef from Mullan's organic farm in 'Derry, and have some nice vegetarian choices. (Tricia Kealy, The Harbour, Greencastle ☎ 074-938 1010 📫 kealysseafoodbar@yahoo.ie 🖱 www.kealysseafood-bar.ie – Restaurant open 12.30pm-3pm, 7pm-9.30pm. Bar food available 12.30pm-9.30pm)

Letterkenny

Wine Shop

● The Wine Buff

Richard Finney is showing himself to be a Northwest mover and shaker in Letterkenny's Wine Buff. He has great wines, and he is a great communicator about the character and charm of those wines, and he is not afraid to put himself about, gadding all around the place for wine dinners and whatnot. Really essential, not least the very smart Xmas hampers filled with good Donegal things. (Richard Finney, Canal Road ☎ 074-912 0075 http://www.facebook.com/TheWineBuffLetterkenny Open 10.30am-7pm Mon-Sat, 'til 8pm Thu-Fri)

made in Donegal
McGettigan's Sausages

Malin Head

Coffee Cart
● Caffe Banba

Dominic and Andrea aren't just the most Northerly baristas in Ireland, they are also surely the bravest. For when the wind whips around Banba's Head at the most northerly extremity of Ireland it is a fearsome proposition to even be brave enough to get out of the car. So summon up your courage, climb out and head over for a beautiful coffee and some lovely buns and cakes, all sold from the beautiful Banba coffee bar on wheels. (Dominic & Andrea McDermott, Ballyhillion, Malin Head ☎ 074-937 0538 dominic@caffebanba.com www.caffebanba.com – Open Mar-Sept, 11am-6pm Mon-Sun. Also available to hire throughout the year for special events.)

Mountcharles

Country House
● The Village Tavern

Enda O'Rourke is one of the guiding lights behind the Donegal Good Food Taverns, a laudable collection of Donegal pubs making an effort to serve quality food – see www.donegalgoodfoodtaverns.com. The founding philosophy and mission statement of the DGFT is very much practised in The Village Tavern, ie a commitment to locally sourced food, and seafood, including loyal oysters; cultural nights to showcase Donegal's uniqueness; home-baked breads and cakes, and the serving of local Tyrconnell Whiskey. Enda allies this philosophy to a solid restaurant grounding, and the Village Tavern attracts diners from all over the county. (Enda O'Rourke, Main Street, Mountcharles ☎ 074-973 5622 villagetavern@live.ie)

Moville

Farm Shop

● The Farm Shop

Jo and Geoff breed the most Northerly and most delicious Inishowen mountain pigs way up in Moville, in addition to running the farm shop. Here you will find organic vegetables and leaves from local growers as well as organic eggs, chickens and Angus beef. There are also lots of pretty crafts and if they don't have it, they'll get it for you. (Jo & Geoff Fowler, Main Street, Moville ☎ 074-938 5526 🖱 www.movilleinishowen.com/farmshop)

Raphoe

Rapeseed Oil

● Donegal Rapeseed Oil

Since our last edition, Donegal Rapeseed Oil has pretty much conquered the country as the go-to cooking oil for both professional and domestic chefs. It's tolerance for high temperatures and its health-filled DNA make it an essential part of the kitchen armoury. Do note that the latest craze with hip chefs is to make a rapeseed oil mayonnaise: nice with asparagus! (Maura McHugh, Oakfield Demesne, Raphoe ☎ 074-914 5386 📫 info@donegalrapeseedoilco.com 🖱 www.donegalrapeseedoilco.com)

Ramelton

Guesthouse

● Moorfield Lodge

Lin and Bobby Crossle's boutique B&B has raised the bar for levels of contemporary comfort and design in Donegal. Moorfield has three suites – The Spa, the Bayview and the Classic. Ms Crossle has hospitality in her bones, and a sincere love of good food. Her breakfast granola is superb, as is the signature strawberry and blueberry crêpe. 'We try to please the guest in every way possible. We are doing this for the love of it,' she explains. The luxury would be empty without the friendliness the couple exude, and it is this charm that animates Moorfield. The Crossles spent a long time looking for just the right property to develop as a B&B, but even if they ran a Nissen hut, you would stay with them. (Lin & Bobby Crossle, Letterkenny, Ramelton ☎ 074-915 2655 ✉ lin@moorfieldlodge.com 🖱 www.moorfieldlodge.com)

Rathmullan

Craft Brewer

● Kinnegar Brewing

You will need your beer antennae working at full tilt to find the three Kinnegar brews, as they are currently produced on a nano scale. Limeburner is a pale ale, Scraggy Bay is a copper ale, whilst Devil's Backbone is an amber ale. Beautifully designed labels make them easy to spot, if you have the good luck to find yourself in their zone. (Rick Le Vert, Rathmullan ☎ 074-915 8875 ✉ greenbox@cartonlevert.ie 🖱 www.kinnegarbrewing.com)

Craft Beer

● Rathmullan House

"Most beguiling of all, there was also an indefinable comfiness about the hotel; grand, but lived-in, few airs, but many graces". That's Judith Woods, writing in the *Daily Telegraph* about Rathmullan House, and you couldn't sum up the place better than Mrs Woods' fine aphorism: few airs, but many graces. That's Rathmullan alright, a place where the Wheeler family show their dynamic hospitality, their generosity, and their genius for setting the mood at just the right pitch. You need a few days to get into Rathmullan, to slow down to its pace, to get at the level of those many graces. It's a most beloved house, especially for regular visitors from Northern Ireland who adore it. But the calmness is created simply because the Wheelers work so hard, and there is a continual smorgasbord of events and happenings to divert and delight everyone. Kelan McMicheal's food is at just the right pitch also, ennobling superb local foods with sympathetic culinary skills. Few airs, many graces. (Mark Wheeler, Lough Swilly, Rathmullan ☎ 074-915 8188 ✉ info@rathmullanhouse.com 🖱 www.rathmullanhouse.com – Open all year, apart from mid Jan-mid Feb)

County Dublin

Written by Caroline Byrne

with additional reporting from our editors

Dublin City Centre 172

North Dublin 233

Dublin 3: (Clontarf, Fairview, North Strand) 233; Dublin 5 (Raheny) 236; Dublin 7: (Smithfield, Stoneybatter) 238; Dublin 9: Drumcondra, Glasnevin 243; Dublin 11: Finglas, Glasnevin 244; Dublin 15: (Ballycoolin) 246

North County Dublin 247

Howth 247; Lusk 252; Malahide 253; Naul 254; Oldtown 255; Portmarnock 255; Skerries 256; Swords 257; The Ward 258

South Dublin 259

Dublin 4: (Ballsbridge, Donnybrook, Sandymount 259; Dublin 6: Ranelagh, Rathmines, Rathgar, Terenure 269; Dublin 8: Harold's Cross, Liberties, Crumlin, Portobello, Rialto 282; Dublin 12 & 14: Churchtown, Dundrum, Rathfarnham 287; Dublin 18: Foxrock, Sandyford, Stepaside 289

South County Dublin 292

Blackrock 292; Dalkey 293; Dun Laoghaire 296; Glasthule 299; Goatstown 300; Killiney 300; Leopardstown 301; Monkstown 301; Mount Merrion 30; Newcastle 304; Rathcoole 304; Stillorgan 305; Tallaght 306

DUBLIN CITY CENTRE

Dublin Central

Gastropub

● Against the Grain

The litmus test for a good gastropub is not merely the presence of good food, but also how people use the place. Do punters come in for drinks and to have the craic? If not, then you're only a restaurant with a bar. That is most definitely not the case with ATG, one of the city's few genuine gastropubs. With over 100 bottled beers, interesting draught, tasty ciders and a nice selection of wines and spirits, this spot gets banging of an evening. The food is also pretty good: fresh Greek salad or falafel wrap at lunch, hearty pies and meaty curries for dinner, darn good chips at any time. (Andrew Byrne, 11 Wexford St, D2 ☎ 01-470 5100 – Open Lunch/dinner 12pm-11.30pm Mon-Thurs, 12pm-12.30am Fri-Sat, 12pm-11pm Sun

Café/deli/bistro

● Angel Park Eatery

A nifty bistro, just a stone's throw from Merrion Square. Upstairs does take-away, with good coffee, loverly confections, and savoury food, including good big fat sandwiches, wraps, salads, and soups. Downstairs the bistro opens for lunch all week, and dinner from Wednesday to Friday. As in the café, the food is fresh and great value with starters such as Kennebunkport seafood chowder; prawns pil pil; mains such as spiced lemon prawn and scallop linguine, and roast pork fillet with spiced pan-roasted apples and pears. Add it all up and you get a great all-rounder. (Tanya McGouran, 5 Lr Mount St, D2 ☎ 01-676 3010 www.angelparkeatery.com – Open Mon-Fri (breakfast) 7.30am-11am, (lunch) 12pm-3pm, café closes 4pm, bistro open for dinner Weds-Fri evenings)

Pub

● Anseo

Not a place for food. It's just one of Dublin's better pubs, and happens to be in the vicinity of good food. Of an evening in Anseo you may enjoy some well-sourced beers and spirits, some good rowdy atmosphere, and a DJ set playing anything from ska to funk. (18 Camden St Lr, D2 ☎ 01-475 1321 – Open Mon-Thurs 10.30am-11.30pm, Fri-Sat 10.30am-12.30am, Sun 11am-11pm)

Food Shop

● Asia Market

The ageless Asia Market stocks everything you could possibly need for whiz-bang Asian cooking, from a myriad of noodle styles to exotic fish and some excellent fresh vegetables. The staff are funkier than the customers, and that's saying something. (Helen Pau, 18 Drury Street, D2 ☎ 01-677 9764 – Open 10am-7pm Mon-Sun)

Dublin Central

Casual dining/café/deli

● Avoca

Simon Pratt's Avoca is a luxury, homely foodie empire, with super cute homeware and fashion on the side. The kitchen ranges and feminine accessories alone could keep you browsing for hours, as their cookbooks keep you flipping pages, and their freshly-made baked goods leave you standing undecided for long periods. At the Suffolk Street store, the basement café turns out fresh Avoca breads and pastries every day – delicious apple and Stilton scones with the very popular field mushroom soup, or walnut and raisin toast, served with Avoca's homemade duck terrine. Try to resist Avoca's wares – it's not easy! (Simon Pratt, Suffolk St, D2 ☎ 01-672 6019 info@avoca.ie www.avoca.ie – Open 10am-6pm Mon-Fri, 10am-8pm Thurs, 10am-6.30pm Sat, 11am-6pm Sun. Also in Rathcoole, Naas Road, Co Dublin, and Counties Wicklow, Cork and Galway)

Restaurant/Italian

● Il Baccaro

A fun, atmospheric cellar-like restaurant that does worthy, good value Italian food and wine, the latter usually consumed in plentiful quantities of an evening, such is the vibe here. Service has been criticised in the past but is generally good these days. (Meeting House Square, Temple Bar, D2 ☎ 01-671 4597 www.ilbaccaro.com – Open 5.30pm-10.30pm Mon-Sun, noon-3pm Sat)

Bakery & Eatery

● The Bakehouse

When Caroline Hennessy enjoyed a creamy, chive-flecked chowder in a bread bowl in The Bakehouse, she reckoned the bread loaf was the size of a baby's head. Conveniently, Caroline had her baby – Small Girl – with her, so the analysis was entirely scientific. Joanne and

Chris's retro-style bakehouse is the place for batch loaves and Dublin coddle, corned beef sandwiches and a beef and Guinness pie. The cooking is clean and homely, so see you here for gur cake and a pot of tea. (Joanne Peat & Chris Morrissey, 6 Bachelors Walk, D2 ☎ 01-873 4279 www.the-bakehouse.ie – Open 10am-6pm Mon-Wed, 9am-10pm Thur-Fri, 10am-10pm Sat, 10am-3pm Sun)

Off Licence

● Baggot Street Wines

Garret Connolly and his team have the rock-steady pedigree of Oddbins backgrounds, and their range is stellar, the service hip, smart, informed. (Garret Connolly, Baggot Street, D4 ☎ 01-667 3033 baggotstreetwines@gmail.com www.baggotstreetwines.com – Open 10.30am-10pm Mon-Sat, 12.30pm-10pm Sun)

Café

● The Bald Barista

New Zealander Buzz Fendall has been called a coffee guru, an innovator, a visionary and, since 2007, has been bringing his passion for this vital beverage to the people of Dublin. In 2009 he opened his second café on Harcourt Road, and recently teamed up with coffee supplier Café de Cuba to bring his own Arabica blend, 'Fixx', to the Irish market, which you'll find at Bald Barista cafés and the Fixx Coffee House on Dawson Street. A member of the Barista Guild of Ireland and a lecturer to future baristas, his credentials and commitment to the development of Ireland's coffee culture are undeniable. (Buzz Fendall, 55 Aungier St (Avalon House) & Harcourt Rd ☎ 086-312 9980 thebaldbarista@yahoo.com www.thebaldbarista.com. Accepts cash only. Open (Avalon) 6.30am-8pm Mon-Fri, 7.30am-6pm Sat, 7.30am-4pm Sun; (Harcourt) 7am-4pm Mon-Fri)

Restaurant

● Bang Restaurant

When the wondrously popular Bang Café closed its doors in early 2010, legions of fans mourned the loss of their beloved brunch and lazy long lunch destination of choice. Thankfully, however, café magnate Bobby Kerr and his business partners decided they couldn't let the old haunt go down in flames. Today you'll find Bang Restaurant alive and well, and turning out possibly smarter food than before. Lunch of two courses for less than twenty euro is good value – fresh chargrilled sardines on a crunchy fennel salad with potatoes is an example of a tasty main that Phil Yeang delivers perfectly. They know how to cook risotto in this joint too. Service, says Aoife Cox, is "highly polished and friendly."(Bobby Kerr, Joe & Anne Barrett, 11 Merrion Row, D2 ☎ 01-400 4229 www.bangrestaurant.com – Open 12.30pm-3pm Mon-Sat (open till 4pm Fri & Sat); 6pm-10.30pm Mon-Wed; 6pm-11pm Thu-Sat. Closed Sun)

Restaurant/Italian

● Bar Italia

David Izzo and Stefano Crescenzi's casual eatery serves to acquaint Dublin with some authentic Italian food and drink, with particular care and attention paid to their coffee. Expect popular fare from their native cuisine, done well, with friendly efficient service. There's a second branch in the IFSC. (David Izzo, 26 Lwr Ormond Quay, D2, ☎ 01-874 1000; Lwr Mayor St, IFSC, D1, ☎ 01-670 2887 www.baritalia.ie – Open 12pm-10.30pm Mon-Thurs, 12pm-11pm Fri-Sat, 1pm-9pm Sun)

Tapas/Spanish

● Bar Pintxo

Bar Pintxo is the livelier sister of the more atmospheric tapas restaurant The Port House. Located in Dublin's 'cultural quarter' Temple Bar, it's popular for drinks and good tasty bites, or just a good time. The food consists mostly of Spanish tapas, especially 'pintxos' (those on a stick or crusty bread), but expect to find the usual array of hot and cold dishes too. Good list of wines, sherries and ports. The bathrooms are an interesting experience! (Lee Sim, 12 Eustace St, Temple Bar, D2 ☎ 01-672 8590 ali@porthouse.ie – Open Mon-Thurs 5pm-11.30pm, Fri 4pm-12.30pm, Sat 12pm-12.30am, Sun 12.30pm-11.30pm)

Restaurant

● Bear

"Really like Bear" says Leslie Williams, and Leslie is not alone. The fourth Joe Macken production, after Jo'Burger, Crackbird and Skinflint, Bear is all about pope's eye, rosary steak, rump and feather blade, i.e. the sticky, delicious, richly gelatinous cuts of meat that others discard. In Bear, which enjoys Macken's hip, bricolage salvage-chic style, the cuts are cooked slowly and served quickly, and the kitchen has invested time and thought into smart sides like the signature millionaire's chips. "Affordable treats in places that are surprising" is how William Barry sums up what young Dubliners want, and "Macken has this down to a T". He sure has. (Joe Macken & Jamie Heaslip, 34-35 South William Street, D2 ☎ no reservations taken 🖱 http://bear.joburger.ie – Open noon-late Mon-Sun)

Dublin Central

Pub

● The Bernard Shaw

This historic Dublin pub now owned by music promoters Bodytonic is probably the hippest pub in Dublin. It's a freedom-loving fun place that anyone can enjoy, but be warned: there are hipsters in this pub, so don't venture in if you can't handle the prolific self-expression through personal style. If you're down with that vibe, then get stuck in because the place is bangin' every weekend, often housing exhibitions, craft markets, gigs, barbecues, T-shirt painting and all kinds of other fun stuff. During the day the Italian Coffee To Get Her Café serves good coffee and tasty Italian quick dishes – panini with speck and gorgonzola; arrosticini lamb skewers; the very best cannoli in town – in the bar or through the street-side hatch for take-away. From Thursday to Sunday the festival-tastic Big Blue Bus serves pizza in the outdoor area. If this is your scene, then don't come to Dublin without seeing 'The Shaw.' (Bodytonic, 11-12 Sth Richmond St, D1 ☎ 085-712 8342 ✉ feedback@bodytonicmusic.com. Open (café) Mon-Sat 9am-4pm, (full bar) from 4pm Mon-Sun, (pizza bus) Thurs-Sun from 6pm)

Restaurant

● Bite

"Shiny happy people and good eats" is how Catherine Cleary of *The Irish Times* summed up Ronan Ryan's funky new eatery, with chef Malcolm Starmer taking care of the cooking. Bite draws in music-biz heads as well as ordinary citizens, all of them thirsty for good cocktails and hungry for snappy, direct, tasty cooking – fish and chips for hipsters, chicken kiev for retro fun, popping candy ice cream for the kids, Grey Goose martini if you have just wrapped the album. Lean and smart, Bite looks very much like a franchise-in-development to us. (Ronan Ryan, 29 Sth Frederick Street, D2 ☎ 01-679 7000 🖱 www.bitedublin.com)

Bistro/French

Blackboard Bistro

We love this basement bistro on Clare Street (just at the end of Nassau Street), where they cook up smart simple food five days a week. The ambience is cosy – the kind of place you could go on a first date – but with a buzzy atmosphere. And it's good value too, especially the early bird menu. Unlike many places, the BB understands the simple art of risotto, and a starter of leek and bacon risotto with fresh oregano, lemon zest and crème fraîche proves this point beautifully. Giving Dublin a taste of the simple French food the French like to eat. (Jean & Pierre Heyraud, 4 Clare St, D2 ☎ 01-676 6839 theblackboardbistro@gmail.com. Accepts credit cards. Open 12.30pm-2.30pm Tue-Fri, 5.30pm-9.30pm Tue-Sat)

Pub

The Black Sheep

With 100 or more craft beers from Ireland and the rest of the world, and Galway Bay beers on tap, the Black Sheep is a key element of the Capel Street renaissance. (61 Capel Street, D2 ☎ 01-873 0013 www.winefoodbeer.com)

Deli/bakery

Blazing Salads Food Company

As foodie yoda John McKenna so aptly says of Lorraine, Joe and Pamela Fitzmaurice, the expertise which fills the pages of their *Blazing Salads Cookbook* transmits into "delicious, tactile reality every day in their bustling deli and shop, and via their splendid naturally leavened breads," which are sold in other outlets apart from the Drury Street shop. The siblings are the second generation of a talented baking family. (The Fitzmaurice family, 42 Drury Street, D2 ☎ 01-671 9552 info@blazingsalads.com www.blazingsalads.com – Open 9am-6pm Mon-Fri, 9am-5.30pm Sat)

Restaurant

Bloom Brasserie

Established by a former head chef of Dax, Bloom Brasserie is one of Dublin's little underground gems. The food is quality bistro fare, expertly cooked using admirable produce: good Irish Black Angus beef, seasonal fish (often a special), 'grade A' foie gras and good Irish farmhouse cheeses. There's terrific value on the lunch and dinner menus, and you may also stop in for some tapas and a cocktail at the bar (available from 5pm). (Pol OhEannraich, 11 Upr Baggot St. D4 ☎ 01-668 7170 info@bloombrasserie.ie www.bloombrasserie.ie – Open 12pm-2.30pm, 5pm-10.30pm Mon-Fri; 4pm-1pm Sat. Closed Sun)

Dublin Central

Casual dining/burgers

● Bóbós

Following an extensive survey of Dublin's gourmet burger restaurants a while back, Guide editor Leslie Williams deemed Bóbós to be dishing up the best patties. Recently, he was able to report that the burgers, and indeed the chips, are still the best. Of particular note are 'The Applewood' (7oz pork burger with cured smoked bacon, smoked Applewood cheese, iceberg and Bobo's own apple relish), and 'The Cashel' (7oz prime Irish beef burger with Cashel Blue cheese, cured smoked bacon, red onion, rocket, black pepper and the house relish), while the skinny and chubby chips are, as they say, 'proper'. (Jay Bourke, 22 Wexford St, D2 ☎ 01-40 5750 info@bobos.ie www.bobos.ie – Open 9am-11.30pm Mon-Fri, noon-11.30pm Sat, 1pm-10pm Sun)

Café

● Le Bon Crubeen

Terrific value for money for good cooking has been the driver for Talbot Street's latest arrival, and they do their take on French Food's Greatest Hits very well: goose rillettes; smoked fish chowder; belly pork with scallops; duck confit; crème brulée. The keen pricing makes for a busy, buzzy room, and consistency has been consistently impressive. (81-82 Talbot Street, D1 ☎ 01-704 0126 info@leboncrubeen.ie www.leboncrubeen.ie – Open from noon-10pm Mon-Sat, 5pm-9pm Sun)

Café/Argentine

● Bondiola Argentina

'Bondiola,' or pork shoulder, is a specialty of this establishment. We are grateful to husband and wife team Antonio and Gabriela for educating us on the benefits of putting this and other Argentine cuts of meat into baps, sometimes with chimichurri, as in their eponymous sandwich, or cheese and ham, as in the beefy lomito, a favourite among regulars. Their empanadas go down just as good, hot or cold. As if this wasn't enough, the very friendly pair do a hearty asado on Saturdays, when they fill the neighbourhood with the smell of grilled rib of beef. A new wine licence means we can enjoy a drop of Argentina's other finest export while chowing down gaucho style. (Antonio Romeo & Gabriela Ramirez Sousa, 53 Haddington Rd, D4 ☎ 01-667 5692 ✉ info@bondiolaargentina.com 🖱 www.bondiolaargentina.com – Open 8am-6pm Mon-Fri, 10am-6pm Sat, closed Sun)

Mexican/takeaway

● Boojum

The burrito is a burgeoning industry in Dublin and John and Karen Blisard's authentic healthy homage to this Mexican wonder food is a good place to start. Boojum is proof there's something happening with Dublin and the burrito: with epazote herb in the black beans, achiote paste in the marinades, and tomatillos in the salsa verde and salsa roja, serious Mexican fans will know they're in safe hands. For their burritos, fajitas, tacos and salads, all ingredients are fresh and high quality, and served with pinto or black bean, lime and coriander rice, salsas, guacamole, cheese and/or sour cream. For fillings you can expect all the usual fare, beef barbacoa, carnitas (pulled pork), chicken, veggie and steak. House salsas range from mild to hot, portions are not for the faint-hearted. (John & Karen Blisard, Millennium Walkway, D1 ☎ 01-872 9499 🖱 www.boojummex.com – Open 12pm-9pm Mon-Sat, closed Sun)

Ice Cream Parlour

● Botticelli

Authentic Italian gelato made using good Irish milk and cream is a recipe for deliciousness, which is what you get by the bowlful in Botticelli. Stay in to eat one of their more decadent desserts or just grab a couple of scoops to go – chocolate and Amaretto are a good combo – and sample some of their good Italian coffee. Leave your guilty conscience at the door. (3 Temple Bar, D2 ☎ 01-672 7289 ✉ botticelli@eircom.net 🖱 www.botticelli.ie – Open 12pm-12am Mon-Sun)

Restaurant

● Brasserie Le Pont

A pretty downstairs room near the Leeson Street end of Fitzwilliam Place, BLP is understated and calm, with the sort of clientele who have money but don't want to make a big deal about it, just like Dubliners used to do back in the 1990's. James Doyle is a good cook, and his cooking is sharp and savoury. He makes a good bouillabaisse, he makes a good risotto, he cooks a lovely Hereford rib-eye steak, but he never grandstands the food: it's good cooking for grown-ups, and it's food that simply wants to make you happy. Were we happy after our last lunch at BLP? Indeed we were. (Fiona Kelly, 25 Fitzwilliam Place, D2 ☎ 01-669 4600 info@brasserielepont.ie www.brasserielepont.ie – Open for pastries from 10am, lunch from noon Mon-Fri, dinner from 5.30pm Tue-Sat)

Café

● Brook's Hotel

One of the things that makes Brooks so special – that make it the best hotel in Dublin – is that it has a Mom'n'Pop feel, thanks to manager Anne McKiernan and chef Patrick McLarnon. Their brilliance gives Brooks an entirely different feel from other city centre addresses: Brooks feels personal, intimate, and real, a place run by people, whereas other places feel they are run by a manual. The team who work with them are as vivid as the manager and the chef, and they all sync together perfectly. Brooks exemplifies the hotel-ness of an hotel, offering not just a welcome, but a real sense of well-being. (Anne McKiernan, Drury Street, D2 ☎ 01-670 4000 reservations@brookshotel.ie www.brookshotel.ie)

Café

● Brother Hubbard

"Well worth the inevitable queues you'll face at lunchtime", said Rosemary McCabe, fashion maven for *The Irish Times*. Rosemary was writing after BH had been open a single month, so did James Boland and Garret Fitzgerald get their chic café right, or did they get it right? A rad interior by Designgoat shows the attention to detail that defines these guys, and Garrett's food draws instruction and inspiration from masters such as Ottolenghi to lift and animate his baking, his salads, his sandwiches. It's impossibly cool, and it's on Capel Street, which makes this the new Coolsville. (Garret Fitzgerald & James Boland, 153 Capel St, D1 ☎ 01-441 1112 hello@brotherhubbard.ie www.brotherhubbard.ie – Open 7.30am-6pm Mon-Fri, 11am-5pm Sat)

Gastropub/beer hall

● The Bull & Castle

Belonging to the FXB restaurant group, the Bull & Castle houses Dublin's only Bavarian-style beer hall, where it serves a staggering list of bottled Irish and imported craft beers, as well as a good selection on draught, including: Blarney Blonde from the Franciscan Well brewery in Cork, Galway Hooker IPA from the Galway brewing company, as well as imports Erdinger Weissbier, Budejovice Budvar, Staropramen and Krombacher. B&C is also a gastropub – the food is decent and they love to recommend beer pairings to go with your nosh. It's a must for beer lovers. (Christchurch, D2 ☎ 01-475 1122 info@bullandcastle.ie www.fxbrestaurants.com/bullcastle. Open 11am-11.30pm Mon-Thurs, 11am-12.30am Fri-Sat, 12pm-11pm Sun)

Mexican/casual dining/takeaway

● Burritos & Blues

Does anything make you happier on a miserable Monday than a piping hot delicious burrito, bulging with fresh ingredients and the house hot sauce? Burritos & Blues know this magic cure and are now bringing it to Dubliners at two city centre locations. All meat and poultry is 100% Irish and all other ingredients are as fresh as a daisy and organic where possible. Everything from the marinades to the guacamole is made fresh in-store every day, and you've not had the real B&B experience 'til you've blown your head off with the house salsa (Level 4, that is). Don't worry, Level 1 provides a mild option for wussies. (2 Wexford St, D2, and Stephen St Upr, D2 ☎ 01-425 4022 http://burritos.ie – Open 12pm-10pm Mon-Thurs, 12pm-4am Fri-Sat, closed Sun)

Restaurant/tapas

● Café Bar H

Local developer Harry Crosbie did well when he recruited chef Johnny Cooke (formerly Cooke's Café, Castle Market) to head up his newest venture. Within weeks of opening Dublin's critics were hailing the tapas and sliders of this cool café-bar as 'seriously good,' accompanied by some pretty slick service and a decent European wine list (if a tad lacking in sherry). This is authentic food that does justice to the Spanish original, and Mr Cooke has long been one of of the most talented chefs at work in the capital. His food has the rare quality of being definitive:

he can nail a dish like few others. Besides the tapas offering there's decadent non-Spanish options to choose from, such as the McH mini-burger (with foie gras and truffle mayo) and some very special veal sweetbreads with a Pedro Ximenez sauce. All is delicious so you may find it hard not to over-indulge, and while some of the prices may hurt your pocket as much as your waistline, other items are reasonable. (Harry Crosbie, Grand Canal Plaza, D2 ☎ 01-899 2216 – Open til late Mon-Sat)

Café/deli/vegetarian

● Café Fresh

Mary Farrell's restaurant is one of the staples of the Powerscourt Town House, and one of the staples of Dublin's tiny vegetarian scene. Her deli on Leeson Street, Deli Fresh, offers signature dishes from the café to take away, another smart aspect of an operation that includes cookery classes, a catering wing, and Mary's own *Café Fresh Cookbook*. (Mary Farrell, Top Floor, Powerscourt Townhouse Ctr, D2 ☎ 01-671 9669 info@cafe-fresh.com www.cafe-fresh.com – Cafe Open 9am-6pm Mon-Sat, Deli Open 7.30am-3.30pm Mon-Fri)

Café/Italian

● Caffe Cagliostro

Terrific Italian coffee and a nice range of hot chocolate (including white hot choc!) with some darn good native confections such as tiramisu and cannoli to boot. Also has one of the best outdoor seating areas of any café in the city. Bellissimo! (Bloom's Lane, 24 Ormond Quay Lr, D1 ☎ 01-888 0860 – Open 7am-6pm Mon-Fri, 8am-6pm Sat, 9am-6pm Sun)

Café/casual dining/Italian/pizza

● Caffe di Napoli

A popular eatery since 1992, Il Caffe ably handles Italian staples such as risotto, good pastas, buffalo mozzarella, and good coffee, as you'd expect. Perhaps the favourite treat on offer here though is their pizza, which you can order to collect. Delicious toppings, liberally applied on a crispy yet doughy base. That'll do nicely. (41 Westland Row, D2 ☎ 01-611 4836 info@napoli.ie www.napoli.ie – Open (restaurant) 12pm-11pm Mon-Sat, closed Sun; (cafe) 7am-11pm, Mon-Fri, 9am-11pm Sat, 9am-6pm Sun)

Café/bakery

The Cake Café

This boho-chic café sums up a certain vibe in the quirky neighbourhood in which it resides. Cute but deliberate, seemingly jumble-sale but actually more Avoca, and filled of a weekend with stylish North Face and Birkenstock clad 30-somethings and their equally stylish little ones, reading *The Guardian* and brunching on the house egg and soldiers. For all the image-consciousness though, Michelle Darmody's café is true to its name – it does cake exceedingly well. Unusually modern in their simplicity and nostalgia, her confections, such as apple & cinnamon, coffee & walnut, or sumptuous orange Victorian sponge, are all the more satisfying for it. Cookery classes and cakes to order are also available. (Michelle Darmody, 62 Pleasant's Place, D8 ☎ 01-478 9394 thecakecafe@gmail.com www.thecakecafe.ie – Open 8.30am-6pm Mon, 8.30am-8pm Tue-Fri, 9am-5.30pm Sat)

made in Dublin

Hick's Sausages

Bistro/Mediterranean

Camden Kitchen

Camden Kitchen was barely open a wet week when it had resident critic tongues wagging, describing it as polished, accomplished and many other such descriptors that one would apply to a seasoned chef like Padraic Hayden. Well after a year open, local fans have been using other words, like 'charming' and 'obliging' and 'favourite.' These words perhaps are even more encouraging than the first lot, and put together tell you everything you need to know about CK. It ticks all the boxes and then some, serving up delicious Spanish, French and Italian dishes using excellent Irish ingredients: roast Fermanagh pork with chorizo and red pepper casserole; roast rump of lamb with mustard pomme purée. Staff are helpful and knowledgeable, and coeliacs are well looked after. It's the closest thing you'll get to a fine local bistro in the centre of town, minus the city centre prices. It's deserving of all plaudits, especially from the locals. (Padraic Hayden, 3a Camden Market, Grantham St, D8 ☎ 01-476 0125 info@camdenkitchen.ie www.camdenkitchen.ie – Open (lunch) 12pm-2.30pm Tues-Fri, 12pm-4pm Sun, (dinner) 5.30pm-10pm Tues-Sat)

Gastropub

● The Cellar Bar

Like the restaurant at the five-star Merrion Hotel, The Cellar Bar manages to be all at once sophisticated yet relaxed and understated. It's one of the best bars for food in Dublin, and manager Damian Corr's combination of energy, enthusiasm, and wine knowledge is a rare thing in any bar. (Damian Corr, Merrion Hotel, Upr Merrion Street, D2 ☎ 01-603 0600 ⌖ www.merrionhotel.com – Open noon-2.30pm, from 6pm Mon-Sun)

Restaurant/brunch

● The Cellar Restaurant

Chef Ed Cooney, who has cooked at The Cellar Restaurant since it opened, delivers food that is polished and impeccably sourced. Contrary to the stuffy image hotel dining in Ireland has acquired, Cooney's cooking is contemporary and vivid, and available for surprisingly good value since the onset of tighter economic times. The 'Cellar Steal' menu allows you to dine in the five-star hotel at terrific prices for three courses such as: confit of Galway salmon with horseradish potato salad, pickled cucumber, sesame seed and cucumber gel; truffle-crusted corn-fed chicken breast with chicory, sweet corn pureé, and red pepper salsa; and mango and pineapple baked Alaska with coconut and Malibu sauce. (Ed Cooney, The Merrion Hotel, Upr Merrion Street, D2 ☎ 01-603 0600 ⌖ www.merrionhotel.com – Open (breakfast) 7am-10.30am Mon-Sun, (lunch) 12.30pm-2pm Mon-Fri (no lunch Sat), (brunch) 12.30pm-2.30pm Sun, (dinner) 6pm-10pm Mon-Sun)

Spirits and wine shop

● The Celtic Whiskey Shop

Want to see a shop packed wall to wall with whiskey? CWS's collection includes a massive range of Irish whiskeys, as well as Scottish, American, Canadian and Japanese whiskys, and a fairly impressive cache of other spirits and liqueurs. Their vinous arm Wines on the Green has a fair stock of wines, the vast majority of which they import themselves. Visit the website to see the online shop, which is also an education on whiskey. The water of life indeed. (Ally Alpine, 27-28 Dawson St, D2 ☎ 01-675 9744 ✉ ally@celticwhiskeyshop.com ⌖ www.celticwhiskeyshop.com. Accepts credit cards. Open 10.30am-8pm Mon-Sat, 12.30pm-6pm Sun)

Restaurant/Indonesian

● Chameleon

Since opening in 1994, the Chameleon has remained true to its bohemian roots, and also remained one of the most popular and talked-about restaurants in Temple Bar, while other pretenders have come and gone around them. Offering generous, simple Indonesian food with personal and friendly service has been the key to their success. For example, their Nasi Goreng (fried rice with free-range chicken, pork, tiger prawns, kecap manis and egg) is not only great value, it's true food for the soul. (Carol Walshe & Kevin O'Toole, 1 Fownes Street, Temple Bar, D2 ☎ 01-671 0362 book@chameleonrestaurant.com www.chameleonrestaurant.com – Open from 5pm Tue-Sat and Sat lunch)

Restaurant/Irish

● Chapter One

It's hard to write about Chapter One in such a short space. Quite simply, it's considered the best restaurant in Ireland by almost everyone who knows it and it's certainly the best-loved in Dublin – with very good reason. If you're in the city and you want to taste the best of Irish food and delicious cooking, come to Chapter One. If you want to experience first hand the old school hospitality for which Ireland is famed, come to Chapter One. What chef Ross Lewis lacks in ego, he makes up for in abundance in class. His food never fails to put a smile on your face and in your heart, and you can't say that about many Michelin-starred chefs. The front of house team, led by co-proprietor (and Dublin treasure) Martin Corbett, make you feel like an old friend. An unmissable experience. (Ross Lewis & Martin Corbett, 18-19 Parnell Square, D1 ☎ 01-873 2266 www.chapteronerestaurant.com – Open 12.30pm-2pm Tue-Fri; 6pm-10.30pm Tue-Sat)

Bistro/French

● Chez Max

Chez Max is something of an oddity. It has the ability to divide opinions so as to have one faction claiming it to be the best Francophile eatery in town and another, eh, not so complimentary. Odder yet, almost all are agreed the second restaurant on Baggot Street is the better and more authentic of the two Chez Max, for which reason you may consider the plaudits awarded in this review attributable to that site. For those familiar with, and partial to, the kind of good casual dining you get in typical bistros in France, this is where you go to get a taste of it in Dublin. Good rustic food: classic pan-fried frogs' legs in garlic butter; confit duck with puy lentils and chicory. And true to its Francophile roots, service is prompt but not fawningly friendly. For the ultimate French bistro experience, go in November for the release of the latest Beaujolais nouveau and a quick bowl of moules frites or minute steak (bavette) with proper French fries. (Max de Laloubie, 1 Palace St (☎ 01-633 7215) and 133 Lr Baggot St (☎ 01-661 8899) chezmaxpalace@gmail.com; chezmax.baggot@gmail.com www.chezmax.ie – Open 8am–12am Mon-Fri, 11am–12am Sat-Sun)

Casual dining/Italian

● Ciao Bella Roma

The city centre pizza place of choice for most Italians (from always-reliable anecdotal evidence), CBR boasts an authentic pizza oven and defies the impression you may get from its fairly typical oversized menu. You'll find pretty much all the usual suspects on the menu but the pizza is the main event in this restaurant and probably among the best value you can find in the city centre. The early bird is one of Dublin's best bargains. (24/25 Parliament St, D2 ☎ 01-677 0004 – Open 12pm-11.30pm Sun-Thurs, 12pm-12am Fri-Sat)

Restaurant

● The Cliff Townhouse Hotel

From the people behind Waterford's acclaimed Cliff House Hotel, the Dublin townhouse outpost has acquired some serious ambition, not to mention a crack team from Waterford who are working hard to create a truly serious destination. Chef Sean Smith has devised a classic offering that gives him plenty of room to riff on ingredients such as Yawl Bay crab, wild seabass, TJ Crowe pork, Donald Russell beef and Skeaghanore duck, and he knows what he wants to do with these blue-chip ingredients. The menu has the poetry of logic to it, the wines and drinks are superb, and it would be very easy to see yourself in here for breakfast, and coming back for dinner. There are nice rooms upstairs if you seek lodging. (Paul Finnegan, 22 St. Stephen's Green, D2 ☎ 01-638 3939; http://thecliftownhouse.com – Open (Lunch) 12pm-2.45pm Mon-Sun, (dinner) 5.30pm-10.30pm Mon-Thurs, 5pm-10.30pm Fri-Sat)

Café

● Cobblers

A perfect little lunch place for busy people, with an informal seating and self-service arrangement, and no-fuss take-away for when there's no time to sit down. On offer is a variety of gourmet wraps, ciabattas and pizzas – including tasty Parma ham & mozzarella and cheddar & mushroom pizzas – which are available in good value combination deals with soup and/or drinks. There's also a high-quality fresh salad bar and daily hot mains including the likes of lamb stew served with brown bread. The soup is hearty and changes every day, and there's always a choice of two, such as country lentil, potato & cheddar, sweet potato & split pea, and Indian vegetable. (Eilis Davy, 4 Leeson Lane ☎ 01-678 5945 – Open 8am-4pm Mon-Fri)

Chocolates & Macaroons

● Cocoa Atelier

The shop is as perfect as the chocolates, and the chocolates are pretty perfect. Marc Amand's little workshop for chocolate, macaroons and eclairs is delectable, and the discipline and seriousness of purpose evident in every aspect of their work is a thrill. One of the great Dublin treats. (Marc Amand, 30 Drury Street, D2 ☎ 01-675 3616 shop@cocoaatelier.ie www.cocoaatelier.ie – Open 10.30am-6pm Tue-Sat, open til 7pm Thur)

Cookery School

● Cooks Academy

Tim and Vanessa acquired a mighty reputation before they moved to the city centre, and they offer an invigorating mix of cookery classes, distinguished by really gifted, entertaining guest chefs. (Tim and Vanessa Greenwood, 19 South William Street, D2 ☎ 01-611 1666 info@cooksacademy.com www.cooksacademy.com)

Coffee Stall

● Coffee Angel

In John McKenna's words: "Karl Purdy is an autodidactic perfectionist and so, whenever you come across a Coffee Angel coffee cart, you are in for a caffeine-fuelled experience that navigates the sublime via the narcotic. Every year at the Irish barista championships, Mr Purdy's crew do exceptionally well, inspired by the dedication – and sheer hard work and vision – of their boss." No arguing with that! You'll find these great coffee carts at CHQ, in Dun Laoghaire, and at various events. (Karl Purdy, CHQ, D1 info@coffeeangel.com www.coffeeangel.com)

Restaurant

Coppinger Row

What opened as a cool and promising spot in the heart of one of Dublin's nightlife districts, has blossomed into a seriously good bistro and cocktail bar. The flavour is still Mediterranean – French, North African, Spanish, Italian and Greek all nicely represented on the dinner menu – while the ingredients are quality Irish. And the drinks are hella good! The 'Zelda' Martini, for instance, combines vodka, almond liqueur, fresh lime and chopped mint, perfect for an after-dinner tipple. Their signature cocktail, the 'Flo & Basy', blends fresh basil, lime juice, agave nectar, gin and elderflower liqueur, and makes a great aperitif – or anytime – drink. To eat there's many, many good things: a creamy and flavoursome polenta so good it convinced a non-polenta lover; so simple yet so lovely roast stuffed chicken leg with Italian sausage and braised baby gem; and garnishes and salads of fresh seasonal leaves and shoots that fill you with summery goodness. Their baklava and 'mascarpone gelato' proves worth the effort even when full. Add to this a good wine list, great service, a buzzy room, bar and terrace, and you have too many reasons not to miss CR. No reservations for parties under six. (Conor & Marc Bereen, Coppinger Row, D2 ☎ 01-672 9884 www.coppingerrow.com – Open noon-11pm Tue-Sat, 1pm-8pm Sun)

Wine shop

The Corkscrew

A superb little shop just off Dublin's busy Grafton Street, the Corkscrew is known to loyal fans for offering some of the best value going on top-quality wines. They're also adept at finding unfamiliar gems at around the ten euro mark. Staff are knowledgeable and enthusiastic about wine, just like the owners. Shopping here is a pleasure for wine lovers and novices alike. (Colm Douglas, Paul Foley & Peter Foley. 4 Chatham St ☎ 01-674 5731 info@thecorkscrew.ie www.thecorkscrew.ie – Open 10.30am-7pm Mon-Sat, 10.30am-8pm Thurs)

Casual dining/vegetarian

● Cornucopia

"For us it is one of the great Dublin addresses, and the enlargement of the original restaurant into a funky new space bodes well for the next 25 years of Cornucopia," are the sentiments of John and Sally McKenna. So that means this address is one that should be on the 'must visit' list, for veggies and keen foodies. The menu is varied (two soups, five mains and 10 salads) and changes every day. The service is usually friendly, the food is always tasty. Good value and handy for a quick bite or chilled out lunch. (Deirdre McCafferty, 19-20 Wicklow St, D2 ☎ 01-677 7583 ✉ cornucopia@eircom.net 🖱 www.cornucopia.ie – Open 8.30am-9pm Mon-Fri, 8.30am-8pm Sat, noon-7pm Sun)

Café/deli/casual dining/Italian

● La Corte del Caffè

A partnership between Stefano Crescenzi (of Dunne & Crescenzi) and fellow Italian ex-pat David Izzo resulting in serious authentic Italian coffee and food which has been delighting Dubliners lucky enough to appreciate it for some years now. Deli produce is also worthy of note. (Epicurean Food Hall, 13 Lower Liffey St, D1 ☎ 01-873 4200 🖱 www.lacortedelcaffe.ie – Open 9am-6pm Mon-Sat, Thurs 'til 7pm, 11am-6.30pm Sun. IFSC, Custom House Square, D1, ☎ 01-672 1929 – Open 7.30am-5pm Mon-Fri. Powerscourt SC, South William St, D2, ☎ 01-633 4477 – Open 10am-6pm Sat, 10am-7pm Thur, 10am-5pm all other days)

Restaurant

● Crackbird

Joe Macken is smart. He does restaurants one at a time, and each restaurant does one thing at a time. Crackbird does chicken, and only chicken, and does it well, which meant the restaurant had to relocate to a bigger premises on Dame Street after just a few months on Crane Lane. Get there early or you will have to wait in line to enjoy a taste of the Dublin zeitgeist, along with your chicken. Sublime fun. (Joe Macken, 60 Dame Street, D2)

Café

● Crunch

"For breakfast, dinner and tay," they describe themselves on Facebook. That's 'tea' to those not familiar with Irish vernacular, and it means light evening meal, usually including tea. Well the tay and the tea are mighty, and the coffee and delectable confections brought in daily from the Sugarlump bakery – try the white chocolate fruit of the forest muffin – and the sandwiches made from good fresh ingredients and real farmhouse cheese, and the specials such as fresh line-caught mackerel, or breakfast of good scrambled eggs on toast, or seasonal fruit with yoghurt and toasted almonds, and all the other nice little touches that make Crunch Café more than just any old café. Owner Emmet Kealy's a lovely fella too and always there, so do say hello. (Emmet Kealy, 10a Aungier St. Accepts cash only ☎ 087-677 2003. Open 7am–8pm Mon-Fri, 8am–6pm Sat, 11am–6pm Sun)

Restaurant

● Dave's Wood-fired Pizza Co @ The Speak Easy Cafe Bar

Dave is a pizza legend in Dublin, having fed the populace from his pizza van over the last few years. But in the Speak-easy he has a piece of terra firma on which to plant his beehive oven and, as they say on George's Street, the pizzas have been knocking them out of the park from day one. Well wonderful. (David Lennon, 4 South Great George's Street, D2 ☎ 086-772 4744 info@daveswood-firedpizzas.ie www.daveswood-firedpizzas.ie)

Restaurant

● Dax

An old favourite among many foodies, serving classic food in elegant Georgian surrounds. Upstairs the café-bar is a good spot for after work drinks or morning coffee, and downstairs the food and wine has a strong French accent, like the owner, Olivier, who does indeed hail from Dax. Starters include ballottine of foie gras, foie gras crème brulée, and glazed salsify, while mains are knowing riffs on classic pairings such as Irish lamb cutlets, white bean and ratatouille, spinach, garlic and rosemary jus. All in all, Dax is top drawer, one of the city's best offerings, and the wine list is outstanding.
If you can't quite afford a splash in the restaurant, the new café-bar will serve amply, with very reasonably-priced tapas and platters, and live jazz on Thursday and Friday evenings. (Olivier Meissonave. 23 Upr Pembroke St ☎ 01-676 1494 olivier@dax.ie www.dax.ie – Open 12.30pm-2pm Tues-Fri, 6pm-11pm Tues-Sat)

Vegetarian Fast Food

● Delhi O'Deli

Pakora; paneer; uttappam; thalis; lime sodas! Hand me my rucksack, 'cause I'm off to Moore Street for street food from Delhi O'Deli. This slice of Indian vegetarian street food is authentic, from the garish lighting in a straightforward room, right down to the prices, which are as keen as it gets in Dublin. (Vicky Mehta, 12 Moore Street, Smithfield, D1 ☎ 01-872 9129 🖱 www.delhiodeli.com – Open 8am-8.30pm Mon-Thu, 8am-8pm Fri)

Restaurant/Thai

● Diep le Shaker

A stately Thai restaurant that has become something of a dining landmark, not to mention something of an empire with its takeaway/casual dining outlets: Diep Noodle Bar (Ranelagh) and Diep at Home (Drumcondra, Ranelagh, Blackrock). The dining room, on two levels, is elegant but understated, much like the service. The food is delicious and full of vibrant flavours and equally vibrant colour. The house selection of hors d'oeuvres is a good one to go for, especially for those less familiar with Thai cuisine. Larb Ped (shredded roast duck breast mixed with lemongrass, dry chilli, fresh lime, coriander, mint, fish sauce served in lettuce cups with roasted Thai rice), Hoi Shell Yang (spicy grilled scallop), Satay Gai (char-grilled chicken breast marinated in coconut milk, turmeric, coriander, curry powder and peanut sauce), Popia Tort (deep-fried spring rolls), and Muu Grop (roast pork belly with chilli, soy and coriander dip) make up the assembly of tasty bites, and generous portions too for the money. (Matthew Farrell, 55 Pembroke Lane ☎ 01-661 1829 📫 leshaker@diep.net 🖱 www.diep.net/leshaker – Open (lunch)12pm-2.30pm Tues-Thurs, 12pm-5pm Fri, (dinner) 5pm-10.30pm Tues-Weds, 6pm-11.30pm Thurs-Sat, closed Sun-Mon)

Restaurant

● Dublin Wine Rooms

The DWR is restaurant, wine shop, deli and wine bar. Leslie Williams was impressed by James Ainscough's cooking in the upstairs restaurant – crab and smoked salmon roulade; grilled cod with clams and pancetta, one of the best value steak-frites in Dublin, a superb flourless chocolate cake. With everything from a sandwich counter to a list of superlative wines, and the excellent enomatic wine system which allows you to sample wines by the glass, the DWR pushes all the right buttons. (James Ainscough, Custom House Sq, IFSC, D1 Restaurant ☎ 01-605 4912 Wine Bar ☎ 01-636 0616 dublinwinerooms@gmail.com www.dublinwinerooms.com)

Wine school

● The Dublin Wine School

Unsuspecting initiates of Nigel Donnan's class might think his sense of humour a little acerbic, but they soon realise his sharp repartee is applied indiscriminately and is even essential for a successful tasting. At the Dublin Wine School he has devised classes for connoisseurs and novices alike, from six-week appreciation courses to single evening tastings focused on specific regions. An evening with Nigel promises to be educational, droll, often controversial, and always enjoyable thanks to his great generosity of spirit. (Nigel Donnan, ☎ 01-288 2288 courses@dublinwineschool.ie www.dublinwineschool.ie)

made in Dublin

Natasha's Living Foods

Café/deli/wine bar/Italian

● Dunne & Crescenzi

More or less a household name now, D&C has been a port of call for coffee, wine and food lovers in the city for many years. From the same husband and wife team that brought us the smart, authentic and delectable Italian casual eatery L'Officina, along with Bar Italia and La Corte del Caffe in another partnership, D&C is a place to chill out and enjoy some good Italian delicatessen foods, such as the plate of bresaola with Parmesan, good Italian olive oil and lemon juice on warm bread, with a glass of good Italian vino from the very extensive list, which covers almost every region for both reds and whites. Booking ahead is advisable to ensure getting a table because, as you might expect by the sounds of such a place, it is very, very popular. (Eileen Dunne & Stefano Crescenzi, 22 Sth Frederick St (☎ 01-677 3815) and 11 Seafort Ave, Sandymount, D4 (☎ 01-667 3252) www.dunneandcrescenzi.com – Open 7.30am (8.30am in D4) until late Mon-Sat, 9am-9pm Sun (9.30am until late in D4)

Restaurant

● L'Écrivain

The words "make yourself at home" are not ones you normally associate with a fine dining, multi-starred restaurant. Yet that's the kind of service you get in L'Écrivain. Yes, they have a lot of suits in for lunch, and yes, they have a lot of suits in for dinner too, but L'Écrivain is truly a place for all to enjoy. They offer some superb value set menus but, whenever possible, do dip into the à la carte too and see what's really coming out of that kitchen. Wild turbot with delicate flakes of white crab meat in mayonnaise, topped with barely cooked fennel, sweet little brown shrimp and tart briny capers in a nutty beurre noisette; quail with onion mousseline; beef fillet accompanied with other succulent parts such as the ox tail and neck, all humble yet elegant in presentation, all adding up to the certain graciousness which characterises L'Écrivain. Come here when you really want to eat, and order well. It bears mentioning that they have a first-rate sommelier, Martina Delaney, who can look after you admirably whatever your budget or palate. (Derry & Sallyanne Clarke, 109 Lr Baggot St ☎ 01-661 1919 enquiries@lecrivain.com www.lecrivain.com – Open 10am-11pm Mon-Fri, 3pm-1am Sat, closed Sun)

Restaurant

● Eden

Eden boasts one of the most sought-after terraces in the city and, when on top form, the food matches the delight of its outdoor dining experience. It's especially nice for weekend brunch (when cocktails are two-for-one in the afternoon), when they do a pretty good Irish fry-up featuring legendary Dublin butchers Hick's gourmet sausages and black pudding. Or you could indulge in a stack of delish buttermilk pancakes with apple compote and cinnamon crumble (or caramelised banana and maple syrup). Now that's how to spend a Sunday afternoon. (Jay Bourke, Meeting House Sq, Temple Bar, D2 ☎ 01-670 5372 eden@edenrestaurant.ie www.edenrestaurant.ie – Open 12.30pm-3pm Mon-Sun, 6pm-10.30pm Mon-Sat, 6pm-10pm Sun, noon-3pm brunch Sat & Sun)

Restaurant/wine bar

● Ely Bar & Brasserie

Known to Dubliners as Ely CHQ, the second outpost of the Ely group is often the favourite of the three, mostly for its striking location in the CHQ building in the north docklands. Upstairs is bright and airy with a bustling terrace during the summer, downstairs is atmospheric and mysterious, in the vaulted cellars once used by merchants to store wine and tobacco. The wine cellar there today is impressive, and the establishment has been known to offer generous substitutions in the case of customers finding their chosen wines out of stock. The menu is also good: Burren fillet of beef Wellington; Dublin Bay prawn gnocchi with globe artichoke and pea & basil marinière sauce; fresh Galway Bay oysters. Often, upon finding success, a business spoils the original by expanding: in the case of Ely the opposite is true. (Erik & Michelle Robson, Custom House Quay (CHQ), D2 ☎ 01-672 0010 elybrasserie@elywinebar.com www.elywinebar.ie – Open 12pm until late Mon-Fri, 12pm-3pm, 5pm until late Sat-Sun)

Gastropub

● Ely Gastropub

The third member of the Ely family, HQ (Hanover Quay) has all the things its new neighbourhood needs: a good pub on rugby days (it's but a 10-minute walk from Lansdowne Road); a proper wine list with interesting choices by the glass; a good theatre menu for those heading to the brand new Grand Canal Theatre next door; good food on that menu, such as organic Burren beef carpaccio with rocket, Parmesan and horseradish, and wild Lough Neagh brown trout with puy lentils, spinach and tomato & caper vierge; a heated terrace in the winter with blankets so you can watch the frozen water of the Grand Canal basin; a barbecue on the terrace in summer so you can while away the warm evenings watching the water sports in the Grand Canal basin. Since this corner of the south docklands has come alive, so has Ely HQ. (Erik & Michelle Robson, Grand Canal Square, D2 ☎ 01-633 9986 elygastropub@elywinebar.com www.elywinebar.ie – Open 12pm-4pm Mon-Sat, 5pm until late Mon-Sun)

Wine bar

● Ely Wine Bar

The original Ely, first opened in 1999 in its picturesque Georgian home on Ely Place, remains as popular as ever among Dublin gastronauts. With two successful additions under its belt, Ely has proven it has what it takes to weather the worst recession and still stay true to its roots: good wine, good food and good service. In Ely Place, customers can walk in and pull up a stool around the bar, and lap up the atmosphere however they like. Perhaps a glass of Charpentier or Taittinger Champagne with a quarter or half dozen fresh Kilkee Pacific oysters, or maybe the Irish and continental farmhouse cheese plate with any of their scores of wine by the glass. Formal sit-down dining is also an option, although many would rather stay sipping and nibbling at the bar. (Erik & Michelle Robson, 22 Ely Place, D2 ☎ 01-676 8986 ✉ elyplace@elywinebar.com 🖱 www.elywinebar.ie – Open 12pm-11.30pm Mon-Thurs, 12pm-12.30pm Fri, 5pm-12.30pm Sat, closed Sun and bank holidays)

Wine bar/Italian

● Enoteca delle Langhe

A solid Italian wine bar, doing a nice list of wines and decent Italian cheese boards and light meals, is the classic offering of the stylish Enotecas. Blooms Lane is a lovely place to linger over a glass and a plate, whilst the suburban outposts are reasonably priced, casual eateries, offering tasty Italian dishes and wine of a refreshingly good standard for local places. (Mick Wallace, Blooms Lane, D1 ☎ 01-888 0834 ✉ enoteca@wallace.ie – Open 12.30pm-11pm Mon-Sat. Also Enoteca Torino, Grattan Crescent, Inchicore, D8 ☎ 01-453 7791, and Enoteca d'Asti, 11-16 Russell St, D9 ☎ 01-884 7500)

Café/deli/casual dining

● Epicurean Food Mall

Opened in 1999 near the bustling shopping district of the north city centre, EFH is still one of the most popular destinations for casual eats this side of the river. With a choice of fish and chips from Leo Burdock's, some of Dublin's best Mexican food from Taco Taco, some excellent Italian coffee and gourmet produce from La Corte, and a range of other cuisines from all over the world, you're spoilt for choice. (Middle Abbey St, D1 – Open 10am-6pm Mon-Sat)

Dublin Central

Fruit & Veg Shop

● Evergreen

Quietly bringing a lovely array of fresh produce and other essential grocery items – such as truffle oil or wine and cheese – to the people of this part of town normally reserved for nocturnal activity of the booze-filled variety. Not a big name on the foodie scene but much loved by locals, and for very good reason. Staff are knowledgeable and always very friendly. Evergreen is one of the city's secret gems. (Damien Madden, 34 Wexford St, D2 ☎ 01-478 5265 – Open 9am-5pm Mon-Sat)

Gastropub

● The Exchequer

The shot in the arm Dublin's pub scene needed, is a good way of describing The Exchequer. In fact, it's what the Irish pub scene needed and needs more of. A kicking bar – especially on Friday and Saturday nights – with a drinks list boasting a very good selection of wines, an admirable line-up of Irish and international beers and spirits that goes way beyond the typical offering, and a choice of 32 outstanding cocktails created by champion mixologist Darren Gerraghty. The Exchequer also does seriously good food, cooked by chef Lee Doyle into delicious seasonal menus featuring a gladdening array of Irish speciality and artisan produce, and excellent Irish ingredients. The food is hearty and great value, offering a broad range from classics, such as Doran's smoked chowder with potato and leek, to original and innovative dishes, such as pork belly with crisp fried squid with fish caramel sauce and a carrot and chilli purée. Highly recommended. (Peter Rock & Ian Tucker, 3-5 Exchequer St, D2 ☎ 01-670 6787 info@theexchequer.ie www.theexchequer.ie. Accepts cards. Booking required for Sunday roast. Open 12pm-11.30pm Mon-Thurs, 12pm-2.30am Fri-Sat, 12pm-11pm Sun)

Gastropub/brunch

● No. 3 Fade Street

The 'Secret Apartment,' 'Snail Bar,' 'No. 3 Fade Street,' 'Bar with No Name.' This establishment is known by all of these titles, and probably more, as it does in fact have no name, only a picture of a snail outside. It's also locatable through its proximity to French bistro L'Gueuleton, which also belongs to Kelly's Hotel on Fade Street and which lies directly beneath the 'secret bar.' By now it's far from secret though and often packed to bursting, especially on Friday and Saturday nights. It also packs out quite quickly for its weekend brunch, which features among the city's top spots for that meal. (3 Fade St, Kelly's Hotel, D2 ☎ 01-648 0010 info@kellysdublin.com www.kellysdublin.com – Open seven days, brunch Sat-Sun from 1pm)

Café/deli/food shop/restaurant/wine bar

● Fallon & Byrne

Since opening in 2006, F&B has transformed the city's food scene. It's the thing to beat for food shopping, with excellent meat and fish, fresh fruit and veg, cheese and charcuterie, wine and confectionery, and all manner of exotic and gourmet products, all under one roof. It is Dublin's Dean & Deluca, with a restaurant and wine bar to boot. Besides the foodhall – which while pricey does offer some pretty fantastic fare – it's the wine bar that really earns this great institution a place in Dubliners' hearts. It has a good varied list, all by the glass, in a cavernous cellar that fills with the best buzz achieved by any wine bar in the city, amply assisted by exceptionally good, friendly, knowledgeable staff. Wine and a cheese board in Fallon & Byrne's big basement has become a staple of Dublin social life. Long may it last. (Paul Byrne & Fiona McHugh, 11-17 Exchequer St, D2 ☎ 01-472 1010 office@fallonandbyrne.com www.fallonandbyrne.com – Open noon-4pm Sun, noon-3pm Mon-Sat, 6pm-9pm Sun, Mon-Tue, 6pm-10pm Wed-Thur, 6pm-11pm Fri & Sat (Restaurant). Wine Cellar & Food Hall open seven days.

Café

● Farmer Brown's

Tarot readings. Clairvoyants. Mystic mediums. Food and fortune evenings. All this along with pan-seared cod with pea purée, lamb and chorizo tagine, chilli cheese burger with paprika fries, and a BYO set-up? FB is different, and delightfully so. Finnuala and Grace like things to be left-field, hippyish, and everything is wonderfully, deliberately mis-matched. Delightful. Oh, and we can see your future: a visit to Farmer Brown's, delightful cooking, great value, excellent service, and a happy, delighted you. Bring on the future. (Finnuala & Grace Caffrey, Bath Avenue, D2 ☎ 085-858 6000 - farmerbrownsdublin@gmail.com – Open 8am-7pm Mon-Thur, 8am-10.30pm Fri, 10am-10.30pm Sat, 10m-6pm Sun)

Dublin Central

Casual dining/Italian

● Il Fornaio

A well-established eatery doing nice bruschetta, good pizza and classic pastas that have been pleasing Dubliners with a taste for Italian for some years. Find them in the IFSC and Raheny. (Bruce Cinelli, 1B Valenta House, IFSC, D1 (01-672 1852), and 55 Kilbarrack Rd, Raheny, D15 (01-832 0277) info@ilfornaio.ie www.ilfornaio.ie – Open 9am-10pm Mon-Fri, 11am-10pm Sat, 11am-9pm Sun)

local knowledge

A good sandwich?

● Bondiola Argentina ● The Chuck Wagon ● Crunch ● Fallon & Byrne ● Foodware Store ● Honest to Goodness ● Juno's Café ● Morton's ● Pig & Heifer ● Simon's Place

Restaurant

● Number Forty One

Head chef Graham Neville's skilled cooking has been lauded right from the beginning, and thankfully his restaurant stands apart from the private club in which it resides, so those in search of culinary rewards can come and dine without the need for a membership. As a chef, Mr Neville is polished, discerning, imaginative, and with an eye for beautiful detail. His raw ingredients are the best available and in season – wild turbot, sirloin from O'Coileáin Butchers in south county Dublin, Irish rose veal, black sole and Annagassan smoked salmon, to give you an idea. Under the care of the newly installed general managers, staff are professional but friendly. Altogether the restaurant has blossomed into one of Dublin's don't-miss destinations. This is the way to visit Georgian Dublin! (Graham Neville, Residence Members Club, 41 St Stephen's Green, D2 ☎ 01-662 0000 info@residence.ie www.residence.ie – Open 12.30pm-2pm (lunch) 5.30pm–10.30pm (dinner) Tues-Sat, closed Sun-Mon)

Food shop/deli

● Fresh The Good Food Market

When is a grocery shop more than a grocery shop? When it's a Fresh, is the answer. Enter any of the four stores within this 'good food' retail chain and you'll see why it's different. At your disposal are all the usual grocery staples but you'll also find buckets of marinated olives and Irish farmhouse cheese, at one of their ubiquitous cheese counters, and a delectable array at the hot and cold deli, and a good selection of wines lovingly put together by Cassidy Wines' most passionate expert, Philip O'Shea. Lucky is the city dweller who lives near a Fresh. (Noel Smith, Smithfield (☎ 01-485 0271), Camden St, Grand Canal Square 🖱 www.freshthegoodfoodmarket.com – Open 7am-10pm Mon-Sat, 8am-10pm Sun, bank holidays)

Restaurant/Chinese

● Good World Chinese Restaurant

A long-standing favourite 'Chinese' among Dubliners and especially noted for its tasty good value dim sum, which are all under a fiver. The dim sum are not too challenging: quail egg and meat dumpling, shan chin bun, curry whelks and other little treats of that nature. There's an interesting Chinese menu of authentic dishes well-frequented by regular ex-pat customers, or more adventurous other diners. Dishes, for instance, such as the combination of duck, roast pork, char siu (barbecued meat) and jelly fish, is worth a go even if only for the value to be had. The long life of Good World is a recommendation in itself, and the staff are always friendly. (18 Sth Great Georges St, D2 ☎ 01-677 5373 – Open 12.30pm-2am Mon-Sun)

Casual dining/vegetarian

● Govindas

Since the late 1990s Govindas has been one of Dublin's greatest ambassadors for tasty vegetarian food, so much so that husband and wife owners Praghosa and Goloka guesstimate around 60 percent of their customers are non-vegetarian. Govinda, in ancient Sanskrit, means "protector of the cows and bringer of pleasure to the senses," and this Dublin chain is fulfilling its brief. The top regulars' favourite from the buffet menu is paneer subji, the veg special of the day with a delicious Indian curd cheese cooked in an aromatic spiced tomato sauce

They make their own paneer fresh every day and, best of all, source the majority of their vegetables from their farm in Fermanagh, where they've also planted over 80 fruit and nut trees – healthy food, in every sense of the words. Govindas' vegetarianism is deeply linked with Krishna way of life and the ancient Vaishnava faith. For more info on this, their classes and their Kirtan Centre, visit the website. (Praghosa & Goloka Murphy, 4 Aungier St, D2, ☎ 01-4750309; 18 Merrion Row, D2, ☎ 01-6615095; 83 Middle Abbey St, D1 restaurants@govindas.ie www.govindas.ie – Open 12pm–9pm Mon-Sat, 12pm–7pm Sun, Abbey St only)

Casual dining

● Green 19

Green 19 pushes all the right buttons, straight from that welcoming cocktail – Green Mexican is a personal fave (Tequila, maraschino liqueur, lime, pink grapefruit juice, fresh chilli and bitters) – to the tasty food and amazing value on main courses, such as corned beef with cabbage and mash, or slow-braised pork belly with chorizo, white bean cassoulet and sautéed cabbage. The sarnies are good – though not such great value – and the atmosphere is funky and relaxed, especially after a couple of those really good cocktails. Make sure you book for the evening time, because chances are the place will be packed. (Stephen Murray, 19 Camden Street Lower, D2 ☎ 01-478 9626 www.green19.ie – Open 10am-11pm Mon-Sat, noon-6pm Sun)

Bistro/French

● The Green Hen

Opened in 2010, TGH's interior is an admirable representation of a typical French bistro, with the addition of a broad bar counter at which to perch for snacks and a glass of wine or a cocktail. The menus are short and sweet with a great value 'plat du jour' from 6.30pm to 7pm which changes daily: confit pork belly, coq au vin, ox cheek pie, sautéed lamb's liver and so on. Sunday to Thursday there's also early bird options until 7.30pm, but in general pricing is mid-range and good value. The starter of rabbit terrine with plum relish, watercress and sourdough toast is rustic and tasty, and they'll happily furnish more sourdough if asked. Mains meanwhile, for example grilled sea trout with fricassee of clam, pea and smoked bacon, or lamb and black pudding with home-made white bean cassoulet with smoked tomato, are consistently good renditions of French bistro food, and good value for your money. Service is friendly and knowledgeable, and the wine list includes some very good southern French reds, especially the Minervois and Coteaux du Languedoc. (Paul Rooney, 33 Exchequer St, D2 ☎ 01-670 7238 ⌂ www.thegreenhen.com – Open 12pm-11pm Mon-Sat (dinner 6pm-11pm), 11am-9pm Sun (brunch 11am-4pm Sat-Sun)

Restaurant

● The Greenhouse

The most high-profile opening of 2012 quickly became the success story of 2012, as it quickly became very, very difficult to secure a table at The Greenhouse. Chef Mickael Viljanen is one of the great contemporary talents, and his food is simply shining here, and eliciting a rare unanimity of acclaim amongst Dubliners. Mr Viljanen's cooking is one of the sublime experiences, as he fuses a Mugaritz-like sensitivity to a Noma-like ruddiness: roasted mackerel with veal tongue and eel cannelloni; celeriac baked in salt and rye with roasted Skeaghanore duck hearts; celery with rhubarb, rose, white chocolate and dill. "Accomplished, innovative, inventive, memorable", said Aoife Cox. Service matches the standards of the cooking, and the only problem is getting that table. (Mickael Viljanen, Eamonn O'Reilly, Joshua House, Dawson St, D2 ☎ 01-676 7015 ✉ thegreenhouse@ireland.com ⌂ www.thegreenhouserestaurant.ie – Open noon-2.30pm, 6pm-10.15pm Tue-Sat)

Bistro

● L'Gueuleton

L'Gueuleton changed the game for French restaurants in Dublin when it opened in 2004, and it's testament of its mettle that it remains a standard-bearer on the city's restaurant circuit today. Atmospheric and inviting from the outside, buzzy and full of great aromas on the inside, it's no surprise the bistro continues to lure the punters in droves, which is the reason it can be hard to get a table (that and they don't take reservations). Another reason for its unwavering success is, of course, the food, which includes French classics such as Burgundy snails in garlic butter, Jane Russell's Toulouse sausages with choucroute and Lyonnaise potatoes, and one of the best chargrilled rib-eye steaks in Dublin, with 'Café de Paris' béarnaise, watercress and chips. L'Gueuleton's menu never strays far from its classic French roots, but is deserving of its many accolades. (Declan O'Regan, 1 Fade St, D2 ☎ 01-675 3708 lgueuleton@gmail.com www.lgueuleton.com – Open 12.30pm-3pm, 6pm-10pm Mon-Sat, 1pm-3pm, 6pm-9pm Sun)

Café/wine bar/Mediterranean

● Harry's

A fixture on Dawson Street for some time now, Harry's has become known for good food and good value, whether it's dinner you're after or a snack and a glass of wine. The style is Mediterranean 'with an Irish twist' (think along the lines of Carlingford mussels with white wine and chorizo) although in reality you'll mostly see classic Med dishes or rather typical Irish ones, such as Irish lamb shank with roast carrots and parsnips, or spicy sausage penne with peppers. The two-course value menu is on every day, and there is a value dinner for two including wine, seven days a week from 5pm. They do over 20 wines by the glass and the service is always easygoing, friendly and obliging. A popular choice for a class of Dublin folk who like a bit of good food and wine, plain and simple. (22 Dawson St, D2 ☎ 01-639 4889 info@harryscaf.ie www.harryscaf.ie – Open 10am-11pm Mon-Sun: dinner only from 5pm Mon)

Tapas/Spanish

● Havana

Buzzy tapas bar with a young vibe and great atmosphere, serving very tasty snacks and bites, including their popular chicken wings. The menu has traditional options, including Spanish meatballs and chorizo in red wine, and a range of Spanish omelettes at lunch. They also do some Mexican-inspired wraps, served with salsa and nachos at lunch, and gooey banoffee pie that brings some punters in just for that. They're also fully licensed and have mojito, caipirinha and Cuba libre by the pitcher and, of course, sangria. The food is generally yummy – their paella is definitely worth a go – and the atmosphere is always terrific and promises a great night out. Spontaneous salsa dancing welcome. (Stephen, Zelda & Paul Quilligan, 10 Sth Great George's St, D2 ☎ 01-400 5990 havanatapasbar@gmail.com www.havana.ie – Open 11am-10.30pm Mon-Wed, 11am-11.30pm Fri, 1pm-11.30pm Sat, 5pm-11pm Sun)

Casual dining

● Herbstreet

Grand Canal Dock is a newly developed, cool part of Dublin, and partners Siobhan Mullen and Vinnie Murphy really get how to work the place with their cool and casual eatery Herbstreet. They're all about being relaxed yet carbon footprint aware, while serving good food and playing good music. The interior is quirky, fun and casual, the food is wholesome and scrumptious. Zingy fried shrimp and calamari salad with chilli, 10oz grilled rib-eye with homemade béarnaise and chips, orzo pasta with tiger prawns and chorizo with lemon, saffron and harissa, and those addictive spicy chicken wings of Elephant & Castle fame, are some of the reasons to make your way to Herbstreet. Menus change with the seasons and everything is homemade, environmentally friendly and as happy as possible. (Siobhan Mullen & Vinnie Murphy, Grand Canal Dock, D2 ☎ 01-675 3875 herbstreetdublin@gmail.com www.herbstreet.ie – Open 8.30am-5pm Mon-Fri, 10.30am-7.30pm Sat-Sat)

Café

● Honest to Goodness

They bake (fully, from scratch) their own breads, they toast their own granola, everything is made in-house, so you know these guys are serious about making good grub. And so, too, have regulars become serious about their sandwiches, especially the renowned Sloppy Joe, which oftentimes comes back for a guest appearance on the specials board. They also do good breakfast options, including unusual ones such as the Upstart toasted sandwich, with scrummy scrambled eggs, salsa, smoked salmon or semi-sun-dried tomatoes. All-round yumminess. (Darragh Birkett, 25 George's St Arcade, Sth Great George's St, D2 ☎ 01-633 7727 www.honesttogoodness.ie. Accepts cash only – Open 9am-5pm Mon-Sat)

Restaurant/wine bar

● Hugo's

Gina Murphy knows how to throw a party, which probably explains how Hugo's manages to maintain its constant buzz. It's probably also down to the effortless warmth and friendliness of the staff, which puts customers at ease among the glamorous surrounds of Hugo's richly decorated rooms. The food is good and often interesting, such as roast pork fillet mignon marinated in green tea leaves with a maple syrup butter, wholegrain mustard mash, mangetout, apple sauce and a sage jus, and they also like to feature good Irish ingredients as centrepieces of simpler dishes, such as Ardsallagh goats' cheese, leek and walnut terrine, with pear and soy coulis, or Irish sea mussels cooked in cream, white wine and garlic. Whether you come for a party or just a glass of wine and a bite, a visit to Hugo's always feels like an occasion. Live jazz on Thursday evenings and for Sunday brunch. (Gina Murphy, 6 Merrion Row. D2 ☎ 01-676 5955 info@thewolftrap.ie www.hugos.ie – Open 12pm-11pm Mon-Sat, 11am-10.30pm Sun)

Restaurant/Indian

● Jaipur

A high-end Indian chain, established in 1998 by entrepreneur Asheesh Dewan, Jaipur is still going strong and is a favourite among Dubliners in its multiple locations, including Dalkey, Malahide, Ongar, and Greystones (under the name Chakra), in addition to the original city centre restaurant on George's Street. While not inexpensive, Jaipur's popular dishes, such as purdah gosht dumdaar (slow braised lamb cooked overnight with aromatic spices, roasted potatoes and shallots, with screw pine saffron and sandalwood extracts), pork vindaloo, or duck chettiyar (free range barbary duck breast with southern spiced coconut and tamarind marinade, and onion and potato mash) keep the punters coming year after year. The recent introduction of an Indian 'tapas' menu for lunch gives Indian fans and uninitiated diners a chance to sample a range of flavours in one go. In 2008 Dewan partnered up with internationally esteemed chef Atul Kochhar to bring the award-winning Ananda to Dundrum. (Asheesh Dewan, 41 Georges St, D2 ☎ 01-677 0999 info@jaipur.ie http://jaipur.ie – Open seven days from 5pm until late)

Takeaway/Thai

● Kanum

Some say it's the best Thai takeaway going, especially in terms of value for money. Kanum has a small space for sitting in and even a small selection of wines, but the bulk of its business is takeaway and that it does very well indeed. Noodle fans will love their zingy pad Thai or hot and spicy ko soi, and the stock and trade tom yam soup packs a fiery punch too. Kanum has its own flavour and it's a hit with local Dubs. (77 Mespil Rd, D2, ☎ 01-660 8616; 16 Orwell Rd, Rathgar, D6 ☎ 01-406 2080 info@kanum.ie www.kanum.ie – Open (Mespil Rd) 11am–11pm Mon-Thurs, 11am–12pm Fri-Sat, 12pm–11pm Sun; (Rathgar) 12pm–11pm Sun-Thur, 12pm–12am Fri-Sat)

Gastropub

● WJ Kavanagh's

The firebrands from Mulligan's of Stoneybatter have opened up on Dorset Street, and Dorset Street has seen nothing like this crew in decades: wasabi mushy peas? Janey Mac! Terrific food, amazing beers, ace cocktails, the coolest staff, and a beautiful pub is what you get in Kavanagh's. The energy and enthusiasm of the crew is as affecting as their creativity and their punchy savoury cooking, and Kavanagh's is the coolest kid on the street. (Colin Hession, Michael Foggarty & Seáneen Sullivan, 4-5 Dorset Street, D1 ☎ 01-873 0990 hello@wjkavanaghs.com www.wjkavanaghs.com – Open noon-11.30pm Mon-Thur, noon-12.30pm Fri, 4pm-12.30pm Sat, 4pm-11pm Sun)

Café-deil/caterer

● KC Peaches

Now in its sixth year and expanded to its second location on Nassau Street, KCP is an ambassador of the US west coast here in Dublin. The food is healthy and tasty and of the homely variety: hearty soups such as tomato and cheddar; tasty salads like Mexican bean with fresh lime, coriander, chilli and onion; and too-tempting-to-resist mains such as KCP mac & cheese, baked to scrumptious perfection. They're also a must for brunch in the city, and definitely don't miss their exceptionally good baked treats, all of which are terrific by any standards, and additive-free like the rest of the food here. Winners of the 2011 Dublin City Soul Festival 'Best Soul Food' award for some smokin' chilli beef tacos and house gumbo. Finally, the Wine Cave in the basement of their Nassau Street store serves some of the best and best value grub in the city, with a well-thought out and fairly priced wine list, and superb live jazz on Saturday nights. Do not miss this. (Katie Cantwell & Vincent Carroll, Unit 10A Trinity Enterprise Cr, Pearse St, D2 ☎ 01-677 0333 thekitchen@kcpeaches.com http://kcpeaches.com – Open 8am-8pm Mon-Fri, 10am-4pm Sat, 11am-4pm Sun)

Dublin Central

Casual dining/Korean

● Kimchi@The Hop House

Kyoung Hee Lee's hip and happening restaurant, pub and music venue is the real deal, so look forward to tofu broth with seafood, bibimbap, beef with sweet potato noodles, pork with chilli sauce, and, of course, you must have some kimchi on the side, and a shot of Chum Churum soju. "Go and be charmed by Kimchi", says Leslie Williams. Kimchi is fab, a shining light on the Korean scene, and they have even kept the old bar from the pub. (Kyoung Hee Lee, 160 Parnell St, D1 ☎ 01-872 8536 – Open Mon-Sun)

Kitchen Equipment

● Kitchen Complements

No food, no, but "the Rolls Royce equipment for many happy years," says the *McKennas' Guide* gang. So you know where to go if serious baking is on your horizon. (Ann McNamee, Chatham St, D2 ☎ 01-677 0734 www.kitchencomplements.ie – Open 10am-6pm Mon-Sat, till 7pm Thur)

Restaurant/Thai

● Koh

Koh is a hip northside bastion of modern Thai (and some 'Asian fusion') cuisine, with a cosmopolitan vibe including that essential accessory – the cocktail bar. Their cocktail recipes are original and delicious, and their food is damn tasty too. Bar bites are available should you not make it into the restaurant, but if you do, the Thai ceviche and green papaya salad and/or the roast spicy pork chops are among the 'don't miss' items. (Conor Sexton & Conor Kilkenny, Millennium Walkway, D1 ☎ 01-814 6777 enquiries@koh.ie www.koh.ie – Open noon-5pm Mon-Sun, 5pm-10.30pm Sun & Mon, 5pm-11pm Tue-Thur, 5pm-11.30pm Fri & Sat)

Café/bistro

● Lennox Café

There are a few places around the city where you may encounter a bit of a scrum for a table at breakfast or brunch hour, and Lennox is one of them. In the heart of the trendy, shabby-chic neighbourhood of Portobello, this tiny doll's house-like café draws in the punters with its quesadillas and eggs Benedict – or Florentine if you're that way inclined. Good lunch options include such dishes as smoked haddock with creamed potatoes and black pudding, or the mixed leaf salad with warm figs, crispy Parma ham, caramelised walnuts and Parmesan. They also stock nice pastries including lurvely cupcakes from Cupcake Kisses. (Huibrecht Lukyx, 31 Lennox St. D8 ☎ 01-478 9966 info@lennoxcafe.ie www.lennoxcafe.ie – Open 9am-5pm Mon-Sat, 9.30am-5pm Sun)

Takeaway/fish & chips

● Leo Burdock's

Established in the minds of many Dubliners as the best chipper in Ireland, the fish and chip aficionado has been doling out piping hot perfect chips and battered fish since 1913. In particular, its Christchurch shop has become a fixture of Dublin nightlife and a noted spot for superlative fare, providing sustenance after an evening sampling the local recreational establishments. Cod, ray, lemon sole – there's not a batter burger in sight. So if it's pints you've been having and it's a good chipper you're after, make your way to Leo Burdock's. Also found in Rathmines, Phibsboro, Liffey Street, Dundrum and Temple Bar. (Burdock family & Charles McGrachan, 2 Werburgh St, Christchurch, D2 ☎ 01-454 0306 info@leoburdocks.com www.burdocks.ie. Accepts cash only – Open 12pm-12am Mon-Sun)

Bakery

● Le Levain

Rossa Crowe is a good baker, and you will find his sourdough breads in some of the city's hippest restaurants. We found some at the Temple Bar market on a recent trip – currently his only retail outlet – and they were delightful: good crust, good crumb, a satisfying chew and a wealth of natural flavour notes permeating through the slices. Mr Crowe has what it takes to emulate the huge success of Cork's Arbutus Breads, and Dublin needs these healthful sourdoughs. (Rossa Crowe, Unit 1, Behan Square, 11 Russell Street, D1 ☎ 01-856 0222 lelevain@gmail.com www.lelevain.com)

Deli/food shop

● Liston's

"If they haven't got it, then you actually don't need it. Everything that you do need, however, you will find in Karen Liston's exemplary deli, cum traiteur, cum wine store," is how the *Irish Food Guide* publishers describe this long-established emporium of all things good, and that includes service. Karen Liston was ahead of the curve when she opened her store and, by some unearthly magic, she manages to remain ahead of the curve. Respect! You will have to join a healthy queue at lunchtime, but there are few waits so worth the waiting. Everything is good, but Ms Liston's soups, in particular, deserve a shout out: they are formidable concoctions that could and would sustain the nation, and they show the care that is given to every detail in Liston's. (Karen Liston, 25 Camden Street, D2 ☎ 01-405 4779 listonsfood@eircom.net www.listonsfoodstore.ie – Open 8am-6.30pm Mon-Thu, 8am-7pm Fri, 10am-6pm Sat)

Dublin Central

Takeaway/café/patisserie

● Lolly & Cooks

Addictive buttery cupcakes have made this adorable stall a destination for Dubliners in search of indulgent treats, including personal favourites such as gingerbread and lime, and coconut and raspberry (wow!). However, the giant delectable sausage rolls seem to have caught up in popularity and are pulling a crowd of their own now: proper order as these are mighty! Lovely coffee too. (Laragh Strahan, George's St Arcade, Sth Great George's St, D2 ☎ 01-675 0865 laragh@lollyandcooks.com www.lollyandcooks.com – Open 9am-6.30pm Mon-Sat, 9am-9pm Thurs, 10am-6pm Sun)

Bistro

● Louie's

A much loved local bistro in one of the Georgian quarters of the north city centre, Louie's has set out to do good food made from fresh locally sourced ingredients right from the first day. Head Chef Dan Courtney directs the kitchen with a practised hand, turning out professionally executed yet very moreish dishes, such as garlic and chilli prawns with mango and coconut salad, roast pork belly with spiced apples and creamed potatoes, and prime Irish beef burger with strong cheddar caramelised onions and fresh hand-cut chips. Mains are mostly under a tenner and starters are around half that, which is the sort of value for money you don't find often. Top marks for this joint. (Eoin Olin, 20 Mountjoy Sq, D1 ☎ 01-836 4588 info@louies.ie, reservations@louies.ie www.louies.ie – Open Mon-Sun 12pm-3pm, Wed-Sat 5pm-11pm)

Restaurant/Indian

● Madina Desi Curry Co

This strangely-shaped, designed-on-a-shoestring room is where you head to for dosas, rice flour panckes that come with various fillings, come in voluminous sizes, and come at rock-bottom prices. It sounds like student heaven, and it is, save that there are no beers. The best choices are the vegetarian options, but everything is simple, true and soulful and well worth the trip to Mary Street. (The Madina Family, 60 Mary Street, D1 ☎ 01-872 6007 🖱 www.madina.ie – Open noon-11.30pm Mon-Sun)

Restaurant/French

● La Maison

Having made a great success at Vaughan's pub in Terenure, Olivier Quenet has transformed La Maison into a stylish, seriously good French restaurant. The menu, written in French and English, sets forth a list of accomplished dishes: the terrines plate is a good place to start – with delicious terrines and quenelles of duck liver pâté served with pickles – before moving on, perhaps, to pan-roasted cod with morels, rocket and gnocchi, or tarte Provençale, or the keenly priced mixed seafood platter. Crisp linen, crisply attired waiters, and a nice slice of La France profonde in central Dublin. Quenet has also taken over one of Dublin's most prized pubs, the Schoolhouse on Northumberland Road, where his top-notch fare does justice to the beautiful old site. (Olivier Quenet, 15 Castle Market, D2 ☎ 01-672 7258 🖱 www.lamaisonrestaurant.ie – Open 12.30pm-3pm Tue-Sat, 6.30pm-10.30pm Tue-Wed, 6.30pm-1am Thur-Sat)

Restaurant/Chinese

● M&L

A certain Dublin food writer who doesn't take 'no' for an answer started the M&L bushfire a while back, after a visit that revealed the possibility of 'egg-yoked soft shell crabs' or 'velvet crabs in ginger sauce,' if only you could get your hands on the menu reserved for ex pats. Following this early review adventurous foodies made the pilgrimage in droves in search of the elusive 'Chinese menu' and the delicacies hidden within. Those who've eaten from the ex-pat carte swear you won't find a better Chinese restaurant in the city. Those who haven't are still impressed by the offering deemed more suitable for western palates: Cantonese roast duck, razor clams with angel hair noodles, chilli squid, and many more. Whether this is the best you will have to find out for yourselves, by exploring the maze of little eateries lining Parnell Street and its surrounds, all with their own secrets, which they may or may not reveal, depending on who you're with and what hour of the day or night you wander in. One thing for sure, it's great fun finding out. (13 Cathedral St, D1 ☎ 01-874 8038 – Open 11.30am-11.30pm Mon-Sat, 12pm-11.30pm Sun)

Restaurant/Indian

● Mantraa

Given the limited number of proper Indian restaurants in the city, it is easy to identify the ones that stand out, and Mantraa is definitely one that stands out. First off, it does a three-course lunch for around a tenner, and the à la carte prices aren't bad either. Secondly, owners Deepak and Avinash fulfil their promise of a varied authentic menu of quality dishes beyond the typical offering. Starters such as Kerala rice pancakes, sambhar (a spiced vegetable stew) and fresh coconut chutney give a taste of Southern India, while mains such as paneer khurchan (Indian curd cheese) and murgh ka mokul (an aromatic take on divine Punjabi buttered chicken) demonstrate flavours of the northern part of the country. Unmissable dishes are squid churmura (crisp calamari with tamarind and tomato confit) and meen manga (grilled sea bream wrapped in banana leaf with fresh mango sauce), which are also the restaurant's most popular menu items. (Avinash Mohan & Deepak Sarath, 132 Lr Baggot St ☎ 01-662 0102 info@mantraa.ie www.mantraa.ie – Open 11am-3pm, 6pm-11pm Mon-Fri, 5pm-11pm Sat, closed Sun)

Restaurant

● La Mere Zou

Praise to Eric Tydgat and his team! Open since 1994, refurbed in 2011, and still doing the good thing in this charming basement on St Stephen's Green. It takes a real pro to navigate the changing tastes of Dubliners and visitors over all those years, and M. Tydgat has managed just that. So, step downstairs for classics such as Lyonnaise salad; foie gras terrine; coq au vin; entrecote of Donald Russell rib-eye. Excellent. (Eric Tydgat, 22 St Stephen's Green, D2 ☎ 01-661 6669 info@lamerezou.ie www.lamerezou.ie – noon-2.30pm, from 5.30pm Mon-Sat)

Hotel/afternoon tea

● The Merrion Hotel

Recessionary times may mean that your cash availability for afternoon tea is a little less than it was at the height of the boom. But, if you do have money to splash and somebody special to meet, then afternoon tea at the Merrion is a textbook example of honouring and respecting this great tradition. (Peter MacCann, The Merrion Hotel, Upper Merrion Street, D2 ☎ 01-603 0600 ⁍ www.merrionhotel.com)

Dublin Central

Brewery/Pub

● Messrs Maguire

Brewer Cullan Loughnane's four craft beers are what makes Messrs Maguire stand out in the city. That, and the many, many mad nights passed within its walls. So head here for Plain Porter, Weiss, Haus and Rusty Red Ale, and try to leave at a reasonable hour. Try. (1-2 Burgh Quay, D2 ☎ 01-670 5777 ⁍ www.messrsmaguire.ie – Open 10.30am-12.30am Mon-Tue, 10.30am-1.30am Wed, 10.30am-2.30am Thu-Sat, noon-midnight Sun)

Wine Merchant

● Mitchell & Son

Mitchell's was established in 1886, when it opened its Kildare Street shop from which it traded until moving to its home in Dublin's Custom House Quay. Strangely enough, when CHQ originally opened in 1820 it was used as a bonded warehouse, so the tradition of great wines in Mitchell's has gone even further into the past. The selection of wines is superb, their knowledge and service is first rate, and their very own Green Spot Whiskey, one of the only remaining bonded Irish whiskeys, is one of the great Irish drinks.
(Peter Dunne. CHQ building, IFSC, Docklands, D1 ☎ 01-612 5540 ✉ chq@mitchellandson.com – Open 10.30am-7pm Mon-Fri, 11am-6pm Sat. Also at 54 Glasthule Road, Sandycove, Co. Dublin ☎ 01-230 2301 ✉ glasthule@mitchellandson.com – Open 10.30am-7pm Mon-Sat, 12.30am-5pm Sun.
Also at Grange Road Retail Centre, Grange Road, Rathfarnham, Co Dublin ☎ 01-493 3816 ✉ grangeroad@mitchellandson.com – Open noon-7pm Mon, 11am-8pm Tue-Thu, 11am-8.30pm Fri, 10.30am-8.30pm Sat, 12.30pm-8pm Sun ⁍ www.mitchellandson.com)

Restaurant/Nepalese

● Monty's of Kathmandu

Offering unique Nepalese cooking since 1997, this great Temple Bar stalwart of Shiva Gautam's continues to raise the tone of its neighbourhood, with tasty, fine Nepalese cooking and politely friendly service. This unique offering is now also available in Shiva's handsome Rathgar restaurant – a slightly more plush affair but with equally good authentic food. The sizzling Tandoori specialities are worth a try (especially the spiced baby squid), although there's really nothing on the menu that disappoints. (Shiva & Lina Gautam, 28 Eustace St, Temple Bar, D2 ☎ 01-670 4911, 88 Rathgar Rd, D6 ☎ 01-492 0633 ✉ shiva@tinet.ie 🖱 www.montys.ie – Open noon-2.30pm, 6pm-11.30pm Mon-Sat, 6pm-11pm Sun)

Dublin Central

Noodle Bar and Sushi Restaurant

● Musashi

"Half the restaurateurs in the city have been spotted here", says Leslie Williams. Catherine Cleary, of *The Irish Times*, put her finger on why Musashi has become the chef's fave haunt: "Great Japanese food, without gimmicks, for the price of a burger and chips". Affordable sushi! Who knew! So, after a few pints of Irish craft beer in The Black Sheep across the street, head into this lean little space and hand over your wine whilst they uncork it (corkage is only a few euro) and tear into vegetable tempura, a sakura selection, teppan tuna teriyaki, or maybe some gyoza plates. Bet you that you will be back tomorrow at lunchtime for a bento box. (Capel Street, D1 ☎ 01-532 8068 ✉ info@musashidublin.com 🖱 www.musashidublin.com – Open noon-10pm, till 11pm Fri & Sat)

Chinese Restaurant

● Neon Asian Street Food

Emmet Daly is the man behind the Café Sol chain in Dublin, and neon is his Thai and Vietnamese street food venture. Purists will always rage about authenticity when it comes to Asian street food, so do note that Neon is a westernised version of street food. It's a clean, crisp room, the food arrives quickly in white cardboard tubes, and it's a very family friendly destination.
(Emmet Daly, 17 Camden Street, D2 ☎ 01-405 2222 ✉ info@neon17.ie 🖱 www.neon17.ie – Open noon-11pm Mon-Sun)

Chinese Restaurant

● New Millennium Chinese Restaurant

The NM is one of the best destinations for dim sum in Dublin city: prawn dumplings; char siu puffs; crispy squid rings; cheung fun; crispy fried bean curd. Don't let them give you the western menu that is ritually handed out to diners: ask for the special menus that the Chinese customers get and that show what they can really do. (Colin Tang, 51 South King Street, D2 ☎ 01-635 1525 – Open noon-11pm Sun-Thu, noon-midnight Fri & Sat)

Dublin Central

Restaurant

● 101 Talbot

Neal and Jenny were chef and manager of 101 before assuming the mantle of owners and operators of this historical northside restaurant. The transition has been smooth, the tradition of serving good simple food – pan-roast saddle of rabbit with mushroom and pancetta gravy, cannelloni of Fivemiletown Irish goat cheese with spinach and roast butternut squash, for instance – continues with modest aplomb. The room has an awesome energy when full, the service is generally very good, and vegetarians are well looked after. (Neal Magee, 101 Talbot St, D1 ☎ 01-874 5011 www.101talbot.com – Open 5pm-11pm Tue-Sat)

Restaurant

● One Pico

These days One Pico can do no wrong, with chef-proprietor Eamonn O'Reilly being nominated and receiving 'chef of the year' awards left, right and centre. One Pico has always been a successful restaurant, thanks in part to its swanky digs near the capital's house of parliament. Recently, however, the focus of the kitchen has sharpened in on simpler classic cooking, using good Irish ingredients and, in short, serving up seriously fine food. Starters of pan-fried quail in a red wine jus with courgette and truffle gnocchi and mains such as roast wild venison with beetroot and potato gratin, pumpkin puree, fig jam, and star anise froth are a taste of the talent and vision at work in the kitchen of One Pico. There's also good value to be had on the set, lunch and pre-theatre menus. (Eamonn O'Reilly, 5-6 Molesworth Pl, Schoolhouse Lane, D2 ☎ 01-676 0300 www.onepico.com – Open 12pm-11.30pm Mon-Sun)

Takeaway/Mexican

● Pablo Picante

Imaginary Mexican wrestler and Californian-style burrito bar, Pablo Picante is the brainchild of northside Dub Colm McNamara. 'What?' you ask. Well, after much time spent in California, Señor McNamara returned to Dublin and suffered extreme panini fatigue, upon which he decided to bring us this fantastic snack food, which has "cult appeal" in sunny CA. El luchador, being an icon of popular Mexican culture, is a perfect brand device for communicating the muy bueno-ness of burritos, without resorting to poor sombrero-laden clichés. Colm's background is one part marketing to two parts habanero. Los burritos are very buenos too, especially the popular Carnitas (slow roast pulled pork), with fiery house-made chilli sauce if you are so inclined. Although a lot of folks reckon the veggie option with roasted veg, feta, black beans and refried beans, homemade guacamole, rice, lime, coriander and salsa is even tastier than the meat feasts on offer. Pablo Picante and his equipo have recently opened a bigger store on Clarendon Market where you can eat in too. He dares you to taste his spicy sauce with sting like a Baja scorpion! (Colm McNamara, 131 Baggot St (and 4 Clarendon Market), D2 ✉ pablopicanteirl@gmail.com 🖱 www.pablopicante.org – Open 11.30am-8pm Mon-Fri, 12pm-8pm Sat, closed Sun)

Café/deli/bakery

● Panem

Ann Murphy's little Italian-style bakery and café, a bit down the ways on Ormond Quay (northside), is a destination address since 1996. Little has changed in that time: the same attention to detail and the high quality of the baking, and the same care in fashioning superb drinks. A filled focaccia, a sunny day on the boardwalk, all is well with the world. (Ann Murphy, 21 Lwr Ormond Quay, D1 ☎ 01-872 8510 – Open 8am-6pm Mon-Fri, 9am-6pm Sat, 10am-4.30pm Sun)

Bakery/Café

● The Paris Bakery

Yannick Forel and his team work through the night to produce irresistible – literally irresistible! – breads and patisserie. M Forel baked in Wicklow's Brook Lodge and in Fallon & Byrne before joining the Moore Street renaissance. The breads are superlative – satisfying, adept, true, authentic – the patisserie is delicate and lush. If you can get the breads and cakes home without eating them en route, you are made of sterner stuff than us. (Yannick Forel, 18 Moore Street, Dublin 1 ☎ 01-804 4112 ✉ info@parisbakery.ie 🖱 www.parisbakery.ie – Open 8am-8pm Mon-Sat, 11am-8pm Sun)

local knowledge

Best cup of coffee?

● The Bald Barista ● Coffee Angel ● Crunch ● Dunne & Crescenzi ● Fallon & Byrne ● KC Peaches ● La Corte del Caffè ● Taste of Emilia ● Temple Bar Market ● Third Floor Espresso

Restaurant/French

● Pearl Brasserie

The team of Kirsten Batt and Sebastian Masi, front of house and head chef respectively, has been on to a winner since the day they first opened the doors of their elegant Merrion Street brasserie. A decade, multiple awards and widespread critical acclaim later, Pearl continues to be one of the city's brightest gems, and still one of the best places to enjoy a long lunch when you should be working. Over one such lunch one might savour a succulent favourite of crispy Dublin Bay prawns with mango and black pepper dressing, perhaps followed by rare-breed pork belly with wholegrain mustard mousseline and balsamic apple, all for the keenest prices. While pricier than the set lunch and early bird, the à la carte menus offer some of the finest cooking around at that price range, and with it you can always expect pitch perfect service and atmosphere. Happily, Kristen and Sebastian have also commandeered Locks on the Grand Canal (Portobello), where their outstanding brand of brasserie dining has lent an elegance to the trendy neighbourhood. Long may they last. (Kirsten Batt & Sebastian Masi, 20 Merrion St Upr, D2 ☎ 01-661 3572 ✉ info@pearl-brasserie.com 🖱 www.pearl-brasserie.com – Open 12pm-2.30pm Mon-Fri, 6pm-10.30pm Mon-Sat)

Dublin Central

Restaurant

● Peploe's

A stylish room serving polished food with a side of polished service, Peploe's has maintained very high standards over the years in its elegant Georgian home on St Stephen's Green. Great wines complete a happy picture. (Barry Canny, 16 St Stephen's Green, D2 ☎ 01-676 3144 ✉ info@peploes.com 🖰 www.peploes.com – Open noon-midnight Mon-Sun)

Café

● The Pepper Pot

The PP is a pretty little perch on the first floor of the Powerscourt Townhouse, with terrace seats perfect for people-watching over a leisurely lunch or afternoon coffee and cake. However, foodie partners Dervla and Marian haven't settled for mere cutesiness over substance. Organic soups, spanking fresh salads, and thick yummy sandwiches, such as their much talked about roasted pear, bacon and Mount Callan cheddar show what they can do. They also offer delectable breakfast options, ranging from sausage sandwich to creamy scrambled eggs, and specials such as mackerel pâté on toast with organic radish and cucumber pickle. Teas and coffees are good, especially accompanied by any of the girls' gorgeous cakes or pies like gooey pecan and whiskey tart and an unusual but scrummy frosted courgette cake. It's all yum, and the Pepper Pot is a runner for best café in the city. (Dervla James & Marian Kilcoyne, Powerscourt Shopping Ctr, Sth William St, D2 ☎ 087-790 3204 ✉ hello@thepepperpot.ie. Accepts cash only – Open 10am-6pm Mon-Wed, Fri, 10am-8pm Thurs, 9am-6pm Sat)

Bistro

● Pichet

This bistro-cum-café-cum-bar-cum-restaurant is the fusion of talents between chef Stephen Gibson and sommelier Nick Munier, culminating in superlative cooking and a wine list to be proud of (available by the glass, pichet or bottle). By day the café-bar serves light meals and snacks, including breakfast, by evening the kitchen dishes out bold bistro fare, including the likes of suckling pig with puy lentils, Toulouse sausage, sauerkraut and wholegrain mustard and its now famous 'crispy hen's egg' with Serrano ham, baby leeks and caper vinaigrette

The prices are bistro, the offering exceeds the modest title, and Pichet is one of the busiest, most happening places in the whole city. (Stephen Gibson & Nick Munier, 14-15 Trinity St, D2 ☎ 01-677 1060 info@pichetrestaurant.com www.pichetrestaurant.com – Open 8am-10.30pm Mon-Fri, 10am-11pm Sat, noon-9pm Sun)

Dublin Central

Café/deli

● Pig & Heifer

A New York-style sandwich deli serving NYC classics such as the 'Ruben' (pastrami and sauerkraut on rye) and beef and horseradish. Since opening in 1996 they've expanded to four locations around the city and the standards have remained high. Breakfast includes the quintessential breakfast roll (bacon, sausages and scrambled eggs in a roll) or a bacon and Ballymaloe relish bagel. They also do a mean BLT and other specials such as chorizo and feta bap, Greek lamb and goat cheese and the 'Maldini Melt' (grilled peppers, milano salami, Taleggio cheese and red chard on toasted bread. Bring your appetite: these sarnies are NYC size too. (21-23 City Quay/6 Guild Court, Amiens St/151 Pearse St/2 Charlotte Way, Harcourt Hall, D2 ☎ 01-478 3182 (Charlotte Way) info@pigandheifer.ie www.pigandheifer.ie – Open 8.30am-4.30pm Mon-Sat, closed Sun)

Restaurant/Irish

● The Pig's Ear

The Pig's Ear has been doing a good job on Irish nosh since it opened only a few short years ago. Its signature dish of chewy, crispy strips of fried breaded pig's ear features on the dinner menu, although there are more satisfying starters to be had, such as roasted butternut squash soup with toasted seeds and cream cheese, or Clonakilty black pudding and new potato salad with mustard and toasted hazelnuts. Mains get pricey if you go for Kettyle's dry-age rib-eye, but generally tend towards good value, such as The 'Pig's Ear' – Lough Erne milk-fed lamb shepherd's pie. The wine list leans towards extravagant, but the restaurant makes up for this with some reasonable offerings on the lunch and early bird menus. (Andrea Hussey & Stephen McAllister, 4 Nassau St, D2 ☎ 01-670 3865 info@thepigsear.ie www.thepigsear.com – Open (lunch) 12pm-2.45pm, (dinner) 5.30pm-10pm Mon-Sat, closed Sun)

Brewery/gastropub

● The Porterhouse Brewing Co

Now something of a beer empire, with bars/gastropubs at multiple locations, including one in Covent Garden, London, and a hotel (Porterhouse Inn at the Bray site), The Porterhouse seems on a mission to bring its unique beers to as wide an audience as possible – much to the delight of local and visiting beer fans. Try its IPA 'Hop Head' for a twangy, fruity triple hop ale. Or stout fans have much to choose from, from the popular Oyster, which is smooth and aromatic, to the award-winning hearty (and not for the faint-hearted) Wrasslers XXXX Full Stout made from a blend including chocolate malt. These are serious brewers for serious beer fans, but those not so keen will still enjoy the rambunctious atmosphere of the pub. Liam and Oliver are two of the great food pioneers in Ireland, and we all owe them a lot. (Liam La Hart & Oliver Hughes, 16-18 Parliament St (Temple Bar), D2 ☎ 01-679 8847; 45-47 Nassau St (Central), D2, ☎ 01-677 4180; Cross Guns Bridge (North), D11 ☎ 01-830 9884; Strand Road (Bray) ☎ 01-286 0668; www.porterhousebrewco.com – Open seven days until late)

Tapas/Spanish

● The Port House

A decent tapas offering in the city and possibly the most romantic place to go for a date, with its cave-like dining room lit by only a smattering of tiny dim spotlights and wall-to-wall candles. Discerning Spanish cuisine fans should stick to the dishes done best in this kitchen, such as pulpo a la Gallega, chorizo in red wine, spicy lamb stew with hot smoked paprika, peppers and garlic, or any of the pintxos which are generally good. The plates of Spanish charcuterie and cheeses are very generous, and other small nibbles, such as pickled hot peppers and salted almonds, all make for tasty accompaniments with a glass of fino. They've a good list of regional wines including sherry and port, so it's worth taking advice on what to go for. A seductive atmosphere, nice food, and good wine keep the punters coming back in droves – and there's no reservations so be prepared for a wait during busy times. (Lee Sim, 64a South William St, D2 ☎ 01-677 0298 info@porthouse.ie www.porthouse.ie – Open 11.30am-11pm Mon-Fri, 12.30am-midnight Sat & Sun)

Café

Queen of Tarts

Not just a pretty name, Queen of Tarts has acquired a cult following over the last decade or so, demonstrated by daily morning contests for a seat in the tiny Cork Hill café, as devotees en route to work are prepared to queue and make themselves late for the chance of a steaming bowl of porridge with apple compote and maple syrup while they soak up the Billie Holiday and bakery-scented ambience. As they trudge onwards to the office afterward, they enviously eye tourists lingering over leisurely breakfasts of bacon and eggs, potato cakes and relish. But they know they have the warm savoury tarts in perfect short pastry and other fresh baked treats to look forward to for lunch. Such was the demand for the Queen's homely goodness she had to open a second larger store just around the corner. Like most royalty, her services don't come cheap – weekend brunch of (delicious) buttermilk pancakes will set you back, but so will most things that are really good. Walking past and breathing in the fresh-baked aromas is free, however. (Regina & Yvonne Fallon, Cows Lane, Dame St, D2 (☎ 01-633 4681) and Cork Hill, Dame St, D2 (☎ 01-670 7499) www.queenoftarts.ie – Open 8am-7pm Mon-Fri, 9am-7pm Sat, 10am-6pm (7pm Cork Hill) Sun)

Restaurant

Ray's Pizza

A slice from Ray's is a very good slice of pizza indeed, and it's perennially popular. They have a second branch up on Harcourt Street. (2 Fownes Street, Temple Bar – Open noon-10pm Mon, noon-10.30pm Tue, noon-4am Wed-Fri, 1pm-4am Sat, 1.30pm-11.30pm Sun)

Restaurant/French

Restaurant Patrick Guilbaud

"Grand and expensive and for many people personifies the very essence of bourgeois dining," say John and Sally McKenna, which is pretty much the impression most people have of this old French multi-starred establishment. With starters in the region of forty euro and mains in the region of sixty euro, it is the most outrageously priced restaurant in the city, and some (those privileged few regulars) believe it is truly worth it. Most would agree, though, the two course lunch for less than forty euro is the better value way to access something akin to the RPG experience. Their refusal to 'market' themselves and create a better impression has left the restaurant's food somewhat underappreciated, albeit the fault of their own old-fashioned and misguided notions. However, it must be acknowledged that there is some seriously special cooking going on at the hands of head chef Guillaume Lebrun, using some of Ireland finest raw materials. Why they're not shouting about this is an enigma. (Patrick Guilbaud, Merrion Hotel, 21 Upr Merrion St ☎ 01-676 4192 info@restaurantpatrickguilbaud.ie www.restaurantpatrickguilbaud.ie – Open (lunch) 12.30pm-2.15pm Tues-Fri, 1pm-2.15pm Sat, (dinner) 7pm-10.15pm Tues Sat, closed Sun)

Restaurant/Lebanese

● Rotana Cafe

Leslie Williams rates the Rotana dolmades as being amongst the best in the city. Others will nominate the falafels – served in Lebanese bread with tahini, pickles and salad. And others always go for the Lebanese special dishes – the rice with minced lamb; the meatballs with Lebanese rice, the moussaka dishes. It's great food, and terrific value, and BYOB makes for one of the best value nights-out in the city. (Mahammed Abuissa, 31 South Richmond Street, Portobello, D2 ☎ 01-475 9969 info@rotanacafe.ie www.rotanacafe.ie – Open 4pm-11.30pm Mon, 11.30am-midnight Tue-Sat)

Restaurant

● Rustic Stone

Dylan McGrath is a genuine celebrity chef, which is to say he is a magnificent chef who has become a celebrity not just for his cooking, but also for his complicated personality as well as his ideas on food. Rustic Stone tends to divide people – love the smartness of the many distinct details; love the raw food menus with their careful consideration of taste, texture and nutrition; love the crab mayo toasts, love the mango chutney with quail, love the beetroot broth, but hate the cook-it-yourself hot stone concept. In truth, the RS concept seems to us to be still-evolving, as McGrath works out his way in the world. You may not like it all, but the journey is pretty fascinating. (Dylan McGrath, Sth George's St, D2 ☎ 01-707 9596 www.rusticstone.ie – Open noon-2.30pm, 7.50pm-10.30pm Mon-Thur, noon-2.30pm, 5pm-10.30pm Fri, 1pm-10.30pm Sat, 2pm-9pm Sun)

Restaurant/Thai/Vietnamese

Saba

Paul Cadden's Saba was a great idea from the get-go: a classy restaurant with a cocktail bar in front, and a great atmosphere. This formula is found more commonly in London and it's not hard to see the attraction. The food is good but not astronomically priced, and the place is chic but buzzy, so Saba works for any kind of occasion. Whether it's a birthday party, a date, a casual bite and a cocktail, this joint fits the bill. And the cocktails are now legendary – we are currently loving the 'Flirtini' with raspberry infused vodka, raspberries, pineapple and champagne. As this place is so cool, booking is a necessity. However, on quieter nights you might be able to squeeze in by the bar for a drink and some crispy black pepper squid, and that's really the perfect place to be. Takeaway is available from Saba-to-Go in Rathmines, Dublin 6. (Paul Cadden, 26-28 Clarendon Street, D2 ☎ 01-679 2000 feedback@sabadublin.com www.sabadublin.com, www.sabatogo.com – Open noon-late Mon-Sun)

Mexican/takeaway

Sabores de Mexico

"Muy auténtico y muy bueuno! This is the first and only time I've found real Mexican food in Ireland in the last four years," gushed one enthusiast for Gustavo and Theresa Hernandez's authentic street food. Newly installed at the Harcourt Street food market, Sabores de Mexico has been on the Dublin market circuit for some time. Fancy a chorizo taco with frijoles refritos and homemade salsa? You'll also find them at the Temple Bar Market on Saturdays, Leopardstown on Fridays, or further afield in Brooklodge in Wicklow on the first Sunday of every month. (Theresa & Gustavo Hernandez, 3 North Great Strand Street ☎ 01-282 4614/086-353 4369 mail@meromeromexico.com www.meromeromexico.com)

Restaurant/Italian

San Lorenzo's

"Gorgeous Italian ingredients and flavours, New York-style" is what you get in San Lorenzo's according to Leslie Williams. Which means the food is "expressive like John Gotti and punchy as a Saturday night in Madison Square Gardens". Chef Temple Garner has always liked

Dublin Central

big flavours in his food, and SL delivers those in dishes such as porchetto tonnato, a riff on vitello tonnata, or scallops with peperonata, or rabbit legs with pancetta with cider and rabbit hotpot. Mr Garner's food has blessed each of his various locations in town over the past 15 years, and San Lorenzo's has the confidence and chutzpah of one of the city's very best cooks. (Temple Garner, Gerry Crossan, South Great George's Street, D2 ☎ 01-478 9383 reservations@sanlorenzos.ie www.sanlorenzos.ie – Open 5.30pm-10pm Mon-Wed, 12.30pm-3pm, 5.30pm-11pm Thur-Sun, closed 10pm Sun)

Dublin Central

Restaurant

● Seagrass

Sean Drugan continues to offer serious cooking at prices you won't find elsewhere in the city. It can't be stressed enough how good the food is for the money you pay – mains such as generously sized whole lamb shank with honey turnip and carrot purée, star anise gravy and crushed baby potatoes for only twenty euro – and they let you bring your own wine with no corkage charge. Open for lunch and dinner and brunch at weekends, and a very generous early bird of three courses every evening. (Susannah Jackson & Sean Drugan, 30 Sth Richmond St, Portobello, D2 ☎ 01-478 9595 info@seagrassdublin.com www.seagrassdublin.com – Open 12pm until late Tue-Sun)

Restaurant

● 777

"An instant classic" was Leslie Williams' take on 777, after a visit with some Mexican friends. The design fuses Tijuana dive-bar chic with beatnik New York-diner, which is fairly hallucinogenic even before you have a Turbo Peligroso. "One of the coolest interiors", says Leslie, who got stuck into vuelve a la vida, a shrimp and clam ceviche, some hamburguesa callejera, a torta Cubana and fine chilaquiles. Food and drinks are right on the money, and 777 is rockin'. Nightowls in search of mezcal and tuna ceviche should note that they serve a menu from 11pm to midnight on Fridays and Saturdays. (John Farrell, 7 Castle House, South Great Georges Street, D2 ☎ 01-425 4052 info@777.ie www.777.ie – Open noon-4pm Sat & Sun, 5.30pm-10pm Sun-Wed, 5.30pm-11pm Thur, 5.30pm-midnight Fri & Sat)

Restaurant/steakhouse

● Shanahan's

One of the few places left in Dublin which people only visit when someone else is paying, hence the largely corporate clientele. One lucky colleague who was recently the recipient of such an invitation sickened the rest of us with news of how good the black sole à la Portugaise, 24oz T-bone, and head-spinningly expensive wines were: he wore the smug expression of someone who'd just won an outlandish car he'd never have bought for himself. The four-course breakfast starring fillet steak and eggs is a much-coveted invite. (John Shanahan, 119 St Stephen's Green, D2 ☎ 01-407 0939 management@shanahans.ie www.shanahans.ie – Open for lunch Fri from 12.30pm, breakfast (contact restaurant), dinner Mon-Sun 6pm-10pm)

Dublin Central

Cheesemonger

● Sheridan's Cheesemongers

So much more than a cheesemonger, Sheridan's is a beacon for Irish artisans of all description around Ireland, such has been their passion for driving the artisan food industry. At their warehouse site at Virginia Road Station, Carnaross, Co Meath, they host a local food market every Saturday, as well as the odd nationwide event with artisans and food heroes from all over the country. In its stores in Galway, Dublin and Waterford, it sells a great variety of Irish farmhouse cheese and charcuterie, as well as a selection of their favourite discoveries from around Europe. In addition, Sheridan's stocks a range of other deli products, such as gourmet pasta and sauces, tinned fish, chocolates, wine and accompaniments for cheese. Hampers can be bought online. Sheridan's is an institution and a must for visiting foodies. (Kevin & Seamus Sheridan, Fiona Corbett, 11 Anne St Sth, D2 ☎ 01-679 3143 dublinshop@sheridanscheesemongers.com www.sheridanscheesemongers.com – Open 10am-6pm Mon-Fri, 9.30am-6pm Sat)

Casual dining/Chinese

● Sichuan House

If you like it hot, make your way to Sichuan House on Parnell Street – it's got more fiery Sichuan pepper heat than you can shake a stick at. The wonton soup with chilli oil, peppery hot dan dan noodles, the whole steamed seabass with ginger and scallions and – of course – chilli, and the duck hot pot, are just some of the spicy delights in this authentic little eatery. The food is rustic but really, really good. (100 Parnell St, D1 ☎ 01-878 3400 Accepts cash only – Open 11.30am until late Mon-Sun)

Café/Middle Eastern

● The Silk Road Café

The Silk Road Café is a Middle Eastern, North African and Mediterranean restaurant, which makes it quite possibly the perfect food offering for Dublin Castle's Chester Beatty Library, which holds some of the most treasured papyri, art objects and exhibits from those very parts. It serves up delicious vegetarian and halal non-veggie dishes, including Greek mousakka, Turkish and Palestinian-style chicken, and stuffed red snapper. The food here is simply wonderful: authentic, nuanced, teasingly delicious and genuine. It's also great value, with a lunchtime buffet offering a substantial main course plus coffee and cake. If going to see the Chester Beatty collection or Dublin Castle, this is a super, if unexpected, part of the experience. All museum cafés should be like this. (Abraham Phelan, Chester Beaty Library, Dublin Castle, D2 ☎ 01-407 0770 silkroadcafe@hotmail.com www.silkroadcafe.ie – Open 10am-4.30pm Mon-Fri, 11am-4.30pm Sat, 1pm-4.30pm Sun. Closed Mondays Oct-May)

Café

● Simon's Place

Simon's Place is genuinely idiosyncratic of Dublin – a 'gentler Dublin' John McKenna calls it – from a time before the words 'Celtic Tiger' had entered our lexicon. And being genuine and of true Dublin spirit is a rare enough thing in the city's café scene. The window counter is a bit wonky, facing out into the George's Street Arcade, and the poster-laden décor is a bit haphazard and circa the mid-90s, but that's all part of why we like it. That, and they do the nicest fresh sandwiches (especially chicken salad or egg), like the kind your mam would make, as well as nice scones and cakes and a good cup o' tea. It's just unpretentious and original and great all-round. And if you're lucky enough to get a good seat, you'll be very happy to sit there for a while. (Simon McWilliams, 22 Sth Great Georges St, D2 ☎ 01-679 7821 – Open 8.30am-5.15pm Mon-Sat)

local knowledge

The Botanic Gardens

Dublin's Botanic Gardens aim to work in the fields of conservation, education and science. This is a phenological garden, a place where records are kept, there is a ever increasing plant collection, including tropical plants, a herbarium and a library. All this, and it is absolutely beautiful too. Genuinely, an oasis, with a good, and busy café.

● Botanic Gardens ☎ 01-804 0200

www.botanicgardens.ie

Pizzas

● Skinflint

Joe Macken's pizza restaurant on Crane Lane follows his usual style: good food, fast, with limited choice, and limitless good vibes. They use Odlums flour for the pizza bases, fermented for 3 days, and after the pizza base is grilled it is dressed with the toppings. There is also a daily meatball dish, and a fine beetroot caviar that took the fancy of Aoife Cox who relished her Maria – potato pizza with mushrooms, mozzarella, a truffle oil and cream – a right royal flibbertigibbet of a pizza. (Joe Macken, 19 Crane Lane, D2 http://skinflint.joburger.ie – Open noon-midnight Mon-Sun)

Café/takeaway

● Soup Dragon

Fiona Fairbrother and Niamh Healion took inspiration from an NYC soup kitchen and conceived of their own healthy, additive-free, gluten-free, delicious soup haven, which they opened in 2006. Soups like dahl (Indian lentil), roasted red pepper, tomato and goats' cheese, chunky chicken and corn chowder, and low fat spicy veg gumbo, are a taster of such deliciousness. In addition to soups, they also do tasty breakfast options, bagels, wraps, sarnies, quiches, curries, stews and salads, all filling and reasonably priced for what you get. Enter the dragon! (Fiona Fairbrother & Niamh Healion, 168 Capel Street, D1 ☎ 01-872 3277 events@soupdragon.com www.soupdragon.com – Open 8am-5pm Mon-Fri, 10am-4pm Sat)

Casual dining/Japanese/takeaway

● Sushi King

Thanks to Rodney and Audrey Gargan's commitment to provisioning sushi to Dublin's city centre, residents, grateful office workers and shoppers now have three locations where they can obtain this essential luncheon alternative when sandwich fatigue sets in. Simple, fresh and good value for money. Sushi King sushi can also be found in various food shops and supermarkets. (Rodney & Audrey Gargan, 146 Lr Baggot St, D2 (takeaway only) ☎ 01-644 9836; Dawson St, ☎ 01-675 2000 and Upr Camden St (takeaway only) ☎ 01-478 9231 www.sushiking.ie – Open Mon-Fri, 8am-6pm)

Dublin Central

Restaurant/Cajun

● Tante Zoe's

Now under the ownership of Dublin hotelier Johnny Moran, this Temple Bar fixture is still doing a good job of bringing Creole-Cajun 'soul food' to Dublin. Since the change of management, the establishment has acquired a strong lean towards cocktails – once featuring a very tasty but somewhat unfortunately-named creation called 'Hurricane'. Non-PC titles aside though, the drinks are good and made by people who know what they're doing. Likewise, the kitchen enlisted the help of legendary London soul food master, Momma Cherri, and turns out hearty representations of all the classics from dooky gumbo (Cajun stew with smoked chorizo and pork) with a side of hushpuppies (corn bread balls) to blackened catfish with rice'n'beans. A good reason to venture into tourist trap-laden Temple Bar. (Johnny Moran, 1 Crow St, Temple Bar, D2 ☎ 01-679 4407 reservations@tantezoes.com www.tantezoes.com – Open from 5pm Wed-Thurs, from 12pm Fri-Sat, from 2.30pm Sun, closed Mon-Tues)

Café/deli/wine bar/Italian

● Taste of Emilia

A place dear to the hearts of Italian inhabitants of the city and a growing following of anybody else who appreciates fine Italian food, wine and coffee. It certainly deserves the attention, and judging from the crowds that squeeze into its little one-room space any night of the week, it's well on its way. The fare is simple but seriously good. The tagliere reggio Emilia offers a board of regional specialities including a DOP prosciutto, some of the best mortadella going in Dublin, some equally delicious coppa and salami, and a 27-month aged DOP Parmesan, all served with pitch-perfect little cipollini onions in vinegar. The board of Parma ham and artichokes is a favourite, but it's worth it to push the boat out for the tagliere Zibello, which offers mouth-watering folds of wafer-thin culatello, the most prized of Italian cold cuts. The cheese board of young and mature Provolone, Parmesan and Pecorino is accompanied by honey, fig compote, balsamic onions, and chutney. Or you could plump for any of the bruschetta or paninis – the artichoke and mozzarella bruschetta is exceptionally delicious. The passionate owner Cristiana Righi and her right-hand men Davide Di Meo and Luca Volpe could not be nicer or more welcoming. (Cristiana Righi, 1 Lower Liffey St ☎ 087-640 2448 – Open Tues 5pm-10.30pm, Wed-Sat 12.30pm-10.30pm, Sun 3.30pm-10pm. Closed Mon)

Restaurant

● Tea Room @ The Clarence

Most people in the world are aware of U2 and consequently many tourists arriving in Dublin have the Clarence Hotel on their list of must-see attractions – the trendy spot being owned by none other than Bono and The Edge. As they might expect, the Octogan bar is trendy as all get out, and a popular watering hole when hanging out at this end of Temple Bar. What they may not expect is the Tea Room restaurant, which can be reasonable price-wise (especially on the Early Bird) and delivers very good cooking. The menu consists of quality Irish food fashioned into contemporary European dishes: slow-cooked Fermanagh pork loin with delicious trimmings and nicely cooked artichoke and lemon risotto are an indication of the good value available on the à la carte. Other items are a bit pricier, but all in all you'll get a good night out here. (6-8 Wellington Quay, D2 ☎ 01-407 0813 reservations@theclarence.ie www.theclarence.ie – Open breakfast, lunch, dinner 7am-10pm Mon-Wed (10.30pm Thurs-Fri), brunch and dinner 12pm-10.30pm/9.30pm Sat/Sun)

Food market

● Temple Bar Market

It's a meeting place for friends on a Saturday morning, a grocery market for gourmands, for some Dubliners it's

an institution and an essential weekend ritual. If visiting Dublin, a trip to the TB market makes for a joyous way to spend a few hours: you can grab a coffee from Ariosa, peruse the bakery stalls for something to nibble while shopping the local and imported produce on offer, or pull up a stool for a glass of wine and half dozen oysters at John McInerney's oyster bar. Warning: you may wonder where all your money's gone at the end of your visit. It's gone to many good homes. (Meeting House Square and around Temple Bar, Temple Bar, D2
www.templebar.ie – Trading on Saturdays)

Casual dining/Japanese

● Ten Thousand

Be careful to enter this establishment by the Liffey Street entrance, coming in the Abbey Street door leads to a not so interesting Asian buffet. In the right door, however, you'll find what is arguably the best value sushi in the city, and decent quality for what you pay too: good food with friendly service and nice variety. (20 Lr Liffey St, D1 ☎ 01-872 9656. Accepts cash only – Open noon-11pm Mon-Sun)

Casual dining/Italian

● Terra Madre

Outside it may be rainin', but downstairs in Terra Madre you will find an oasis of Italian warmth, emanating from both the cooking and the spirit of this tiny basement joint – there are only 17 seats. The menu is an A4 sheet, but expect surprises such as the first tomatoes of the season, sliced and dressed with oregano and olive oil. You can eat a dish of cotechino sausages and lentils here that will make you happy as a sandboy, and everything is offered with respectful simplicity and grace. A simply darling place with darling cooking that has already stolen many a heart. Look out for their "Stop good food here" sign. (13a Bachelor's Walk, D1 ☎ 01-873 5300)

Café

● Third Floor Espresso @ the Twisted Pepper

Do you know your coffee? Do you really care about the coffee that passes your lips? Then you can't come to Dublin without a visit to 3FE, barista champion Colin Harmon's brainchild and ode to coffee, situated above the Twisted Pepper club on the northside of the fair city.

His filter coffee changes every week, he offers tastings of different filter coffees (8 euro per person, served three ways), and any drink ordered comes with encyclopaedic knowledge of the beans, roasting techniques, blending and anything else worth knowing about the coffee you're about to imbibe. Colin 3FE is a legend among his particular tribe of anoraks – we salute him! Check out his newest outpost on Grand Canal Street too. (Colin Harmon, 54 Middle Abbey St, D1 ☎ 085-752 2573. Also 32/34 Grand Canal St, D2 ☎ 085-752 2573 hello@thirdfloorespresso.com www.3fe.com – Open 10am-6pm Mon-Fri, 12pm-5pm Sat, closed Sun)

Restaurant

● Thornton's

Kevin Thornton is one of Ireland's most revered chefs. After an up-and-down affair with public opinion, due in part to his own sassy tongue, certain established food critics have become strangely defensive about him. Critics aside though, it serves the public well to remind them just how good Thornton's food is, and has always been in his more-than 20-year career. Go if you can for his dinner menus, as the set value lunch is only a pale shade of the real Thornton cuisine. At dinner you will enjoy aesthetically stunning, masterful cooking that is uniquely his own. A sensual experience that should be had by all who love to eat. (Kevin & Muriel Thornton, Fitzwilliam Hotel, St. Stephen's Green, D2 ☎ 01-478 7008 thorntonsrestaurant@eircom.net www.thorntonsrestaurant.com – Open 5.30pm-10.30pm Tue-Wed, 12.30pm-2pm, 6pm-10.30pm Thu-Sat, closed Sun-Mon)

Café/deli/Italian

● Toffoli

Known also as Bottega Toffoli or sometimes Café Toffoli, whatever it's called it's damn good. Mostly people cram into the tiny café for their excellent handmade pizzas, which they serve between 1pm and 5pm, and later on Fri and Sat. The spicy salami-laden 'Sculacciata' is popular. But they also do some exceptionally good (and some extremely filling) sandwiches, on good bread with nice ingredients, with everything made in-house. Try a piadina sandwich (Italian flat bread) with some of their lovely meats. Great spot. (Elaine McArdle & Carlo Eremita, 34 Castle St ☎ 01-633 4022 – Open 11am-9pm Tues-Thurs, 11am-11pm Fri-Sat, closed Sun)

Café/caterers

● Urban Picnic

A worthy food establishment that hopes to give the customer some tasty nosh - mostly Asian, US, and Mediterranean – for very good value prices, Urban Picnic has been laid on for Dublin gastronauts by friendly Cavan chef Vincent Donohoe. He doesn't mind you asking him to wrap up your Sesame and Ginger Salmon to go, or any of his lunch specials which he announces to loyal fans over Facebook: char-grilled chicken breast with wild mushroom and pancetta sauce; or roast cod with zucchini. What's more, he keeps each dish under a tenner, with his fresh soup of the day and homemade bread well under a fiver. Lovely wraps and ciabatta sandwiches abound, and he also knocks out a few nice treats for afters too. Find Vinny and his good grub in the George's St Arcade. (Vincent Donohoe, 30-31 George's St Arcade, Sth Great George's St, D2 ☎ 087-977 5822. Accepts cash only – Open 9am-6pm Mon-Wed, Fri-Sat, 9am-8pm Thurs)

Bakery/café

● Il Valentino

A genuine artisanal Italian bakery on the waterfront at the evolving Grand Canal Square, where those who value good coffee and good breads and pastries will often sit and enjoy a fix of the real, uncompromised thing. Black olive bread, fresh focaccia, ricotta or marzipan cookies, are but some of the treats in store, and Il Valentino is a great spot for lunch. It's a must for bread lovers, who arrive and fill the car boot with these unique breads, for there are no other breads like these in the city, indeed in the country. (Owen & Valentina Doorly, 5 Gallery Quay, Grand Canal Harbour, D2 ☎ 01-633 1100 🖱 www.ilvalentino.ie – Open 7am-7pm Mon-Fri, 9am-5pm Sat-Sun, bank holidays)

Restaurant/Italian

● Il Vicoletto

Since being taken over by new management, this restaurant has gone way up in discerning diners' estimation. The new management recruited real talent in the kitchen and source good ingredients for their tasty Italian menu. You can expect all the usual suspects: pappadelle with ragu of the day; linguine alle vongole; spaghetti carbonara, all very reasonably priced. There are other less-known dishes, such as chitarra (homemade pasta using a guitar-like device, hence the name) or escalopes of milk-fed veal with sage and prosciutto, red wine sauce and vegetable flan. You're guaranteed a meal to make you happy wherever you roam on this menu. (5 Crow St, Temple Bar, D2 ☎ 01-670 8633 vicolettorestaurant@yahoo.com www.ilvicoletto.ie – Open (dinner only) Sun-Thurs, from 12pm Fri-Sat)

made in Dublin
Porterhouse Beers

Café/patisserie

Voilà

A pretty French-style patisserie and café in one of the city centre's business districts, offering an array of satisfying pastries, tartines, sandwiches, soups and specials made in-house every day. Coffee of your choice and a home-baked scone is pretty outstanding value from this little gem too. (14 Lower Baggot St, D2 ☎ 01-662 9353 – Open breakfast and lunch 7am-5pm Mon-Fri, 9am-5pm Sat, closed Sun)

Tea & Sushi

Wall & Keogh

Be prepared to take your time. In Wall and Keogh, that time is the time needed for your tea to infuse. Maybe five minutes, maybe eight minutes, maybe fifteen minutes. If your normal cuppa involves squashing a tea bag against the side of a cup with a teaspoon, you may be in the wrong place. If you wish to get Zen with your tea – and with the bricolage surroundings, the cool sounds, the wry books, Oliver's chat, the chess board, their fine sushi, the courtyard – then W&K is your little oasis. "The calmest half an hour of my year", said Catherine Cleary in *The Irish Times*. W&K is a massage for the mind, and the tastebuds. So, just take your time, take your time. And who are/were Wall & Keogh? Sure, just ask. (Oliver Cunningham, 45 Richmond St, Rathmines, D2 ☎ 01-475 9052 wallandkeogh@live.com – Open 8am-8.30pm Mon-Fri, 10.30am-7.30pm Sat-Sun)

Restaurant/Irish

● The Winding Stair

The mighty Winding Stair has long been one of the most recommended places to eat in Dublin. It's fair to say their signature style of contemporary Irish cooking is the original, the beginning of the trend that went on to spawn several of the city's other favourite Irish restaurants. The menu is seasonal and throws out great specials, such as roast neck of pork, succulent shoulder of lamb, or their now famous collar of bacon with parsley sauce and cabbage. However, the regulars such as smoked haddock poached in milk with cheddar mash, potted crab with soda bread, or the smoked fish platter with dillisk bread and crème fraiche, remain good as ever. In general, the wines, style, service and the buzz are consistently, impressively good. (Elaine Murphy, 40 Lwr Ormond Quay, D1 ☎ 01-872 7320 ✉ restaurant@winding-stair.com 🖱 www.winding-stair.com – Open 12.30pm-3.30pm Mon-Sun, 6pm-10.30pm Tue-Sat, 6pm-9.30pm Sun)

local knowledge

Rothar Bicycle Café

Rothar is a social enterprise, using bikes to tackle environmental, social and economic challenges through the promotion of sustainable urban transport with cycling. They now have a rather sweet café in central Dublin, where you can peruse both a food & drink menu and a bike menu. Admirable.

The Rothar Café, 16 Fade Street, D2 ☎ 01-677 2233 🖱 www.rothar.ie – Open 10am-6pm Mon-Sat, 10am-8pm Thur

NORTH DUBLIN

DUBLIN 3: CLONTARF, FAIRVIEW, NORTH STRAND

Casual dining/Italian/takeaway

● Da Tommaso

Tommaso is a Roman, so Roman hospitality is what you get at his place. Warm, unpretentious and friendly, and of course some damn lovely, simple Italian cooking. The house pizza – pizza Tommaso – is topped with good quality ingredients. The pasta is cooked to Italian standards. The hugs and handshakes are hearty and genuine. And if you can't stop in, you can get their great value grub to go. (Tommaso Stennato, 24 Fairview Strand, D3 ☎ 01-887 5939/087 294 3750 – Open 5pm-11pm Tue-Sun)

Casual dining/Italian/takeaway

● Dom Mimi

Dom Mimi has caused awesome waves in Dublin's gastro scene – between opening in its original site in Monkstown and moving to its current digs in the humble neighbourhood just north of the Five Lamps. Humble is indeed how the place looks, but awesome is indeed what their pizzas are. Great quality ingredients, including the all important dough, great value, and utterly delicious: try 'diavola' (mozzarella, salami piccante, mixed peppers and chilli flakes); 'toto mare' (mozzarella, king prawns, garlic, cherry tomatoes and rocket); or the Dom Mimi (Parma ham, shaved Parmesan, cherry tomatoes, rocket and extra virgin olive oil) and taste some of the best pizzas in the city. They also serve a small range of other Italian staples, to takeaway or eat-in in the tiny space provided. The coffee is also excellent. (Paolo Marinuzzi, 148 North Strand, D3 ☎ 01-8561714 info@donmimi.ie www.donmimi.ie – Open 10am-10pm Mon-Sun)

Café/deli/food shop

● The Food Room

Alison and Barry Stephens run a really fine shop on the main Clontarf Road, and Barry's cooking draws in queues of locals, especially at lunchtime when the place is jammers with hungry folk hunting the good stuff. (Barry & Alison Stephens, 46 Clontarf Rd, D3 ☎ 01-833 2258 info@thefoodroom.ie www.thefoodroom.ie – Open 8am-7pm Mon-Fri, 9am-6pm Sat & Sun)

Dublin North

Restaurant

Hemmingway's

A long-time favourite among locals and one that, despite changes over the years, has remained committed to sourcing good fresh seafood. Check the specials board for the daily catch and find very good value on the midweek 'cheap and cheerful' menu. (Brian Creedon, Vernon Ave ☎ 01-833 3338 www.hemmingways.ie – Open from 5.30pm Wed-Sun)

Bistro/deli

Kennedy's

Catherine Cleary, in *The Irish Times*, put her finger on the importance of local food specialists such as Kennedy's of Fairview. A small, friendly restaurant, she wrote "feeds the longing to connect and belong". Aha, so Kennedy's feeds you once, and then feeds you twice: food for the body, and food for the (social) soul. And Sarah Kennedy does all this at terrific prices: "not much more than a splurge at the local takeaway" wrote Ms Cleary, and this keen pricing is a vital element of what makes Kennedy's such a local treasure. Leslie Williams was so impressed he reckoned every community needed a Kennedy's. Aingeala Flannery in *The Irish Independent* reckoned it was worth leaving your own neighbourhood to eat in a neighbourhood restaurant like this. Lucky Fairview. (Sarah Kennedy, 5 Fairview Strand, D3 ☎ 01-833 1400 www.kennedysfoodstore.com – Bistro open 6pm-9.30pm Tue-Sat, Shop open 9am-8pm Mon-Fri, 9am-7pm Sat, 10am-4pm Sun)

Restaurant/Pakistani

Kinara

Kinara has consistently delivered outstanding Pakistani (and some Indian) food to a grateful Dublin audience since it opened in 2001. Never failing to impress critics and punters with its assured and delicious cooking, it is one of the best ethnic restaurants in the city. Its sister restaurant – the more casual affair Kinara Kitchen – does equally well in the southside borough of Ranelagh. Its early bird menu (5-8pm Mon-Thurs) offers three courses for under twenty euro, which makes it one of the best value early birds going in any restaurant. (Sean Collender, 318 Clontarf Rd, D3 ☎ 01-833 6759 info@kinara.ie www.kinara.ie – Open 12-4.30pm, 4.30pm-11pm Mon-Sun)

Restaurant

● Moloughney's

A family connection to Phibsborough's excellent Woodstock café sets the tone for Moloughney's: it is a smart set-up, a restaurant that manages to cook for everyone yet makes no compromises. So, settle into the pretty room and start with some wild garlic soup, or some of their home-smoked salmon, then some Irish lamb with wild garlic pesto, or Silverhill duck with parsnips, then a lovely carrageen moss panna cotta. And we can think of nothing nicer than settling in for a dinner menu like this: duck rillette with blood orange compote; honey roast fig with goat's cheese and pomegranate; coq au vin with potato purée; tarte au citron, especially with a bottle or two of Dungarvan Ale. Very impressive, and heading for the stars. (Liam & Michelle Moloughney, 9 Vernon Avenue, Clontarf, D3 ☎ 01-833 0002 🖱 www.moloughneys.ie – Open 8.30am-midnight Mon-Fri, 9.30am-1.30am Sat-Sun)

Food shop/Café

● Nolan's

Everyone wishes they lived near a shop like Nolan's. At the heart of this business is total dedication to sourcing excellent produce, offering a fantastic range of the kinds of food and wines you really want, and providing the kind of experience that makes shopping a pleasure. If you have time you can even relax with a coffee and a bun and read the paper when you're finished browsing the vast array of artisan goods in the deli and on the shelves. (Richard Nolan, 49 Vernon Avenue, Clontarf, D3 ☎ 01-833 8361 – Open 9am-7pm Mon-Wed, 9am-9pm Sat, 11am-4pm Sun)

Café/food market

● The Red Stables Food Market

Red Stables is one of the great Dublin markets, with everything from Omega beef to Corleggy Cheese to Hemmingway's ready meals, to Burke's Farm ice cream, and there are even gourmet dog biscuits for that special someone in your life. The popular café is open during the week too. (Andy O'Reilly, Andre Jenkinson, The Red Stables, St Anne's Park, Mount Prospect Ave, D3 ☎ 01-2227377 ✉ info@redstables.ie 🖱 www.redstables.ie – Open Sat 10am-5pm, till 4pm in winter)

Dublin
North

Restaurant

● Restaurant Ten Fourteen

1014 is owned by CASA, the Caring and Sharing Association, and caring and sharing is just what they do at Gareth Smith's terrific restaurant. Don't be fooled by the fact that this restaurant is run by a charity, it is a seriously good restaurant. On a recent visit to try a tasting menu of local delights every morsel was flawless. It's simple cooking: wild Lissadell mussels with lemon, coriander and sauvignon broth; slow-roast rare breed pork belly with champ, caramelised veg and lip smacking 'pork gravy.' But it's beyond delicious, excellent value, and served with a smile in a perfect little space facing the sea. If you can, try to get a table by the window. Whatever you eat you'll leave satisfied and happy, including the kids who are very well catered for with proper food. (Gareth Smith, 324 Clontarf Rd, D3 ☎ 01-805 4877 🖱 www.restaurant1014.com – Open 10am until late Mon-Sun, closed Mondays in January)

Fish shop

● Wright's of Marino

Wrights of Marino has been selling fresh fish to Dubliners, from the same spot, for 100 years now, so they know a thing or two about fish and how to treat it. They are actually big players in the fish business, but we like the fact that they have held onto their modest Fairview shop, and that they pay such kind attention to their customers. That's how you last for a century. (John Wright, 21 Marino Mart, Fairview, D3 ☎ 01-833 3636 📫 info@wrightsofmarino.com 🖱 www.wrightsofmarino.com – Open 10.30am-2.30pm Mon, 9am-5pm Tue-Thu, 9am-5.30pm Fri, 10am-3.30pm Sat)

DUBLIN 5: RAHENY

Café/deli/Italian

● Il Fornaio

Formerly a well-kept Northside secret until it opened a branch in the IFSC in the financial quarter, Il Fornaio has always done good pastas and pizzas, and contented itself with doing them right, just the way an Italian restaurant in Italy would. The pizzas are classic and crisply crunchy, the pastas are ace, again sticking to classic dishes and making sure they are true and precise. The coffee, of course, is also excellent. (Bruno Cinelli, 55 Kilbarrack Rd, Raheny, D5 ☎ 01-832 0277 info@ilfornaio.ie www.ilfornaio.ie – Open 8.30am-10pm Mon-Thu, 8.30am-11pm Fri, 10am-11pm Sat, 10am-10pm Sun. Also at 1b Valencia House, Custom House Sq, D1 ☎ 01-672 1852)

made in Dublin

Llewellyn's Orchard

Wine shop

● McHugh's Off Licence

McHugh's is a hugely respected wine shop and never a year goes by without them deservedly garnering more awards. Their new bistro in Raheny (see entry below) has, as you would have hoped, a really good wine list, which offers terrific value for money. Also find them in Artane. (Cathal McHugh, 57 Kilbarrack Rd, D5 ☎ 01-839 4692 and 25e Malahide Rd, Artane, D5 ☎ 01-831 1867 good-drinks@mchughs.ie www.mchughs.ie – Open 10.30am-10pm Mon-Sat, 12.30-10pm Sun)

Bistro

● McHugh's Wine & Dine

A solid local eatery turning out simple, honest food and doing it very, very well. The early bird is available all night Monday to Thursday (5-7pm Fri-Sat), via which you can enjoy superlative casual fare for exceptionally good value. Two courses of, say, mackerel fillets in light batter with wasabi mayo and mixed baby leaves, followed by an 8oz flat iron steak with skinny chips and pepper sauce, will set you back around twenty euro if you add dessert. And we have it on good authority that their burgers are top notch. McHugh's also own two award-winning off-licences (in Raheny and Malahide), so it comes as no surprise that their wine list and neat selection of craft beers is well above average. Terrific spot. (Cathal McHugh, 59 St Assams Park, D5 ☎ 01-832 7435 dine@mchughs.ie www.mchughs.ie/dine – Open (lunch) 12-3pm dinner (5-10pm) Mon-Sat, 12-9pm Sun)

DUBLIN 7: SMITHFIELD, STONEYBATTER

Artisan Bakery

● Arún Bakery

Gimme a bohemian! Gimme a batard! Gimme a Vlaa! Gimme a sourdough! Gimme a sourdough with rye! Gimme a spelt with pumpkin seeds! Heck, just give us everything that Vlad Rainis bakes and we will be happy. Mr Rainis bakes in Dublin 7 and delivers his breads there, and you will find these superb sourdoughs and other breads in shops such as Liston's, Fresh, Lilliput Stores, Lawlor's and Fothergill's in Rathmines, and meet the baker himself at the superb Honest 2 Goodness market in Glasnevin every Saturday. (Vlad Rainis, Spade Enterprise Centre, D7 ☎ 01-617 4804 📫 bakeryarun@gmail.com)

Dublin North

Patisserie

● Buns Cup Cakes

Paula and Ger Coyne bake marvellous – and marvellously colourful – cup cakes and macaroons – macaroons are the new cup cake, by the way. To get hold of these little marvels of taste, hunt Buns down at Harcourt Street market, at Christchurch market, in Cleary's department store, and at Howth market on Sunday, or you can also order online and have your buns delivered by hand if you're in the Leinster area. Check out their custom bun arrangements for weddings. (Paula & Ger Coyne, North King St, D7 🖱 www.buns.ie)

Café

● Cinnamon Café

Besides the odd service issue, Cinnamon is a welcome little oasis in the heart of Smithfield, serving decent coffee and pastries, lovely muffins and pancakes for brekkie, and a fine array of hot and cold foods throughout the day, including vegan-friendly salads from Blazing Salads. (Coke Lane, Smithfield, D7 ☎ 01-872 6567 📫 cinnamoncafe@gmail.com 🖱 www.cinnamoncafe.ie – Open 6.45am-5.30 pm Mon-Sat)

On-Line Off Licence

● Drink Store

A Manor Street gem, and a place of serious pilgrimage for beer lovers. (The Butler family, 87 Manor Street, Stoneybatter, D7 ☎ 01-671 9760 🖱 www.drinkstore.ie)

Gastropub/wine shop

● Hole in the Wall

Martin McCaffrey's famous pub – it's the longest bar in Ireland – has a fine wine shop, with hundreds of bottles on the shelves, in the centre of this meandering, historic pub, and you can buy a bottle and take it into either the pub or into the restaurant, where there is good cooking. (Martin McCaffrey, Blackhorse Ave, D7 ☎ 01-838 9491 – Open 2pm-10pm Mon-Thu, 2pm-10.30pm Fri, noon-10.30pm Sat, noon-10pm Sun)

Dublin North

Restaurant

● Juno's Café

Think of a New York diner, like Zabaar's, only Irish, distinguished by quality Irish ingredients and the wholesome carby-ness of Irish cooking. Dressed home-smoked organic salmon on the house brown bread; beetroot and Ryefield Goat Cheese salad with walnuts and croutons; air-dried Connemara ham with pickled fennel, dressed rocket and olives; the 'roast roll of the day,' such as corned beef with saurkraut and pickles. Breakfasts are ample, the house-made confections are scrumptious (lemon polenta and almond cake served with lemon syrup, for instance), and the signature dish – a 'chip buttie' with fat homemade chips between thick wedges of buttered batch loaf – is suitably epic. The owners have managed to make something funky and appealing out of this narrow, unusually situated space, and the easy friendly manner of the staff will leave you happy to linger on. (Paul Kelly, Juha Salo, 26 Parkgate St, D7 ☎ 01-670 9820 junoscafe@gmail.com www.junoscafe.com – Open 8am–3pm Mon-Fri, 5pm–9:30pm Tues-Sat, 10am-4pm Sun.)

Fish shop

● Kish Fish

Where do Bill, Tadgh, Damian and Fedelmia put all the trophies for fish retailing excellence that they win? We ask because Kish wins awards year in, year out. Every year brings new garlands, gongs, trophies, and all because Kish are the best. Both the Bow Street and Coolock shops are benchmark destinations for the best fish, the best displays of fish, the best presentation, the best service. And which one of the family has to polish all the trophies? (Bill, Tadgh, Damian & Fedelmia O'Meara, 40/42 Bow St, Smithfield, D7 ☎ 01-8543900 www.kishfish.ie – Open 9am-4.30pm

Tues-Fri, 9am-1pm Sat. Also Malahide Rd Industrial Park, Coolock, North Co Dublin ☎ 01-8543925 – Open 8am-5pm Mon-Fri, 8am-2pm Sat)

Dublin North

Cookie Mixes

● Kooky Dough

Graham and Sophie make some very good, very convenient cookie mixes, in flavours that kids love. Most recently, they have headed south to begin to conquer the market in France with "des cookies délicieux en quelques minutes". Voila! (Sophie Morris & Graham Clarke, Spade Centre, Dublin ☎ 087-614 8480 info@kookydough.ie www.kookydough.ie)

Deli/food shop

● Lilliput Stores

Brendan O'Mahony's Lilliput Stores is an ace place. An avalanche of good things are jam-packed into one tiny store, from locally sourced fresh vegetables to locally baked bread and pastries to wine to charcuterie. Mr O'Mahony is superbly discriminating, so what comes in to here and what goes out from here is all fantastic. (Brendan O'Mahony, Arbour Hill, Stoneybatter ☎ 01-672 9516 – Open 8am-7.30pm Mon-Fri, 8am-6.30pm Sat, 9am-4pm Sun)

Gastropub

● L Mulligan Grocer

This is the pub that beer and whiskey drinkers always wanted. If there's a craft brewer worth knowing in Ireland, you'll find them behind this bar. If there's a whiskey/whisky worth quaffing, whether Irish, Scottish, Welsh, European or Japanese, Michael Foggarty is the man to see. Or if you just want to sit in a really good pub with all the character and atmosphere that hopeful visitors to Ireland long for, then L Mulligan Grocer is your only man. Colin Hession will sort you out whatever your pint may be, and resident foodie Seaneen has your gastronomical needs very well taken care of. The menu may be designed for beer and pub-type conviviality, but Mulligan's food rocks the socks off most of its rivals. Their homemade relish with a tranche of Jack McCarthy's famous pudding, or their own free-range egg and rare breed pork Scotch egg, (both only a fiver) are good examples, or their perfect twice-cooked chips and Hoegaarden mayo, and even butter with locally foraged wild garlic and homemade brown soda bread. The food, the drink, the people and the craic are mighty indeed in this pub. (Colin Hession, Michael Foggarty & Seáneen Sullivan, 18 Stoneybatter, D7 ☎ 01-670 9889 table@lmulligangrocer.com www.lmulligangrocer.com – Open 4pm weekdays, 2pm weekends. Food hours: from 5pm Mon-Fri, from 12.30pm Fri-Sat)

Health Foods

● Natasha's Living Foods

Before you dismiss the idea of 'raw and living foods' as some crusty notion not within the remit of genuine foodies, have a taste of Natasha Czopor's incredible coconut raw chocolate ganache, or her delectable sprouted chickpea hummus with cumin and coriander, or her tasty spicy kale snacks, and be prepared to change your mind. A worthy recipient of our Electric Picnic 'Healthy Buzz' award, and an all-round renegade when it comes to food and life, Natasha and her living food will certainly always give you something to think about. Find her products at farmers' markets, including Dublin Food-Co-op, Temple Bar and Dun Laoghaire, and in various independent shops. (Natasha Czopor, North King St, Stoneybatter, D7 ☎ 01-617 4807 www.natashaslivingfood.ie)

Casual dining/Italian

● Plan B

The very unassuming Plan B just off Manor Street is surprising, turning out good honest Italian cooking in a warm environment that leaves you feeling all fuzzy inside. Order the simplest of things in Linda Madigan's little place – bresaola salad with rocket; spaghetti with courgettes and chilli; their lasagne – and you'll see what we mean. Many regard the lasagne as one of the best you will find. The room may not look like much, but there is a magic at work here, and it is accentuated by wonderful, relaxed service that gets you right into the groove of this peachy place. (Linda Madigan, Manor Place, Stoneybatter, D7 ☎ 01-670 6431 lindmadigan@hotmail.com – Open 12.30pm-late)

Restaurant

● Seven Social

Sit us down in Emma Bowe's pretty, lean room, bring us a cherry, toasted hazelnut and Barry's tea muffin, and we are happy as all get out. Ms Bowe is doing something funky here on Benburb Street, and SS reminds us of Galway's iconic Ard Bia. It has the same hippyish smarts, the same left-field cooking – linguini with broad beans and ewe's cheese; pork and leek sausages with mash; shredded pork belly ciabatta. Very, very promising. (Emma Bowe, 76 Benburb Street, D7 ☎ 01-672 9080 info@sevensocial.ie www.sevensocial.ie – Open 8am-10pm Mon-Fri, noon-10pm Sat)

local knowledge

Great Pub Grub?

● The Bernard Shaw ● The Bull & Castle ● The Chop House ● The Exchequer ● WJ Kavanagh's ● John Kavanagh (The Gravedigers) ● Kimchi@The Hop House ● L Mulligan Grocer ● The Merrion Inn ● Stoop Your Head

Deli/Gift Shop

● Treat Deli & Gift Shop

A vivid, colourful and uplifting gift shop that also stocks ace artisan foods and makes good sarnies and soups, Treat does just what it says on the door: it is a treat to be here, in a feelgood space with feelgood food. (Lindley Jones & Sally-Anne Bennett, 3 Imaal Mart, Imaal Road, Cabra, D7 ☎ 01-838 9473 treat@dublin.ie – Open 8am-6pm Mon-Sat)

Café

● Woodstock Café

They are particular in the Woodstock, so don't call those snappy buns "cup cakes". They are "fairy cakes", as they were for generations before the cup cake tyranny steamrolled us. But it's not just the fairy cakes they are particular about, for the sourcing of ingredients in Woodstock is ace, the baking is inspiring, and the healthfulness of everything they serve is a joy. Their lovely new livery has also made Woodstock even better. A key Phibsborough destination. (Angela Ruttledge, 156 Phibsboro Road, D7 ☎ 01-830 0265 www.woodstockcafe.ie – Open 7.30am-8pm Mon-Sun)

Café, Deli & Creperie

● Anderson's and Anderson's Creperie

Anderson's was revolutionary when it opened in Glasnevin in 2003, and Noel Delaney's café and deli has stayed ahead of the curve, meanwhile begetting the excellent Anderson's creperie in Drumcondra and, most recently, opening Anderson's at the Highlane Gallery in Drogheda. Its secret is judiciousness: they source the right foods and treat them with respect, and they look after their customers, and have done so for a happy decade or thereabouts. Anderson's Creperie is the Drumcondra destination of Noel Delaney's little north-side empire and serves the best crepes you can find. A buckwheat galette, a bottle of cider, and bliss is yours for a tiny stipend. Excellent service, and a really lovely, modest slice of culinary culture. (Noel Delaney, Food Hall & Cafe, 3 The Rise, Glasnevin D9 ☎ 01-937 8394. Anderson's Creperie 1a Carlingford Road, Drumcondra, D9 ☎ 01-830 5171 ☝ www.andersons.ie)

Cheesemonger/café/deli

● The Cheese Pantry

Ireland needs the Cheese Pantry. Not just because it is impossibly stylish and profoundly hip, is blessed with the wittiest staff, and is a joyful place to eat and hang out in. It is all of these things, but, just as importantly, it gives a focus to the food scene in Drumcondra because it is loved by young and old, established residents and wan-nabe students. It is all things to all men and women. Take a look at any part of its constituent elements – the food offer, the wine offer, the cheese room offer, the eating offer – and every part is considered and considerate, and yet unclichéd. It's a maverick place, and owners Aidan and Karen McNeice achieve their ambitions beautifully. (Aidan & Karen McNeice, 104 Upper Drumcondra Road, Drumcondra, D9 ☎ 01-797 8936 ✉ aidan@thecheese-pantry.com ☝ www.thecheesepantry.com – Open 9am-8pm Mon-Tue, 9am-10pm Wed-Sat, 10am-4pm Sun)

Casual dining/Italian

● Enoteca d'Asti

Part of Mick Wallace's group of casual Italian eateries and wine bars, Enoteca d'Asti is a handy spot for a good midweek dinner out that won't blow the bank and ticks all the boxes – decent food and wine, comfy pleasant surrounds, and friendly service. They now offer pretty good pizzas too. (Mick Wallace, 15 Russell St, D9 01-884 7500 – Open (lunch) 12.30pm-3pm Mon-Fri, (dinner) 5.30pm-10pm Mon-Sun. Also Blooms Lane, D1 ☎ 01-888 0834, and Enoteca Torino, Grattan Crescent, Inchicore, D8 ☎ 01-453 7791)

DUBLIN 11: FINGLAS, GLASNEVIN

Food market

● Honest2Goodness Market

Although relatively new to the food market scene in Dublin, H2G is definitely one of the best in the city. Brid Carter's passion for excellent locally produced fresh and artisanal foods and her warm fun-loving nature make the market a joy to visit, as well as a place where you could do a week's shop, for less than you might spend in the supermarket. This is what a food market should be: excellent meat straight from Ryan's farm in Meath; dairy produce from David Tiernan (Glebe Brethan cheese), Killowen Yoghurts, Cooleeney cheese, Burke's Farm Ice Cream, and Moonshine dairy; sausage and other pork products from Hick's; fruit and veg from the Dublin Meath Growers; and fresh fish from off the Wexford coast courtesy of Johnny Fish. Brid's brother Colm offers a nice selection of European wines – which you can buy and imbibe on site – or you could relax with an Ariosa coffee and a cake in the café after a good morning's shop. A children's play area completes the whole perfect experience. May H2G live forever! (Brid & Colm Carter, Paul O'Hara, and Veronica O'Hara. 136a Slaney Close, Dublin Industrial Estate, Glasnevin, D11 ☎ 087-629 4713 ✉ brid@honest2goodness.ie; (for wine sales) ☎ 087-9914291 ✉ colm@honest2goodness.ie 🖱 www.honest2goodness.ie – Open 9.30am-4pm Saturdays)

Pub/gastropub/tapas

● John Kavanagh ('The Gravediggers')

John Kavanagh has long been known to everyone lucky enough to be local to this tucked away spot as one of the best pubs in Dublin. It is also widely known as 'The Gravediggers' on account of its location next to beautiful Glasnevin cemetery. There's nothing morbid about the pub, however, in its picturesque nook in the secluded community surrounding De Courcy Square. On a sunny summer evening the green in front is packed with throngs of people drinking frosty pints and possibly nibbling on some of Ciaran Kavanagh's terrific tapas. As pub food and tapas go they do a pretty good job – it's worth a visit though just for the experience of a great quintessential old Dublin pub, which is a rarity these days. A place where you might find the 6th, 7th and 8th generation of owners all behind the bar. (Eugene Kavanagh, 1 Prospect Sq, Glasnevin, D9 ☎ 01-830 7978 No cards – Open 10.30am-11.30pm Mon-Thu, 10.30am-12am Fri-Sat, 12.30pm-11pm Sun)

Fish stall

● Out of the Blue

The East Coast Inshore Fishing Company act as commission agents for fishing boats, sourcing fresh fish direct from the boats and distributing them to independent fishmongers and shops, and supplying their own renowned market fish vans (called Out of the Blue) in various city and south city Dublin farmers' markets. No visit to the Leopardstown, Temple Bar or Naas farmers markets should be undertaken without buying fish from these notable sellers. The company East Coast actually dates back to 1942, and has been in the O'Callaghan family since 1971. (Brian O'Callaghan, Unit 28 Millennium Business Park, Cappagh Rd, D11 ☎ 01-864 9233. Leopardstown Friday Market, Temple Bar and Naas Saturday Markets)

Fish shop

● Connolly's Fish Company

Stevie Connolly's company has been in expansion mode, so there is now a second store at 135 Upper Rathmines Road. The original store in the old Dublin village of Finglas is well known and well used by local people. With such an outstanding selection of fresh fish and shellfish, from whole fresh sardines to razor clams, it's no wonder Mr Connolly is taking over the city. Super service with great seasonal knowledge, and expert advice. (Stevie Connolly, Unit 3 Finglas Main Shopping Centre, D11 ☎ 01-856 8564 – Open 8am-6pm Tue-Fri, 8am-2pm Sat)

Wine Shop

● Sweeney's Wine Merchants

Finian Sweeney has crammed more than 1,000 wines into his shop at Hart's Corner, so whatever you seek, you will find it here. The beer selection is as capacious as the wine offer, and all the other elements of a great wine shop – a delivery service, tastings, wine appreciation classes, a party service – are all present and correct. They also stock a nice selection of gourmet foods, including cheeses from Sheridan's and charcuterie from On the Pig's Back and Gubbeen, and fresh breads. (Finian Sweeney, 6 Finglas Rd, Hart's Corner, D11 ☎ 01-830 9593 www.sweeneyswine.ie – Open 10.30am-10pm Mon-Sat, 12.30pm-10pm Sun)

local knowledge

Gur Cake

Gur Cake was a lowly snack, unique to Dublin, made from, frankly, leftover stale bits of bread and cake, sandwiching poor quality fruit. Needless to say it was immensely popular, due to being both sweet and cheap. The word "gur" still has slang associations: "gurrier" is someone up to no good, and the verb "to gur", meaning to mitch from school. Nowdays, a much posher, more reputable, version is available from many Dublin bakeries, sometimes called a Fruit Slice.

DUBLIN 15: BALLYCOOLIN

Coffee roaster

● Java Republic

David McKiernan's amazing, state-of-the-art, mega-million coffee roastery at Ballycoolin is a fab spot for taking time to enjoy some Java Republic tea and coffee, and for enjoying a nice bite of something tasty at lunchtime. Mr McKiernan is one of the great movers and shakers in Irish speciality food, and Java Republic has played a pivotal role in the Irish coffee revolution. A lot done, but we reckon Mr McKiernan feels there is still a whole lot more he wants to do, so keep an eye on him. (David McKiernan, 510 Mitchelstown Rd, Northwest Business Park, Ballycoolin, D15 ☎ 01-8809300 www.javarepublic.com – Open 7am-4.30pm Mon-Fri)

NORTH COUNTY DUBLIN

HOWTH

Restaurant/seafood

● Aqua

A longstanding and perenially popular seafood restaurant in one of Dublin's poshest suburbs. Howth is one of the more beautiful parts of the city, and Aqua is possibly best situated to show it off, with panoramic views of the bay from its perch right on the end of the pier. The traditional seafood cookery going on here is confident and classy – think Dover sole meuniere on the bone and lobster Thermidor – and of an old world sort that so befits its environs. They also serve up pretty good meat mains and starters for the non-fish fan. (Richard Clery & Charlie Smith, 1 West Pier ☎ 01-832 0690 www.aqua.ie – Open (lunch) 12.30pm-3.30pm (Tues-Sat) and noon-5pm Sun, (dinner) 5.30pm-10pm (Tues-Sat), 5pm-8.30pm Sun)

Fish shop/food shop/café/deli

● Beshoff's The Market

Beshoff's covers all the bases here on the pier in Howth. The Market is their superlative seafood store and deli, but there is also food to eat in the Market Café – Balscadden crab; shellfish bisque; Dublin Bay prawns – as well as a Grill Bar where they cook the fish you select from the counter, in addition to a tapas and oyster offer. The shop is a beauty, and they know their fish from A to Z. See also the entry for Ivan's, their seafood restaurant, page 250. (Alan Beshoff, 17-18 West Pier, ☎ 01-839 0766 sales@beshoffs.ie www.beshoffs.com – Open 8am-6pm Mon-Sat, 9am-6pm Sun)

Butcher's Shop

● Ray Collier

A staple of Howth shopping for two decades, Ray Collier's traditional shop is of interest to food lovers as he sources Lambay Island beef, real pré-salé beef, which is dry-aged on the premises ("Best beef in North Dublin!", says Aisling in Malahide's Foodware Store). Ray also has fine free-range pork from The Naul. (Ray Collier, 3 Main St ☎ 01-8322002 raycollierbutchers@gmail.com – Open Mon-Sat 8.30am-5.30pm)

Café/deli/bakery

● The Country Market

Downstairs is the Country Market deli, with lots of organics, good baking, signature sandwiches for lunchtime and plenty of food to go, in addition to a good range of standard shopping needs. Upstairs in the Country Market café, chef Lyndsay Cooney makes good savoury and sweet dishes, approachable and enjoyable food that always hits the spot. They also do home catering for those of you who have just gotten off the DART. (Joseph Dogherty, 16 Main St ☎ 01-832 2033 – Cafe Open 8am-6pm Mon-Sat, 8am-5pm Sun. Shop open 7am-7pm Mon-Sat, 7am-5pm Sun)

Casual dining/seafood

● Deep

A cosy, friendly, unfussy local restaurant that serves up reliable food in a warm atmosphere that puts you at ease. The menu carries plenty of favourites: spicy chicken wings, calamari, rib-eye steak with pepper sauce, supreme of chicken with chorizo – all done well and reasonably priced. The special touch is their seafood offering which changes with availability – catch of the day (available on the early bird six days a week), seafood sharing platters, fish pie and other tasty seafood-based mains and starters, giving you a taste of Howth's greatest produce in uncomplicated, honest cooking. The early bird, which is available all day Mon-Fri and from 12.30pm to 7pm on Sat, offers two courses for outstanding value in this location. (Debbie & Brendan O'Connor, West Pier ☎ 01-806 3921 www.deep.ie. – Open 12.30pm-9.30pm Mon-Sat, 12.30pm-8.30pm Sun)

Fish shop

● Doran's on the Pier

Sean Doran's fish shop on the pier is both a bricks-and-mortar shop and on line website (www.seafood2go.ie) which is open to both the trade and the public. The fish selection and quality is superb and as if this wasn't enough, they also run the fine Oar House restaurant, right next door to the shop. (Sean Doran, 7 West Pier ☎ 01-839 2419 🖱 www.lettdoran.ie – Open 9am-6pm Mon-Sat, 10am-5pm Sun)

Wine Bar

● Ella Wine Bar

Aoife Healy's wine bar is a classic local restaurant. The people who come here have been here before, they know what they like and know what they want, and the staff are more than happy to ensure they get exactly what they want. It's all wonderfully logical and simple, just like the food: deep-fried calamari; Ella smokies; tempura of Dublin Bay prawns; Kilkenny beef with a whiskey cream sauce; chocolate nemesis. The lunch offering is a smart selection of sandwiches, quiches and salads, and every village needs an Ella. (Aoife Healy, 7 Main St ☎ 01-839 6264 📧 info@ellawinebar.com 🖱 www.ellawinebar.com – Open 12.45pm-2.45pm Thur-Sat, 6pm-late Mon-Sat)

Café/deli/restaurant

● The House

Smart restaurants give the customer what they want to give the customer, which is to say that they give you what they do best, and not some stuff that they aren't confident about or happy to cook and serve. The House is one of those smart places. They offer you what they like to cook and eat themselves, which means the food isn't really like restaurant cooking. Instead, it's polished domestic cooking that greets the hungry with open arms at any time of day, from their breakfast bacon sandwich through a lunchtime dish of courgette and potato pancakes with asparagus and crispy eggs to an early dinner of West Cork mussels with crab cream and fries to a lazy weekend dinner of Rockwell chicken with sage and onion polenta with bacon gravy. The cooking keynotes are a seesawing sweet and savoury punch that you find in everything Ian Connolly sends out from the kitchen. They want to feed you, to feed you well, and they want you to come back. That's a laudable ambition, and they achieve it with gracious ease. (Karl Dillon & Ian Connolly, 4 Main St ☎ 01-839 6388 📧 info@thehouse-howth.ie 🖱 www.thehouse-howth.ie – Open 8.45am-5pm Mon, 8.45am-9.30pm Tues-Thurs, 8.45am-10.30pm Fri, (brunch) 10am-3.30pm (dinner) 6pm-10.30pm Sat, (brunch) 10am-4pm (dinner) 5pm-9.30pm Sun)

Dublin North

Farmer's Market

● Howth Farmers' Market

Sunday morning opposite the harbour brings more than 40 stallholders to feed the citizens. (Sun & Bank Holidays 10am-5pm.

Café/deli/wine bar/Italian

● Il Panorama Café

As the name suggests, you have a splendid panoramic view of the bay sitting in the window or outside this bijou café-deli and wine bar. As if that wasn't enough, though, the charming young proprietors – known to all as Fitzy and Graziano (or the Ozzie and the Italian) – have infused the place with effortless cool and great craic, especially of a Friday or Saturday night. Expect great coffee, tasty panini and bruschetta, and a small but fab selection of Italian delicatessen fare. There is a short list of decent wines to enjoy by the glass, or you can choose one of 40 (mostly Italian and Australian) bottles from off the shelf. One of the coolest spots in Howth. (Fitzy and Graziano, 1A Island View, Harbour Rd ☎ 01-839 7282 ⌂ www.ilpanoramacafe.com – Open 10am-6pm Mon, 9.30am-11.30pm Tues-Fri, 10.30am-12.30am Sat, 10.30am-11pm Sun).

Restaurant/seafood

● Ivan's Oyster Bar & Grill

Ivan's is the restaurant arm of the Beshoff family's mightily impressive Howth fish operation, and adjoins their Beshoff's The Market emporium. There is both an oyster bar and a grill bar, and sparklingly fresh seafood is what you get in this slick room. They keep the cooking simple and straightforward: crab cakes with citrus mayonnaise; gambas a la plancha; silver hake with herb-crushed potatoes; haddock and chips with pea purée. It's a delightful room, so head here after you have walked the hills. (Alan Beshoff, West Pier ☎ 01-839 0285 ⌂ www.ivans.ie – Open (lunch) 12pm-3pm Mon-Fri, 12pm-5pm Sat, (dinner) 6pm-9.30pm Thurs-Sat, 12pm-7pm Sun)

Restaurant/seafood/guesthouse

● King Sitric

One of the longest established restaurants in all of Dublin, and how splendidly Aidan and Joan McManus continue to fly the flag for good seafood cookery and great white wines. A worthy experience, but it is expensive and booking is essential. (Aidan & Joan MacManus, East Pier, Howth ☎ 01-832 5235 ✉ info@kingsitric.ie 🖱 www.kingsitric.ie – Open from 6.30pm Mon-Sat, 1pm-7pm Sun. Closed Tues and bank hols)

Cookery School

● The Kitchen in the Castle

A cookery school set in the Georgian kitchens of Howth Castle, the KITC offers an extensive range of classes from a crack team of instructors. The courses are of varying length – mornings, evenings, daylong, several days – and the range is comprehensive, from cup cakes and macaroons to Vietnamese cooking. (Christine & Edwina St Lawrence, Howth Castle, ☎ 01-839 6182 ✉ info@thekitcheninthecastle.com 🖱 www.thekitcheninthecastle.com)

Fish Shop

● Nicky's Plaice

Martin McLoughlin today heads the business in which four generations of the McLoughlin family have played their part in establishing Nicky's Plaice as an iconic destination in Irish fish retailing. The location – down towards the very end of Howth Pier – makes it an archetype of what every fish shop should look like, and the quality of fish is second-to-none. Nicky's Plaice is a proud shop with a real sense of mission, and Martin McLoughlin makes much of his respect for the sea. "Fish is one of the last things that man has gone out to hunt," says Martin, and we need to have respect for the hunters. (Martin McLoughlin, West Pier ☎ 01-832 3557 – Open 10am-1pm Mon, 9am-6pm Tue-Fri, 9am-8pm Thur, 9am-1pm Sat)

Restaurant/seafood

● The Oar House

Catch of the day means catch of the day in The Oar House – Sean Doran gathers his fish directly from the trawlers – and Mr Doran doesn't need to do much to his product when it's so good: crab claws with garlic and lemon butter; their classic fish and chips; linguine with squid, prawns, clams and mussels; plaice with almond butter. Pricing is good for such high-quality fish, and make sure to get there early. (Sean Doran, West Pier ☎ 01-839 4562 🖱 www.oarhouse.ie – Open 12.30pm-10.30pm Mon-Sun)

Fish shop

● Ocean Path

Alan Ecock's Ocean Path are the largest processors of fresh seafood in Ireland, supplying most of the biggest supermarket groups with a vast range of fresh seafood, frozen fish and value-added seafood products, and their traditionally smoked salmon under the brand Dunns of Dublin. Their shop front for retailing to the public can be found in Ireland's seafood Mecca, the West Pier at Howth, where you will find a superb range of Irish fish, deep-sea fish, shellfish and exotics. This is the oldest fish company in Ireland – established back in 1822 – and it is still family-run. (Alan Ecock, West Pier ☎ 01-839 8900 www.dunns.ie – Open 9am-6pm Tue-Fri)

Dublin North

LUSK

Artisan apple products

● Llewellyn's Orchard Produce

David Llewellyn fed the Queen of England when she came to Ireland – as did Jenny McNally, another north Dublin entrant in this book and, with David, a stalwart of the Saturday Temple Bar market. We have enjoyed Mr Llewellyn's progress over the last fifteen years with great delight, as he has fashioned his apples, his apple juices, his ciders, his apple balsamic cider vinegar and, most surprisingly, his fine wines – a red wine and two white wines. All the while, he has simply gotten better and better and better, and he has that alchemist's touch, along with a good dose of bloody mindedness. So, you can't mke good wine in Ireland? David will make you think otherwise. Inspiring. (David Llewellyn, Quickpenny Road, Lusk ☎ 01-843 1650 pureapple@eircom.net www.llewellynsorchard.ie)

made in Dublin

Dublin Coddle

Restaurant

● Bon Appetit

Oliver Dunne is one of the great modern Irish chefs, and the latest talk about Bon Appetit has been his ground-breaking Bovine menus in the Brasserie element of the complex (BA is restaurant, brasserie and Le Bon Vin wine bar). They offer unusual cuts, such as popeseye, braised shin, wagyu sirloin, point-end, and you select from a large range of sauces and accompaniments. Bovine shows a chef who is still pushing, pushing, pushing, still searching, staying ahead of the curve. It would be easy for Mr Dunne to sit back and hoover up the Malahide money, but he isn't that sort of chef. Do note that you can eat at very decent prices here, as well as splashing the cash on a big night if that is your thing. (Oliver Dunne, 9 St James Terrace ☎ 01-845 0314 ✉ reservations@bonappetit.ie 🖱 www.bonappetit.ie – Open (restaurant) lunch 12.30pm-2.30pm Thurs-Sat, dinner 6pm-9.30pm Wed-Sat, (brasserie) dinner from 6pm Tues-Sat, lunch from 12pm Sun, (wine bar) open from 6pm Wed-Sat)

Deli/caterer

● Foodware Store

Aisling and Jill have been feeding the good people of Malahide well for almost a dozen years, their confident cookery expertise evident in every loaf of bread, every Tunisian orange cake, every lamb korma and every roast vegetable pie. Foodware is a lovely store, and there is a healthfulness, a zest in everything they cook. Foodware makes your life better, simple as that. (Aisling Boyle, Old St ☎ 01-845 1830 ✉ aislingfood@mac.com 🖱 www.foodwarestore.com – Open 9.30am-6pm Mon-Sat)

Café/deli/Garden Centre

● Garden Works

There are two Garden Works stores (Mabestown, Malahide and Clonee, County Meath) and they are beloved amongst keen gardeners, not just for being excellent plants people, but also for having exceptionally good food halls and cafes in which to shop and eat. Among the selection of gourmet products on offer you'll find excellent coffee, teas, wine, cheese and artisan breads. A delightful surprise. (Mabestown ☎ 01-845 0110. Also at

Dunboyne, Co Meath ☎ 01-8255375 info@gardenworks.ie www.gardenworks.ie – Open 9.30am-5pm Mon-Fri, 9.30am-5.30pm Sat, noon-5.30pm Sun & bank hols)

Wine Shop

● Gibney's Fine Wines

Gibney's is a famous Malahide pub, and just as famous as the pub is their off licence. They have won so many awards for their excellence as an independent wine merchant that they have likely lost count at this stage, but the gimlet crack ambition and desire to be their best never wavers here: this is a brilliant wine shop and off licence.(New St ☎ 01-845 0606 www.gibneys.com – Open 10.30am-11.30pm Mon-Thu, 10.30am-12.30am Fri-Sat, 12.30pm-11pm Sun)

Farmers Market

● Malahide Farmers' Market

You will find food outside the Malahide Market at the GAA club, and inside is a nice bevy of crafts and crafts people. (Church St (side of St Sylvester's GAA hall) Open 2pm-6pm Sat)

NAUL

Organic Herb Nursery

● The Herb Garden

Denise Dunne is the herb guru you need if a bounteous organic herb garden is what you want to see every time you look out the window. Denise grows and sells the herbs and designs herb gardens and offers a consultancy service. (Denise Dunne, Forde-de-Fyne ☎ 01-841 3907 info@theherbgarden.ie www.theherbgarden.ie – Visitors strictly by appointment only)

Organic Vegetable Farm

● McNally Family Farm

Jenny and Patrick McNally and their family produce beautiful organic foods, and produce them the way nature intended. They produce beautiful salad leaves, herbs and crops and a whole lot more – last time at Temple Bar Market, for example, they had some delicious country butter which we snapped up along with a whole lot more wonderful things – so keep your eyes open for their stall at Temple Bar and Leopardstown markets on Saturdays and Fridays respectively, where their stalls are amongst the busiest and buzziest. (Jenny & Pat McNally, Balrickard, Ring Commons ☎ 01-841 3023)

OLDTOWN

Crisp Fryers

● Keogh's Crisps

Derek, Ross and Tom Keogh are changing the way we think about potatoes, and changing the way we think about potato crisps. The Keogh family have been growing spuds in north Dublin for two centuries, but it has been their diversion into making potato crisps that has seen their visibility skyrocket – Roisin Ingle wrote three pages about them in *The Irish Times!* It's quite simple: their crisps are delicious, they know what variety is used and what field it came from, and who fried it, so they have changed the rules of crisp manufacturing. When you buy a bag of their Atlantic sea salt and vinegar crisps, the man who made that vinegar is artisan-alchemist David Llewellyn, who farms in nearby Lusk. They use Dungarvan Brewery stout in the roast beef and stout crisps. Respect! The Keoghs are just the coolest farmers in Ireland. (Derek, Ross & Tom Keogh, Westpalstown, Oldtown ☎ 01-843 3175 admin@keoghs.ie www.keoghs.ie)

PORTMARNOCK

Wine Shop

● Jus de Vine

Jus de Vine is the world of wine in a single place. It is an incredible place, and it is in Portmarnock. Today, the store rocks on under the stewardship of daughter Julie Cullen and its defining characteristic is the modestly worn knowledge of the staff, their quiet confidence that makes them so good and that helps JDV win so many awards. So you can expect incredible wines and really great service, and an incredible experience. (Julie Cullen, 7 Portmarnock Town Centre ☎ 01-846 1192 www.jusdevine.ie – Open 10.30am-10.30pm Mon-Sat, 12.30pm-10.30pm Sun)

Fish shop

Egan's Ocean Fresh

Third generation fishmonger Tony Gunnery runs this excellent fish shop in the picturesque area of Strand Street, next to the fishing harbour. "We're here to sell fish" says Mr Gunnery, and that's what they do: good fresh fish, beautifully prepared and presented. (Tony Gunnery, 85a Strand St ☎ 01-849 5244 www.egansfreshfish.com – Open 9am-6pm Tue-Sat, 11am-3pm Mon)

Café/deli

Olive

Deirdre Dorrity uses the word "pride" to describe what she and her husband, Peter, and their team do at Skerries' iconic Olive Deli and Café. It's a telling word, a telling adjective, and it fits this operation, for they try hard, and then try even harder. Every detail of every element here is considered, and curated – how to make the best coffee, the best panini, the best bowl of soup. The Dorritys have a total vision of their work, they understand how to mine the seam of culture that lies within food and fine cooking and fine ingredients, something they showed way back in the day when they ran the cult Café Iris in Temple Bar, before they headed north to the sea. They are different by nature, different by desire, and that is Olive Café's USP. (Peter Dorrity & Deirdre Fahy, 86 Strand St ☎ 01-849 0310 sales@olive.ie www.olive.ie – Open 8.30am-6pm Mon-Sat, 9.30am-5pm Sun)

Restaurant/hotel

Red Bank House

Terry McCoy will soon knock up thirty years of cooking and service, for he first opened the doors of The Red Bank as long ago as 1983. The Red Bank's reputation has been built on Terry and his son, Ross's, magnificent seafood cookery, though there are of course meat dishes on the menu. The Red Bank also has comfortable rooms, and the hospitality for thirty years has always been genuine, distinctive and true. (Terry & Ross McCoy, 5-7 Church St ☎ 01-849 1005 www.redbank.ie – Open 6.30pm-9.45pm Mon-Sat, 12.30pm-4.30pm Sun)

Wine shop

● Red Island Wines

Dougie Stewart is a superb Facebooker. Read his wine notes on his Facebook page and you will learn quickly and clearly about wine and the culture of wine. Mr Stewart strikes just the right note, wearing his learning lightly, providing tips and suggestions, making you want to step into the car and head to Church Street. Many of the bottles on the shelves are regularly chosen by the weekend wine writers as outstanding examples of what you should be drinking. (Dougie Stewart, 64 Church St ☎ 01-849 4032 ✉ info@redislandwine.com – Open 12pm-8pm Wed-Thurs, 12pm-9pm Fri, 11am-8pm Sat, 1pm-7pm Sun)

Gastropub/seafood

● Stoop Your Head

SYH is a very successful bar and restaurant, so waiting for a table – either at the bar or next door in Joe May's – will likely be a reality. The cooking is punchy and tasty and generous – Dublin Bay prawns in garlic butter; moules mariniere; seafood paella; cod frites. There are choices other than fish and shellfish, but seafood is what the locals who pack the place out tend to go for. (David May, Harbour Rd ☎ 01-849 2085 – Food served 12-3pm, 5.30-9.30pm Mon-Thu, 12pm-3pm, 5.30pm-10pm Fri-Sat, 12.30pm-3pm, 4pm-8pm Sun)

SWORDS

Bakery/café/deli

● La Boulangerie Francaise

You might have to navigate a little around Applewood Village to find Florence and Damian's excellent bakery, deli and café, but keep going: it's worth the detour to find this tasty destination. Damian's baking is true and expert, and the lunches are delightful and delicious, but do get there early as it's tiny and there aren't many seats. You can also find these fine breads and cakes in the Temple Bar Market on Saturdays. (Florence & Damian Cusack, Unit 77, Applewood Village Sq ☎ 086-102 2786 🖱 www.laboulangeriefrancaise.ie – Open 9am-5pm Mon & Sat, 9am-6pm Tue-Fri, also at Temple Bar Market on Saturdays)

Dublin North

Deli and Tapas Bar

● Gourmet Food Company

Lorraine and Lorraine's GFP has doubled in size in Swords, proof that this dynamic duo are giving the people what the people want when it comes to good food and good wines. GFP is now a 72-seater and, in addition to their barnstorming daytime food, there is a super tapas offer on Thursday, Friday and Saturday evening. (Lorraine Heskin & Lorraine Byrne, Unit 2.2 St Fintan's, North Street ☎ 01-897 1496 ⌘ www.gourmetfoodparlour.com)

Takeaway

● The Chuck Wagon

The legendary Chuck Wagon has moved to the R132 near to Corduff, so that is where you need to head to for stellar sausage sandwiches and inimitably insouciant service. (Martin Crosby, R132, Corduff ☎ 085-702 5446. Cash only – Open 7.30am-5.30pm Mon-Sat)

THE WARD

Chocolatier

● Chez Emily

Ferdinand and Helena are superb chocolatiers, and one could go quite crazy in their chocolate boutiques, such is the excellence of their work and the delectable aesthetic of everything they make. The chocolates are true tempered productions, and the good news is that they are steadily, surely becoming more widely available across the country. Any trip to Emily's house is a very good trip indeed. (Ferdinand Vandaele & Helena Hemeryck, Cool Quay ☎ 01-835 2252. Also at Main St, Ashbourne, Co Meath ✉ Helena@chezemily.ie ⌘ www.chezemily.ie)

DUBLIN SOUTH

DUBLIN 4: BALLSBRIDGE, DONNYBROOK, SANDYMOUNT

Townhouse

● Ariel House

Deirdre McDonald runs a great show in Ariel House, and she is backed up by a great team who match the boss's inspiration. It's a favourite place to stay in Dublin for many discerning travellers, and one bite of their bountiful breakfasts will help you understand why. (Deirdre McDonald, 50-54 Lansdowne Road, D4 ☎ 01-668 5512 reservations@ariel-house.net www.ariel-house.net)

Pizza/takeaway

● Base

Shane and Aengus's Terenure classic comes to D4, letting locals ponder the eternal Base question: is this the best pizza in Ireland, or is this the best pizza in the world? Life is too short to disagree over such matters, so you order the Diablo, I'll order the Verona, and we'll fight over who gets to pay for them. (Shane Crilly & Aengus Lacey, 18 Merrion Road, Ballsbridge, D4 ☎ 01-440 5100 info@basewfp.ie www.basewfp.ie – Open noon-11pm Mon-Sun)

Restaurant/Italian

● Bianconi's

The Macari family's long, bright room is always a good spot for accessible and very polished Italian cooking, and it always attracts a very Tony crowd who want something straight from the textbook of Italian classics: antipasto misto; pizza Margherita; ricotta and spinach tortelloni; spaghetti carbonara. (Tony Macari, 232 Merrion Road, Ballsbridge, D4 ☎ 01-219 6033 – Open 9.30am-10pm Mon-Fri, 10.30am-10pm Sat, 10.30am-9pm Sun)

Bistro/deli

● Browne's Deli and Café

Peter Bark's coffee shop and deli counts among its local regulars a heavyweight in Irish food writing – you don't get much better recommendation than that. Come for dinner and you'll see why: effortlessly accomplished cooking, unpretentious presentation, relaxed and easy service, and pretty much everything you'd want from a local bistro. They're regularly counted among the city's best casual dining restaurants, and that's fair praise indeed for this worthy spot. (Peter Bark, Sandymount Green, D4 ☎ 01-269 7316 pbark@eircom.net – Open 7.30am-9.15pm Mon-Fri, 9am-9.15pm Sat, 10am-5pm Sun)

Spanish Produce Deli

● The Black Pig

Paul Walsh got his wine education in Oddbins back in the good old days when those shops were staffed by passionate wineheads who pored over their Andrew Jefford books while they worked. Mr Walsh's focus crystallised in a love affair with Spanish wines, and Spanish foods. Step in the door of the Black Pig, and you can feel the love. Fresh padron peppers, artisan manchego cheese, superb bomba rice, amazing cured meats and 200 hand-picked Spanish wines will see you re-emerging back into Donnybrook with a cartful of delights from the Iberian peninsula. (Paul Walsh, 95b Morehampton Road, Donnybrook, D4 ☎ 087-275 4718 info@blackpig.ie www.blackpig.ie – Open 10.30am-7pm Mon-Wed, till 8pm Thur-Sat)

Deli/caterer

● The Butler's Pantry

Now a chain of multiple locations around Dublin, this gourmet stalwart has been doing good food back since before it was really trendy to be a caterer. The Sandymount deli, one of the older sites, still graces the local village with its tasty salads, hot dishes and sweet treats, and loyal customers would go nowhere else for party food when a caterer of some substance is required. Friendly, personal, and great quality, are just some of the reasons why The Butler's Pantry remains favourite. (Eileen Bergin. 3 Sandymount Green, D4 ☎ 01-215 1700 events@thebutlerspantry.ie www.thebutlerspantry.ie – Open Mon-Sun 9am-7pm. Also at Southern Cross Bus Pk, Boghall Rd, Bray; 2B Vernon Ave, Clontarf; 97B Morehampton Rd, Donnybrook; 53 Mt Merrion Ave; 99 Rathgar Rd; 1a Montpellier Place, Temple Hill, Monkstown; Burnaby Buildings, Church Rd, Greystones; and 19 Sandycove Rd)

Butcher & Deli

● Michael Byrne Craft Butcher

This much-respected butcher's shop is actually part of a double act, for Michael and Raymond Byrne also have a fine deli and vegetable shop right across the road, just as you come into the green at Sandymount. Excellent meats, an especially invaluable haunt for game birds and other wild game, and excellent service brings the D4 crowd back time after time. (Michael & Raymond Byrne, 92 Sandymount Rd, D4 ☎ 01-660 7072)

Gastropub

● The Chop House

One of the most exciting gastro ventures to hit Dublin 4 in recent years, and one that has cemented this particular corner of the sought-after Dublin locale as 'the' foodie destination for D4 dwellers. The Chop House does it all: changing selections of oysters, depending on what varieties are available; carefully sourced meat and fowl, with a particular penchant for aged Charolais beef; and confident, accomplished, delicious cooking that gives just the right amount of theatre without over-complicating your pub lunch. The wine list is thoughtful, and on match day you'll be as much in the thick of it as in any pub that brings in the crowd. This is what a gastropub should be - a real pub that cares about gastronomy, as opposed to just a restaurant with a bar in, or a bar with a restaurant in. (Kevin Arundel, 2 Shelbourne Rd, D4 ☎ 01-6602390 info@thechophouse.ie www.thechophouse.ie – Open (food) 12-10pm Mon-Fri, 6-10pm Sat, 1-8pm Sun)

Food shop/deli/restaurant

● Donnybrook Fair

For the owner of Ireland's most famous chain of gourmet food shops, you probably wouldn't expect a man as unassuming as former butcher Joe Doyle. Modest and humble, he shrugs off praise and passes all credit to his daughters who now run the empire. Don't be fooled, however, as his influence is all over this landmark Irish food business. Ed Hick's artisan sausages, and an in-house beef-buyer who is himself a master butcher and beef producer, show the mark of a butcher with a pride in his product behind this operation. This is the legacy Mr. Doyle leaves to DF, and the reason it remains so high in our esteem. (Joe Doyle, 91 Morehampton Rd, Donnybrook, D4 ☎ 01-668 3556 info@donnybrookfair.ie www.donnybrookfair.ie – Shop open 7am-10pm Mon-Sat, 9am-10pm Sun. Restaurant open 7.30am-10pm Mon-Thur, 7.30am-10.30pm Fri-Sat, 9am-10pm Sun. Also 13 Baggot Street ☎ 01-668 3556 – Open 7am-9pm Mon-Fri, 8am-10pm Sat, 9am-6pm Sun. Also Grattan Court, Greystones ☎ 01-287 6346 – Open 7am-8pm Mon-Thur & Sat, 7am-9pm Fri, 8am-8pm Sun)

Craft Butcher

● Dunne's of Donnybrook

Fintan Dunne's butcher's shop is just the sort of class act you hope to find in a glam place like Donnybrook. Superbly sourced and aged meats are handled with skill, deftness and knowledge, and the shop and the service standards are totally customer-orientated. A glass-fronted cabinet lets you see the grass-fed meats as they hang, developing pristinely through the maturation process, and Mr Dunne himself reckons a steak hung for 32 days is where perfection lies. Aside from the beef and lamb, everything else is available, and just as carefully selected and prepared. A benchmark butcher's address in every possible way. (Fintan Dunne, 53 Main Street, Donnybrook, D4 ☎ 01-283 9679)

Food Store & Coffee Shop

● Food Game

"Hearty, homemade stuff that tastes real", says our friend Mary. Ross Staunton has a Ballymaloe-school background, so he knows about real tasting food. The shop is smart and stocked with everything you want and need, from Clive McCabe coffee to Colman Andrews' newest book. Their soup and sambo deal is a lunch-time steal, and prices are really keen for such careful, loved-up cooking. Excellent. See you there for brunch on Saturday. (Ross Staunton, 10 South Lotts Road, Ringsend D4 ☎ 01-281 5002 foodgamedublin@gmail.com www.foodgame.ie – 8am-6pm Mon-Fri, 9.30am-3.20pm Sat-Sun)

Wine bar/French

● The French Paradox

Simple plates of good food and some zinging wines make up the rock-steady formula of Tanya and Pierre Chapeau's original and intriguing eaterie. The FP is in a paradoxical position, somewhere between a French deli and a wine bar, but it works superbly, with tasty food spurring on the desire to order another glass of wine. The wine shop downstairs is terrific. (Tanya & Pierre Chapeau, 53 Shelbourne Road, Ballsbridge, D4 ☎ 01-660 4068 wineshop@thefrenchparadox.com www.thefrenchparadox.com www.chapeauwines.com – Open noon-3pm, 6pm-10.30pm Mon-Fri, noon-10.30pm Sat. Amuses gueules served from 3pm-7pm)

Dublin South

Restaurant/Chinese

● Furama

Rodney Mak's Chinese restaurant has been a reliable and consistent destination for over two decades. His is a homely style of Chinese restaurant for which many Irish people have a great affection. (Rodney Mak, Ground Floor, Eirpage House, Donnybrook Main Road, D4 ☎ 01-283 0522 www.furama.ie – Open 12.30pm-2pm Mon-Fri, 5.30pm-10.30pm Mon-Thu till 11pm Fri-Sat)

Food Market

● Irish Village Markets

Tara Dalton and Des Vallely's company runs markets in Dublin city – the Mespil Road market, in its perfect setting along the Grand Canal, is a particular favourite for local townies – but you'll also find them in Blanchardstown, Christchurch, East Point, Grand Canal, Sandyford, Spencer Dock, Stillorgan Luas stop, and Whitewater SC in Newbridge. At Mespil Road, for instance, you'll find a delightful array including wood-fired pizza, rotisserie chicken, lamb skewers, Thai cuisine, Spanish stews and paella, German bratwurst, Palestinian wraps and salads, Mediterranean Grill, Chinese noodles, Mexican burritos, Hungarian Goulash, Irish chocolates, and artisan coffee and breads...to name a few things. These Irish Villages are as cosmopolitan as it gets! (Des Vallely & Tara Dalton ☎ 01-2841197 info@irishvillagemarkets.com www.irishvillagemarkets.com. Lunch market open 11am-2pm Thurs)

Bistro

● Itsa4

It's hard work keeping up with the brilliant Kemp sisters, Domini and Peaches. In addition to opening up a tea room in Dublin Castle, planning a new venture – Hatch – on St Stephen's Green, running the restaurant in Brown

Thomas, manning their various bagel bars and opening a new Itsa in Ranelagh, they switched the Sandymount Itsa to a day-time café, serving breakfast and lunches. So, good soups, sarnies, bagels, smoothies and sweet things and, as ever, excellent service. (Domini & Peaches Kemp, 6A Sandymount Green, D4 ☎ 01-219 4676 www.itsabagel.com. Open breakfast & lunch)

local knowledge

Need a late night feed?

● Bóbós Burritos & Blues ● The Good World ● Jo'burger ● Leo Burdocks ● Little Jerusalem ● Sichuan House ● The Bernard Shaw ● Sagaar ● Kanum

Café/deli/brunch/pizza

● Juniors (and Paulie's Pizza)

A blackboard menu, the tiniest wee room imaginable, and half the neighbourhood vying for a table. Weekend brunch at Juniors is an institution in leafy old D4, and tucked between the Aviva rugby stadium and legendary rugger pub Slattery's, you can expect a scrum for a seat, especially on the terrace during summer. Portions are generous and the eggs are great, whatever way you like them. It ain't cheap but the locals wouldn't change a thing. (Paul & Barry McNerney, 4 Bath Avenue, Ballsbridge ☎ 01-664 3648 8 www.juniors.ie – Open all day). Around the corner you'll find sister diner Paulie's Pizza, which attracts an equally loyal local fan base and turns out some pretty good Neapolitan-style pizza and gourmet sarnies to boot. (☎ 01-664 3658 paulies@juniors.ie)

Casual dining/Mediterranean/Egyptian

● Keshk Café

Keshk has become popular with young and old not just for the food, which is rather good, but because it is one of those rare, much appreciated BYOB places, of which the city needs a lot more. Bringing your own beer or wine considerably eases the bill and also lets you pick exactly what you'd like to drink. It also lessens costs for the establishment, allowing them, as is definitely the case at Keshk, to offer their food for very good value prices. Tasty charcoaled kafta (minced lamb), grilled chicken and meatballs, or great vegetarian options like okra with fresh coriander in tomato sauce, and Maghmour, a traditional stew of aubergines, chickpeas, onions, fresh mint and tomato sauce are examples of this high quality, good value food. A second depot is on Mespil Road. (Mosy Keshk, 129 Upper Leeson St ☎ 01-668 9793 ✉ moustafa7777@hotmail.com – Open 12pm-late)

Restaurant/seafood

● The Lobster Pot

Tommy Crean, John Rigby and chef Don McGuinness have been doing good fish and shellfish cookery for years, serving their good food with good wines, and it ain't broke and they sure ain't gonna fix it. Charming, fashion-free, so let's have sole bonne femme and coquilles St Jacques and some Chablis and off we go. (Tommy Crean, 9 Ballsbridge Tce, Ballsbridge, D4 ☎ 01-668 0025 🖱 www.thelobsterpot.ie – Open 12.30pm-2pm Mon-Fri, 6pm-10.30pm Mon-Sat)

Wine shop

● Louis Albrouze

A great wine shop close to BYOB restaurant Keshk, LA specialise in finding less common, artisan-grower wines, and they also have a very good website where you can buy the wines online. They also stock Riedel speciality glassware. (Nathalie Hennebert, 127 Upper Leeson St ☎ 01-6674455 ✉ leesonstreet@louisalbrouze.com 🖱 www.louisalbrouze.com – Open 10.30am-9pm Mon-Sat)

On-Line Bakery

● Lou Lou Bakery

"Utterly delicious showstoppers" is how Marie-Claire Digby described Fiona Wymes cakes in *The Irish Times*. And with comparisons to London's legendary Hummingbird Bakery having already been made, Fiona Wymes' on-line bakery already has the kudos necessary to persuade you that you do indeed need a Lou Lou layer cake, or a pistachio and orange blossom cake, or a lavender and honey cup cake. With a Ballymaloe School background and a spell at the Violet Bakery in London, Ms Wymes has those magic hands, and she is a purist: no artificial gunk here, just quality ingredients and exacting skill and care. (Fiona Wymes, Sandymount, D4 ☎ 086-847 6029 ✉ sales@louloubakery.com 🖱 www.louloubakery.com)

Dublin South

Gastropub

● Merrion Inn

Fearghus McCormack and his team are working hard in the Merrion Inn to get beyond the traditional ideas – and expectations – of what people think about Irish pub cooking. They are an ambitious bunch, and Vincent Kelly's cooking begins with very well-sourced ingredients from blue chip suppliers, so keep an eye on these guys. (Fearghus McCormack, 188 Merrion Road, Ballsbridge D4 ☎ 01 269 3816 info@themerrioninn.com www.themerrioninn.com – Food served noon-9.30pm Mon-Sun)

Deli

● Molloy's of Donnybrook

"The only place I have ever managed to find La Ratte potatoes", is Leslie Williams' delighted endorsement of Molly's, a really fine deli with lots of rare and arcane good things. (Peter Molloy, 47 Donnybrook Road, D4 ☎ 01-269 1678 petermolloy@gmail.com – Open 9am-6pm Tue-Sat)

Restaurant

● Mulberry Garden

Now here's a strange one. A restaurant that only opens three nights a week, only does dinner, only offers a choice of two starters, mains and afters (dessert du jour or cheese), often doesn't offer steak as one of the choices, and Dubliners are raving about it. If we needed proof that Dublin has grown up into a cosmopolitan food capital, Mulberry Garden is it. The cooking is confident but not needlessly showy. The ingredients are the best of local Irish produce and change every week with the menus. The dining room is chic but laid back and buzzing. Every detail of this restaurant conforms to the desires of a cosmopolitan foodie - including the essential cocktail menu and surprisingly good wine list. And it's very delicious: rack of pork with caper sauce; slow-braised short rib of beef; herb-crusted whiting; Jerusalem artichoke velouté; crubeens with poached hen's egg; roast Silverhill duck leg - it's all about the produce and it sings off the plate at you. That's music to our ears. (Brian Lennon, Mulberry Lane, Donnybrook, D4 ☎ 01-269 3300 eat@mulberrygarden.ie mulberrygarden.ie – Open (dinner only) 6pm-10.30pm Thurs-Sat)

Restaurant/Irish

● O'Connell's

You're greeted by long-time restaurateur Tom O'Connell himself and treated to some of his old-school charm and dry wit while he shows you to your table. They offer a most interesting wine list which is divided into House, Super House, and Very Special reds and whites, listing everything from each wine's alcohol by volume to its wine merchant. The food is a very tempting array of delights on every menu – lunch, dinner, high tea, supper and Sunday buffet – and there's good value to be had. O'Connell's deals in fine Irish produce and their menus proudly showcase this: Catalonian charcoal oven-roasted free-range Irish chicken (raised by Donal Nash in Co Limerick), char-grilled rib steak of Irish Hereford on the bone, grilled fillets of Castletownbere landed plaice. The cooking is simple, the food is honest and hearty, and it's a sublime taste of Irish hospitality. (Tom O'Connell, 135 Morehampton Road, Donnybrook ☎ 01-269 6116 info@oconnellsdonnybrook.com www.oconnellsdonnybrook.com – Open 10.30am-10.30pm Tues-Sat, 9am-7.30pm Sun)

Hotel

● Pembroke Townhouse

A beautiful location on tree-lined Pembroke Road is the major asset of the PT, though the exceptionally fine staff match the grandeur of the house. The bedrooms are calm and very comfortable, the public rooms are cosy and the breakfast is truly one of the best in the city, a feast to set you up for the day and what the city promises. (Fiona Teehan, 90 Pembroke Rd, Ballsbridge, D4 ☎ 01-660 0277 www.pembroketownhouse.ie)

Cookery School

● Pink Ginger

What you need to know about Eimer Rainsford is simply that she was the head chef of Avoca, Ireland's leading luxury food brand, for more than a decade. Head chef of Ireland's leading luxury food brand is as good as it gets, so if you want to know how Eimear made all that magic for many years, you need to enrol in one of the inspiring classes Ms Rainsford holds in her own home. (Eimer Rainsford, 4 Serpentine Road, Sandymount, D4 ☎ 087-986 4964 www.pinkginger.ie)

Dublin South

Deli/Restaurant

● Rigby's Deli

"Assured, delicious cooking" is our how great mate Mary Dowey describes James Rigby's splendidly left-field little diner. It's a deli and sandwich bar by day but for three nights each week it morphs into a menu-free restaurant, and James Rigby cooks what's in the market. We like this: seared scallops with black pudding and ruby grapefruit; smoked chicken and pea risotto;monkfish with langoustine. Mr Rigby used to do the standard style of cooking and got sick of it. Here, he does his own thing, and it's strange, delicious, inspiring. A second outlet on Dame Street has just opened. (James Rigby, 126 Upper Leeson St, D4 ☎ 087-793 9195 rigbys.deli.and.dining.room@gmail.com – Open 7.30am-6pm Mon-Wed, 7.30am-10pm Thur-Fri, 10.30am-10pm Sat)

Deli/Restaurant

● Roly's Bistro

Twenty years of mighty service to Dublin is the proud achievement of Roly's, one of the city's most beautiful places to eat. Today it is a bistro, an all-day café and a catering service. It is also a timeless, ageless legend. (John O'Sullivan, Paul Cartwright, 7 Ballsbridge Terrace, D4 ☎ 01-668 2611 info@rolysbistro.ie www.rolysbistro.ie – Open noon-3pm, 5.45pm-10pm Mon-Sun)

Restaurant/Irish

● The Sussex (at M O'Brien's)

This site has seen a few incarnations in the recent past but the current resident over M. O'Brien's pub seems to be ticking all the boxes. Good value, solid Irish cookery showcasing the national produce of which we are so proud. Ted Browne's Dingle Bay prawns on toast with lemon and garlic is a fine example of the simple deliciousness on offer, and you can wash it down with a decent pint from the bar if you so wish. Restaurant prices are upper mid range – there's a simpler more economical menu available in the pub below too. If you're in this neck of the woods and in need of sustenance, chances are you'll be very happy with your lot in The Sussex. (Trevor Browne & Ger Foot, 9 Sussex Terrace, Upr Leeson St. D4 ☎ 01-676 2851 info@thesussex.ie www.thesussex.ie – Open 7 days for lunch and dinner from 12 noon until 11pm)

Wine Merchant

● Terroirs

Terroirs heads towards two decades of service to Dubliners and wine lovers, and their great achievement in all that time has been to stay always relevant, always surprising, always enterprising. Françoise and Sean created a timeless aesthetic in their store when they opened, and age has only improved it. Their combined knowledge means they are able to keep finding good bottles, most especially from their beloved France, and their treasure trove of good things to eat is always intriguing and special. (Sean & Françoise Gilley, 103 Morehampton Road, Donnybrook, D4 ☎ 01-667 1311 ✉ info@terroirs.ie 🖱 www.terroirs.ie – Open 1pm-7pm Mon, 10.30am-7pm Tue-Sat)

Dublin South

DUBLIN 6: RANELAGH, RATHMINES, RATHGAR, TERENURE

Pizza/takeaway

● Base

According to our editor Leslie Williams, Shane Crilly and Aengus Lacey make the best pizzas in the country. Editor Caroline Byrne seconds that. Not just the best in Dublin, but the best in Ireland. Caroline is addicted to the 'Diablo' with its molten chunks of chorizo and fiery jalapenos, but you will find your own addiction amidst their delectable, meticulous menu. Everything about Base is smart and hip, and it's no surprise that they have a second branch in Ballsbridge and, one feels, even more to come. Bring it on: Dublin and Ireland needs these fabulous pizzas. (Shane Crilly & Aengus Lacey, Terenure Road East, D6 ☎ 01-440 4800 ✉ info@basewfp.ie 🖱 www.basewfp.ie – Open noon-11pm Mon-Sun)

Casual dining

● Beckett & Bull

"The emphasis is on the casual", Leslie Williams says of Amanda and Jonathan's American-style eaterie, so tuck in to mussels with garlic bread; panko-crumbed calamari; sirloin with wedges and onion rings; good pizzas; some nice battered fish, and a gooey chocolate chilli cake. B&B is a pivotal new addition to D6 dining, and the good things to eat are served alongside an admirable list of wines and beers. (Amanda & Jonathan Kirwan, 53 Rathgar Ave, D6 ☎ 01-498 0011 hello@beckettandbull.ie http://beckettandbull.ie – Open 12-3pm and 6-10pm Wed-Fri, 11am-4pm and 6pm-10pm Sat-Sun)

Restaurant/Italian

● Bellagio

An Italian fixture in Terenure, Bellagio is the local place to bring your other half, family or friends when there's a special occasion to be celebrated. When owners Vincenzo or Fabio are at front of house the service is oh so Italian, especially for the ladies! The food is authentic and makes use of fine ingredients: 21-day dry aged Irish beef, Italian cured meats and cheeses. They know their onions when it comes to classic staples such as pizza and risotto too. Leslie Williams gives it the nod. (Fabio Cirello & Vincenzo Morelli, 92 Terenure Rd North, D 6W ☎ 01-492 7625 info@bellagiorestaurant.ie www.bellagiorestaurant.ie – Open 12.30-11.30pm Mon-Sun)

Bistro

● Bijou

The name is apt: Bijou shows both elegant workmanship in its design, and in the food on the plate, and as a destination it is highly prized by D6 locals who know a good thing when they eat it. The food is ageless – duck confit with lentils; pork belly with scallops; rib-eye with mustard mash and green beans; battered fish with minted peas; chocolate fondant with cinnamon ice cream – the room is relaxed and glamorous, and Bijou hits the spot. (Linda Smith, 47 Highfield Rd, Rathgar, D6 ☎ 01-496 1518 bijourestaurant@eircom.net www.bijourathgar.ie – Bistro open noon-late, restaurant open from 5pm Wed-Fri, from 6pm Sat, 12.30pm-5pm Sun)

Indian/takeaway

● Bombay Pantry

The Bombay Pantry is a dynamic, meticulous business that achieves their self-assured goal of being the best Indian takeaway in Dublin. Their food is consistently, reliably good, and the spread of branches throughout the city – there are Pantries available in Ashtown, Bray, Clonskeagh, Fairview, Glenageary, Rathfarnham, and Rathmines, and they have an efficient delivery service – which means you are never far from some fine, authentic Indian food. We can recall it from way back in the day, when there was just one simple shop in Glenageary: my baby, how you've grown! (Emma Sheehan, 14 Rathgar Rd, Rathmines, D6 ☎ 01-4969695 bombaypantry.com – Open 4pm-11pm Mon-Sat, 4pm-10pm Sun)

Casual dining/steakhouse

● The Butcher Grill

Following hot on the heels of the very successful Dillinger's, TBG opened just down the road in the hands of the same team, and once again they've proven they really know how to work this business. TBG does exactly what it says on the tin – it's a meat fest. Choose from the wood smoked grill: barbecue baby back ribs; beef and bone marrow cheese burger; 10oz dry age ribeye; or the 24oz cote de boeuf for two, if you bring the right sort to dine with you. Some beef aficionados feel the promise is greater than the product in TBG, but most would probably agree it's a damn fine feed, and a joy even just to watch. At the bar in front of the grill are possibly the best seats in the house. They welcome walk-ins but booking is advisable for busy times and be sure to ring if you're going to be late to avoid having your table given away. (John Farrell, 92 Ranelagh Village, D6 ☎ 01-498 1805 eat@thebutchergrill.ie www.thebutchergrill.ie – Open Dinner: 5.30–9.30pm Sun-Wed, 5.30–10.30pm Thurs-Sat; brunch/roasts noon-4pm Sat-Sun)

Café

● Cinnamon Café

The Cinnamon is a chilled-out series of eating spaces, characterised by a funky, mis-match bricolage style, where you can share platters of various vegetables, terrines, dips and breads, have confit duck leg or Moroccan meatballs, have some wine, or just enjoy tea and some rather fetching cakes. There is a good selection of foods, breads and wines to take away, and it's another nice little fixture in the culinary grotto that Ranelagh is speedily becoming. (Grainne Walsh, 87 Ranelagh, D6 ☎ 01-901 3020 info@cinnamon.ie – Open 9am-11pm Mon-Sun)

Dublin South

Bakery

● The Corner Bakery

They make real bread in the Corner Bakery. Proper stuff, made from scratch, made by a human being, a person with skills, who works through the night so that when you break through that baguette with your morning coffee, what you are getting is a cultural and culinary artefact, a piece of goodness itself. It is impossible to overestimate the importance of local bakeries such as The Corner; they are truly the cornerstone of any food culture, and Terenure is lucky to have Fiona, Cara and David working hard to bring forth the best breads and cakes they can. Don't miss the challah bread, the apple and cinnamon cake and, of course, their signature cupcakes. (David Brown & Cara Lloyd, 17 Terenure Rd North, D6W ☎ 01-490 6210 – Open 8am-5.30pm Mon-Sat, 9am-1pm Sun)

Casual dining/American

● Dillinger's

Another of the American-inspired joints that have sprung up in the last few years, whose raison d'être is to offer American-style food and drinks at that lower mid-range price level that has been so elusive in Ireland (during Celtic Tiger years anyway). Good burgers and steaks, 'Cal-Ital' pastas and salads, clam chowder, and the odd Asian or Med fusion dish to bring a little variety to the otherwise steady but satisfying menu. There's good value in their wines by the glass, and happy hour on Tuesdays and Wednesdays allows you to enjoy their cocktails for less. Tasty, consistent and good value. (John Farrell, 47 Ranelagh Village, D6 ☎ 01-497 8010 info@dillingers.ie www.dillingers.ie – Open lunch/brunch 12.00-4pm Fri-Sun; dinner 5.30-9.30pm Sun-Tue, 5.30-10.30pm Wed-Thurs, 5.30-11pm Fri-Sat)

Café/deli/Italian

● Er Buchetto

Situated on a busy corner in Ranelagh village, this buzzy little café offers tasty Italian snacks – such as soups, panini, and a range of deli foods – good Italian coffee, and wine by the glass if you're feeling that way inclined. Grab a seat near a window if you can. (71 Ranelagh Village, D6 ☎ 01-496 7584 – Open 8:30am-5pm Mon-Fri, 9:30am-5pm Sat, 9:30am-5pm Sun)

Restaurant

● Eatery 120

120 is a stylish, straight-ahead Ranelagh favourite, a room that is always buzzing. Its dinner and weekend brunch menus are a collation of sure-fire classics: cod smokies; scallops with black pudding; beer-battered fish with peas and tartare; the Eatery burger. Mid-week menus offer very good value, and 120 has proven itself to be a real solid-sender. (Brian Lennon, 120 Ranelagh Village, D6 ☎ 01-470 4120 eat@eatery120.ie www.eatery120.ie – Open 5pm-10pm Mon-Thur, 5pm-10.30pm Fri, 11am-3pm, 6pm-11pm Sat, 11am-3.30pm, 5.30pm-8.30pm Sun)

Dublin South

Grocer

● Field and Vine

Field & Vine is a superb grocer's shop, of a style that has almost become unfashionable as retail hovers between supermarkets and delis. You can get fresh fruit and veg here, along with organic produce, nice wines and lots of speciality foods. They also make a fine sandwich. (151 Upper Rathmines Rd, D6 ☎ 01-496 2636 marketfresh1@eircom.net – Open 11am-6pm Mon-Sun)

Patisserie

● Fothergill's

Do *not* go in here if you are attempting to stick to a diet; this is not for the weak-willed. It's a veritable paradise of cake and patisserie, a Dublin 6 legend for decades now, and yet the energy and enthusiasm of the crew in Fothergill's remains as youthful as ever. (Tom O'Connor, 141 Rathmines Rd Upr, D6 ☎ 01-496 2511 – Open 9.30am-6pm Mon, 9am-6.30pm Tue-Fri, 9am-6pm Sat)

Casual dining/burgers

● Gourmet Burger Co

With a name like this you'd expect the burgers to be decent – and thankfully they are. All are 8oz organic Irish beef, or Irish free-range chicken, or Irish Organic lamb, and you may expect to find the odd hunk of Kobe beef or wild boar too. The fillings are inventive and suitably gourmet: bacon, grilled pineapple and homemade relish; Burgundy marinade with grilled plums and Dijon mustard; red chard and truffle wasabi dressing. The space could be a touch more glam, but the chips are alright and you can't say that for every so-called gourmet burger joint. (Jonathan Dockrell, 97 Ranelagh Road, D6 ☎ 01-497 7821 www.gourmetburgercompany.ie – Open noon-10pm Mon-Thu, noon-11pm Fri & Sat)

Health Foods

● The Hopsack

The Hopsack is today as dynamic as ever, capably in the hands of the second generation of the family, brother and sister Kate & Finn Murray. Come for friendly service, and a wholefoods offering they're proud to say is three-quarters food, rather than pharmaceutical. (Erica, Finn & Kate Murray, Swan Centre, Rathmines, D6 ☎ 01-496 0399 www.hopsack.ie – Open 9am-7.30pm Mon-Wed, 9am-9pm Thu-Fri, 9am-6.30pm Sat, 1pm-6pm Sun)

Casual dining/burgers

● Jo'burger

Jo'B is the hippest incarnation amongst the current generation of burger boundary-pushers. Queues can be long, the crowd is hipster light, and the burgers good: try the Dube (bacon and relish); Pimville (fresh salsa and avocado); or Zondi (green Thai curry mayo, coriander and chilli), with a 100% Irish organic beef or lamb pattie. It's painfully hip and the chips could be improved, but there's no denying the quality of these burgers. Also owned by this outfit are the hipster-laden Crackbird (fried chicken and beer), Skinflint (pizzas and stuff) and Bear, a steakhouse deserving of special mention for its interesting cuts, moreish 'million dollar fries' and homemade sauces. Find Bear on South William Street, Crackbird on Dame Street, and Skinflint on Crane Lane, Temple Bar. (Joe Macken, 137 Rathmines Road, D6 ☎ 01-491 3731 info@joburger.ie www.joburger.ie – Open noon-11pm, closes later on Fri & Sat, Mon-Sun)

Butcher

● John Downey & Son

John and Mark Downey's shop is one of Dublin's finest butcher's shops, a place and a team who are always looking to improve, always looking to invent. Ask Leslie Williams for his list of indispensible Dublin shops, and Downey's will be near the top of the list. If they don't have it, they will search heaven and earth to get it for you. Don't miss the spiced beef. (John & Mark Downey, 27 Terenure Rd East, D6W ☎ 01-490 9239 www.organicfoodsireland.com – Open 8.30am-5.30pm Mon-Sat)

Pakistani & Eastern Restaurant

● Kinara Kitchen

The third and equally outstanding offering to come from the people behind Kinara in Clontarf and Kijjal in Malahide, Kinara Kitchen has been receiving rave reviews since opening in Ranelagh in 2011. The vibe is informal but the cooking is seriously good and almost unbearably delicious: melt-in-the-mouth chargrilled lamb chops marinated in garlic, turmeric and chilli with a mint sauce; succulent tandoori monk fish; or fresh seafood (platter for two) with paneer jalfrezi, are but a taste of Pakistan, skilfully rendered and served with a smile and a pretty nice selection of wines. Service has sharpened up since the early days. Come and enjoy and try your best not to gorge. (Sean Collender & Shoaib Yunus, 17 Ranelagh Village, D6 ☎ 01-404 0066 ✉ info@kinarakitchen.ie 🖱 www.kinarakitchen.ie – Open 11am-11pm Mon-Sun

Spanish/tapas

● La Bodega

Another little Ranelagh gem, offering a small but very satisfying menu of authentic Spanish dishes as tapas and mains. Try a dish less commonly seen in Dublin, such as the zarzuela (Catalan fish stew), or any of the favourites, including marinated anchovies or prawns fried with chorizo, and you'll be very happy. Ranelagh is running away with the prize for the best village in Dublin for good eating, and La Bodega is another brick in the wall of excellence. (93 Ranelagh Village, D6 ☎ 01-497 5577 ✉ labodegaranelagh@gmail.com – Open 12-4pm Mon, 12pm-12am Tues-Sat, 12.30pm-11pm Sun)

Butcher

● Lawlor's Butchers

Lawlor's of Rathmines is an archetype of the local butcher's shop, and it is a portal to great foods, a place of superb service, a true asset to the community it serves with such distinction. Just look through the glass at their dry-aged beef room and see the quality of meat as it comes to its full flavour potential. The term "craft butcher" doesn't really describe what James Lawlor and his team are about, for they have transcended the craft element: they are art butchers, and every piece of their stock shows maximum consideration, maximum contemplation, maximum care. Positively life-affirming. (James Lawlor, Upr Rathmines Rd, D6 ☎ 01-497 3313)

Dublin South

Middle Eastern/takeaway

● Little Jerusalem

Abraham Phelan has brought great food to every place he has cooked in Dublin and Little Jerusalem is no exception. The Palestinian and Lebanese cooking has wonderful new tastes, such as Mulihea Pilaranp – a form of spinach which is cooked with rabbit, onion, garlic and olive oil, or Arayess, where Lebanese bread is filled with minced lamb, onion, garlic and tomatoes. High standards all round make for a vital address. (Abraham Phelan, 3 Wynnfield Road, Rathmines, D6 ☎ 01-412 6912/087-971 7196 littlejerusalem@live.ie – Open 1pm-11pm Tue-Sun)

Café/deli/cookery school

● The Lovely Food Company

It wasn't long up and running before D6 dwellers were talking about this little gem. The brainchild of chef and all-round foodophile Paul Breen, TLFC has shown great promise since opening in 2011 and brings a new dimension to lucky D6. Breen and his band of merry chefs have constructed simple, concise yet skilfully-crafted menus for brunch, lunch and dinner, although you'd be welcome to drop in just for a coffee. Produce is fresh and procured locally, food is wholesome and prepared in-house each day, but most of all you savour the welcome, which is omnipresent. They now also offer cookery classes, teaching the basics of baking and dinner party recipes, in fun evening tutorials accompanied by a glass of wine. Lucky D6 is right. (Paul Breen, 14 Terenure Rd West, D6 ☎ 01-492 7717 www.lovelyfood.ie – Open 8.30am-5pm Mon, 8.30am-9.30pm Tues-Fri, 10am-9.30pm Sat, 10am-5pm Sun; dinner menu 6-9.30pm Wed-Sat)

Casual dining/Italian/pizza

● Manifesto

Don't be fooled by the simple appearance of Manifesto – inside there is seriously good food going on, especially the pizzas coming at a steady pace from the real stone oven at the front of the restaurant. Perfectly crisp base, sublimely topped with fresh ingredients, a Manifesto pizza is as nature and Italy intended. Their freshly made pastas are al dente but not stodgy, and their drinks menu is, of course, Italian but affordable and well put together. Good Italian food is hard to find outside Italy, so if you need proof of Manifesto's worth just observe the number of Italian patrons within. This is the kind of family restaurant every neighbourhood wishes it had, and they're quite happy to do pizzas to take away too. (Lucio Paduano & Eugenio Massitelli, 208 Lr Rathmines Rd, D6 ☎ 01-496 8096 www.manifestorestaurant.ie – Open 5pm-11pm Mon-Thurs, 5pm-11.30pm Fri-Sat; 4pm-10pm Sun)

Café/deli/casual dining

● Mayfield & Mayfield @ Union Square

Now expanded into the site next door which is named Mayfield @ Union Square, this winning neighbourhood café and deli is a bona fide food destination, with wine, a food store, workshops, breakfast, lunch, brunch and dinner, and theatre productions. The fare is simple: good salads, good homemade bread, open gourmet sandwiches, good coffee, and lovely homemade baked treats. The ambience is cosy and local, the décor quirky and fun. Mayfield is a great option for dinner if you're in the area Thursday to Saturday, for which guide editor Leslie Williams can vouch, and watch out for their theatre evenings. (Kevin Byrne & Kevin Byrne, Terenure Rd North, D6W ☎ 01-492 6830 mayfieldeatery@gmail.com – Open 9:30am-7pm Mon-Weds, 10am-11pm Thurs-Sat, 11am-4pm Sun)

local knowledge

Best for Brunch

● Dillinger's ● The Exchequer ● Juniors ● Juno's Café ● KC Peaches ● Lennox Café ● The Lovely Food Company ● Nosh ● No 3 Fade Street ● The Cellar Restaurant

Restaurant/takeaway/Japanese

● Michie Sushi

This is the best sushi restaurant in Dublin. That's the consensus among those in the know so no qualms here about putting it in black and white. You may have trouble finding the disarmingly modest little nook, hidden down a lane off the main street in Ranelagh, but this of course adds to its charm. Depending on what owner and chef Michel Piare puts up for the day's sashimi special, raw fish lovers could be anywhere between heaven and even more heaven. One day it's butter soft beautiful tranches of swordfish, another (if you're exceptionally lucky) it's gleaming sea urchin, melt in the mouth and fresh as the sea. Everything that passes your lips is breathtakingly fresh and full of vibrant flavour, which is the simple beauty of good sushi. Michel's inventive special rolls are delicious too, particularly the soft shell crab roll, made with spring onion, flying fish roe and avocado. Non-fish needs are also catered for, with popular choices such as chicken yakitori or hot dishes like vegetable yaki soba. Pricing in general is in the mid-range, which is good value for the quality on offer. Service is friendly and relaxed, managed by Michel's wife Anna, and there's a small but fair selection of sake, beers, and wines. Michie Sushi is an absolute must for sushi fans and, for those yet to succumb to its pleasures, this is the place to start. (Michel Piare & Anna van Exel, 11 Chelmsford Lane, Ranelagh, Dublin 6 ☎ 01-497 6438 info@michiesushi.com www.michiesushi.com – Open Tue-Sun 12pm-10pm)

Food shop/café/deli

● Morton's

The Morton family's supermarket has been a beacon of fine food shopping in Dublin for decades. Under the guidance of Gary Morton, the empire has expanded to a particularly beautiful site in Park Place off Hatch Street in town – where it doles out good coffee and gourmet sandwiches to hungry office workers in the Harcourt Street area – and to the convenience shop at the Beechwood Luas stop. At Dunville Avenue, the offering has expanded in recent years to include a butcher counter from Lawlor's of Rathmines, a cheese counter from Sheridan's Cheesemongers, in addition to the usual terrific range of Irish artisan and speciality products, fresh fruit and veg, and interesting wines. If you fancy a break while shopping you can stop into their Café 21 next door, or you can get them to do all your shopping and cooking for you, by using their super catering service. Vital. (Gary Morton, 15-17 Dunville Ave, Ranelagh, D6 ☎ 01-497 1913 info@mortons.ie www.mortons.ie – Open 8am-8pm Mon-Fri, 8am-6.30pm Sat, 11am-4pm Sun. Also at Park Place, Hatch St ☎ 01-478 2758)

Casual dining/Spanish/tapas

● Ochos

A funky space with a relaxed vibe and some very tasty

tapas indeed. The house 'albondigas' (meatballs in slightly spicy tomato sauce) and the green beans with crushed anchovies and toasted flaked almonds are especially worth a lash. Nice little wine list too. (Jerome Fernandez, 53 Ranelagh Village, D6 ☎ 01-496 8825 eat@ochos.ie http://ochostapas.com – Open 5pm-11pm Mon-Sun. Brunch from 11am Sat, from noon Sun)

Café

● 161 Café & Bistro

Greg Kira manned front of house at the Lennox Café before moving to this pretty room, and hitting the ground running with a failsafe offer for Dublin 6. It's daytime during the week, with dinner from Wednesday through Saturday, and the menus collate all your favourite things – 161 burger; club sandwich; fish and chips; tian of crab; sweet potato pie; chargrilled prawns. 161 is very Bill Granger, so you can wear your Quiksilver and Roxy threads. (Greg Kira, Hugh Palmer, 161 Upper Rathmines Road, D6 ☎ 01-497 8049 www.161cafebistro.com – Open 9am-6pm Mon-Tue, 9am-10pm Wed-Sat, 11am-5.30pm Sun)

made in Dublin

Pizza da Piero

Butcher

● O'Toole's Butchers

Hailed by fans as one of the best master butchers in Dublin, O'Toole's has been a purveyor of fine organic meats since the early 1990s. In a time when specialists are under fire from soulless supermarket chains, O'Toole's dedication is highly commendable – attested by the quality of their own charcuterie as well as their excellent meat. (O'Toole family, 138 Terenure Rd North D6W ☎ 01-490 5457 info@otoolesbutchers.com www.otoolesbutchers.com – Open 8.30am-6pm Mon-Sat. Also at 12 Fitzwilliam St, D2 ☎ 01-668 0456 clynes@otoolesbutchers.com)

Café/deli/Italian/wine bar

● Pinocchio

Pinocchio is part of a truly dynamic organisation – Campo de Fiori, based in Bray – that runs this bustling Ranelagh address, as well as a cookery school, a catering company, and a travel company. They also send out very amusing e-mails to people like us, which are always stuffed with cheery, sunshiney best wishes. And cheery, sunshiney best wishes is what you will be feeling yourself after some of their superbly authentic cooking, and the very authentic wines which they import. It's great to take a seat and order the salami or seafood plates with a glass of wine, or else to make an evening of it with some precise Italian cooking – gnocchi with Gorgonzola; prawns with tomato; pasta fagioli. They do Italian food the way it should be done, the way you want it to be done. (Luca Mazza, Luas Kiosk, Ranelagh D6 ☎ 01-497 0111 www.pinocchiodublin.com – Open 7.30am-10.30pm Mon-Fri, 9.30am-11pm Sat, 11am-10pm Sun)

Restaurant/Indian

● Punjab Balti

Gursharan Singh's restaurant endures and thrives in Ranelagh, thanks to solid, delicious, honest Indian cooking, at very fair prices. (Gursharan Singh, 15 Ranelagh Village, Ranelagh, D6 ☎ 01-496 0808 gsingh@punjabbalti.ie www.punjabbalti.ie – Open from 5pm Mon-Sun)

Wine shop

● Redmond's of Ranelagh

One of the best wine shops and off-licences in the city and the country, Jimmy Redmond's store is one of the essential food stars of Ranelagh, and was a major D6 player long before Ranelagh became the gourmet ghetto it has become in the last three years or so. The selection of wines, beers and whatever-you're-having is superlative, and best of all is the fact that it is sold without any pretentiousness: whether you are spending a fiver or five hundred, one and all are treated equally, treated well. (Jimmy Redmond, 25 Ranelagh Village, D6 ☎ 01-496 0552 – Open 10.30am-10pm Mon-Sat, 1pm-10pm Sun)

Restaurant

● Tribeca

They do good burgers and great big house salads, but the main reason patrons beat a path to Tribeca's door is their NYC-style buffalo chicken wings with blue cheese dressing – known to Dubliners from the originals at Elephant & Castle. They make your lips sting with the heat and you won't be able to stop eating them. Find them also at the Canal Bank Café on Leeson Street which belongs to the same folks. (Ger Foote & Trevor Browne, 65 Ranelagh, D6 ☎ 01-497 4174 info@tribeca.ie www.tribeca.ie – Open noon-11pm Mon-Sun)

Dublin South

Wine shop

● The Vintry

Evelyn Jones's wine shop, The Vintry, is a consistent prizewinner for the excellence of the shop's wine offer, and for the knowledge and expertise of the service. If you want to put the swerve on your Soave, then they are here to help you master the arcane world of wine, and to help you discover its delights. A marvellous beacon of the culture of wine. (Evelyn Jones, 102 Rathgar Road, D6 ☎ 01-490 5477 vintry@vintry.ie www.vintry.ie – Open 10.30am-10pm Mon-Sun)

Restaurant

● The Wild Goose Grill

In a neat room above McSorley's pub, Kevin McMahon's restaurant offers excellent wines and good, straight-ahead bistro cooking that matches the wines very well indeed: seared scallops with Iberico ham; chicken with goose potatoes and smoked bacon; Connemara lamb with mint butter. Sunday lunch lasts all day, and early menus offer very good value. (Kevin McMahon. 1 Sandford Rd, Ranelagh, D6 ☎ 01-491 2377 www.thewildgoosegrill.ie – Open 5.30pm-late 7 days, Sun 12.30pm-3pm)

made in Dublin

Green Spot Whiskey

DUBLIN 8: HAROLD'S CROSS, LIBERTIES, CRUMLIN, PORTOBELLO, RIALTO

Café

● Bibis

So, you have the Turkish eggs, I'll have the roast butternut squash eggs with garlic yogurt, chilli butter and coriander, and then we'll agonise over the brownie to share – pure chocolate? cheesecake topped? peanut butter? Ah, life's delicious dilemmas, as supplied by the Lenehan sisters, Maisha and Petria. Bibi's is pure cult, as cultish as the delectable Doll's Boutique next door which the sisters also run. Life enhancing. (Maisha & Petria Lenehan, 14b Emorville Avenue, D8 ☎ 01-454 7421 eat@bibis.ie www.bibis.ie – Open 9am-4pm Tue-Fri, 10am-5pm Sat, noon-5pm Sun)

Café

● Bite of Life

Many would agree that the humble scrambled egg on toast is something of a lost art. Not the gourmet kind with more garnish and other bits than you know what to do with, the proper homemade kind you used to get for brekkie when you were a kid – with real butter on the toast. Jorinde and Conor Moynihan's little café on Patrick Street, however, is the kind of place that understands these simple pleasures, and you'll know this with every tasty bite of their simple homemade soup, sandwiches, salads and cakes. Hearty, healthy comforting food, a nice cuppa tea or coffee, and a space that feels like home. (Jorinde & Conor Moynihan, 55 Patrick St, D8 ☎ 01-454 2949 www.biteoflife.com – Open 7.30am-4pm Mon-Fri, 10am-4pm Sat-Sun)

Bakery

● The Bretzel Bakery

The BB is an essential establishment for all those who are serious about fresh bagels and other kosher bakery items, such as challah and onion rolls. And that, let's face it, is all of us. You can find Bretzel products in other outlets around Dublin, however a trip to the Portobello store is highly recommended. In addition to good white, brown, sourdough and rye, you'll find an array of delicious speciality breads, pizzas and confectionery, whose aromas alone make it worth the trip. Rathmines residents now no longer need to get on their bikes: the second BB is open in Upper Rathmines. (William Despard, 1a Lennox St, Portobello, D8 ☎ 01-475 2724. Also at 8 Upr Rathmines Road. www.bretzel.ie – Open 8.30am-6pm Mon-Fri, 9am-5.30pm Sat, 9am-1.30pm Sun)

Food Market

● Dublin Food Co-Op

The Saturday market at the DFC is one of the great food events of the capital. Whilst their old stomping ground of Pearse Street is now occupied by the Super Natural food market, the move to Newmarket has been smooth and successful, and the Saturday buzz that this unique co-op offers is as addictive as ever. In 2013, the DFC will celebrate 30 years as one of the city's most important food destinations, a unique producer-member co-operative that has managed to stay ever-youthful, ever-relevant, ever-delightful. The DFC, in truth, is actually a community, as well as a co-op, and it is a welcoming, nourishing community for the city. Look out for Caryna's cakes, superlative organic vegetables, beautiful cheeses and dairy products and much, much more. Utterly vital. On Sundays, the room becomes the brilliant Dublin Flea Market, and at other times it is the Peas & Pods Market. (Fintan Molloy, 12 Newmarket, D8 ☎ 01-454 4258 www.dublinfoodcoop.com – Open Saturdays & Thursdays, also some Sunday markets)

Butchers

● Ennis Butchers

Derek Bolger's shop is a treasure trove. There is a treasure of great meats, of course, as you would expect from one of the city's most respected butchers. But there is so much more on offer here, from great artisan foods to great wines, that it is enough to make it worth a special trip down the canal to stock up the fridge and the freezer. Good judgement and good taste characterise a truly special shop. (Derek Bolger, 463 Sth Circular Rd, Rialto, D8 ☎ 01-454 9282 – Open 8am-7pm Mon-Sat)

Food market

● Farmleigh House

Farmleigh is home to some of the very best farmers' markets to be found in the city, and a summer Sunday spent shopping and eating here is a genuine, special family treat. (Phoenix Park, D7 ☎ 01-8155900. Check the website for market days 🖱 www.farmleigh.ie)

Fish shop

● JL Fitzsimons Fish Shop

A staple of the local community for some 16 years, since the shop was first established by fishmonger John Fitzsimons and wife Linda. Now run by their son Philip and his two siblings, Fitzsimons remains one of Dublin's fish shops – the place to go for fresh plaice, or ray, or any other fish popular amongst real Dubs. (Philip Fitzsimons, 183a Kimmage Rd West, Crumlin Cross ☎ 01-4554832 – Open 10am-5.30pm Tue-Fri, 10am-4pm Sat)

Casual dining/take-away/Indian

● Konkan

The excellent Konkan has a second branch in Dundrum in addition to the essential Clanbrassil Street original. Their southern Indian specialities are the signature dishes of the restaurant, and the use of coconut milk in various guises and recipes is very nuanced and expert. (Bala Nayak, 46 Upper Clanbrassil Street, D8 ☎ 01-473 8252 ✉ info@konkan.ie 🖱 www.konkan.ie – Open 5.30pm-11.30pm Mon-Sun)

Restaurant

● Locks Brasserie

Head chef Rory Carville has really made his mark on this outpost from the team behind Dublin's celebrated Pearl Brasserie. His singular style has won him acclaim with the critics and a steady following of those in the know when it comes to superlative dining. The ingredients are top drawer, fashioned into delicious expressions of the season by Carville's elegant yet sensitive hand. New season asparagus with '63°C cooked duck egg,' air-dried duck, Parmesan and truffle custard and duck croutons, is one example of such flair. And he's not afraid to deviate from the usual safe bets, boldly offering the likes of hogget (young sheep meat older than lamb), rabbit, and less commonly seen sustainable fish such as brill and hake. His cooking is fresh and beautiful, and always utterly delicious. Locks is not too far from town for city centre dwellers to make this spot a regular haunt, in fact its pretty setting on the canal is ideal for post-dinner strolling. There is excellent value to be had on the lunch menu and value dinner menu, and service and wine list are also pitch perfect. (Kirsten Batt & Sebastian Masi, 1 Windsor Tce, Portobello, D8 ☎ 01-454 3391 info@locksrestaurant.ie www.locksrestaurant.ie – Open noon-4pm Sat & Sun, 5.30pm-10.30pm Mon-Thur, 5.30pm-11pm Fri-Sat)

Deli/patsserie/caterers

● Lovin' Catering

Kevin and Natasha Doyle now have confident charge of the business that was The Gallic Kitchen, a staple of our books since the very first edition in 1989. The great bakery classics are still pumping proudly in Lovin' Catering – the salmon and broccoli roulade; the ham, tomato and cheddar quiche; the pear and almond tart. In addition to the shop, Kevin and Natasha can also be found at the Dun Laoghaire, Marlay Park and Stillorgan farmers' markets. (Kevin Doyle, 49 Francis Street, D8 ☎ 01-454 4912 lovincatering@gmail.com www.lovincatering.com – Open 9am-4.30pm Mon-Sat)

Café/deli/food shop

● Nelly's

A steady little business that seems to be surviving in this tough site where others have not lasted. The homemade soups, jams and baked goods are of the hearty kind – the kind that stick to your bones. The organic coffee is pretty good too, they use organic Wicklow produce from Gold River Farm, and the rest of the cosy shop is filled with tempting foodie treats to suit all seasons. Rather delightful, and a cult in the making. And: are their chocolate brownies the best in town? Only one way to find out. (12 Sth Circular Road, D8 ☎ 01-473 4775 – Open 8.30am-6pm Mon-Fri, 10am-5pm Sat, closed Sun)

made in Dublin

The Bretzel Bakery

Dunne & Crescenzi

Café

● Phoenix Café

Helen Cunningham's Phoenix Café is the sort of place that gives visitor centres a good name. It's a cult address, where devotees turn up early for the legendary scones, and ordinary citizens arrive for excellent salads and savoury baking. Ms Cunningham has the smarts – she's a real cook, the real deal and her food is worth the trip to the Park. (Helen Cunningham, Phoenix Park Visitor Centre, D8 ☎ 01-677 0090 – Open 9.30am-4pm Jan-Dec, 9.30am-5pm Oct-Mar)

Gastro Pub

● Sean MacD's

Stephen McDonald makes it from scratch, so the food in this big pub is the real thing. Catherine Cleary singled out his cooking as being amongst the best food of the year in *The Irish Times*, and called McDonald – "a proper cook" A proper cook is what he is, so roll out the Parmesan potato gnocchi with mushroom and spinach, the sea trout with prawn and pea risotto; the bangers and mash with onion marmalade; the bread and butter pudding with caramel sauce. And make sure to check out the art works, and the superbly chosen cult movies they screen. (Stephen McDonald, 69 Harold's Cross Road, D6 ☎ 01-497 6832 seanmacds@gmail.com www.seanmacds.com – Food served 12.30pm-3pm, 4.30pm-9pm Mon-Wed, 12.30pm-3pm, 4.30pm-9.30pm Thur, 12.30pm-3pm, 4.30pm-10pm Fri, 10am-10pm Sat, 10am-8pm Sun)

Food Shop

● Shop Easi

Shop Easi is 'the' place to go for mangoes. They fly in ten to twelve different varieties from March to Sep tember, and these are perfumed wonders that smell of jasmine, rose petals and unearthly delights. Lots more good ethnic treats in the store also. (Kashif Mahmood, 63 Clanbrassil St, D8 ☎ 01-473 3565 – Open 10.30am-9.30pm Sat & Sun, 11am-9.30pm Mon-Fri)

DUBLIN 12 & 14: CHURCHTOWN, DUNDRUM, RATHFARNHAM

Restaurant/Indian

● Ananda

Sunil Ghai's southside jewel of a restaurant has gotten better with time. Too many of us think 'Indian' food is all about heat, heat and more heat. We don't realise the country's many regional cuisines are as distinct as they are beautiful, blending spices, herbs, meat, seafood and vegetables in their own unique way. Nutty and fragrant in Hyderabad, the aromatic 'Mangolorean' curries of Tulu Nadu, the elaborate lamb (or mutton) based dishes of Kashmir, or the buttery richness of Punjabi cuisine, to name but a few. Sunil Ghai wants to showcase them all in the most painterly and sensitive manner possible, banishing misplaced chilli and laying on the aromatics with a generous hand. Not to be missed. (Sunil Ghai, Dundrum SC, Sandyford Rd, D14 ☎ 01-296 0099 info@anandarestaurant.ie www.anandarestaurant.ie – Open 5.30pm-11pm Mon-Sun. Lunch from 12.30pm Fri-Sun)

Restaurant

● Arch Bistro

Stephen McArdle is no standard suburban cook. He may be cooking in a room upstairs from a suburban pub, but there is ambition here: Aoife Cox has described it as "the kind of place that you'd be happy to have in your neighbourhood", and satisfied locals eating here testify to the quality of Mr McArdle's cooking. Aoife enjoyed the chicken liver parfait; the trio of seafood; the slow-roast pork belly; the light tempura batter on cod, served with chunky chips; the boozy oranges with bitter chocolate mousse. Good service, good value for set menus, and we shall be hearing more from Mr McArdle. (Stephen McArdle, Landscape Road, Churchtown, D14 ☎ 01-296 6340 info@thearchbistro.com www.thearchbistro.com – Open 12.30pm-3.30pm Thur-Sun, 5.30pm-10pm Tue-Fri, 5pm-10pm Sat, 5pm-8pm Sun)

On-line Beer

● The Beer Club

"No boring beers need apply" is the motto of the on-line beer club. You will get every worthwhile and organoleptically exciting beverage that your heart could possibly desire, whether it's a Porterhouse Brainblasta or a McGrath's Irish Black. The crew also organise beer tastings at the warehouse, so if you are dipping a toe into the sea of craft brewing, then dip those toes in here. (Kimmage, D12 ☎ 01-4428171 🖱 www.thebeer-club.ie)

Fishmonger

● Feeney's Fish

Fergal Feeney knows his fish, and he has improved the quality of life for Rathfarnham residents no end. There is always a great selection of fish in the shop, it's always beautifully presented and if there is something arcane in this piscine world that you seek, Fergal will hunt it down for you. Splendid. (Fergal Feeney, 30 Barton Dr, Rathfarnham ☎ 01-495 8758 🖱 www.feeneysfish.ie)

Café/deli/butcher/food shop

● Flemings Fine Foods

Mick Fleming has set a new standard for butcher's shops with his glittering emporium. A top-class butcher, a gourmet food shop, a café and a deli with a difference – and the difference is, despite the upmarket appearance, the prices are surprisingly keen. In addition to their range of fine foods and good value, Flemings fans rave about the service, which is both friendly and knowledgeable. Fleming's Fine Foods is the prototype for the new era of Irish butcher shops. (Michael Fleming, Dundrum Village Cr, D14 ☎ 01-299 0092 – Open 8am-7pm Mon-Fri, 8am-6pm Sat, 10am-5pm Sun)

Food shop

● Get Fresh

Niall Dermody's shop is one of Leslie Williams' essential Dublin destinations. It's the shop that has everything you need, for whatever style of cooking you want to grapple with, and it's sold with charm and confidence by helpful staff who make every visit here a real delight. (Niall Dermody, Unit 6, Rosemount SC, Marian Rd, D14 ☎ 01-493 7148 📫 getfresh6@eircom.net – Open 9am-6pm Mon-Fri, 8am-6pm Sat)

Casual dining/Italian/food shop

● L'Officina

L'Officina works to a formula – approved denomination Italian foods served by vigorous staff in handsome big rooms – and if only every formula was as consistent, successful and pleasureful as this one. The discipline evident here is incredible, the achievement is considerable. (Eileen Dunne & Stefano Crescenzi, Dundrum Town Centre, D16 ☎ 01-216 6764 – Open 9.30am-10pm Mon-Wed, 8.30am-10.30pm Thu, 8.30am-late Fri & Sat, 11am-10pm Sun. Also at Unit 35 Nurney Road, Kildare Town, Kildare – Open 9.30am-6pm Mon-Wed, 9.30am-8pm Thur-Sat, 10.30am-7pm Sun. Also at Arnott's, Jervis Centre, D1 – Open 9am-6.30pm Mon-Wed, 8.30am-10.30pm Thu, 8.30am-11pm Fri & Sat, 10.30am-7pm Sun)

DUBLIN 18: FOXROCK, SANDYFORD, STEPASIDE

Restaurant

● Bistro One

Bistro One states its aim quite simply: it's all about you the customer and your enjoyment of their food and wine. Simple old-school principles of hospitality are delivered with warmth and a great sensitivity towards their excellently prepared seasonal menus. The food is consistently good and moves with the times – think razor clam and wild garlic risotto, or loin of Wicklow venison with cabbage, smoked bacon and an Amedei chocolate jus – and the service is always on point. Bistro One is restaurateur's restaurant – it's exactly what it aims to be, and exactly what you want it to be. They also sell a rather spiffing olive oil produced in their little hideaway in Italy. (Mark Shannon, 3 Brighton Rd, D18 ☎ 01-289 7711 dining@bistro-one.ie www.bistro-one.ie – Open noon-2.30pm, 6pm-10pm Tue-Sat)

Restaurant

● The Box Tree

The man who brought us One Pico, Bleu Bistro and lately the Greenhouse with legendary chef Mickael Viljanen, has delivered to south county Dublin a restaurant described by one of Ireland's most authoritative critics as: "the most complete dining experience" he'd witnessed in a restaurant for a very long time. And that is exactly what you get. The food is accomplished, honest, made from good Irish ingredients, and good value: wild Wicklow pheasant with celeriac and thyme gratin, savoy cabbage and pancetta, and cauliflower purée, for example. The service is professional but friendly and appropriate to a local family restaurant. It's one of those rare places that is everything you could hope for in a restaurant near you. Lucky Stepaside. (Eamonn O'Reilly, Stepaside Village, D18 ☎ 01-205 2025 www.theboxtree.ie – Open lunch and dinner Mon-Sun)

Dublin South

Restaurant/Chinese

● China Sichuan

Simply put, China Sichuan has been the best and most admired Chinese restaurant in Dublin since it opened in Stillorgan many moons ago, and it remains so in its more recent home in Sandyford. The dining room is elegant and the service smart, although you could have lunch or dinner any day of the week for an absolute bargain. Sunday lunch with their array of delectable dim sum – including melt-in-the-mouth tea-smoked duck rolls, and moreish hon yu guozi (poached dumplings in a hot and spicy oil) – is a very special event. It is worth making the trip to China Sichuan, its quality, ambience and value combined make it one of the best places to eat in the city. (Kevin Hui, The Forum, Ballymoss Road, D18 ☎ 01-293 5100 www.china-sichuan.ie. – Open 12-10pm Mon-Fri, 5-10pm Sat, 12-9pm Sun)

Wine shop

● Nectar Wines

John McGrath puts it simply: "We have to keep focusing on our niche and our USP: personal service, and a specialised, high-quality range of wines." That's what they do in Nectar and that's what they have on the shelves: bespoke wines from bespoke producers sold by a bespoke wine firm. They have excellent wine tasting evenings, they have all the paraphernalia you need to get the most from your wines, and they have the wines you want to drink. Super. (John McGrath & Carl Byrne, 3 Sandyford Village, D18 ☎ 01-294 4067 sales@nectarwines.com www.nectarwines.com)

Deli/food shop

● Thomas's Delicatessen

They seem to make things to last in Foxrock, and Thomas Murphy's inspiring deli is one of the defining destinations of this tony village. As Mr Thomas heads towards thirty years of service, his shop seems ever limber and lush, packed with good things to eat, packed with good bottles to drink, every nook and cranny of the shop revealing something surprising, something delicious. Thomas's is one of the great Dublin shops. It has everything you might need, or could need. (Thomas Murphy, 4 Brighton Rd, D18 ☎ 01-289 4101 🖱 www.thomasoffoxrock.ie – Open 8am-7.30pm Mon-Sat, 9am-4pm Sun)

local knowledge

Kimberley, Mikado & Coconut Cream

These three biscuits, now made and owned by global brand Kraft Foods, were first made in Ireland in 1855. William and Robert Jacob established a factory in Waterford, and then moved it to a premises in Dublin's Liberties. The company later merged with Bolands' biscuits to create the Irish Biscuits Company.

Kimberley, Mikado & Coconut Cream all used a combination of biscuit base and mallow: Mikado biscuits were actually named after the Gilbert & Sullivan operetta. Kimberley, made in the time of the Boer War, was named after the Kimberley diamond mines in South Africa.

Jacobs were also the first company in the world to produce a wheat cracker, called the Cream Cracker. It quickly took on, and was exported all over the world. The cracker is still made in very much the same way today, though not in Dublin.

Jacob's also invented the Fig Roll which is mentioned, incidentally, by James Joyce in *Ulysses*.

Blackrock

Wine Importer

● Burgundy Direct

Writing in *The Irish Times*, John Wilson noted that in early 2012, Conor Richardson of Burgundy Direct was "making their 28th consecutive offer of Burgundy, surely making them the most experienced in the country". It's quite something to be proud of, navigating the treacherous waters of Burgundy with such skill for so long. Mr Wilson's top wines from the BD list are Dancer, de Vogue, Grivot and Gros, but in truth all of Mr Richardson's choices are good, and they don't all require a barrister's stipend. (Conor Richardson, 8 Monaloe Way ☎ 01-289 6615 info@burgundydirect.ie www.burgundydirect.ie. Accepts cards)

Patisserie

● Cakes & Co

Rosanna and Joannie's cake creations are magnificent works of sugarcraft, and they make stunning centre pieces for any occasion. (Rosanna Mulligan & Joannie Langbroek, Jane Cottage, Newtownpark Ave ☎ 01-283 6544 joannie@cakesandco.com, rosanna@cakesandco.com www.cakesandco.com – Open 9.30am-5.30pm Mon-Sat)

Cookery school

● The Dublin Cookery School

Lynda Booth's chic and glam cookery school has been a huge success since opening in 2007. The room and the layout are superb, the standard of teaching from Ms Booth and her collaborators is stellar, and the array of guest chefs is blue chip. The DCS does it right. (Lynda Booth, 2 Brookfield Tce ☎ 01-210 0555 info@dublincookeryschool.ie www.dublincookeryschool.ie. Accepts cards)

Wine shop

● McCabe's Wines

The McCabe family know their onions when it comes to wine and it's for this reason that McCabe's is one of the glories of Irish wine retailing. The Blackrock store is dynamic with a huge range of more than 1500 wines, and they take their beer very seriously here too – the world range has recently expanded and well worth a look for enthusiasts. Their second shop in Foxrock also has a restaurant (The Gables), and you can buy a good bottle in the shop to take in to lunch or dinner, with only a modest corkage charge. (John McCabe, 51/55 Mount Merrion Ave ☎ 01-288 2037 value@mccabeswines.ie www.mccabeswines.ie – Open 10.30am-10pm Mon-Sat, 12.30pm-8pm Sun; The Gables (☎ 01-289 2174 info@thegables.ie) open 8am-10pm Mon-Fri, 9am-10pm Sat, 10am-10pm Sun)

Food shop

● The Organic Supermarket

Meet the affable, energetic Darren Grant and you can already imagine the passion and energy behind his baby, TOS. His is the best range of organic foods you'll find in the country, full stop. Grant is tireless in his pursuit of interesting, high-quality, delicious products, and his loyal fan-base – which includes those willing to travel considerable distances – are proof it's all good value for your money too. If you pick up a lettuce in TOS, chances are it was picked from the ground at 6am that morning and driven the few miles to Blackrock to be on Darren's shelves at 8am. Check out the website and shop online and get yourself some of this delicious, life-affirming food. (Darren Grant. 2c Main St ☎ 01-278 1111 contact@organicsupermarket.ie www.organicsupermarket.ie – Open 8am-8pm Mon-Fri, 10am-8pm Sat, 11am-6pm Sun)

Dalkey

Food market

● Dalkey Farmers' Market

We love the atmospheric hall in which they hold the Dalkey Market – it gives a taste of what Dalkey was like in the old days. Great foods and lovely stallholders complete the picture. (Jackie Spillane, Heritage Cr, Main St ☎ 087-9573647 market@dlrcoco.ie www.dlrcoco.ie/markets. Open Fri 10am-4pm)

Dublin South

Food market

● Dalkey Food Company

Ivan and Ellie of the DFC are pretty cool dudes, interested not just in food but also in music, DJing, design and, well, living well. Their company makes soups and breads and supplies them to local businesses, and there is also a catering service and cookery classes. If you are lucky, you just might find their stall at a local festival, firing out some imaginative burgers, hot dogs and sardines with salsa verde. Nice. (Ivan Varian & Ellie Balfe, Dalkey, Co Dublin ☎ 01-235 2657 www.thedalkeyfoodcompany.com)

Café

● Idlewilde Café

A cosy café where you can linger over a bowl of soup and a BLT or a pampered panini, and they know how to serve a good coffee. (Ruan Healy, 20 St. Patrick's Road ☎ 01-235 4501 – Open 8am-6pm Mon-Sun)

Wine shop

● On the Grapevine

Gabriel and Pamela Cooney opened in Dalkey on St. Patrick's Day in 1999, and have been supplying superlative bottles from all over the world to lucky Dalkey residents for nearly fifteen years. There are hundreds of wines on offer, all of them worthy of your attention and your money. (Gabriel & Pamela Cooney, 21 St Patrick's Rd ☎ 01-2353054 sales@onthegrapevine.ie www.onthegrapevine.ie – Open 11am-8pm Mon-Sat)

Casual dining

● Ouzos

With outlets in Dalkey and Blackrock and a solid reputation as a destination for enjoying fresh fish and shellfish, Ouzos has become a mainstay of the southside. They do offer meats and poultry, but it's their nous with fish that is the real secret. (Fionnuala Quirke, 22 Castle St ☎ 01-285 1890 reservations@ouzos.ie www.ouzos.ie – Open noon-10pm Mon-Sat, 12-9.30pm Sun. Also at Main St, Blackrock ☎ 01-2101000 - blackrock@ouzos.ie)

Casual dining/Italian/pizza

● Ragazzi

A local favourite for some years, who even count among their clientele a local resident Michelin-starred chef who thinks the place a spot worthy enough for himself and his kids of a Sunday afternoon. The hearty homely Italian cooking is honest and possibly a tad clichéd, but so what? It's simple familiar Italian staples done well, and there's nothing wrong with that. Order a delicious calabrese pizza and a bowl of mezze maniche pasta with Italian sausage and chilli and kick back with a nice little Chianti. You know you want to. (Fabio Perozzi, 109 Coliemore Rd ☎ 01-2847280 ✉ ragazzi109@yahoo.com 🖱 www.ragazzi.ie – Open 5.30pm-10.30pm Mon-Sat)

Food shop/health foods

● Select Stores

Oliver and Mairead McCabe have a really unique shop and juice bar, the kind of place that sells all the things you need and want. Oliver is an expert nutritionist and everything he sells is good for you, especially the weekly delivery of organic delights from Denis Healy. A super shop. (Oliver McCabe, 1 Railway Rd ☎ 01-285 9611 🖱 www.selectstores.ie – Open 7.30am-6.30pm Mon-Fri, 8am-6pm Sat, 10am-4pm Sun)

Casual dining/Thai/takeaway

● Thai House

Tony Ecock's Thai House restaurant is a classic example of how good cooking, good service, culinary consistency and an obsession with customer satisfaction can make you a local food hero. The cooking is lovely, so we're here for the soft-shell crab, the papaya salad with pork, the red scallop curry, and do note that there is a great takeaway menu available each evening, for those nights when you just want to watch Mad Men again. (Tony Ecock, 21 Railway Rd ☎ 01-284 7304 ✉ tony@thaihouse.ie 🖱 www.thaihouse.ie – Open 6pm-10.30pm Tue-Sun, till 11pm Sat)

Deli/caterer

● Thyme Out

David and Berna of Thyme Out actually have a long foodie history in Dalkey, for Berna's Mum used to run a cake shop called Yvonne Joan's in the centre of the village. Her recipes are being used to this day in Thyme Out, a rather lovely continuation of a culinary culture that just gives you a warm feeling. Mr and Mrs Williams are a discriminating pair, which means happy customers get food that is prepared with meticulous attention to detail. Look out for their range of salad dressings, most likely coming to a good shop near you sometime soon. (David & Berna Williams, 2a Castle Street, Dalkey ☎ 01-285 1999 ✉ thymeout@eircom.net 🖱 www.thymeout.ie – Open 8.30am-7pm Mon-Sat)

Dun Laoghaire

Restaurant

● Alexis Bar & Grill

Interesting, fun, warms your heart and makes you feel at home – and that's just the owners. Any time spent in the company of brothers Alan and Patrick will help you understand how Alexis has been successfully producing such welcoming yet refined food for over five years now. Finding cooking of such calibre, such as slow-cooked milk-fed veal with smoked marrow, leek and celeriac cream and cep sauce, for under twenty euro is not easily done in any city. Finding it in a warm and welcoming place like Alan and Patrick's Alexis is a rare thing indeed. Understandably it's a very popular spot so be sure to book Thurs-Sun especially. (Alan & Patrick O'Reilly, 17-18 Patrick St, ☎ 01-280 8872 ✉ info@alexis.ie 🖱 www.alexis.ie – Open 12.30pm-2.30pm, 5.30pm-10pm Tue-Fri, 5.30pm-10pm Sat, 12.30pm-3pm, 5.30pm-9pm Sun)

Farmers' Market

● Dun Laoghaire Farmers' Market

From muffins to oysters to County Dublin strawberries and Thai corn cakes, via the best artisan producers the east coast can muster, there seems to be everything on sale at the legendary People's Park market. This is one of the classic markets, so the best plan is to shop first, then decide what you would like to eat, then find a cosy bench. Don't worry: the sun will be shining. It's always shining on Sunday in Dun Laoghaire. They have a sweet and helpful Facebook profile too. (Jackie Spillane, The People's Park ☎ 01-205 4700 and 087-957 3647 ✉ market@dlrcoco.ie 🖱 www.dlrcoco.ie/markets. Cash only – Open Sun 11am-4pm. Also at Dalkey, Fri 10am-4pm; Marlay Park Sat 10am-4pm)

Café/deli/caterer/wine bar

● Gourmet Food Parlour

Lorraine and Lorraine of the busy GFP seem simply unstoppable. Their latest move has seen their Swords store expand exponentially, so that it now has 72 seats as well as a patio area. They are also working in Malahide and Ballyboughal, all the while keeping the original of the species – GFP Dun Laoghaire – thriving. Their achievement in the midst of a savage recession is formidable, and they are succeeding because they do it right, every time. Lovely food, lovely wines, lovely spaces, lovely times. (Lorraine Byrne & Lorraine Heskin, 7 Cumberland St ☎ 01-2805670 ✉ dunlaoghaire@gourmetfoodparlour.com 🖱 www.gourmetfoodparlour.com – Open 8.30am-5pm Mon-Thu, 8.30am-late Fri, 10am-5pm Sat, 12pm-4pm Sun. Also at Unit 2 St Fintans, Nth St, Swords ☎ 01-897 1496 ✉ swords@gourmet-foodparlour.com – Open as above Mon-Sat, 12pm-6pm Sun. Also at The Grange, Oldtown Rd, Ballyboughal ☎ 01-807 8888 ✉ info@gourmetfoodparlour.com. Also at Gannon Park, Coast Road, Malahide ☎ 01- 828 3661 Open 9.30am-5.30pm Tue-Fri, 10am-6pm Sat-Sun)

Fish shop

● The Ice Plant

In what was the old Ice Plant on Dun Laoghaire pier, you will find a great fish shop, selling the day's catch, plus fish to feed the seals. (Coal Quay, Dun Laoghaire Pier ☎ 01-280 5936 – Open Tue-Sat mornings)

Café/bagel bar

● Itsabagel

Sisters Domini and Peaches Kemp are pioneers of the gourmet bagel in Ireland and their empire today runs to six locations around Dublin. From 'The Gourmet Veggie' to the 'Itsa Reuben,' their bagels are top notch and guaranteed to satisfy the best of appetites. Catering platters are also available, and far better than your standard tray of boring sarnies! (Domini & Peaches Kemp, The Pavilion, Royal Marine Rd ☎ 01-236 0644 🖱 www.itsabagel.com. Also at Arnotts, Middle Abbey St, D1 (☎ 01-804 4555); Fitzwilliam Lane, adjacent to the Merrion Hotel, D2 (☎ 01-644 9941); 3 The Triangle, Ranelagh D6 (☎ 01-497 8572); Unit 56a Blackthorn Rd, Sandyford Industrial Estate, D18 (☎ 01-293 5994; 1 The Diamond, New St, Malahide (☎ 01-845 6744)

Dublin South

Butcher

● J Hick & Sons

Ed Hick, the man credited with starting the real sausage revolution in Ireland, really outdid himself in 2011 when he launched a new and now legendary product on the market. So moreish and addictive is this unctuous substance it drove certain food writers to undignified behaviour in their determination to grab the last jar at the Bloom festival. We speak, of course, of Hick's infamous 'bacon jam' – a porky purée flavoured with apple and onion and spices. Spreadable and fat as butter, you won't be able to resist smearing it on everything you eat, from burgers to pancakes, or even just eating it with a spoon until there's none left and the Betty Ford Clinic is knocking at your door to take you away. If you fear you might succumb to its porky goodness, then try your luck with any of Hick's meaty handmade seasonal sausages, or his dry-cured beechwoodsmoked bacon. Try it all if you dare, Mr. Hick is an evil genius! (Ed Hick, 15A George's St Upr ☎ 01-284 2700 🖰 www.thepinkpig.com. Also find them at the Temple Bar and Honest2Goodness markets)

Casual dining/burgers

● Real Gourmet Burger

In the past RGB has been a reliable place for a decent burger. Recent times have seen the menu somewhat abbreviated but the rosemary chips and mighty 'Old Timer,' however, remain ever satisfying to the last bite. (Dave Larcan, The Pavilion ☎ 01-284 6568. Also at Sweepstakes Cr, Ballsbridge D4 ☎ 01-667 0040 ✉ info@realgourmetburger.ie 🖰 www.realgourmetburger.ie – Open 12-9.30pm Mon-Thurs, 12-10pm Fri-Sat, 12-9pm Sun)

Café & Tea Room

● White Tea

"This little wonderland - where a whimsical array of china cups and saucers project from the walls, alongside an artful display of spoons and forks" is how Aoife Cox describes Alice King's brilliant tea rooms and café. Ms King makes deliciously fresh salads, does some lovely savoury baking, and her cakes are fast becoming the stuff of legend – lemon drizzle cake with a tangy lemon curd filling; a bakewell tart with raspberries, the great walnut and coffee cake. And the following is an Important

Announcement: if you arrive late for lunch at White Tea, there is a very good chance that everything will be sold out. So, don't delay, get there early. (Alice Burns, Brian S Nolan Ltd, 102 Upper Georges Street, Dun Laoghaire ☎ 087-361 5600 – Open 9am-4pm Mon-Sat)

Glasthule

Fish shop/deli/food shop/caterer/restaurant/seafood

● Caviston's Food Emporium

Caviston's in Glasthule is legendary and one of 'the' foodie destinations of Dublin. Here, in their unrivalled delicatessen and fish shop, you'll find a picnic-makers paradise, with a beautiful array of freshly made salads, cooked meats and whole roast chickens, pies, soups, cheeses, freshly baked bread, and excellent coffee, all made from the finest ingredients they can find. Their fresh fish and meat offering is also outstanding, and in the restaurant next door they serve some of the country's finest seafood cooking. The menus are prepared simply, using influences from Asia and the Mediterranean: chargrilled mackerel fillet with apricot and chilli blantjang, or Ted Browne's Dingle Bay crab claws in garlic butter, give you a small taste of what's on offer. Caviston's is unmissable for foodies in Dublin, whether residing there or just passing through. (David & Lorraine Caviston, 59 Glasthule Rd ☎ 01-280 9245 www.cavistons.com – Restaurant open (lunch) 12-1.30pm, 1.30pm-3pm, 3pm-5pm Tue-Sat; (dinner) 6pm-8.15pm, 8.15pm-close Fri-Sat only)

Restaurant/Indian

● Rasam

Nisheeth Tak's slinky Indian restaurant up above the Eagle Pub is a classy operation. A large stylish room offers dishes collected from the subcontinent: Baigun cheese bhaja from Kolkotta, tandoori quail from Haryana, gosht awadh from Awadh, safaed maans from Rajasthan. The result of this cherry picking is a menu that is far removed from the conventional, inauthentic Indian cooking which is so widespread. Rasam has consistently been the choice of food writers in Dublin for many years. (Nisheeth Tak, Eagle Pub, 18/19 Glasthule Rd ☎ 01-230 0600 www.rasam.ie – Open 5.30pm-11pm Mon-Sun)

Wine shop

● 64 Wine

64 is a most beautiful wine shop, with shelves filled with great wines, and with speciality artisan foods that you need to go with those wines. It's a model shop, a place that is a delight to linger in, and great service rounds out a great experience. (Gerard Maguire & Richard Moran, 64 Glasthule Rd ☎ 01-280 5664 info@64wine.com www.64wine.com – Open 9.30am-7pm Mon-Wed, 9.30am-8pm Thur-Fri, 9.30am-7pm Sat)

Pizza Restaurant

● Weafer & Cooper

Our great friend Clodagh McKenna rates the Weafer & Cooper pizzas as the hottest in town, and she isn't the only foodie star to make her way to this exciting and hip bistro. They run the gamut from breakfast through to dinners, and there's no question but that Weafer & Cooper is a star in the making. (71 Glasthule Road, Glasthule ☎ 01-231 1971 http://weaferandcooper.com – Open 9am-9pm Mon-Wed, 9am-10pm Thur-Sat, noon-9pm Sun)

Goatstown

Wine Shop

● Bin No 9

Andy Kinsella has such a fantastic range of great wines on the shelves in Bin No 9 that he is a staple of the weekend wine columns, earning endless mentions as his wines are selected by wine writers as the best and best value in their category. Mr Kinsella is also a most obliging and approachable merchant, so even if you know little or nothing, he will guide you safely to that bottle that has your name on it. (Andy Kinsella, 9 Farmhill Rd ☎ 01-296 4844 andrew@binno9.com www.binno9.com – Open 10.30am-10pm Mon-Sat, 12.30pm-8pm Sun)

Killiney

Tea merchant

● Kingfisher Tea

Colm Hassett brings an enviable aesthetic to every aspect of Kingfisher tea. The teas are beautiful, they look beautiful, and you need beautiful pots to make them in and beautiful cups to drink them from. So, yes, it is a cup of tea, except it isn't: a cup of Kingfisher tea is an aesthete's moment, an oasis moment, a mindful moment. Look out for Colm at the brilliant Dun Laoghaire Sunday market and at other markets down the east coast. Life enhancing, life affirming goodness. (Colm Hassett, 121 The Sycamores, Shanganagh Rd ☎ 01-272 1856/ 087-662 5189 ✉ info@kingfishertea.com 🖱 www.kingfishertea.com)

Leopardstown

Food market

● Leopardstown Farmers' Market

Leopardstown is another of Dublin's older markets and has a long-standing loyal following who come to shop and eat every Friday. Among the stallholders are local organic producers McNally's, who grow a range of organic salad leaves and herbs, and Denis Healy, who offers a range of fruit, veg and herbs from his organic farm in Wicklow. Also find fresh fish from Out of the Blue, fresh meat from Coolanowle Organic Farm, cheese from Sheridan's cheesemongers, and a whole host of other gourmet foods to take home or eat in the indoor market – or outdoors by the racecourse if the weather permits. (Sean McArdle, Leopardstown Racecourse ☎ 086-3826377 ✉ info@irishfarmersmarkets.ie 🖱 www.irishfarmersmarkets.ie – Open Friday 10am-4pm)

Monkstown

Café/deli/food market

● Avoca

Avoca, as we've said elsewhere, is something of an empire, but it's worth giving special mention to the Monkstown site. Of all the Avocas in Dublin this is definitely the best – for foodies anyway. This place is dedicated entirely to food with, in addition to the usual foodhall and café (Salt), a beautiful food market showcasing some of Ireland's very best produce. Such are its credentials it even counts among its food offering a glorious church of butchery run by one of Ireland's most renowned butchers, Pat Whelan. This alone is worth the trip out to Monkstown. Add in the superb cooking in Salt, and you have a don't miss! destination in Monkstown. (Simon Pratt, 11a The Crescent ☎ 01-202 0220; Salt Café Reservations ☎ 01-202 0230 monkstown@shop.avoca.ie www.avoca.ie – Food market open 8.30am-7pm Mon-Tues, 8.30am-8pm Wed-Fri, 9am-8pm Sat, 9am-7pm Sun. Café open 8.30am-5pm Mon-Sun, dinner from 6pm Wed-Sat)

Gastropub/steakhouse

● FXB

What began as Francis Xavier Buckley's butcher shop on Moore Street over twenty years ago has turned into something of a steakhouse empire. However, the dedication to great meat remains – the beef is still raised on the Buckley farm in Offaly and aged in the Buckley butchery. You'll find their wares at several locations around Dublin but the gastropub in Monkstown deserves special mention. Officially known as The Pub @ FXB Monkstown, it occupies the ground floor below the original restaurant, and it knocks the socks off most so-called gastropubs. (3 The Crescent ☎ 01 284 6187 www.fxbrestaurants.com. Gastropub open 12-10pm Mon-Sun, restaurant open 6pm-10pm Mon-Sun. Also at: FXB Restaurant Pembroke St, D2 (☎ 01-676 4606); FXB Grill, Temple Bar, D2 (☎ 01-671 1248); FXB Grill @ Ryan's Parkgate St, D8 (☎ 01-677 6097); and FXB @ Bull & Castle Beer Hall.

Gastropub/takeaway

● The Purty Kitchen

Dating back to the early 1700s, this truly is an old Irish pub. Better again, they've taken advantage of their harbour-adjacent situation and built up a decent repertoire of seafood dishes on their menu: prawns pil pil; seafood chowder; mussels in white wine; crab salad open sandwich; or if you're feeling hungry enough go for the 'seafood skillet' which boasts seven kinds of fish and shellfish with veg and baby potatoes. (Conor Martin, 3-5 Old Dunleary Rd ☎ 01-284 3576 www.purtykitchen.com – Food served 12.30pm-10pm. Also at 34/35 Essex St, Temple Bar, D2 ☎ 01-677 0945)

Casual dining/seafood

● Seapoint Fish & Grill

A handsome bistro run by Shane Kenny and chef Nick

Clapham, Seapoint serves up the sort of modern, easy cooking that never fails to please. The operation has recently undergone some changes and has taken on a younger, funkier look and feel. The food with its strong seafood emphasis remains reliable as ever though, and the atmosphere just as easygoing. Seapoint stands out for all the right reasons. (Shane Kenny & Nick Clapham, 4 The Crescent ☎ 01-663 8480 info@seapointrestaurant.com www.seapointrestaurant.com – Open 12-3pm Tue-Sat, 6pm-10.30pm Mon-Sat, 12-9pm Sun)

Wine importer

● Searson's

Charles Searson and his team run one of Dublin's best wine merchant businesses. The shop is delightful, the wines are individual, engaging, cultured, and the entire experience of buying wine here is nothing less than a treat. In Searson's, wine is a culture, not simply a mere liquid. (Charles Searson, Monkstown Crescent ☎ 01-280 0405 sales@searsons.com www.searsons.com – Open 10.30am-6pm Mon-Wed, 10.30am-8pm Thu & Fri, 10.30am-7pm Sat)

Mount Merrion

Café/deli/Italian/casual dining

● Michael's Food & Wine

An ever-popular spot for residents of the Mount Merrion locale, Michael's remains the quintessential south Dublin eatery, with gourmet ingredients, no need for social media or web anything, and prices to match the status of its location. This may not be the vibe everyone digs, but those that do can't get enough – as evidenced by the throngs at lunch every day and brunch every weekend. Expect perfect eggs, beautiful Italian foods and wine served via the deli or trattoria, and a touch of class. (Michael & Mary Lowe, Deerpark Rd, Mount Merrion, D6 ☎ 01-278 0377 – Open from 11.30am Mon-Sat; dinner from 7pm Thurs-Fri only, lunch 12-3pm Sat, closed Sun)

Food shop

● Supervalu Mount Merrion

Heading home from a disappointing episode as part of her *McKennas' Guides* work, Aoife Cox decided to rescue the day with "a chance to take a look around Damien Kiernan's well-stocked SuperValu: some good West Cork representation there with Caherbeg sausages and rashers and lots of Glenilen on the shelves, among others." It's not just West Cork that Mr Kiernan scours for his stock, however: if it is good, then he wants to have it here in Mount Merrion, to the delight of the locals, who are affectionately proud of this excellent supermarket. (Damien Kiernan, 27 The Rise, Mount Merrion, D6 ☎ 01-288 1014 – Open 7.30am-8pm Mon-Fri, 8am-6pm Sat)

Newcastle

Bakery

● The Cake Stand

Iseult Janssens doesn't just have a patissier's precision and artistry, she has a patissier's soul. Her cakes and macaroons exhibit such verve, such dedication, such joie de vivre in her work, that they fair take your breath away. She has learnt her skill, her craft, the hard way, studying at the Ecole Gregoire-Ferrandi in Paris, as well as stages in some great restaurants and a spell in the pastry team at the Bon Marche food hall of the Grande Epicerie. All that time, all that work, seems bundled up in every cake, in every piece of sweet work, and they seem super-charged with ardour and delight, plosive with flavour, texture, proper little temptations. Awards have already begun to come her way in her first year of running and operating The Cake Stand, and she will likely set new standards in a post-cupcake Ireland. Ms Janssens deals in art, and she works in magic. (Iseult Janssens, Skylark Hill, Newcastle ☎ 086-407 7676 iseult@thecakestand.ie www.thecakestand.ie)

Rathcoole

Café/deli/casual dining

● Avoca

The Rathcoole outpost is the third mention for the inimitable Avoca group in the guide. This is the place where food writers and editors, and everyone we know, stop en route from Cork to Belfast. For locals, it's not simply the best stop-over on the main road, it's none other than a Godsend in an area deprived of good food. You need nerve to pour a pink concrete floor in a big store: Simon Pratt has that nerve, and he has the nous to serve superb, moreish food in both the self-service restaurant and the lovely The Egg Café. All in all, Avoca is simply an experience that lifts your spirits. Every time. (Simon Pratt, N7 Naas Rd ☎ 01-257 1800; The Egg Café Reservations ☎ 01-257 1810 www.avoca.ie – Store open 9.30am-6pm Mon-Sat, 10am-6pm Sun, food served until 5pm. Also in Suffolk St, D2 and counties Wicklow, Cork and Galway)

On-Line Butcher

● The Market Butcher

The Market Butcher supplies many of the best Dublin restaurants with their beef and lamb, and this is the place to come if you search for Connemara hill lamb, as they are the exclusive suppliers. Pat O'Doherty's peerless pork products are also for sale. The shop is a bit hard to find, in the middle of a confusing industrial estate, but it's worth persevering – there is lots of good stuff here. (Michael Bermingham & Karl Freeman, Unit 11, Block G, Greenogue Business Park, Rathcoole ☎ 01-458 0577 info@themarketbutcher.eu www.themarketbutcher.eu)

Pizza bases

● Pizza da Piero

All the good shops have Piero's pizza bases and they are the best prepared pizza bases there are. The secret is a two-day fermentation to build the flavour from time, rather than from yeast, so get them from the freezer and then get Bernadette O'Shea's classic book "Pizza Defined" down from the shelves, and what will it be tonight? Black pudding, leeks and pinenuts? Toons Bridge mozzarella Margarita? Ah, the world is your pizza. (Gianpiero de Vallier, Europa Foods Ltd, Unit B9, Aerodrome Business Park, Collegeland, Rathcoole ☎ 01-401 1733 sales@europafoods.ie www.artisanpizza.ie)

Stillorgan

Butcher

● Fenelon's Craft Butchers

We know Cliff Lenehan's shop from way, way back.

Fenelon's was great back then, but Mr Lenehan and his crew have spent the last three decades getting better and better. Their suppliers are blue chip, so you get the best beef, lamb, poultry and game birds, and their fish and deli offer is outstanding. Above all, however, it is the assured, knowledgeable and polite service that wins Fenelon's its devoted customers: they look smart, act smart and they are smart. (Cliff Lenehan, Unit 6 Stillorgan SC ☎ 01-28 81185 www.fenelons.ie – Open 8.30am-6pm Mon-Wed & Sat, 8.30am-8pm Thu & Fri)

Tallaght

Food market

● Hellfire Pigs

When Bref Galligan isn't working at his day job, he is tending to his beloved pigs. We are big fans of his pork, which has beautiful taste and texture: this is the real thing, and anyone who can no longer face the bland nonsense that is industrial pork needs to get some Hellfire Pigs into their life. (Bref Galligan, Tallaght, D25 ☎ 085-728 4692 bref@hellfirepigs.net www.helllfirepigs.net)

Bistro

● Interval Bistro @ the Civic Theatre

Jimmy and Bev serve home-cooked food in a properly run restaurant, here in the Civic Theatre, and they do it with body and soul. Breakfast, lunch and dinner are served every day and there's also a full bar available. Quality and consistency are excellent, and there is some outstanding value too. (Jimmy & Beverly Dunne, Tallaght Civic Theatre ☎ 01-462 6532 www.civictheatre.ie – Open 9am-7.30pm, Mon-Sun)

Accommodation
Ariel House 259
Brook's Hotel 180
Cliff Townhouse Hotel 186
Pembroke Townhouse 267
Against the Grain 172
Alexis Bar & Grill 296
Ananda 287
Anderson's 243
Anderson's Creperie 243
Angel Park Eatery 172
Anseo 172
Aqua 247
Arch Bistro 287
Argentine
Bondiola Argentina 178
Ariel House 259
Arún Bakery 238
Asia Market 173
Avoca 173, 301, 304

Baccaro, Il 173
Baggot Street Wines 173
Bakehouse, The 174
Bald Barista, The 174
Ballsbridge 259
Ballycoolin 246
Bang Restaurant 174
Bar Italia 175
Bar Pintxo 175
Base 259, 269
Bear 175
Beckett & Bull 269
Beer Club, The 288
Bellagio 270
Bernard Shaw, The 176, 242, 264
Beshoff's The Market 247
Bianconi's 259
Bibis 282
Bijou 270
Bin No 9 300
Bistro One 289
Bite 176
Bite of Life 282
Blackboard Bistro 177
Black Pig, The 260
Blackrock 292
Black Sheep, The 177
Blazing Salads Food Company 177
Bloom Brasserie 177
Bóbós 178
Bóbós Burritos & Blues 264
Bodega, La 275
Bombay Pantry 270
Bon Appetit 253
Bon Crubeen, Le 178
Bondiola Argentina 178, 198
Boojum 179
Botanic Gardens 225
Botticelli 179
Boulangerie Francaise, La 257
Box Tree, The 289
Brasserie Le Pont 179
Bretzel Bakery, The 282
Brook's Hotel 180
Brother Hubbard 180
Browne's Deli and Café 259
Buchetto, Er 272
Bull & Castle, The 181, 242
Buns Cup Cakes 238
Burdocks, Leo 207, 264
Burgundy Direct 292
Burritos & Blues 181
Butcher Grill, The 271
Butler's Pantry 260
Byrne, Michael 261

Café Bar H 181
Café Fresh 182
Caffe Cagliostro 182
Caffe di Napoli 182

Cajun
Tante Zoe's 226
Cake Café, The 183
Cakes & Co 292
Cake Stand, The 304
Camden Kitchen 183
Caviston's Food Emporium 299
Cellar Bar, The 184
Cellar Restaurant, The 184, 277
Celtic Whiskey Shop, The 184
Chameleon 185
Chapter One 185
Cheese Pantry, The 243
Chez Emily 258
Chez Max 185
China Sichuan 290
Chinese
China Sichuan 290
Furama 263
M&L 209
Neon Asian Street Food 212
New Millennium 213
Sichuan House 223
Chop House, The 242, 261
Chuck Wagon, The 198, 258
Churchtown 287
Ciao Bella Roma 186
Cinnamon Café 238, 271
Clarence, The 227
Cliff Townhouse 186
Clontarf 233
Cobblers 187
Cocoa Atelier 187
Coddle 252
Coffee
Bald Barista, The 174
Coffee Angel 187, 215
Third Floor Espresso 228
Coffee Angel 187, 215
Collier, Ray 247
Connolly's Fish Company 245
Cookery Schools
Cooks Academy 187
Dublin Cookery School, The 292
Dublin Wine School 192
Kitchen in the Castle, The 251
Lovely Food Company 276, 277
Cooks Academy 187
Coppinger Row 188
Corkscrew, The 188
Corner Bakery, The 272
Cornucopia 189
Corte del Caffè, La 189, 215
Country Market, The 248
Crackbird 189
Crumlin 282
Crunch 189, 198, 215

Dalkey 293
Dalkey Farmers' Market 293
Dalkey Food Company 294
Da Tommaso 233
Dave's Wood-fired Pizza Co 190
Dax 190
Deep 248
Delhi O'Deli 191
Diep le Shaker 191
Dillinger's 272, 277
Dom Mimi 233
Donnybrook 259
Donnybrook Fair 261
Doran's on the Pier 248
Downey, John & Son 274
Drink Store 238

Drumcondra 243
Dublin City Centre 172
Dublin Cookery School, The 292
Dublin Food Co-Op 283
Dublin South 259
Dublin Wine Rooms 191
Dublin Wine School 192
Dundrum 287
Dun Laoghaire 296
Dun Laoghaire Farmers' Market 296
Dunne & Crescenzi 192, 215
Dunne's of Donnybrook 262

Eatery 120 273
Écrivain, L' 193
Eden 193
Egan's Ocean Fresh 256
Ella Wine Bar 249
Ely Bar & Brasserie 194
Ely Gastropub 194
Ely Wine Bar 195
Ennis Butchers 283
Enoteca d'Asti 243
Enoteca delle Langhe 195
Epicurean Food Mall 195
Evergreen 196
Exchequer, The 196, 242, 277

Fade Street, No. 3 196, 277
Fairview 233
Fallon & Byrne 197, 198, 215
Farmer Brown's 197
Farmleigh House 283
Feeney's Fish 288
Fenelon's Craft Butchers 305
Field and Vine 273
Finglas 244
Fitzsimons, JL Fish Shop 284
Flemings Fine Foods 288
Food Game 262
Food Room, The 233
Foodware Store 198, 253
Fornaio, Il 198, 236
Fothergill's 273
Foxrock 289
French
 Blackboard Bistro 177
 Bon Crubeen, Le 178
 Chez Max 185
 Green Hen, The 200
 Guilbaud, Restaurant Patrick 219
 Maison, La 209
French Paradox, The 262
Fresh The Good Food Market 199
Furama 263
FXB 302

Garden Works 253
Get Fresh 288
Gibney's Fine Wines 254
Glasnevin 243, 244
Glasthule 299
Goatstown 300
Good World Chinese Restaurant 199, 264
Gourmet Burger Co 273
Gourmet Food Company 258
Gourmet Food Parlour 297
Govindas 199
Gravediggers, The 242, 244
Green 19 200
Green Hen, The 200
Greenhouse, The 201
Green Spot Whiskey 281
Guilbaud, Patrick 219
Gur Cake 246

Harold's Cross 282
Harry's 202
Havana 202
Hellfire Pigs 306
Hemmingway's 234
Herb Garden, The 254
Herbstreet 203
Hick & Sons, J 298
Hick's Sausages 183
Hole in the Wall 239
Honest2Goodness Market 244
Honest to Goodness 198, 203
Hop House, The 206
Hopsack, The 274
House, The 249
Howth 247
Howth Farmer's Market 250
Hugo's 203

Ice Plant, The 297
Idlewilde Café 294
Il Panorama Café 250
Il Vicoletto 230
Indian
 Ananda 287
 Bombay Pantry 270
 Jaipur 204
 Konkan 284
 Madina Desi Curry Co 209
 Mantraa 210
 Punjab Balti 280
Indonesian
 Chameleon 185
Interval Bistro 306
Irish Village Markets 263
Italian
 Baccaro, Il 173
 Bar Italia 175
 Bellagio 270
 Bianconi's 259
 Botticelli 179
 Caffe Cagliostro 182
 Caffe di Napoli 182
 Ciao Bella Roma 186
 Corte del Caffè, La 189
 Da Tommaso 233
 Dom Mimi 233
 Dunne & Crescenzi 192
 Enoteca d'Asti 243
 Enoteca delle Langhe 195
 Fornaio, Il 198, 236
 Nonna Valentina 285
 Officina, L' 289
 Panorama, Il Café 250
 Plan B 241
 Ragazzi 294
 San Lorenzo's 221
 Taste of Emilia 226
 Terra Madre 228
 Vicoletto, Il 230
Itsa4 263
Itsabagel 297
Ivan's Oyster Bar & Grill 250

Jaipur 204
Japanese & Sushi
 Michie Sushi 277
 Musashi 212
 Sushi King 226
 Ten Thousand 228
 Wall & Keogh 231
Java Republic 246
Jo'burger 2642, 274
John Kavanagh 242, 244
Juniors 264, 277
Juno's Café 198, 239, 277
Jus de Vine 255

Kanum 204, 264
Kavanagh's, WJ 205, 242
KC Peaches 205, 215, 277
Kennedy's 234
Keogh's Crisps 255

Keshk Café 264
Killiney 300
Kimchi@The Hop House 206, 242
Kinara 234
Kinara Kitchen 275
Kingfisher Tea 300
King Sitric 250
Kish Fish 239
Kitchen Complements 206
Kitchen in the Castle, The 251
Koh 206
Konkan 284
Kooky Dough 240
Korean
Kimchi@The Hop House 206

La Boulangerie Francaise 257
Lawlor's Butchers 275
L'Écrivain 193
Le Levain 207
Lennox Café 206, 277
Leo Burdocks 207
Leopardstown Farmers' Market 301
Levain, Le 207
L'Gueuleton 201 Liberties 282
Lilliput Stores 240
Liston's 207
Little Jerusalem 264, 276
Llewellyn's Orchard Produce 237, 252
Lobster Pot, The 265
Locks Brasserie 284
Lolly & Cooks 208
Louie's 208
Louis Albrouze 265
Lou Lou Bakery 265
Lovely Food Company 276, 277
Lovin' Catering 285
Lusk 252

Madina Desi Curry Co 209
Maison, La 209
M&L 209
Malahide 253
Malahide Farmers' Market 254
Manifesto 276
Mantraa 210
Market Butcher, The 305

Markets
Dalkey Farmers' Market 293
Dublin Food Co-Op 283
Dun Laoghaire Farmers Market 296
Honest2Goodness 244
Howth Farmers' Market 250
Irish Village Markets 263
Leopardstown Farmers Market 301
Malahide Farmers' Market 254
Red Stables 235
Temple Bar Market 227
Mayfield & Mayfield Union Square 277
McCabe's Wines 292
McHugh's Off Licence 237
McHugh's Wine & Dine 237
McNally Family Farm 254
Mere Zou, La 210
Merrion Hotel, The 211
Merrion Inn, The 242, 266
Messrs Maguire 211
Mexican
777 222
Boojum 179

Burritos & Blues 181
Pablo Picante 214
Sabores de Mexico 221
Michael's Food & Wine 303
Michie Sushi 277
Middle Eastern
Keshk Café 264
Little Jerusalem 276
Rotana Cafe 220
Silk Road Café 224
Mitchell & Son 211
M&L 209
Molloy's of Donnybrook 266
Moloughney's 235
Monkstown 301
Monty's of Kathmandu 212
Morton's 198, 278
Mount Merrion 303
Mulberry Garden 266
Mulligan, L Grocer 240, 242
Musashi 212

Natasha's Living Foods 192, 241
Naul 254
Nectar Wines 290
Nelly's 285
Neon Asian Street Food 212
Nepalese
Monty's of Kathmandu 212
Newcastle 304
New Millennium 213
Nicky's Plaice 251
Nolan's 235
North Dublin 233
North Strand 233
Number FortyOne 196

Oar House, The 251
O'Brien's, M 268
Ocean Path 252
O'Connell's 267
Officina, L' 289
Oldtown 255
Olive 256
101 Talbot 213
One Pico 213
161 Café & Bistro 279
On the Grapevine 294
Organic Supermarket, The 293
O'Toole's Butchers 280
Out of the Blue 245
Ouzos 294

Pablo Picante 214
Pakistani
Kinara 234
Panem 214
Panorama, Il Café 250
Paris Bakery 214
Paulie's Pizza 264
Pearl Brasserie 215
Pembroke Town House 267
Peploe's 216
Pepper Pot, The 216
Phoenix Café 286
Pichet 216
Pig & Heifer 198, 217
Pig's Ear, The 217
Pink Ginger 267
Pinocchio 279
Pizza da Piero 279, 305
Plan B 241
Porterhouse Brewing Co 218, 231
Port House, The 218
Portmarnock 255
Portobello 282
Pubs
Against the Grain 172
Anseo 172
Bernard Shaw, The 176

Black Sheep, The 177
Bull & Castle, The 181
Chop House, The 261
Exchequer, The 196
Fade Street, No. 3 196
FXB 302
Hole in the Wall 239
John Kavanagh 244
Kavanagh's, WJ 205
Merrion Inn 266
Messrs Maguire 211
Mulligan, L Grocer 240
Porterhouse Brewing Co 218
Purty Kitchen, The 302
Punjab Balti 280
Purty Kitchen, The 302

Queen of Tarts 219

Ragazzi 294
Raheny 236
Ranelagh 269
Rasam 299
Rathcoole 304
Rathfarnham 287
Rathgar 269
Rathmines 269
Ray's Pizza 219
Real Gourmet Burger 298
Red Bank House 256
Red Island Wines 257
Redmond's of Ranelagh 280
Red Stables Food Market 235
Restaurant Ten Fourteen 236
Rialto 282
Rigby's Deli 268
Roly's Bistro 268
Rotana Cafe 220
Rothar Bicycle Café 232
Rustic Stone 220

Saba 221
Sabores de Mexico 221
Sandyford 289
Sandymount 259
San Lorenzo's 221
Seagrass 222
Sean MacD's 286
Seapoint Fish & Grill 302
Searson's 303
Select Stores 295
777 222
Seven Social 241
Shanahan's 223
Sheridan's Cheesemongers 223
Shop Easi 286
Sichuan House 223, 264
Silk Road Café 224
Simon's Place 198, 224
64 Wine 300
Skerries 256
Skinflint 225
Smithfield 238
Soup Dragon 225
South County Dublin 292
Spanish & Tapas
Bar Pintxo 175
Black Pig, The 260
Café Bar H 181
Gourmet Food Company 258
Havana 202
Port House, The 218
Speak Easy Cafe Bar 190
Stepaside 289
Stillorgan 305
Stoneybatter 238
Stoop Your Head 242, 257
Supervalu Mount Merrion 303
Sushi King 226
Sussex, The 268
Sweeney's Wine Merchants 246

Swords 257

Tallaght 306
Tante Zoe's 226
Taste of Emilia 215, 226
Tea Room, The 227
Temple Bar Market 215, 227
Ten Thousand 228
Terenure 269
Terra Madre 228
Terroirs 269
Thai
  Diep le Shaker 191
  Kanum 204
  Koh 206
  Saba 221
  Thai House 295
Third Floor Espresso 215, 228
Thomas's Delicatessen 291
Thornton's 229
Thyme Out 295
Toffoli 229
Treat Deli & Gift Shop 242
Tribeca 280
Twisted Pepper 228

Urban Picnic 230

Valentino, Il 230
Vegetarian
  Blazing Salads 177
  Cafe Fresh 182
  Cafe Fresh 182
  Cornucopia 189
  Delhi O'Deli 191
  Govindas 199
Vicoletto, Il 230
Vintry, The 281
Voilà 231

Wall & Keogh 231
Ward, The 258
Weafer & Cooper 300
White Tea 298
Wild Goose Grill 281
Winding Stair 232
Woodstock Café 242
Wright's of Marino 236

County Galway

GALWAY CITY

Restaurant

● Aniar

Some cooks push the envelope and create the road ahead, and Enda McEvoy is one of those cooks. What he is doing in Aniar (a-neer is the pronunciation), a lean, light room on Dominick Street, is new, inasmuch as his focus is equally attuned to wild and foraged ingredients as to cultivated foods and products. And yet he is part of a tradition that goes back to Ballymaloe House, where innovation only makes sense when you create it out of tradition. To break the rules, he knows, you must first have rules to break. It's this tension that makes his food such a thrill, and he carefully places his wild foods into well-tempered dishes that are a joy: smoked potato and oyster emulsion with scallops and wood-sorrel; sublime glazed sweetbreads with buttermilk, hen egg and girolles; slow-cooked beef short ribs with chickweed; monkfish with kale flower and elderberry; buttermilk pannacotta with sea buckthorn and hazelnut. Discipline and wildness abound in Aniar, and the wildness is all in Mr McEvoy's imagination. (Enda McEvoy, 53 Lower Dominick Street, Galway ☎ 091-535947 ✉ aniarrestaurant@gmail.com 🖱 www.aniarrestaurant.ie – Open 6pm-10pm Tue-Sat)

Galway City

local knowledge

Connemara Hill Lamb

The words "Savage Beauty" have been bandied around to describe various locations - but the phrase was initially coined by Oscar Wilde, about Connemara. The national food of this region is Connemara Hill Lamb, a food which was awarded PGI status in 2007. Connemara Hill Lamb comes from a Blackfaced Horned Ewe, a rugged, adaptable animal that grazes on the particular grasses and sedges and heathers and is well suited to the sometimes punishing climate of these mountainous uplands.

Café and Take-away

● Anton's

A stone's throw from the Corrib, and a pivotal neighborhood player, Anton O'Malley's little corner room on Father Griffin Road does the good thing, and Galwegians are grateful. Everything they make and bake is wholesome, unpretentious, true and good. We like the calmness of the crew, their easy sangfroid somehow making the food taste even better. You don't find places like Anton's away from Galway, so settle in with a coffee and some buttermilk pancakes, check out the artworks, and mainline the culture. (Anton O'Malley, 12a Father Griffin Road, Galway ☎ 091-582067 info@antonscafe.com www.antonscafe.com – Open day time Mon-Fri)

Galway City

made in Galway

Colleran's Black Pudding

Restaurant

● Ard Bia, Nimmo's & The Long Walk Market

Aoibheann McNamara and her team fashion one of the city's best rooms, a pulsing, clamorous, engaged space where the cooking is fresh, vibrant and unpretentious, where the staff are hip to the trip, and where it's always time for the good times. Caroline Byrne and her BNBFs (best new best friends) found the restaurant already packed to the rafters on a Tuesday evening, and here is what the bnbfs ate: a shared mezze plate to start, with three delicious varieties of hummus, a perfect sheek kebab with fresh salad and pitta, then three orders of the evening's special of ray wing, served with a crab butter, albino beetroot and bak choi. They also enjoyed Killary mussels with chorizo and a spicy broth that was sharpened with some harissa, the sauce mopped up with tasty bread. 'The food over-delivered, and at the lower end of mid-range prices', writes Caroline. The service in Ard Bia, in common with many of the best Galway destinations, is amongst the best we have ever enjoyed. (Aoibheann McNamara, 2 Quay Street, Galway ☎ 091-539 897 ardbia@gmail.com www.ardbia.com – Café open 9am-3.30pm, Restaurant open 6pm-10pm)

Restaurant

● Artisan

The architecture of Quay Street has blessed Artisan with a small, long, upstairs room that they have decorated simply and appropriately, with bentwood chairs and strings of lights. Sit at a window table and peer down to the busy street below and its never-ending human procession. The food is as simple and appropriate as the decor: boeuf bourguignon, baked salmon, and some thoughtful, artful sandwiches. (Matt Skeffington, 2 Quay Street, Galway ☎ 091-532 655 ✉ artisanrestaurant@gmail.com 🖱 www.artisangalway.com – Open lunch and dinner Mon-Sun)

Galway City

Asian Tea House

● Asian Tea House Restaurant

Everything is very carefully considered in Terry Commons' restaurant. From the furnishings and decor, to the pan-Asian style of the menu, and especially with their exhaustive range of speciality teas, there is aesthetic and culinary contemplation evident in every gesture, in every bite. So, order a pot of Moon Stars, then set out on an Asian journey – Hong Kong wontons;Chinese hoisin pork belly; Siam ribs; Japanese gyoza. (Terry Commons, 15 Mary Street, Galway ☎ 091-563749 🔔 www.asianteahouse.ie – Open Mon-Sun 5pm-10.30pm, closed Tue off season)

Restaurant

● Bar 8

Tom Sheridan runs a wickedly smart venture in the hip Bar 8. Menus are short, sourcing from West Coast artisans is impeccable, and pricing makes this the closest you can get to gift grub in the region. You could have lamb salad with couscous to start and then a chicken and leek pie with their signature chips and Stephen Gould's wonderful organic leaves, and you would have change from a twenty. You won't, of course – the fantastic wines and beers and the prospect of a long, lovely evening in a great room with your friends will soon drag you from the straight and narrow – but it is theoretically possible. Theory, of course, is bunk: this is Galway, after all. Bar 8 is real smart, real hip. (Tom Sheridan, 8 Dock Road, Galway ☎ 091-565111 ✉ info@eight.ie 🖱 www.eight.ie – Open 4.30pm-11pm Mon-Thu, 12.30pm-11.30pm Fri-Sun)

Wine Warehouse

● Cases

Enthusiasm. Unlike wine, you can't put it in a bottle. But if the person making the wine has enthusiasm, and if the person selling the wine has enthusiasm, then what is in the bottle will taste so much better. Peter Boland and his team at Cases have that enthusiasm, and it makes the world of difference to the wines they sell. Knowledgeable, generous, up-for-it, the Cases team take away the fear factor and replace it with no-nonsense enthusiasm, just the right approach to fit the bright, big warehouse space where they sell the wines. There are brilliant wines to discover here, from enthusiastic winemakers from every part of the wine world, so let Peter and his crew enthusiastically lead you into the culture and pleasure of good wine. Chances are, if you have eaten in a few Galway restaurants, that you will already know some of the spiffing bottles that Cases have in store, waiting for you. (Peter Boland, Riverside Commercial Estate, Tuam Road, Galway ☎ 091-764701 peter@cases.ie www.cases.ie – Open 10am-7pm Mon-Sat)

Galway City

local knowledge

Sweaty Betty

There is hardly a restaurant in Galway that hasn't invented a dish for Sweaty Betty, the locally caught fish that was introduced to the city by Gannet Fishmongers. The firm-fleshed flavourful fish is from the hake family, and is otherwise known as Forked Beard, which is almost as characterful.

Spanish Restaurant & Tapas Bar

● Cava

Jp McMahon and Drigin Gaffney are out of the box. In addition to Cava they are involved in the next-door Aniar, and the down-the-street Massimo. Quite how Mr McMahon's culinary heart came to reside in Spain we don't know, but we do know that he understands his favoured cuisine implicitly: the food in Cava is as real as it gets without transporting yourself to San Sebastian. The salted cod cakes are sublime; the scallops with pancetta and sweet potato purée are divine, we would walk to Galway for the pig cheeks with apple, cinnamon and white wine, and the rack of lamb we enjoyed was one of the best dishes of the year, meat so sweet and moreish that it rendered us speechless. The room heaves with energy, the crowd are cool, the wines and sherries are brilliant and service is as fine as we have ever experienced and enjoyed. A simply brilliant restaurant. (JP McMahon & Drigin Gaffey, 51 Dominick Street Lower, Galway ☎ 091-539884 food@cavarestaurant.ie www.cavarestaurant.ie – Open noon-4pm, 6pm-10pm, tapas all day, Sat & Sun brunch 11am-5pm, late opening Fri & Sat)

Restaurant

● Chi

This exciting new Asian venture is the brainchild of Catherine O'Brien, who since 1997 has been feeding authentic Chinese cooking to Galwegians in the Da Tang Noodle House. Chi broadens the purist approach of Da Tang, with chef Andy Banderas offering a pan-Asian array of dishes from Malaysia, Singapore, Thailand, Vietnam, and China. So, I'll have the beef brisket noodles, you try the Mi Hoo Goreng, and let's chase that desire for balance and energy – and pleasure – which great Asian cooking offers in every bite. (Catherine O'Brien, Unit 4, Westside Enterprise Park, Westside, Galway ☎ 091-861687 info@chigalway.com www.chigalway.com – Open 4pm-10pm Tue-Sun)

Bakery

● The Cupcake Bakery

Jennie had all the good stuff at her stall at the Galway Food Festival: minty mint; galaxy caramel; strawberry sundae; rhubarb, ginger and white chocolate; snicker doodle; cream egg surprise were just a few of her beauties, as handsome to look at as they are to eat. Ms Browne has a wild imagination, and the discipline of a fine baker. (Jennie Browne, Ard Alainn, Galway ☎ 086-1543843 lovethecupcakebakery@gmail.com www.lovethecupcakebakery.com)

Restaurant

● Cupan Tae

The western outpost of the Kenmare original serves excellent tea and nice things to eat in a girly, flowery, flamboyant fashion. We like it, being girly, flowery and flamboyant in our own quiet way. (Alison McArdle, Flood Street, Galway ☎ 091-895000 www.cupantae.eu – Open 10am-6pm Mon-Sat, 11am-6pm Sun)

B&B

● 7 Cross Street

Paris has lots of little hotels where you walk through a single narrow door, then down a narrow entrance to a little reception desk and, having checked in, you climb steep stairs to the warren of little bedrooms. Olivia O'Reilly's No 7 Cross Street is one of those hotels – the narrow doorway on the street, the narrow hall, the tiny reception space, the tiny rooms, the city centre location, the bustle and noise, and it brought back to us floods of memories of staying in inexpensive Parisian hotels when we used to backpack. So, No 7 suits us perfectly, and if you like petite rooms – let's call them intimate – and cheek-by-jowl eating, then you will love this chic little space on Cross Street. (Olivia O'Reilly, 7 Cross Street, Galway ☎ 091-530100 info@7crossstreet.com www.7crossstreet.com – Open all year)

Butcher

● John E Colleran & Sons

Colleran's is a legend in Galway, a legend that Raymond Colleran is amplifying every day with his cutting-edge skills. Mr Colleran did a nose-to-tail cooking presentation at the Galway Food Festival, and he is a star performer – funny, relaxed, witty, cultured – and all of these qualities are evident in his charcuterie and his meat preparation. Their cooked hams are peerless, the meats are as good as it gets, and they really know their stuff: Mr Colleran advised his audience, for instance, to never fry black pudding. It's already a cooked product he said, so warm it through in the oven, which will lighten the texture and amplify the flavour. He is dead right. (Raymond Colleran, 18 Mainguard Street, Galway ☎ 091-562582 colleransbutchershop@eircom.net – Open 8am-6pm Mon-Fri, 7am-6pm Sat)

Restaurant and Lunch Box Take Out

● Da Tang Noodle House

The Da Tang has become one of the staples of Galway's food culture, a cultured little room in which to enjoy true, subtle, Chinese cooking. The cooking style here is Northern Chinese, so it is quite different from the hybrid Chinese food served elsewhere: it is much, much better. Noodles and pork dumplings for me, and tofu in yellow bean sauce with noodles for you, and everyone is happy. (Du Han Tuo & Catherine O'Brien,

2 Middle Street, Galway ☎ 091-788638 ✉ info@datangnoodlehouse.com 🖱 www.datangnoodlehouse.com – Open noon-3pm Mon-Fri, 6pm-11.30pm Mon-Fri, noon-11pm Sat)

Café

● Delight

Paula Lawrence's health café is at the Kingfisher Club in Renmore, in the east of the city. Their focus is on health-giving, energising food, so there are power salads and detoxing juices, smart sandwiches and good toasted bagels. It's lovely to see a destination that balances health and satisfaction so implicitly and successfully in its food. (Paula Lawrence, Renmore Avenue, Galway ☎ 091-761 466 🖱 www.delight.ie – Open 8.30am-4.30pm Mon-Fri, 10am-3pm Sat)

B&B

● Devon Dell

Devon Dell may be a simple house, set in a quiet cul-de-sac a short stroll from the centre of Galway, but it's precisely the kind of place that Galway does well: individual; aspirational, a bit naive, pure delight. It's pure Galway, in the way that some places are pure West Cork. Hard to define, but you know it when you get it. And that is what you get in Devon Dell: pure Galway. The city spirit is here. (Berna Kelly, 47 Devon Park, Lower Salthill, Galway ☎ 091-528306 ✉ devondell@iol.ie 🖱 www.devondell.com – Open Mar-Oct. No credit cards.)

Craft Butcher

● Martin Divilly

Martin Divilly has been winning awards from the moment he took up the reins of this third-generation butchers, back in the 1990's. Since then, he hasn't stopped innovating, improving, expanding, and today Divilly's has radicalised the very concept of the traditional Irish butcher's shop, transforming it into a deli-food hall-emporium-butcher's shop. The one thing that hasn't changed, as the shop has expanded and the range has broadened, is the top-class quality of the meat they source and prepare. (Martin Divilly, Unit 9/10 Westside Shopping Centre, Galway ☎ 091-523947 🖱 www.martindivillybutchers.com – Open 8.30am-7pm Mon-Thu, 8.30am-8pm Fri, 8am-6pm Sat)

Fish Store

● Ernie's Fish Stores

Fish Store is a bit of a misleading description for Ernie's venerable old family business. You can buy everything from fresh cut turf to tins of vegetables, to spices and teas, to a good selection of fresh fish. And, guaranteed, there'll be a story to go with every purchase. (Ernie Deacy, Sea Road, Galway ☎ 091-586812 ✉ erniedeacy@gmail.com – Open 9am-6pm Mon-Sat)

Fishmonger

● The Fisherman

Galway City

Galway is a maritime city with an enviable choice of fish sold by knowledgeable fishmongers. These guys are tripping over themselves to provide a modern, positive experience in fish retailing, and at the vanguard of this is Patrick O'Malley's Fisherman. Expect perfectly served fish, of course, but also sushi, tapas and very good live shellfish. Lookout also for the Fisherman Freezers which are placed in shops around Galway, adding convenience to an already go-ahead offer. (Patrick O'Malley, Galway Shopping Centre, Headford Road, Galway ☎ 091-561966 ✉ info@fisherman.ie 🖱 www.fisherman.ie – Open 8am-6pm Mon, 9am-6pm Tue-Sat (till 8pm Thur & Fri), noon-5pm Sun)

Restaurant

● Food For Thought

Kenneth Walsh's restaurant has had a neat new facelift, which may serve to awaken many people – as it did us – that FFT is not just a vegetarian-wholefood stop-over, but has a more extensive menu, whilst still cooking interesting meat-free dishes. There is nice fresh baking and get-up-and-go smoothies for breakfast, and alongside the vegan and vegetarian dishes there are nice pies and bakes. "Wholesome" they call it, and wholesome it is. (Kenneth Walsh, Lower Abbeygate Street, Galway ☎ 091-565854 ✉ food4thoughtgalway@gmail.com – Open 7.30am-6pm Mon-Fri, 8am-6pm Sat, 12.30pm-4pm Sun)

Hotel

● The G Hotel & Matz at the G

Seven years on from its opening at the height of Ireland's boomtime, and The G remains a sublime piece of contemporary design, in a curious location. The rooms are fabulous, both the public rooms and the bedrooms, and it's always a treat to swan here for a few hours, enjoying a cocktail and having a bite to eat. (Gerry Barrett, Wellpark, Galway ☎ 091-865 200 www.theghotel.ie – Open 7am-10am Mon-Fri, 7am-11am Sat-Sun, 6.30pm-9.30pm Sun-Thu, 6pm-11pm Fri-Sat, 1pm-3pm Sun)

made in Galway
Killeen Farmhouse Cheese

Market

● The Galway Saturday Market

Galway is on such a roll these days that one hesitates to criticise something as iconic as the Saturday Market. Two decades ago, it led the field, the most left-field, inspiring, iconoclastic place to shop in the west. And its core of great producers – Cait Curran, Brekish Dairy, Dirk Flake, Joachim Hess and others – are as resolute and creative as ever. Whilst new arrivals such as Castlemine Farm, Gannet Fishmongers and Coolfinn Bakery have added new colour and new quality, one still can't help but feel that Galway has lost its pole position. What should they do? Stop the traffic and let the market expand organically onto both sides of the road opposite the church, for the extra space will attract new blood, new energy that will get Galway back on top again. And, having said all that, it is still a fantastic market, with its own unique swerve, its own chaotic grace and covetable clamour. (Beside St Nicholas's Church galwaymarket@eircom.net www.galwaymarket.net – Open 8.30am-4pm Sat, 2pm-6pm Sun)

Fishmonger

● Gannet Fish Pantry

"You should be proud to be a fishmonger", says Stephane Griesbach. Well, if every fishmonger practised their craft at the level at which they practise it in Gannet, then Ireland's fishmongers would be the proudest people in the world. Mr Griesbach and his team are a benchmark fish operation, selling the finest Irish fish in the most customer-friendly way. Their market stalls and Eyre Square shop are legendary, because they don't just sell you fillets and whatnot: they sell you the culture of the sea, the culture of fish cookery, the pleasures of fish cookery. Gannet is a paragon food business, as good as it gets. (Stephane Griesbach, 32 Dun Ri, Athenry ☎ 086-3488591 www.fishmongers.ie Also Eyre Square Shopping Centre – Open 9am-6.30pm Tue-Sat. Also selling at markets in Ballinasloe, Fri 9am-1pm; Loughrea, Thu 9am-1pm; Oranmore, Thur noon-6pm; Moycullen, Fri noon-6pm; Gort, Fri 10am-2pm; Claregalway, Sat 10am-2pm, Galway, Sat 9am-6pm)

made in Galway

Kylemore Acres Herb Mixes

Bakery

● The Gourmet Tart Company

There's a definite touch of Yotam Ottolenghi about this wonderful Galway operation: pristine white surfaces coupled with outrageous displays of the most amazing cakes and savouries are a signature of the London based chef, and here they are augmented by great Irish service. The Henry Street bakery is deceptively spartan but it's immediately obvious that some serious bakers are at work – huge croissants, swirly pink meringues, delicious coffee eclairs and sandwiches that are the polar opposite of those miserable damp slabs that fill so many petrol station shelves. A superb operation that Galway is extremely lucky to have. (Michelle & Fintan Hyland, 65 Henry Street, Galway ☎ 091-5883847 www.gourmettartco.com – Open 8am-6.30pm Mon-Sat, 9am-6pm Sun. Also Lower Abbeygate Street, Galway, Salthill & Galway Shopping Centre)

Patisserie & Coffee Shop

● Goya's

Emer Murray's status as the best baker in Galway has never been challenged in two decades. When Ms Murray first opened her little store on Shop Street, she was immediately the best. In her hip Kirwan's Lane café and shop, she remains the best, a patissier of infinite patience, exactitude and accomplishment. Nothing comes out of the kitchen at Goya's – from the simplest sandwich to the most mellifluously ethereal cake – unless it is the best it can possibly be. Goya's is endlessly inspiring. (Emer Murray, 2/3 Kirwans Lane, Galway ☎ 091-567010 info@goyas.ie www.goyas.ie – Open 9.30am-6pm Mon-Sat)

Bakery

● Griffin's Bakery

Saturday morning, and the queue to buy breads at Griffin's is well out the door, and winding well down Shop Street. Jimmy Griffin's bakery is no mere food store. Instead, it is a temple, a temple of good things, and we all come here to worship, to pledge fealty to Mr Griffin's devotion to making beautiful things to eat. Mr Griffin hasn't just continued the family business. Instead, he has super-charged it, steadily broadening the list of breads and cakes, running a superb tea rooms, and yet never losing their focus on the fact that "Bread is not bread unless it is made by an artisan bakery". Mr Griffin bakes the staff of life, and your life is better every time you walk in their door. (James Griffin, 21 Shop Street, Galway ☎ 091-563683 ✉ sales@griffinsbakery.com 🖱 www.griffinsbakery.com – Open 8am-6pm Mon-Sat, 10am-6pm Sun)

Galway City

B&B

● The Heron's Rest

There is a heron, you know, who likes to rest right outside Sorcha Mulloy's riverside house at the Spanish Arch. He's called Jack. In Galway, Heron's Rest means just that: the place where the heron – Jack – comes to rest. You couldn't make it up. Mind you, you could hardly make Sorcha Mulloy up, either. There is no more meticulous hostess in Ireland. But she's funky, too, and she creates a breakfast that has no parallel in Ireland. Last time we started with beautiful fruit salad with goji berries and yogurt, then pearl barley porridge with poached cinnamon pears and honeyed dates. We felt like we could have taken to the skies, just like Jack. (Sorcha Molloy, 16a Longwalk, Spanish Arch, Galway ☎ 086-337 9343 ✉ theheronsrest@gmail.com 🖱 www.theheronsrest.com – Open May-Oct)

Hotel

● The House Hotel

The House Hotel has got more and more confident about finding ways to be alluring as it has settled into Galway life. The downstairs lobby seems pinker with each visit, the uniforms more modish. It has become a nadir of girliness, and is popular with Hen Parties. But all this vogueishness hasn't replaced a down-to-earth professionalism, with well-designed rooms, comfort, and smooth operating. At what point does somewhere become an institution? The House has got to that point. (James Griffin, Lower Merchants Road, The Latin Quarter, Galway ☎ 091-538900 ✉ info@thehouse.ie 🖱 www.thehouse.ie – Open all year)

Pub/Restaurant

● The Huntsman Inn

There are certain people, places and performers whose professionalism makes you smile: Beyoncé; the Killarney Park Hotel; Roger Federer; the American bar at the Savoy; the Murphy brothers of Dingle. Galway's iconic Huntsman fits into that pantheon of professionalism with svelte ease. It is a meticulous operation – restaurant; rooms; bars – all glow with a professional sheen whereby the staff make their work look easy, whilst working incredibly hard to maintain that illusion.They serve food from early until late, all of it characterised by good judgement and sure delivery: chicken with mushroom stuffing and creamy mash; spinach and ricotta ravioli with broccoli; fish cakes with caper, lime and coriander. It's people-pleasing food, and it hits the spot. (Stephen Francis, 164 College Road, Galway ☎ 091-562849 🖱 www.huntsmaninn.com – Open 8am-9.30pm Mon-Sun)

local knowledge

Galway's Latin Quarter

There is nothing quite like the infectious and spirited buzz of Galway. Much of it is centred around "The Latin Quarter" - a physical space which includes heritage sites such as the Druid Theatre, Spanish Arch, the City Museum and St Nicholas' Church, but has become more associated with food and drink and nightlife.

Restaurant

● Kettle of Fish

The big city outpost of the fish and chip masters from Gort is perenially packed, and for good reason. KofF do great fish and chips, so nobody minds the wait, nobody minds the crush, nobody minds the paucity of space. The staff are as sharp as the cooking, and whilst there are choices other than fresh fish, you should always go for the catch of the day, with chips, and a gentle splash of vinegar. Bliss! (Siobhan Fahey, 4 Lower Cross Street, Galway ☎ 091-569 881 – Open noon-late)

made in Galway

Connemara Smokehouse

Restaurant

● The Malt House

Is there another restaurant team that tries as hard as the crew in the Malt House? These guys and girls put body and soul into their work, and their effort makes for a thunderously pleasing destination. What is perhaps most striking is the fact that customers love the Malt House to bits: actually, they aren't customers, they are devotees, they are disciples, and we understand their faith. The cooking is delicious, the service is fantastic, and the totality of the exprience of eating here is one of the highlights of Galway. (Mary & Paul Grealish, Olde Malt Mall, High Street ☎ 091-567866 info@themalthouse.ie www.themalthouse.ie – Open noon-2.30pm, 6pm-9.30pm Mon-Sat)

Gastro Pub

● Massimo

What can you do with chicken and chips? Well, in Eat @ Massimo, a seriously stylish bar, they coat the chicken in a saffron batter, then deep fry it. They leave the skins on the chips. They give you a little pot of mustard mayonnaise, and they sprinkle wilted salad leaves on top. The food comes in a small, deep-fat fryer basket, on a plate. The result? The best chicken and chips we have ever eaten, simple as that. Eat is the gastro-pub brainchild of Jp McMahon of Cava, and every detail of the concept is as smart as it gets. We would like to see an Eat in every town in Ireland. (Jp McMahon, William Street, Galway ☎ 091-582239 www.eatgalway.com – Food served noon-6pm Mon, noon-9pm Tue-Thur, noon-10pm Fri-Sat, noon-8pm Sun)

Galway City

local knowledge

Cloon Keen Atelier

"Dramatic simplicity" is a phrase used by Cloon Keen Atelier to describe their products, and scents of Cloon Keen are a way of capturing everything that is lovely about this county and bringing it home to enjoy. Their fragrances, when experienced through the medium of liquid soaps or scented candles, are generous, powerful and superbly crafted. The best thing is that you can buy them on line, which is good, because once you start to use these you'll never want to be without them. www.cloonkeenatelier.com. Note also, that just around the corner from Cloon Keen Atelier, there is a little antique shop (9 Cross Street, 091-562282) which stocks a mesmerising collection of art deco tableware and cutlery. Another Don't Miss whilst in Galway city.

Delicatessen

● McCambridge's

You need to hunt for the big words to describe McCambridge's of Galway. Ostensibly, it's a grocery shop. But it's actually a bazaar of good things, a cornucopia of delicious delights. At each point of the store, something singular and seductive is waiting for you – superb wines; brilliant sandwiches; great savouries; sublime coffees; artisan meats; agrestic breads. Everything Natalie McCambridge and her family have chosen to grace their shelves is worth the detour. Vitally, for Galway city, the McCambridge family have been demonstrating their careful, wise judgement since 1925, providing not just a destination in the city centre, but a true landmark, a culinary landmark. The new wine bar and café upstairs is a thrilling new direction, gathering together all the McCambridge qualities of enthusiasm, dedication, and service. They have been servants to the city of Galway, distinguished servants indeed. (Natalie McCambridge, 38/39 Shop Street, Galway ☎ 091-562259 retail@mccambridges.com www.mccambridges.com – Open 8.30am-7pm Mon-Wed, 8.30am-9pm Thu-Sat, noon-6pm Sun)

Wine Bar

● Martine's Quay Street Wine Bar

Martine put a hip, smart new facade on her hip, smart wine bar in 2012, but behind the new surface, this Galway institution does what it does the way it has always done it: cooking nice food, making people happy, ensuring they come back time and time again, and doing everything with a smile. Martine and her team could coast on the tourist trade, but they don't: every day they make it new, and we salute their energy. (Martine McDonagh, 21 Quay Street, Galway ☎ 091-565662 www.winebar.ie – Open 4pm-10pm Mon-Fri, 1pm-10pm Sat-Sun)

Galway City

Restaurant

● Maxwell's Restaurant

The McKenna boys – Sam and PJ – were well impressed with Maxwell's on their first visit to Paul O'Meara's bistro. PJ had the tomato and basil soup with the terrific brown bread, whilst Sam had the nicely spicy chicken wings. They noticed – as you do – that most of the customers in this bright, colourful and well-designed space were twenty-something Galway girls. They enjoyed the attentive service. And they vowed to make sure that Maxwell's is part of every future Galway visit. Oh, and their Dad was well impressed also. (Paul O'Meara, Williamsgate Street, Galway ☎ 091-568974 bookings@maxwellsrestaurant.ie www.maxwellsrestaurant.ie – Open 10am-9.30pm Mon-Sun)

Restaurant

● Kai

Kai is the Maori term for 'food', but we like to think of it as the right word for Jess Murphy's attitude to food. Some cooks may be Zen, some may be bonkers, but Ms Murphy has a way of seeing food that is definitely 'Kai'. She is a singular cook, stubborn and smart, and she and her husband, David, opened with a bang when Kai launched in mid-2011. Kai opened with a bang because of some stonkingly fine cooking, food that chases the naked earthiness of the ingredients used – razor clams with garlic butter and samphire; roasted rhubarb with Bluebell Falls goat's cheese and almonds; Lough Boora farm plate; megrim roasted on the bone with lemon aioli; hake with clams and chorizo; gorse flower ice cream; elderflower sorbet with toasted oats. Every plate has just what it needs, and no more, just great cooking. (Jess & David Murphy, Galway ☎ 091-526003 kaicaferestaurant@gmail.com www.kaicaferestaurant.com – Open 9.30am-4pm. Lunch served noon-3pm Mon-Sat, noon-3pm Sun, 6.30pm-10.30pm Wed-Sun)

made in Galway

McGeough's Smoked Sausages

Galway City

Restaurant

● The Kitchen @ Galway City Museum

Did they know we were coming? First time we came to the Kitchen, the soundtrack was "Merriweather Post Pavilion", by Animal Collective. If you want to make us love you, it sure helps to play this weirded-out classic of indie rock. Even better: as we listened we ate Kilbeggan porridge, and Sean Kelly's black pudding for our breakfast, with excellent coffee. Friends, it doesn't get better than that. The Kitchen is our kind of place. (Spanish Parade, Galway ☎ 091-534883 thekitchengalway@gmail.com www.galwaycitymuseum.ie – Open 10am-5.30pm Mon-Sat, noon-5.30pm Sun)

Restaurant & Fish'n'Chip bar

● McDonagh's Seafood House

Is McDonagh's the busiest restaurant in Ireland? We ask for a simple reason: the room is always packed – just like their chip shop, next door to the restaurant, which is also always picked. You come to McDonagh's for fresh fish, fish that they source and cook correctly, and they send it out with confidence, consistency, and charm. The only hard part is actually getting a table. (Colm McDonagh, 22 Quay Street ☎ 091-565001 fish@mcdonaghs.net www.mcdonaghs.net – Restaurant open 5pm-10pm Mon-Sat, Fish and Chip bar open noon-11pm Mon-Sat, 4pm-10pm Sun)

Deli & Cafe

● Olio & Farina

O&F is both shop and café, the former essential for well sourced and chosen Italian food treasures, the latter for nice light food and good drinks. (Liam & Maria Payne, 50 Upper Abbeygate Street, Galway ☎ 091-539742 www.olioefarina.com – Open 9.30am-6.30pm Mon-Thur, 9.30am-8pm Fri, 9.30am-6.30pm Sat)

Restaurant

● Oscar's

Oscar's latest innovation, where the weekly fixed price menu is available all evening, has seen the room packed with happy punters who share a plate of little amuse-gueules to begin, then choose the day's fresh fish dish, or a Hereford beef sirloin steak, or the day's vegetarian dish. At 15 euro, this is a steal for such clever cooking, and it's another example of how Michael O'Meara is steadily working his way towards an ever more impressive simplicity. He used to do complex, fancy stuff, but that is all gone now, and he pays homage to his great suppliers by letting the food speak for itself – Clare Island salmon with dillisk potatoes; Sweaty Betty with brown shrimp; Galway seafood coddle; Connemara lamb with wild crab apple jelly. Sinead Hughes runs the room with pure Galway panache and confidence. (Michael O'Meara & Sinead Hughes, 22 Upper Dominick Street, Galway ☎ 091-582180 ✉ oscarsgalway@eircom.net 🖱 www.oscarsbistro.ie – Open 6.30pm-late Mon-Fri, 6pm-late Sat)

Galway City

Bakery and Coffee Shop

● Le Petit Delice

Bread lovers will tell you that the baguette baked here in the little Petit Delice is the best in town. It is indeed very good, but so is everything else they make, and the few chairs and tables at the rere of the store make for an excellent spot for taking tea and nice sweet treats. (Alexandra Saivre, 7 Mainguard Street, Galway ☎ 091-500751 – Open 8am-6.30pm Sat, 10.30am-6pm Sun)

Café

● Providence Market Kitchen

Lovely food in an art gallery space is the irresistible concoction from Orla Fox and her team in the PMK. The cooking is as true and structured as a good painting – healthy breakfasts; clean, fresh salads; superb gourmet sandwiches; enlivening drinks. Ms Fox and her team make it look terribly easy, but it's not easy to be this good. It takes a clear vision, and discipline, and they have both. (Orla Fox, corner of Abbeygate and St Augustine Street ☎ 091-533906 ✉ orla@providencemarketkitchen.com 🖱 www.providencemarketkitchen.com – Open 8am-6pm Mon-Sat)

Brew Pub

● The Salt House

The Salt House is the third member of the Cottage-Oslo group, and their reach stretches as far as the capital, where they run Against the Grain, The Brew Dock and The Black Sheep. Good beers and good brewing underpin this slick, charmismatic collection of atmospheric destinations. (Jason O'Connell, Niall Walsh, Ravens Terrace, Galway ☎ 091-581204 www.winefoodbeer.com)

Galway City

Fishmonger

● Seafood Centre @ Galway Bay Seafoods

The Seafood Centre in Galway is an authoritative one-stop shop for fresh fish. "Quality is our first, second and last thought of every day" Noel Holland once said to us, and this shop is energised by passion and experience. (Noel Holland, New Docks, Galway City ☎ 091-563011 galwaybayseafoods.com – Open 8.15am-5pm Mon-Wed & Sat, 8.15am-7.30pm Thu & Fri)

Winebar

● Sheridan's Winebar

There is nowhere like it. Sheridan's is a wine bar, but it is also a salon. It is always filled with fascinating people, perched on their stools, sipping wine, taking bites of delicious cheeses and charcuterie, people who seem on the verge of asking "Is there a bigger plonker than Bernard Henri Levy?", or of saying "Julie Feeney is the real Galway Girl, don't you think". The place is intoxicating even before you have a sip of their brilliant wines, and no visitor to the city should miss one of the most quixotic and defining destinations in Galway. (Seamus & Kevin Sheridan, Fiona Corbett, 16 Church Yard Street, Galway shop ☎ 091-564829, wine shop ☎ 091-564832 www.sheridanscheesemongers.com – Shop Open 9.30am-6pm Mon-Fri, 9am-6pm Sat, (and 1pm-6pm Sun June-Aug only), Winebar open 2pm-9pm Tue-Fri, noon-8pm Sat)

made in Galway

Solaris Botanicals

Cheesemonger, Delicatessen & Wine Shop

● Sheridan's Cheesemongers

The Sheridans deal in archetypes, so their cheese shop feels and looks exactly like the cheese shop of your dreams. The mix of cheeses, speciality foods and fresh foods, allied to a standard of service that has no peers, quickly leads one into economic unconsciousness: if they have it, then you want it. Sheridan's is one of the greatest shops in the world. (Seamus & Kevin Sheridan, Fiona Corbett, 16 Church Yard Street, Galway shop ☎ 091-564829, wine shop ☎ 091-564832 www.sheridanscheesemongers.com – Shop Open 9.30am-6pm Mon-Fri, 9am-6pm Sat, (and 1pm-6pm Sun June-Aug only), Winebar open 2pm-9pm Tue-Fri, noon-8pm Sat)

Tea Blenders

● Solaris Botanicals

Jorg Muller is an advocate of Goethian science, so his search as a tea bleander is on understanding how the plants and leaves he uses actually work, and catching them and their essential properties at their optimum. "What is the plant signature?" is the question he asks himself, and his handsome Solaris teas are his search for the answer. We are devoted to them, their vibrancy, their cleanness and health-giving properties. Solaris teas make your life better. (Jorg Muller & Karin Wieland, Unit 3, Ballybane Enterprise Centre, Galway ☎ 091-750020 info@solarisbotanicals.com www.solarisbotanicals.com)

Bakery Cafe

● Sweetie Pies

A cake café: bring it on! Maureen and Jenny, sisters in sweetness, bring a real sense of retro mania to their day-glo-glam cakes in Sweetie Pies, and the girls themselves are like performers in their own cake drama. A cake drama in a cake café: only in Galway. (Maureen Foley & Jenny Griffin, 3 Middle Street, Galway ☎ 087-2566887 info@sweetiepies.ie www.sweetiepies.ie – Open 10am-5pm Mon-Thu, 10am-6pm Fri-Sat, noon-6pm Sun)

Butcher

● C.R. Tormey & Sons

The Tormey family opened our eyes to the magnificence of Irish beef. It was many years go now when we first met James Tormey and his dad, at Crookedwood House, near to Mullingar, and listened, gobsmacked, as father and son explained just how they achieved the standards of beef production that characterised the family's three butcher's shops. Those skills, and that experience, are evident in every piece of meat one buys from the family's three shops, in Mullingar, Tullamore, and Galway. Of course, being experts, they don't shout about their expertise: they just quietly look after customers who admire them and respect them and trust them. So, go to Tormey's, and get your eyes opened. (John Tormey, Unit 17 Headford Shopping Centre, Headford Road, Galway ☎ 091-564067 info@crtormeys.ie www.crtormeys.ie – Open 9am-6pm Mon-Wed, 9am-7pm Thu, 9am-8.30pm Fri, 9am-6pm Sat, 9am-5.15pm Sun. Also at Harbour Place, Mullingar ☎ 044-934 5433; Bridge Street, Tullamore ☎ 057-932 1426)

Galway City

made in Galway

Beechlawn Organics

Restaurant

● Tulsi

A tiny room with a big menu that delivers excellent Indian cooking is the Tulsi signature. It's modest and simple, and the service is wonderful. (Mukther Ahmmed, 3 Buttermilk Walk, Middle Street, Galway ☎ 091-564831 www.tulsigalway.com– Open 1pm-2.30pm, 6pm-11pm Mon-Sat (closed 11.30pm Fri & Sat), 1pm-10pm Sun)

Bakery

● Il Vicolo

The fact that all the restaurant staff of Galway eat here on their day off says just about all that you need to know about Il Vicolo. So, step right in, hang your coat on the rack and squeeze in with the other shoppers, locals and visitors. Now allow yourself to be charmed by this not-quite-Italian, not-quite-Irish hybrid of Galway meets southern-Med café. Let yourself be tempted by the pasta specials of the day - a bowl of orecchiette with caramelised red onion, spinach and pecorino, or a classic pasta like spaghetti carbonara or puttanesca. The coffee is good and there's probably no better place in Galway to have breakfast – especially The Full Italian: Italian sausage, fried eggs, portobello mushroom, pan-fried potato and pancetta. (Gerry McMahon, 5 Buttermilk Walk, Galway ☎ 091-535922 – Open 9am-6pm Mon-Tue & Sun, 9am-midnight Wed-Fri, 10am-midnight Sat)

Restaurant

● Vina Mara

Eileen Feeney does a superb job in keeping Vina Mara right up to the mark, endlessly introducing new menu ideas – most recently their steakhouse menu offering sirloin, fillet, rib-eye, T-bone and cote de boeuf – organising food and wine evenings, and all the while cooking lovely food in a classic room. Such energy and creativity after a decade at the coalface is simply inspiring. (Eileen Feeney, 19 Middle Street, Galway ☎ 091-561610 info@vinamara.com www.vinamara.com – Open from 12.30pm lunch, from 6pm dinner, Mon-Sat. Opens 5.30pm Sat)

Japanese Café

● Wa Café

Everything you love about Japanese food – the use of colour; the sense of proportion; the deep wisdom; the quiet focus on nutrition; the enlivening hit of umami flavours – can be found in the small, perfectly-proportioned space that is Yoshimi Hayakawa's Wa Café. Ms Hayakawa and her crew prepare beautiful food – simple, soulful, generous, respectful – and serve it with the utmost grace. Ms Hayakawa hopes to open a Sushi Academy in the future: sign us up, for we want to know the way of Wa. (Yoshimi Hayakawa, 13 New Dock Street ☎ 091-895850 info@wacafe.net www.wacafe.net – Open 11.30am-9pm Mon-Sun)

Wine Shop

● Thomas Woodberry's

"Wines with personality" is how Declan and Sandra describe their range in Woodberry's, but they could equally add "A wine shop with personality", and "Staff with personality". All the wines are good, but those from producers with whom they have a particularly close relationhip – O'Leary Walker in Australia; Douro Estates in Portugal; Closerie des Alisiers, to name just three – show the myriad benefits of a close and enduring winemaker-wine seller nexus. (Declan & Sandra Owens, 3 Middle Street Mews, Middle Street, Galway ☎ 091-533706 woodberrys@eircom.net www.woodberrys.ie – Open 10.30am-7pm Mon-Fri, 10am-7pm Sat)

ARAN ISLANDS – INIS MEÁIN

Restaurant and Suites

● Inis Meáin Restaurant and Suites

We don't want to get all Zen on you, but if you come to beautiful Inis Meain and stay and eat at Ruari and Marie-Thérèse de Blacam's gorgeous restaurant and suites, what you will experience is: Oneness. This extraordinary place brings everything that is special about these islands together – the light, the stone, the sea, the colours, the food, the sense of time. It all becomes One. The cooking is simple, perfect: island vegetable soup; dressed crab; seafood pot with tomato and fennel; saddle of lamb with peppers; apple tart and crème anglaise. The calmness of the food, the fact that it is grown and reared and caught outside the door, the charming service, is almost overwhelming. And so everything at Inis Meain is at One, at Oneness. Bliss. (Ruari & Marie-Therese de Blácam, Inis Meain ☎ 086-826 6026 ✉ post@inismeain.com 🖱 www.inismeain.com – Apr-Sept, dinner only)

B&B

● An Dún

Potatoes from the garden. Fresh mackerel. Carrageen pudding for dessert. And Inis Meain winding itself into your soul as the sun sets on another lovely day as you enjoy dinner in Teresa Faherty's simple, lovely B&B and restaurant. Mrs Faherty has been looking after guests here since 1989, and doing so with grace and sympathy. (Teresa & Padraic Faherty, Inis Meain, Aran Islands ☎ 099-73047 ✉ anduninismeain@eircom.net 🖱 www.inismeainaccommodation.com)

INIS MÓR

Guesthouse

● Kilmurvey House

Most visitors to the Aran Islands make a disastrous mistake: they don't stay here. Instead, they arrive on the morning ferry, scoot around the island on a bike or in a minibus and then they leave on an afternoon ferry. There! Aran Islands done! Next?! That's not how you do it. To understand these mystical islands requires one thing: time. So, book yourself into Treasa and Bertie's lovely house. Swim in Kilmurvey Bay. Trek the island. Explore Dun Aengus. Relax in the bars of Kilronan. Enjoy Treasa's stupendous breakfasts. Enjoy Bertie's hospitality. Borrow a bike and cycle slowly around the perimeter of Inis Mor. Kilmurvey House is your portal for these pleasures. (Treasa & Bertie Joyce, Kilmurvey, Inis Mór, Aran Islands ☎ 099-61218 ✉ kilmurveyhouse@eircom.net 🖱 www.kilmurveyhouse.com – Open 1 Apr-16 Oct)

INIS OIRR

Restaurant & Study Centre

● South Aran Guesthouse & Restaurant

Enda and Maria have created a world unto themselves in Fisherman's Cottage. As well as accommodation and delicious cooking in the restaurant, they run many varied cookery courses in addition to health and lifestyle courses. They are wise and holistic people, attuned to nature, and they can tune you into it as well: just surrender to the natural charms of this beautiful island. (Maria & Enda Conneely, Fisherman's Cottage, Inis Oirr, Aran Islands ☎ 099-75073 ✉ foodwise@eircom.net 🖱 www.southaran.com)

local knowledge

Aran Island Potatoes

The story of the soil on the Aran Islands is a magical tale of endeavour. The islanders built the soil by piling sand and seaweed on top of the limestone rocks, and it is now extremely fertile. Aran Island potatoes, grown in this salty, temperate environment, are a particular treat.

Athenry

Bakery

● The Foods of Athenry

Siobhan and Paul describe their work as creating artisan products for "the food conscious". And for those conscious about what they eat the Athenry bakery provides food low in salt, yeast-free, rich in vitamins and flavinoids, breads without preservatives, additives or hydrogenated fats. These are breads that are proud of their heritage, created and informed by their climate and culture. What sets the Lawless family apart is their espousal of an ethos, and their ability to deliver it with every fine product. They are resilient people, too: the bakery was destroyed in a fire not so long ago, a heart-breaking event for a family business on the family farm. Undaunted, they rebuilt, re-started, and made it even better. That's the sort of questing, unstoppable people they are. (Siobhan & Paul Lawless, Oldcastle, Kilconieron, Athenry ☎ 091-848152 siobhan@foodsofathenry.ie www.foodsofathenry.ie)

Galway County

Café

● The Nook

Julie Murphy first made a splash with her excellent Braingrain health bars, the sort of power-packed snack bar that we need to see more of. But, not being content with creating delicious snack bars, she has also opened The Nook, where she makes crepes from local eggs and artisan ingredients, brews the excellent McCabes coffee, and showcases local arts and artisans. Our kind of funky. (Julie Murphy, Church Street, Athenry ☎ 087-9448185 braingrainfoodco@gmail.com www.thenookathenry.ie www.thebraingrainbar.com)

made in Galway

Galway Native Oyster

Restaurant, Shop and Bakery

● The Old Barracks

Fiona King and Cathal O'Malley's handsome stone-and-shutters building in Athenry is pretty much a one-stop-shop for all your food needs. TOB is bakery, café, restaurant, caterer, wedding cake baker, you name it. This is an ambitious and dynamic food adventure, which enjoys the enviable advantage of being able to source meats for their menus from their own farm in Craughwell, so a home-reared Angus beef burger should be top of your list for lunch. (Fiona King & Cathal O Malley, Athenry ☎ 091-877406 cathal@oldbarracks.ie www.oldbarracks.ie – Open 9am-6pm Mon-Sat, 10am-6pm Sun, 6.30pm-9.30pm Thur-Sat)

Grass Farmer

● The Friendly Farmer

Someone will make a television series about Ronan Byrne sometime soon, and the Friendly Farmer will become a national celebrity. Not before time: Mr Byrne explains the attractions and dissatisfactions of farming better than just about anyone, and we need charismatic advocates to explain to the people of Ireland why farming is our natural and characteristic industry. Meantime, he continues to rear the most beautiful pasture-fed produce. "The better you treat animals, the better they taste", he says, as succinct a statment of animal and human welfare as you will find. Not just the Friendly Farmer, then, but also the Future Farmer. (Ronan Byrne, Knockbrack, Athenry ☎ 087-620 3765 thefriendlyfarmer@gmail.com thefriendlyfarmer.blogspot.com)

Galway County

Ballinafad

Hotel & Restaurant

● Ballynahinch Castle

So here is what Sam, PJ and John McKenna had for dinner on their last trip to Ballynahinch: slow-cooked McGeough's pork neck in air-dried ham; galantine of duck foie gras and confit duck leg; tomato and ginger soup; raspberry sorbet; assiette of McGeough's Irish pork; McGeough's beef filet; black sole cooked on the bone; pecan pie and vanilla ice cream. It was all delicious, proof of Xin Sun's excellence as a cook. Breakfast-time, meanwhile, offered a superb buffet table and beautifully cooked food, and the dining room is always a special place in which to enjoy such peachy cooking. Good judgement and excellent staff are the keys to Ballynahinch, as well as a jaw-dropping estate which is essentially a world-unto-itself. (Patrick O'Flaherty, Ballinafad, Recess, Connemara ☎ 095-31006 bhinch@iol.ie www.ballynahinch-castle.com – Open all year, except Feb and Christmas)

Ballinasloe

Organic fruit and vegetables

● Beechlawn Organic Farm

Padraig and Una's beautiful organic produce is widely available throughout the best shops and supermarkets in County Galway, and Beechlawn is an archetype of the sort of organic farm that could and should be the norm for Irish farming. Their produce is beautifully produced, life-giving and health-giving, which may explain why the pair of them are such mighty craic. (Padraig Fahy & Úna Ní Bhroin, Ballinasloe ☎ 090-964 6713 ✉ info@beechlawnfarm.org 🖱 www.beechlawnfarm.org)

Galway County

made in Galway

Oslo Bay Ale

Farmhouse Cheese

● Killeen Farmhouse Cheese

A month after joining Facebook, Marion Roeleveld posted some pictures of herself making cheese using raw milk which was still warm from their herd of goats. Consider that: the milk from their animals who graze on their farm, still with the temperature of the animal's body, and transformed by this master cheesemaker. If you have ever asked yourself why Ms Roeleveld's goat's and cow's milk cheeses are so good, now you know: you cannot get closer to making a natural product the way nature intended than this. Lucky us, also, that Ms Roeleveld is one of the most gifted of modern cheesemakers, her signature style in both of her goudas a liminal sweetness, and a clean, lactic purity. It doesn't get better than this. (Marion Roeleveld, Killeen Millhouse, Ballyshrule, Ballinasloe ☎ 090-974 1319 ✉ haske-marion@iolfree.ie)

Herb mixes

● Kylemore Acres

Richard and Diana Murray are true epicureans. Their Kylemore Acres herb and spice blends aren't like anyone else's. Instead, the Kylemore mixes bring structure and definition to a dish – a robustness to a bolognaise, a cleanness to a chowder, a warmth and depth to a seasonal glass of mulled wine. They are tweakers, endlessly refining the balance of their herb packages, looking for the maximum sensual congratulation to deliver to a dish. Kylemore Acres may be the shortest route you can take to being an accomplished cook. (Diana & Richard Murray, Kylemore, Laurencetown, Ballinasloe ☎ 090-968 5857 ✉ sales@kylemoreacres.com 🖱 www.kylemoreacres.com)

Ballyconneely

Smokehouse

● The Connemara Smokehouse

Galway County

Graham Roberts works hard, and has always worked hard. Aged four, he was scoring a penny every time he washed a fish box for his dad. Aged six, he was helping out with everything. Today, in the Connemara Smokehouse, it is the boss himself who hand-fillets the fish, salts it, smokes it. This is artisanship. His tenure has been marked not just by superb smoked fish, but by an impish need to innovate, which has led him to create smoked tuna recipes and products that are the clearest expression of his signature style, using both cold- and hot-smoking techniques. Rick Stein buys it for his Padstow restaurants, a genuine accolade, and a richly deserved one. (Graham & Saoirse Roberts, Bunowen Pier, Ailebrack, Ballyconneely ☎ 095-23739 ✉ info@smokehouse.ie 🖱 www.smokehouse.ie)

Bearna

Restaurant

● O'Grady's on the Pier

Mike O'Grady's waterside restaurant is atmospheric and has been consistently professional for more than a decade. Seafood is their main man, and the team like to veer away from the classics to show their swerve: Clare Island salmon with smoked potato purée; plaice with Killary mussels, smoked tomato and chervil butter; silver hake with smoked paprika vermouth. There are dishes apart from fish and shellfish, of course, but those are the ones we go for. The restaurant has a sister establishment, Kirwan's Lane, in Galway city. (Michael O'Grady, Seapoint, Barna, Galway ☎ 091-592223 ✉ ogradysonthepier@hotmail.com 🖱 www.ogradysonthepier.com – Open from 6pm daily. Sun lunch 12.30pm-2.45pm)

Bakery and Café

● The Pins Bakery

The Pins Bakery is the third food stop that is part of the Twelve Hotel. Sitting just beside Pizza Dozzina, this little café bakery bakes bread and pastries and has a good deli counter. Perfect for picnickers heading West. (Fergus O'Halloran, Bearna Village, Galway ☎ 091-597000 ✉ enquire@thetwelvehotel.ie/pins-bakery-shop 🖱 www.thetwelvehotel.ie – Open all year, but always check off season)

Galway County

Pizza Restaurant

● Pizza Dozzina

Dozzina made news locally when the two-and-a-half ton Napoliforni oven was manoeuvred into the lower ground floor kitchen in a tight squeeze through the window. Connemara traffic was brought to a standstill. It was a great start to the restaurant as locals and visitors flocked to its doors to see what all the fun was about. Now it looks as if it's always been there, and what is more, it always seems as if we Irish have put our fine ingredients on a pizza, because after all what better showcase could you get for some Connemara charcuterie, or some of our farmhouse cheeses. Each pizza is tossed together by hand by a motivated, enthusiastic team, and Dozzina is a winner. (Fergus O'Halloran, Bearna Village, Galway ☎ 091-597012 ✉ enquire@thetwelvehotel.ie 🖱 www.thetwelvehotel.ie/pizza-dozzina – Pizzas available to eat in or takeaway. Pizza parties arranged)

Hotel

● The Twelve

The Twelve, a groovy, colourful hotel at the junction in Barna, west of Galway city, is a fascinating place. It's as modern as all-get-out and yet… and yet, it's actually utterly traditional in a uniquely Irish way.
How so? Because of the team who work with manager Fergus O'Halloran, who work in the old Irish way, which is to say: they look after you. They are patient, funny, generous, and unselfconscious. They make the experience of staying here utterly special and, in the bar and restaurant (and pizzeria), you see this social genius at work at pell-mell pace: Barna, New York. In their West restaurant, chef Martin O'Donnell has worked his

way into the top position and looks set to be a major player, creating a cuisine that smartly uses his native foods but with a confident, avant-garde touch. The wine list is – justly, rightly – celebrated. (Fergus O'Halloran, Bearna Village, Galway ☎ 091-597000 enquire@thetwelvehotel.ie www.thetwelvehotel.ie – Open all year, but always check off season)

Claregalway

Farmers' Market

● Claregalway Farmers' Market

Saturday morning at County Galway's favourite traffic snarl-up is the site for the market. Get there early for the fresh fish. (Sat 10am-2pm)

Clarinbridge

Restaurant

● Providence Market Kitchen

Orla Fox's county outpost to her Galway city Market Kitchen is another lovely space, with new gallery work always on exhibit. The best art, however, is what will be on your plate. The menus are kept tight and concise, and everything is as good as they can possibly make it, from the pinhead oatmeal to the club double-decker. (Orla Fox, Clarinbridge ☎ 091-533906 Orla@providencemarketkitchen.com www.providencemarketkitchen.com – Open 8am-6pm Mon-Sat)

Restaurant

● Claire's Tearooms

Stone walled. Richly furnished. Elegant china. A classy bit of retail. Oh, it would be great to have Claire Walsh's singular, special tearooms as your local, rather than experiencing it – as the rest of us have to – as a roadside stop when heading North or South. But then, that might be like people who move to Galway and regret no longer having the experience of being able to visit Galway for the weekend. What better, calmer, roadside destination could one have than this little oasis of civility and culture. (Claire Walsh, Clarinbridge ☎ 091-776606 – Open 9.30am-5pm Tue-Sat, noon-5pm Sun)

Pasta

● Magnetti Pasta

Sean, Marco and Paolo peer out from the windows of a tiny cinquecento on the bright, fun packaging that wraps around their fine pasta products, and they have always shown an impish sense of fun, as well as serious culinary chops, when it comes to making good Italian food. Fresh pastas, filled pastas and ready meals can be found in supermarkets and speciality shops throughout the country, and they bring a smile to your face, they really do. (Marco, Paolo & Sean Magnetti, Unit 1A Clarinbridge Business Park, Clarinbridge ☎ 091-776580 ✉ info@magnettibrothers.com 🖱 www.magnettibrothers.com. Trattoria Magnetti, 12 Quay Street, Galway ☎ 091-563910)

Cleggan

Seaweed Relishes and Seafood

● Cleggan Seaweed Company

The Cleggan Seaweed Co have always had a vision of their seaweeds as a connoisseur product, something that sits comfortably in gourmet hampers, or on the shelves of the best delicatessens. Their Sea Pickle looks like the sort of jar you would expect to buy in Fortnum & Mason. They have always demonstrated confidence and finesse with their boxes of seaweed – five varieties, which are hand-picked from the clean local shoreline and packed and sold without need of any further processing. (Shane Forsythe, Cleggan Fishing Village, Connemara ☎ 095-44649 ✉ info@clegganseaweed.com 🖱 www.clegganseaweed.com)

Clifden

Shop

● The Connemara Hamper

The Connemara Hamper is just that: a little space, packed chock-a-block with lovely things from near, and from far. Like a good hamper, it unveils itself slowly, as you come to realise just how many things Eileen and Louise have managed to pack onto the shelves and into the deli. Superlative sandwiches and rolls to take away just solved your lunchtime dilemma. (Eileen & Louise Halliday, Market Street, Clifden ☎ 095-21054 ✉ info@connemarahamper.com 🖱 www.connemarahamper.com – Open 10am-5.30pm Mon-Sat, with more limited hours off season)

Country House

● Dolphin Beach

In Dolphin Beach, the small details are all there: the comforting pot of tea and biscuits when you arrive; perfect beds with crisp linen; beautiful books to leaf through in the front room; home-made breads and jam; the warm welcome. Clodagh Foyle has innkeeping in her blood, and it shows. She effortlessly juggles a million household tasks, and yet is always ready with a smile. Dolphin is the house in which to truly unwind. (The Foyle family, Lower Sky Road, Clifden, Connemara ☎ 095-21204 🖱 www.dolphinbeachhouse.com ✉ stay@dolphinbeachhouse.com – Open Mar-Oct)

Galway County

Fishmonger

● Duane's Fish Shop

Duane's is an essential destination for anyone self-catering in Clifden, and look out particularly for their very good crab in summertime. (John Duane, Main Street, Clifden ☎ 095-21804 – Open 10am-6pm Mon-Fri, closed Mon off season, 10am-5pm Sat)

Restaurant

● Mitchell's

Mitchell's is one of those restaurants that makes you feel good. The rooms are bright and simple, and everything in the restaurant gleams with polished care. The style is stripped-back and unpretentious, calm and colourful, a room that everyone can enjoy. But it's not just the room that feels right: the service and the food in JJ Mitchell's restaurant enjoy a consistency that you – frankly – don't expect in a busy tourist town like Clifden. JJ and his team know what they do best, and they do it every season, making Mitchell's the real solid-sender in Clifden. (JJ Mitchell, Market Street, Clifden ☎ 095-21867 ✉ jjm.clifden@googlemail.com – Open noon-close, with dinner sittings at 7pm & 9pm Mon-Sun. Closed Hallowe'en-March)

Shop

● Off The Square

PJ and Maureen do a very good job at cooking for the diverse and disparate visitors who pile in to pretty Clifden, so you can come to OTS for breakfast, arrive later to get chowder and a sandwich for lunch, and turn up in the evening for some West Coast fish or a good steak. (PJ & Maureen Heffernan, Clifden ☎ 095-22281 info@offthesquare.ie www.offthesquarerestaurant.com – Open from 9.15am, open breakfast, lunch and dinner)

Guesthouse

● Quay House

Our editor Elizabeth Field's reaction to Paddy and Julia Foyle's gorgeous house articulates every duality that makes this house extra-special: peaceful yet dynamic; stylish yet relaxed; private yet public, a world apart. "This place has tons of style: overstuffed sofas and chairs, walls chock-a-block with paintings and ornaments; plump pillows; meandering corridors, So you feel like you're in your own private, rambling, wisteria-covered residence. The breakfast was outstanding: scrambled eggs with smoked salmon; porridge with berry compote; and all the fixings of the full Irish. The Foyles are absolutely dynamic: funny, warm, urbane and welcoming. An Irish classic." (Paddy & Julia Foyle, Beach Rd, Clifden, Connemara ☎ 095-21369 res@thequayhouse.com www.thequayhouse.com – Open mid Mar-early Nov)

B&B

● Sea Mist House

A stone-clad, handsome house dating from the 1820's, set just down the seaward road off the main square in Clifden, Sheila Griffin's Sea Mist B&B is one of those houses that define the essence of our guides. So, for instance, there are no televisions in the bedrooms. Ms Griffin takes the opposite point of view from those who think every room has to have all the gizmos, and she knows that if you are in Connemara, you should be out on the Twelve Bens, or at least enjoying her lovely garden, or relaxing in the aesthetic of her beautiful house. So, she does things differently, and we like that. (Sheila Griffin, Clifden, Connemara ☎ 095-21441 sheila@seamisthouse.com www.seamisthouse.com)

Coffee Shop

● Steam

Claire and Alan's terrific café had a smart makeover for the 2012 season, so there is now even greater comfort and colour in which to bask as you enjoy parsnip and apple soup, crabmeat on fresh brown bread, or maybe that crabmeat will be in a tart with tomatoes and leeks, or maybe you fancy Steam homecooked ham with cheddar and relish in a sandwich, and then a slice of zesty lemon tart. Great food, great place, great vibe, a room where everything is done as well as they can do it, not least the legendary hot chocolate, the Best in the West. (Claire Griffin & Alan King, Station House, Clifden ☎ 095-30600 www.steam-foods.com – Open 10am-6pm Mon-Sat)

Corrandulla

Organic Box Delivery

● Green Earth Organics

Kenneth and Jenny Keavey run a fab box-delivery system, delivering throughout Galway city and county, bringing their organic produce to lucky recipients. They have polytunnels and farm about 15 of their 30 acres, just five miles from Galway city. They had a great presence at the first Galway Food Festival, both as exhibitors and speakers, and they are key players in the burgeoning Galway food culture. You will also find them at the Moycullen Market, and there is a farm shop at Corrandulla. (Kenneth Keavey, Caherlea, Corrandulla ☎ 091-793768 info@greenearthorganics.ie www.greenearthorganics.ie – Office open 9.30am-11am Mon, 9.30am-noon, Tue, 9.30am-2pm Fri)

Furbo

Hotel

● Connemara Coast Hotel

Charles Synnott understands that to run an hotel, you need to be an hotelier, that most noble, and difficult, of vocations. In fact, Mr Synnott runs two hotels in this book, and it is their difference, and their distinctiveness, that appeals to us. Brooks Hotel in Dublin is the quintessential city hotel. The Connemara Coast, then, is the quintessential resort hotel, a place to escape to from the city, a place to enjoy sea air, good food, a beautiful art collection, along with excellent service led by manager Ann Downey. The Coast is a place to relax, and the staff manage to create the Ocean Liner Effect perfectly: when you stay here, you are away from it all. To create and maintain this feeling is the true art and craft of the hotelier, and you will rarely see it practised better than it is practised in this special West Coast getaway. (Charles Synnott, Furbo, Galway ☎ 091-592 2108 ✉ info@connemaracoast.ie 🖱 www.connemara-coast.ie – Open all year, except Christmas)

made in Galway

Connemara Abalone

Gort

Café and Hostel

● Gallery Cafe

Is this the funkiest place in Galway? Galway does funky better than anywhere else in Ireland, but the Gallery takes funky into a new stratosphere: Super Funky. We love the surreal aspects – hair salon seats; indoor car boot sales! – but the Gallery isn't just nicely weird: the cooking is good, and the service is even better. Respect! (Sarah Harty, Queen Street, Gort ☎ 091-630630 ✉ galcafe@gmail.com – Open Lunch and Dinner)

Market

● Gort Farmers' Market

Friday morning is market time in Gort. (Town Centre, Gort – Open Fri 10am-2pm)

Fish and Chip Shop

● Kettle of Fish

The county outpost of the Galway city solid sender, and one of the best chippers on the west coast, an opinion that is echoed by many other food lovers. We love the clean crispness that they achieve with the fryer, and the quality of ingredients is first class. Worth the detour into town. (Siobhan Fahey, The Square, Gort ☎ 091-630300 – Open noon-10pm Mon-Sun)

Kilcolgan

Oysters

● Michael Kelly Shellfish

The Kelly family produce edulis oysters, and you can't eat anything better on this earth than a Galway edulis oyster. Their delivery system is as efficient as their oysters are delicious, and having an ash basket of Kelly oysters arrive for your birthday – hint, hint – or because it's Thursday is a food lover's idea of heaven. (Diarmuid Kelly, Tyrone, Kilcolgan ☎ 091-796120 kellyoysters@eircom.net www.kellyoysters.com)

Oysters

● Moran's Oyster Cottage

Yes, Moran's is an international tourism staple, but don't worry about that. Catherine Moran is the seventh generation of the family to run this beautiful waterside bar. They do some lovely things – oysters and brown bread, chowders, fish platters – and with a pint of creamy stout, you will wish to be nowhere else. (Catherine Moran, The Weir, Kilcolgan ☎ 091-796 113 www.moransoystercottage.com – Open noon-11.30pm Mon-Thur, noon-midnight Fri-Sat, noon-11pm Sun)

Kinvara

Health Food Shop

● Healing Harvest

Sian Morgan's store is one of those vital neighbourhood addresses. Not just for good wholefoods, though you will find them here. But also for hanging up your posters about this cause or that concert or this benefit or that marathon. Healing Harvest is a neighbourhood place, in that it defines the neighbourhood, and reflects it. Super. (Sian Morgan, Main Street, Kinvara ☎ 091-637176 www.healingharvest.ie – Open 9am-6pm Mon-Sat)

Smokehouse

● Kinvara Smoked Salmon

We first met Declan Droney for a chat in the kitchen of his house near to Kinvara, many years ago. Today, many years later, Kinvara is a powerhouse artisan company, exporting to 27 countries worldwide, winning numerous awards and critics' accolades. And still based in Kinvara, if not quite in the family kitchen. How did Declan do it? Terrific smoked salmon, allied to a brilliant understanding of logistics. He is a cool, anlaytical guy, pretty good qualities all told for a salmon smoker and a businessman. His fish is superb – subtle, delicate, beautifully realised, beautifully packaged. In another decade, we are sure, it will be 77 countries worldwide. (Declan Droney, Kinvara ☎ 091-637489 info@kinvarasmokedsalmon.com www.kinvarasmokedsalmon.com)

Market

● Kinvara Friday Market

Music plays, chickens (such handsome chickens!) cluck, people ramble from stall to stall in the walled garden, shopping and eating and chatting and admiring the chickens, and there is everything from Sri Lankan curries to seaweed to local honey to handsome sweaters. Kinvara is a lovely, left-field market: do not miss it! (Behind Johnston's Hall, Main Street, Kinvara, Friday 10am)

Pub Restaurant

● The Tide Full Inn

Marianne and her husband, Joseph, serve good honest Italian food in this lovely old pub in the centre of town. They keep things nice and tight, with a short list of simple starters, a few pasta dishes and a few main courses. Their signature pizzas are not just good, they are funny: the Berlusconi! the Bastardo! the Tide Full Out! the Drunk! Reading about them is almost as much fun as eating them. And don't miss the fine baking – Rocky Road, orange and polenta cake. A super place, with grown-up cooking that is a quiet treat. (Marianne & Joseph Krause, Main Street, Kinvara ☎ 091-637400 www.thetidefullinn.com – Open noon-10pm Mon-Sun, closed Tue)

Leenane

Country House

● Delphi Lodge

The reason Peter Mantle's country house and estate is world-renowned is not just because of what it is, but also because of what it is not. Yes, it is an especially beautiful house in one of the most beautiful places in Ireland – if not the world. But equally important is the fact that Delphi doesn't try to be an hotel, or to ape hotel-style service. It has stubbornly set its face against the modern blandness many people think of as luxury. So, instead it is quaint, a place that is comfortable with itself, which means you will be comfortable with it too. In Delphi, they know what they can do best, and their best is what they do. It's a simple thing, but it demands a quiet confidence. (Peter Mantle, Leenane ☎ 095-42222 ✉ res@delphilodge.ie 🖱 www.delphilodge.ie – Open Mar-Sep. House parties 18+ off season)

Galway County

made in Galway

Kinvara Smoked Salmon

Letterfrack

Craft Shop & Café

● Avoca

The Avoca crew are a class act, and their utter discrimination is as evident here on the West coast as in their Wicklow and Dublin heartland. (Simon Pratt, Letterfrack ☎ 095-41058 ✉ info@avoca.ie 🖱 www.avoca.ie – Open 9am-6pm Mon-Sun. Closed Jan 15-Mar 15)

Country House

● Renvyle House Hotel

Ronnie and Tim, manager and chef of Renvyle House, are one of the great double acts in Irish hospitality and food. Between them, Mr Ronnie Counihan and Mr Tim O'Sullivan have created a manifesto for Renvyle that is one of the most compelling examples of contemporary Irish ingenuity. It means that Renvyle looks like an hotel and has the scale of an hotel, but feels more like a country house. It means that the food is cutting edge, and yet is also simple and unpretentious, earthy and agrestic, smartly sourced from excellent local artisan suppliers. It means that Renvyle feels traditional, yet is as modern as you need it to be. Reconciling all these seeming contradictions takes a particular form of genius, and these two genial blokes have it in spades. (Ronnie Counihan, Letterfrack, Connemara ☎ 095-43511 ✉ info@renvyle.com 🖱 www.renvyle.com – Open Mar-Nov & Christmas)

Country House

● Rosleague Manor

Mark Foyle's house is one of the prettiest of all the Irish country house. Pretty in pink, with the most to-die-for location and setting, it is a quintessential part of Connemara, fusing the elegant with the elemental in a sublime cocktail. (Mark Foyle, Letterfrack, Connemara ☎ 095-41101 ⌘ www.rosleague.com – Open Mar-Nov)

Loughrea

Food Hall & Café

● Corry's Food Hall & Café

Declan Corry has reinvented the traditional butcher's shop, repositioning it as part of a super-funky modern food hall, and with an excellent café, Sabor, upstairs, run by Nigel Murray. The Sabor team in the kitchens gives the food hall a huge range of baked goods to complement the charcuterie, and after you have filled the shopping bags, it's upstairs for some slow-cooked pork Peruvian-style. Mr Corry and his team aren't content with 100%: for these guys, it's 110%, all the time, and a clutch of awards in the last few years alone show one of the most dynamic operations in the county. (Declan Corry, Station Road, Loughrea ☎ 091-841 109 – Open 8.30am-6pm Mon-Sat, 11am-5.30pm Sun)

Restaurant Pizzeria

● Il Porcetto

You might not expect some echt Italian cooking in Loughrea, but that is what you will find in Il Porchetto. Good fresh pastas and crispy pizzas come in generous portions, served in a room that is simplicity itself – all that is missing is some wax-coated fiascos on the tables and you could be in Calabria, 1963. (Main Street, Loughrea ☎ 091-870 633 ✉ ilporcetto@gmail.com – Open noon-3pm, 5.30pm-late Mon-Sun, from 12.30pm Sun)

Moycullen

Traiteur & Deli

● Enjoy

Enjoy is the traiteur-food hall of Kevin and Ann Dunne's restaurant, White Gables. It's packed with lovely things

– Gingergirl relishes, Badger & Dodo coffee, Connemara Smokehouse fish, Solaris teas, their own superb savoury and sweet baking. It's a lovely room in which to take breakfast or lunch, and to take away something delicious for dinner. (Kevin & Ann Dunne, Moycullen ☎ 091-868200 ✉ info@whitegables.com 🖱 www.whitegables.com – Open 10.30am-8pm Tue-Sat, 10.30am-5pm Sun)

Cupcake Bakery and Café

● The Galway Cakery Café

The Cakery Café is uber-cool, a light, arty, minimalist space in which to enjoy Henrike Elehmer's artful baking. Cup cakes aren't all they do – they also make cakes, baklava, cakeballs and biscuits – and everything is united by precision and a joyful sense of colour and pleasure. (Henrike Elehmer, Unit 17a, Cearnog Nua, Moycullen ☎ 091-555033 ✉ info@cupcakesonline.ie 🖱 www.cupcakesonline.ie – Café open daily for cakes, treats and light lunches)

Galway County

Market

● Moycullen Farmers' Market

Moycullen has one of the best markets in the west. You seek sushi or pancakes, organic breads or fish, organic veg or grass-fed beef, fudge or hot dogs, Pangur Ban pies or Omey oysters? They are all here, including Desperate Housewives and Ballygourmet buns, and a lot more too. A terrific endeavour. (The Forge – Open Fri 1pm-6pm)

Restaurant

● White Gables

It is so refreshing to see a chef like Kevin Dunne decide that he has no interest in chasing culinary fashion, and that he will cook where his heart lies, with the classic dishes of classic French cuisine – snails with garlic and herb butter; beef consommé; roast duckling with orange sauce; beef Wellington; sole on the bone with beurre blanc; pineapple with Kirsch. It takes some nerve in modern cooking to assert that you have no interest in being modern, but the Dunnes have that nerve, they have that conviction, and they do things their way. Oh, and everyone loves it, of course. (Kevin & Ann Dunne, Moycullen Village ☎ 091-555744 ✉ info@whitegables.com 🖱 www.whitegables.com – Open 7pm-9.30pm Wed-Sun 12.30pm-3pm Sun)

Oranmore

Chinese Restaurant

● Royal Villa

One of the Chan family's resilient and rock-steady duo of restaurants. The Villa is calm, classy, always reliable. (Charlie Chan, Castle Court, Castle Road, Oranmore ☎ 091-790823 🖰 www.royalvilla.ie – Open 5pm-11pm Mon-Thur, 5pm-11.30pm Fri & Sat, 3pm-10pm Sun)

Galway County

Restaurant and Hotel

● Basilico

Chef Paolo Sabatini, manager Fabiano Mulas and their team are working super-hard in Oranmore, spinning off new ideas in Basilico at a rate of knots. Ingredients are carefully curated from good suppliers, and show deep culinary understanding – ravioli fritti with Taleggio, walnuts and butternut squash cream; monkfish tagliatelle; wild sea bass baked al cartoccio; ravioli primavera; haddock with tomato risotto; bistecca al vino rosso. (Paolo Sabatini, ☎ 091-788367 📫 basilico.oranmore@yahoo.ie, 🖰 www.coachhousehotel.ie – Open 8am-11pm Mon-Fri, 8am-11.30pm Sat-Sun)

Café and Cookery School

● Kate's Place

At the top of the escalator in the Orantown Centre you will find Kate Wright's sweet little café. Ms Wright was a staple of the *McKennas' Guides* when she ran the Cobblestone Café in the city. Her little room in Oranmore is bright and girly, with a small counter of delicious things begging you to come and taste them – bakewells; apple pies; Tunisian orange cake – and lots of tables and chairs out front on the concourse. In the evening, Kate conducts various cookery classes, so come along and learn from an experienced expert. (Kate Wright, 1st floor, Orantown Centre, Oranmore ☎ 086-6066494 📫 katewright@eircom.net 🖰 www.galwaycookeryclassses.com)

Market

● Oranmore Farmers' Market

The Oranmore Market brings together some of the county's very best producers and food specialists. (Open Thur noon-6pm, behind the church)

Oughterard

Butcher

● Roger Finnerty & Sons

There is a branch of the excellent Finnerty's in Galway city – in the Eyre Square centre – and Billy Morgan's stores are places for pristine, creative charcuterie, and excellent service from skilled butchers. (Billy Morgan, Main Street, Oughterard ☎ 091-552255 ✉ finnertysbutchers@iolfree.ie – Open 8am-6.30pm Mon-Sat, till 7pm Fri)

Butcher

● McGeough's Butchers

McGeough's has been in business for more than forty years. Four decades in which father and son – Eamonn and James – have shown that they have no peers when it comes to being creative charcutiers. Of course, they have the best Connemara lamb and the best beef – aged for 6 weeks and more! But it has been James McGeough's experiments with charcuterie that have chiselled him a singular position, for no one else produces anything like his air-dried lamb, beef and pork, his fantastic smoked sausages, his hams and salamis. You can order them online, but a visit to this singular shop, to see and breathe the culture of charcuterie that runs through the veins of these guys, is a food lover's dream. (James McGeough, Barrack Street, Oughterard ☎ 091-552351 ✉ connemarafinefoods@eircom.net 🖱 www.connemarafinefoods.ie – Open Mon-Sat)

made in Galway

Foods of Athenry Bakery

Wine Merchant

● Probus Wines

Paul Fogarty has been finding and selling superb wines from all over the world for almost 15 years now, providing an invaluable and expert service for wine lovers. Mr Fogarty knows his mind, and his shop is quirky, the range is bespoke, the advice is sage. A marvellous wine shop. (Paul Fogarty, Camp Street, Oughterard ☎ 091-552084 🖱 www.probuswines.ie)

Recess

Country House

● Lough Inagh Lodge

"Sometimes it's the really small things that are memorable", a friend wrote about an afternoon stop-over at Maire O'Connor's pretty hotel. "The warmth of service, welcoming and quietly confident, yet attentive and eager to please, the fact that they may have been doing this for years, yet every visitor is unique and important." Lough Inagh is delightful, a special place. (Maire O'Connor, Recess, Connemara ☎ 095-34706 ✉ inagh@iol.ie 🖱 www.loughinaghlodgehotel.ie – Open Mar-Dec)

Galway County

Roscahill

Garden & Tea Rooms

● Brigit's Garden

My but we had a lovely meander in and around Brigit's garden on our last trip through Roscahill. You could come here just to sample their fine café, but you really should not miss these ingenious and captivating gardens, which fuse an aesthetic beauty with a contemplativeness that is enchanting. It's very Celtic Zen, which we like a lot. The café is excellent, with wholesome, true cooking that fits the aura of the gardens perfectly. Lovely. (Jenny Beale, Pollagh, Roscahill ☎ 091-550905 🖱 www.galwaygarden.com – Café opens 1 May-30 Sept 10.30am-5pm. Open Sun in April. Groups off season by arrangement)

Rossaveal

Shellfish Producer

● Connemara Abalone

Cindy O'Brien's company is one of the small number of abalone producers dotted around the Irish coastline. They specialise in the prized Japanese Ezo abalone. Do look out for the terrific recipe leaflets for abalone created by Tim O'Sullivan, of Renvyle House. (Cindy O'Brien, Ballinahown Industrial Estate, Rossaveal ☎ 091-591307 ✉ info@abalone.ie 🖱 www.abalone.ie)

Roundstone

B&B

● The Angler's Return

Lynn Hill's Angler's Return is a house that you need to lower yourself into, as if it were a beautiful, big, bubble bath. Just staying one night and rushing through Connemara, is madness personified. You have to let this place into your soul. And when you do that, when you get Zen, you suddenly see the birds, and hear the bees – especially if you are lying on a rug in the pretty garden of the Angler's Return! And then there is a cracking fire in the evening time in the sitting room, looking out at the lakes and the sunset and maybe a simple, delicious dinner cooked by Lynn. Now, isn't that the real Connemara? (Lynn Hill, Toombeola, Roundstone, Connemara ☎ 095-31091 ⌘ www.anglersreturn.com – Open Feb-Nov)

Bar & Restaurant

● O'Dowd's Seafood Bar & Restaurant

Four generations of the O'Dowd family have rattled the pots and pans of this Connemara institution, and they have acquired their legendary status by serving simple, consistent, tasty food – seafood gratin; poached salmon; smoked salmon pasta; beef and Guinness stew. And a pint of Guinness to go with it, of course. (O'Dowd family, Roundstone ☎ 095-35923 ✉ odowds@indigo.ie ⌘ www.odowdsbar.com – Open 10am-9.30pm all year)

Salthill

Pizzeria

● Da Roberta Pizzeria

Roberta and Sandro and their son, David, bring Tuscany to Salthill every day of the week, and everyone loves it. The original pizzeria proved to be such a success that it spawned its sister resturant, right next door. The pizzeria is not devoted solely to pizzas – there are classic starters, pasta dishes, meat dishes and so on – but the pizzas and calzones are rock-steady good. It's manic, theatrical, and brilliant fun. (Sandro & Roberta Pieri, 161 Upper Salthill, Galway ☎ 091-585808 – Open noon-11pm Mon-Sun)

Restaurant

● Gourmet Tart Company

We think the GTC in Salthill is one of the most beautifully designed eating spaces we have ever seen. It put Eamon Barrett in mind of the café at Daylesford Organic in Notting Hill. Connie McKenna loved the doodlebook drawings that break up the plain white walls. When Eamon ate here, "We arrived at twelve thirty for lunch and by one o'clock there wasn't a table to be had – always a sign that you're in good hands. The menu is cleverly simple: soup, sandwiches, salads and a small selection of hot food - but everything we ate was prepared with care and was tasty and satisfying. Leaving without trying some of the amazing cakes will be almost an impossibility. A superb operation that Salthill is extremely lucky to have." And so say all of us. (Michelle & Fintan Hyland, Salthill Upper, Galway ☎ 091-861667 📫 info@gourmettartco.com 🖱 www.gourmettartco.com – Open 7.30am-8pm)

Galway County

Independent Supermarket

● Morton's of Galway

Eric Morton's store is one of the masterly pieces of culinary editing in Ireland. Mr Morton sells everything you need, and no more. He has the best of the best, and that's all he has. Breads, vegetables, charcuterie, meat, a fantastic range of traiteur foods to take away, excellent wines. It's all here, beautifully arrayed and presented. A model enterprise. (Eric Morton, Lower Salthill, Galway ☎ 091-522237 📫 sales@mortonsofgalway.ie 🖱 www.mortonsofgalway.ie – Open 9am-7pm Mon-Sat, 10am-5.30pm Sun)

Brew Pub

● Oslo

Oslo is a great big enormodrome of a pub, at the seaside end of Salthill. Of most interest to food lovers is their range of slickly named craft beers, from their Galway Bay Brewery: Strange Brew; Bay Ale, and Stormy Port. The beers are light and clean, and go well with their modern tasty food – bangers and mash; steak burger; salmon and haddock fish cakes; beer-battered fish. Most of the Irish craft beers are also sold, as well as a great range of international brews. (Jason O'Connell, Niall Walsh, Salthill, Galway ☎ 091 448 390 📫 @ 🖱 www.winefoodbeer.com)

Restaurant

● L'Osteria da Roberta

L'Osteria is the (slightly) more formal restaurant sister of the hugly popular Da Roberta Pizzeria, and it's equally atmospheric and enjoyable. The food is Tuscany's Greatest Hits: sea bass with potato crust; chicken wrapped in Parma ham; linguini with seafood. Will you enjoy it? You assuredly will. (Sandro & Roberta Pieri, 157 Upper Salthill, Galway ☎ 091-581111 ✉ daroberta@eircom.net – Open 5pm-11pm Mon-Sat, 12.30pm-11pm Sun)

Chinese Restaurant

● Royal Villa

The smart, handsome National Aquarium is home to one of the great Galway champions, Charles and Yvonne Chan's Royal Villa. The Chan family have run excellent Chinese restaurants – there is a sister branch in Oranmore – for more than two decades, fashioning great, atmospheric rooms and cooking delightful ethnic food. The menus have become more pan-Asian over time, but for us it's the chef's classic Chinese dishes every time. (Yvonne Chan, 1st floor, National Aquarium of Ireland, Salthill, Galway ☎ 091-580131 ✉ salthill@royalvilla.ie 🖱 www.royalvilla.ie – Open 5pm-11pm Mon-Thur, 5pm-11.30pm Fri & Sat, 3pm-10pm Sun)

Galway County

Spiddal

Restaurant

● Builin Blasta

Jamie Peaker is a New Zealander, and he is a local hero in Spiddal where his café in the craft centre is the mecca for local food lovers. Mr Peaker prepares excellent food: funky pizzas; a great bacon, egg and potato omelette cake (breakfast, lunch and dinner in one go, if you like); and there are crisp clean salads, nice puddings and sweet things, and jars of dressings and chutneys to bring home. Delightful and special, a real local hero. (Jamie Peaker, Spiddal Craft & Design Studios, Spiddal ☎ 091-558 559 🖱 www.spiddalcrafts.ie – Open day time)

County Kerry

Annascaul

Black Pudding

● Ashe's Black Pudding

Kerry butchers make good puddings, and Thomas Ashe's is one of the best. The family's black pudding recipe dates back to 1916 and – crucially – is today still made with fresh blood. Thomas also makes superb sausages and rashers, and brilliantly inventive black pudding sausages and pork and black pudding sausage rolls. Mr Ashe is one of the most gifted charcutiers at work today, and he has patiently built Ashe's into one of the best bespoke meat companies. (Thomas Ashe, Annascaul ☎ 066-915 7127 info@annascaulblackpudding.com www.annascaulblackpudding.com)

Kerry

Ballinskelligs

Café

● Cill Rialaig Art Café

There is a logic to Ivor O'Connor's food that can be traced back to his culinary education, his interests and his travels. A Ballymaloe education cemented a produce-based philosophy that began with his mother. Travelling added to his skills, and an interest in foraging and fishing completes the picture. Ivor now cooks in the Cill Rialaig artists' retreat, a centre where artists come to work and study in this peaceful environment. The cafe is open to the public, along with a gallery. (Ivor O'Connor, Ballinskelligs ☎ 066-947 9297 – www.ivorsfood.com Open daily 7 days, Jun-Aug, with dinner on Saturday night)

Chocolate

● Cocoa Bean Artisan Chocolates

Emily and Sarah think sideways. Chocolate with gin and tonic? Spiffing idea. Chocolate with roses? Bring it on. Chocolate with sea salt? Whyever not. We have known the girls since their earliest days in the Limerick market, and their enthusiasm remains undaunted, their creativity undiminished, their ingenuity as infectious as ever, their sense of fun rampant in every bar they make. (Emily Webster & Sarah Hehir, The Glen, Ballinskelligs ☎ 066-947 9119 🖰 www.cocoabeanchocolates.com)

Free range ducks and duck eggs

● O'Connell's Ducks and Poultry

Patrick and Kim produce superlative ducks. These beauties spend so much time running around outside that their level of fat is much less than the couch-potato ducks one normally finds, so they are a cinch to cook – you can roast them just like a chicken. Their geese are just as fine, and this is a vital resource for top-class poultry. (Patrick O'Connell & Kim Cusick, Meeligoleen, Ballinskelligs ☎ 087-7415790 📫 meeligoleeneggs@gmail.com 🖰 www.oconnellspoultry.com)

Kerry

Chocolate

● Skelligs Chocolate Company

Colm Healy's Skelligs Chocolate Company is the yang to the yin of Emily and Sarah's Cocoa Bean in the Ballinskelligs metropolis of chocolate. How extraordinary that two such gifted artisan chocolate companies should work side-by-side at St. Finian's Bay. The Skelligs chocolate bars, boxes and truffles are vividly delicious. (Colm Healy, The Glen, Ballinskelligs ☎ 066-947 9119 📫 info@skelligschocolate.com 🖰 www.skelligschocolate.com – Open to the public 10am-4pm Mon-Fri Sep-Dec, Feb-May, 10am-5pm Mon-Fri Jun, 10am-5pm Mon-Fri, noon-5pm Sat & Sun Jul-Aug)

Ballybunion

Tearooms

● Sundaes Ice Cream Parlour

Pretty floral baskets and al fresco chairs and tables announce Joanna McCarthy's cult ice cream destination in Ballybunion. Honeycomb ice cream and a doughnut or two is your motivation to join the weekend queue, as you agonise over which of the 15 flavours to choose from. Only mighty. (Joanna McCarthy, Main Street, Ballybunion ☎ 086-052 3089 📫 mccarthyicecream@yahoo.ie – Open noon-9pm Apr-Oct, closed 6pm Sundays)

Blackwater

Tearooms

● The Strawberry Field

Pancakes and ice cream are what we head to the Strawberry Fields for, but you might also come here to buy some statuary, an oil painting, some pottery or cast-iron products, or indeed almost any manner of crafty, creative gift. So, start with some apple pie and a cup of tea and see what takes your fancy. (Margaret & Peter Kerssens, Moll's Gap, Sneem Road, Blackwater ☎ 064-668 2977 info@strawberryfield-ireland.com www.strawberryfield-ireland.com – Open 11am-6pm Mon-Sun)

Kerry

Bonane

Chocolatier

● Benoit Lorge

A French chocolatier working out of an old post office at the side of the road in Bonane, between Kenmare and Bantry. Well, that would be Benoit Lorge, then, wouldn't it. If this sounds fanciful, then believe us that it is real, and that M. Lorge makes smashing chocolates, in the old post office. So, stop the car, buy something sweetly delicious, then pinch yourself. See? It's for real, alright. (Benoit Lorge, Releagh Cottage, Bonane, Kenmare ☎ 064-667 9994/087-991 7172 info@lorge.ie www.lorgechocolate.com)

made in Kerry

Ted Browne's Crab Meat

Caherdaniel

Farmers' Market

● Caherdaniel Market

In addition to its weekly country market, Caherdaniel hosts a summertime farmers' market, on all those summertime sunshiny Sundays that bless the Ring of Kerry. (Blind Piper, Caherdaniel – Open 12.30pm-6pm Sundays, May-Oct, weather permitting)

Guesthouse

● Iskeroon

Iskeroon's extraordinary location at the ocean's edge explains its world-wide renown, and David and Geraldine have designed and furnished their suites and self-catering apartment with exactly the right sort of chic rusticity. Iskeroon is pretty unforgettable, pretty amazing. (Geraldine & David Hare, Iskeroon, Caherdaniel ☎ 066-947 5119 res@iskeroon.com www.iskeroon.com)

local knowledge

Dingle Pies

Myrtle Allen first documented the Dingle Pie in her classic book *The Ballymaloe Cookbook*. The pies, she recorded, were made for special occasions in Dingle, on Holy Days and Fair Days, when "nobody had time to sit down to a proper meal, but pie shops flourished." Dingle pies were made to be eaten hot or cold. Mrs Allen continues: "Fishermen brought them to sea in a can and heated them up in the stock over a little fire made in a tin box, at the bottom of the boat. A cold baked pie was better for the farmer's pocket." The Dingle Pie begot the Spiced Mutton Pie, and it is this spicier version that is cooked now, often using lamb rather than the traditional mutton, and flavoured with cumin seed.

Cahersiveen

Farmers' Market

● Cahersiveen Market

Thursday morning during the season is the time to get the goodies in pretty Cahersiveen. (Community Centre, Thurs 11am-2pm, high season)

Bakery

● Nadura Organic Breads

Nadura breads are made with wholegrain flours and

homemade sourdough starter, and you will find Marie-Louise's health-giving baking at the Milltown market and other occasional markets. (Marie-Louise Holst, Kilcolman, Cahersiveen ☎ 066-9473140 ✉ mlholst@eircom.net)

Bistro

● Number Five Bistro

Barry Wallace's food is very logical, very clean, as chefs say – baby squid two ways; monkfish with saffron butter and sauté potatoes; braised belly of pork with Sneem black pudding and scallop; rump of lamb with roasted pumpkin; dark chocolate and cherry brownie with Valentia Island Madagascan vanilla ice cream! It's hidden down a lane and up the stairs, where you will find a simple, plain room that is the ideal showcase for some really exciting cooking. (Barry & Elaine Wallace, 5 Main Street, Cahersiveen ☎ 066-947 2174 ✉ numberfivebistro@gmail.com 🖱 www.no5bistro.ie – Open noon-3pm Wed-Fri, 6pm-10pm Wed-Sat, noon-10pm Sun)

Kerry

Bakery

● Petit Delice

You don't really expect to find a French bakery and tea rooms on the Ring of Kerry, but here it is: Petit Delice is bakery, lunch time destination, ice cream stop, chocolate fix and coffee stop! "You can imagine that you are deep in La France Profonde", said the FT, and you, hunkered into a booth enjoying a Jésuite aux Amandes and a cup of French roast, will soon see what they mean. Precious. (David Aranda, Danny O'Leary, Cahersiveen ☎ 087-990 3572 www.ringofkerrypatisserie.com – Open 9am-6pm Mon-Sat)

Bar & Restaurant

● The Point Seafood Bar (O'Neill's)

O'Neill's source their fish from Quinlan's fish shops, so make sure to get here early – it's a very busy spot – to enjoy spankingly fresh seafood in a charming, family-run pub. (Michael & Bridie O'Neill, Renard Point, Cahersiveen ☎ 066-947 2165/087-2595345 – Open Lunch Mon-Sat, Dinner Mon-Sun during high season. Telephone first off season, especially if visiting during months Nov-Mar)

Bar & Restaurant

● QC's

Kate and Andrew added the most stunningly stylish series of rooms to their fine restaurant in 2011, instantly establishing QC's as the hippest destination on the Ring of Kerry. Eddie Gannon's cooking follows the design ethos of QC's: take top-class materials, and treat with empathy and respect – crabmeat and prawn bisque with avocado oil; pan-seared squid; hake with samphire and lemon risotto. QC's is hip and very happening. (Kate & Andrew Cooke, 3 Main Street, Cahersiveen ☎ 066-947 2244 ✉ info@qcbar.com 🖰 www.qcbar.com – Open for food 12.30pm-2.30pm Mon-Sat, 6pm-11.30pm Mon-Sun with more limited hours off season)

Smoked Salmon, Fishmonger and on-line retailer

● Quinlan's Kerry Fish

More than thirty people work in the Quinlan family's fish business, which includes four terrific fish shops, their smart Killarney seafood bar, a fish processing plant, and two trawlers, so they really do push all the buttons between tide and table, and they have been doing it for almost fifty years. In addition to fresh fish, they also smoke salmon, mackerel and haddock. There are already plans afoot for a second seafood bar in Tralee beside their shop – now, that's a good idea – and one feels Quinlans are really starting something. (Fintan & Liam Quinlan, Main Street, Cahersiveen ☎ 066-947 2686. Also The Square, Killorglin ☎ 066-976 1860. Also 1 The Mall, Tralee ☎ 066-712 3998. Also Park Road, Killarney ☎ 064-663 9333 – Open 10am-6pm Mon-Fri, 10am-2pm Sat 🖰 www.kerryfish.com)

Lamb

● Ring of Kerry Quality Lamb

Established by more than twenty Kerry lamb producers just a few years ago, the RKQL is a radical group: hill and lowland lamb farmers who want to carve out their own destiny, rather than being carved up by the business. You can order all manner of lamb cuts via their website, including spring lamb and hill lamb, and you can specify how you want the larger cuts butchered, and this is a brilliant customer-focused organisation that we would love to see replicated throughout the entire country. (Timmy Fleming, Cahersiveen ☎ 1890 252 978 ✉ info@kerrylamb.ie 🖰 www.ringofkerryqualitylamb.ie)

Castlecove

Shop, Bakery & Accommodation

● Westcove Farmhouse Shop

Jane Urquhart runs a teasure trove of adventures here in Westcove – a bakery, a shop-that-sells-everything, and a self-catering apartment. Her baking expertise extends from soda bread and scones to Norwegian chocolate cake and made-to-order birthday cakes. Jane is also a pivotal player in local markets, so you will find her produce there as well as in the Westcove shop. (Jane Urquhart, Westcove Farmhouse, Westcove Road, Castlecove ☎ 066-947 5479 westcovefarmhouse@oceanfree.net www.westcove.net)

Castlegregory

Kerry

Bakery

● Bácús

Orla Gowen is a wonderful baker. Her loaves have that crucial alliance of skillfulness and succulence that marks out the best bakers, that magic touch that unites crust and crumb into a piece of utter satisfaction. Her loaves are pretty, too, so she has the eye of an artist and the soul of a artisan. Look out for the Bácús loaves in farmers' markets in Dingle and Tralee, and in several local stores. Ms Gowen is developing slowly and organically, and we are already looking forward to her confectionery. (Orla Gowen, Cloghane, Castlegregory ☎ 087-318 5453 orlagowen@gmail.com)

Farmhouse Cheese

● Dingle Peninsula Cheese

Maja Binder seems happy with life-changing circumstances. She originally wanted to be a clothes designer, but three weeks on an organic dairy farm made her change direction. She moved from Germany to Kerry in 1996, and started making cheese, then met Olivier Beaujouan when she needed dilisk to flavour her cheeses. Now, in addition to her brilliant cheesemaking, she also runs the Little Cheese Shop in Dingle. Her cheeses – the original Kilcummin, Beenoskee and Diliskus – are superb, and are supplemented at different times with fresh cheeses – look out for Dingle truffle cheese – and some fine country butter. (Maja Binder, Kilcummin Beg, Castlegregory ☎ 066-713 9028)

Seafood, Relishes and Charcuterie

● On The Wild Side

We do not know of a more skilled artisan than Olivier Beaujouan. He is an expert butcher, an expert forager, an expert at sea vegetables, an expert with fish, and an expert with fish smoking. And he is as modest as all get out, which only serves to amplify his numerous talents. His sea vegetable preparations can now be found in many good shops, but do hunt down his stall at farmers' markets for there are always delightful concoctions to be found, the latest wild improvisations from a man who mainlines food artisanship. (Olivier Beaujouan, Kilcummin, Castlegregory ☎ 066-713 9028 seatoland@hotmail.com)

made in Kerry

Skelligs Chocolate

Castlemaine

Bakery

● Cloudberry Bakery

Samantha Harrison and her Mum, Maureen, bake some wicked cakes. The sugarcraft skill in Cloudberry cakes is quite breathtaking: it is perfectionism incarnate, real OMG! baking. Look out for their cakepops and cupcakes and other geewhizz treats at Kerry markets. (Samantha & Maureen Harrison, Shanahill East, Castlemaine ☎ 087-097 2081 info@cloudberrybakery.com www.cloudberrybakery.com

Organic restaurant

● The Phoenix

Lorna and Billy have created a world unto themselves at The Phoenix. Arrive here and you'll quickly forget about everything in the outside world as you tumble into their quixotic and charming universe, eagerly awaiting a scrummy vegetarian dinner – Phoenix salad; chick pea, sweet potato and tofu curry; lentil quinoa bake, and fab puddings – and then maybe even a night's rest in one of their gypsy caravans. Every county should have a Phoenix, a sublime, left-field idyll. (Billy & Lorna Tyther, Shanahill East, Castlemaine ☎ 066-976 6284 phoenixtyther@hotmail.com www.thephoenixorganic.com – Open 11am-6pm Thu-Sun)

Cromane

Pub and Restaurant

● Jack's Coastguard Restaurant

Sunday lunchtime, you head off to Jack's in Cromane for a quiet lunch, and when you get there Brian and Grainne Keary's place is mobbed. Don't be surprised: when you ally the gorgeous beachside location of Jack's with a art-deco style interior and rock-solid cooking, then being mobbed with customers is a racing certainty. Seafood should be the first thing on your mind, and get there early. (Grainne & Brian Keary, Cromane Lower, Killorglin ☎ 066-976 9102 ✉ info@jackscromane.com 🖱 www.jackscromane.com – Bar open noon-11.30pm, till 12.30am Fri & Sat, Restaurant open 6pm-9pm, till 9.30pm weekends. Closed Tues all year, & Weds during low season)

Kerry

Dingle

Tea Room

● Béile le Chéile

Blogger, cupcake-maker, marketeer and teacher Sharon Ni Chonchuir has opened this upstairs café in the centre of town, and it's a simple and profound showcase for this warm-hearted perfectionist. We don't know how Sharon does all she does, but we're just glad she does, so it's a chocolate custard muffin and a properly made cup of coffee for me, please. (Sharon Ní Chonchuir, Green Street, Dingle ☎ 087-915 1350 ✉ sharondingle@yahoo.com 🖱 www.foodiefancies.com – Open 10.30am-5.30pm)

Dairy

● Bric Farm

Look out for Dingle Farmhouse Milk from Tom and Mae's farm when touring the peninsula – you will find it in The Little Cheese Shop in Dingle and other stores. (Tomas & Mae Bric, Baile na nGall ☎ 066-9155218)

Brew Pub

● Bric's Brew Pub

The West Kerry Brewery is a collaboration between two local pubs, and there are two beers available – Béal Bán, a dark ale, and Cúl Dorcha, a pale ale. The beers are served from the cask, which is extremely rare, so beer nuts should not miss the trip out to the Gaeltacht in Ballyferriter. There is food available in the bar. (Paul O'Loinsigh & Adrienne Heslin ☎ 066-915 6325 ✉ aheslin@tigbhric.com 🖱 www.tigbhric.com)

Seafood

● Ted Browne's of Dingle

Happily for the people of Ireland, Ted Browne's brilliant crab meat is now very widely available, and it is just the best. Mind you, the frozen prawns are superb, the scampi perfect, and the smoked salmon as good as everything else. A textbook seafood company, with benchmark standards. (Ted Browne, Ballinaboula, Dingle ☎ 066-915 1933 ✉ tbrowne@indigo.ie)

Accommodation

● Castlewood House

"Breakfast is king at Castlewood", wrote Pol O Conghaile in *The Examiner.* Pol recommended in particular the oranges in caramel and the plums in star anise syrup, and we suspect that every guest at this fine house has a breakfast favourite. (Us? Helen's porridge with Cooley whiskey. Come on: we're on holiday!) Castlewood is as customer-focused a destination as you will find in Ireland, and everyone simply loves this smart B&B. (Brian & Helen Heaton, The Wood, Dingle ☎ 066-915 2788 ✉ castlewoodhouse@eircom.net 🖱 www.castlewooddingle.com)

Restaurant

● The Chart House

Owner Jim McCarthy and chef Noel Enright have formed a mighty duo over the last several years in The Chart House. The pair are blessed with a very clear idea of what they want to achieve, and the way in which they want to achieve it. Both like comfort – Mr McCarthy's service is de luxe and comforting, so five minutes after you have settled in, the outside world will have disappeared. Mr Enright then brings a de luxe comfort to tip-top local foods that he knows intimately. The Chart House is as rock-solid and reliable as a restaurant can be. (Jim & Carmel McCarthy, The Mall, Dingle ☎ 066-915 2255 ✉ charthousedingle@gmail.com 🖱 www.thecharthousedingle.com – Open 6.30pm-10pm Mon-Sun, closed Mon & Tue off season)

Craft Brewer

● Dingle Brewing Company

Set in the old Dingle Creamery Building, the DBC's beer is named after the legendary Antarctic explorer Tom Crean, from nearby Annascaul. The beer is widely available in pubs throughout the county, and further afield, but there is something special about enjoying a pint at the brewery at the foot of the Conor Pass. (Jerry O'Sullivan, Spa Road, Dingle ☎ 066-915 0743 ✉ hello@dinglebrewingcompany.com 🖱 www.dinglebrewingcompany.com)

Beef

● Dingle Dexter Beef

Paddy Fenton is a vet and a Dexter devotee, who rears these adorable animals – they only grow to three feet tall! – in partnership with five other farmers. These guys are more than enterprising, for they have also converted a van modelled on the old Dingle railway carriages, – the Dingle Dexter – which they bring to food festivals. Dexter beef is wonderfully flavoured – Paddy calls it "Ireland's Kobe beef" – and we reckon they are going to conquer the planet. (Paddy Fenton, Ventry, Dingle ✉ office@dexterbeef.ie 🖱 www.dexterbeef.ie)

Kerry

Market

● Dingle Local Produce and Craft Market

When John McKenna said a few words and smashed the champagne against the trestle table to launch the reconstituted Dingle market just a few years go, the bedrock of bakers, cheesemakers, milliners, growers, chocolatiers, chefs and cupcake makers were already in place in this happy space. And it's just gotten better ever since. (The Harbour, Dingle, Fridays 10am-3pm)

Fish & Chips

● Dingle Reel Fish & Chip Shop

When *The Irish Times* conducted its survey of the best fish and chips in Ireland, on St Patrick's Day 2012, Marie-Claire Digby reported that "Eleanor Walsh says the chips at Reel Dingle Fish are worth driving 220 miles for". So, there you have it: 220 miles for a bag of chips and some freshly fried fish. Yeah, that seems about the right value for Mark Grealy's seriously fine cooking. (Mark Grealy, Holy Ground, Dingle ☎ 066-915 1713 – Open 1pm-10pm)

Chocolatier

● Dovinia

Saorla's chocolates have a nice, hippyish look and feel to them, though maybe it's the hemp and almond milk chocolate bar, or the absinthe chocs, that makes us say that. Rich, wild, boozy flavours – prosecco and raspberry; brandy and apricot; salted caramel – are perfectly rendered, and colourfully packaged (Saorla O'Corrain, Baile Ghanín Beag, Ballydavid 🖱 www.dovinia.com)

Restaurant

● Fish at The Marina

OK, so I'm having the seared tuna burger with black olive relish and chips and you're having the organic salmon fillet with gnocchi, spinach, tomato and basil, and my aren't we having a lovely time here in Alex Barr's place on the Marina. Dingle restaurants are good at encapsulating the zeitgeist of the town, and Mr Barr does that brilliantly. (Alex Barr, Marina Buildings, Dingle ☎ 086-378 8584)

Kerry

Guesthouse

● Emlagh House

Emlagh is a beautiful, serenely comfortable house that has featured in our annual 100 Best Places to Stay in Ireland book ever since it opened. (Marion & Gráinne Kavanagh, Emlagh, Dingle ☎ 066-915 2345 🖱 www.emlaghhouse.com – Open Mar-mid Nov)

Café

● Garden Café

Consider how cool this is: when legendary local butcher Jerry Kennedy launched his Dingle Dog, the launch took place in Sheila Egan's Garden Café, and was marked by a poem specially written about the new hot dog by Gene Courtney. Respect! So, everyday Sheila serves a Dingle Dog, along with good soups, good tarts and quiches and some lovely, domestic baking that is pure goodness. (Sheila Egan, Green Street, Dingle 🖱 www.thegardencafedingle.eu – Open 10am-5pm Mon, Wed-Sat, noon-4pm Sun)

Restaurant

● Global Village

When it comes to smart cooking, Martin Bealin doesn't miss a beat. Fish from day boats, local meats from the peninsula, fresh sustainable vegetables, and then the experienced, generous capacities of Mr Bealin's skills bring the very best from all that he sources. It's a particularly lovely room and, despite the restaurant's title, Global Village is a quintessential Kerry restaurant. (Martin Bealin & Nuala Cassidy, Upper Main Street, Dingle ☎ 066-915 2325/087 917 7700 www.globalvillagedingle.com – Open 5.30pm-10pm Mon-Sat)

Café

● Goat Street Café

Ed Mulvihill does nice things with his ingredients in the GSC: corn-fed chicken with Annascaul black pudding and leek and chorizo cream; smoked salmon and feta frittata; duo of hake and pollock; raspberry crème brulée. The rooms also double as a gallery for the staff's art works, and there is always a nice community vibe here, both downstairs and in the smarter upstairs room. Value is very keen, the cooking is fresh and true and Goat Street is a no nonsense place you'll quickly be back to. (Ed Mulvihill, Main Street, Dingle ☎ 066-915 2770/086 8264118 www.thegoatstreetcafe.com – Open 10am-5pm Mon-Sun, 6pm-9pm Thur-Sat)

Guesthouse with Restaurant

● Gorman's Clifftop House

Quite how Vincent and Sile manage to maintain such a productive herb and vegetable garden, here at the edge of Smerwick Harbour, we don't quite know. But their fresh leaves and herbs add mightily to Vincent's classic cooking, bringing colour and contrast to the culinary canvas in Gorman's. Great comfort, great views. (Vincent & Sile Gorman, Glaise Bheag, Ballydavid, Dingle ☎ 066-915 5162 info@gormans-clifftophouse.com www.gormans-clifftophouse.com – Food served 6.30pm-9pm Mon-Sat. Closed Nov-Mar)

B&B

● Greenmount House

John and Mary's stylish, modern house offers elegant comfort, great views, lovely cooking and instinctive hospitality. For many visitors, booking Greenmount is the first thing you do when planning a trip to Dingle. (John & Mary Curran, Upper John St, Dingle ☎ 066-915 1414 greenmounthouse@eircom.net www.greenmount-house.com)

Accommodation

● Heaton's Guest House

Cameron, Nuala and David Heaton seem able to read their guests' minds, so you will have scarcely made a request for something or other before they have it sorted, solved, dealt with, arranged, taken care of. Their hospitality is only mighty, and David's cooking is the cherry on the icing on the cake. (Nuala & Cameron Heaton, The Wood, Dingle ☎ 066-915 2288 heatons@iol.ie www.heatonsdingle.com)

Butcher

● Jerry Kennedy

Last time we visited Jerry Kennedy's shop, on a Saturday morning, the place was mobbed. Were they giving away free samples of their legendary Blasket lamb? Their fantastic sausages? Their amazing beef? Not a bit of it: it was just a standard Saturday morning in Kennedy's butchers in Dingle, and the place was a riot. This is one of the great butcher's shops, where amazing meats meet great service, and should not be missed on any account. (Jerry Kennedy, 8 Orchard, Dingle ☎ 066-915 2511 – Open 8am-6pm Mon-Sat)

Cheese Shop

● The Little Cheese Shop

Maja Binder is a cheesemaker who also runs a cheese shop: now, that's called being qualified for your job. This is a wonderful place to find wonderful cheeses in mint condition, as well as great foods and – hungry traveller alert! – some really crackingly desirable sandwiches for lunch. Don't miss this Dingle gem. (Maja Binder, Greys Lane, Dingle ☎ 066-7139028 ☎ 087 625 5788 majabinder@hotmail.com – Open 11am-6pm Tue-Fri, 11am-5pm Sat)

ce Cream

● Murphy's Ice Cream

The original Murphy's ice cream store remains a place with a unique ambience, a pivotal player in the renaissance of Dingle, and the place from which the Murphy brothers have steadily marched out to conquer the world (Killarney and Dublin recently stormed, and placated). To say that they make ice cream is to say that Horowitz played the piano, or James Joyce wrote a few books. Better to say that they express their creativity, their intelligence and their culture via the medium of ice cream. Better to say that they are artists, and ice cream is the medium. Unconvinced? Visit the shop in Dingle, and you will see what we mean. (Sean & Kieran Murphy, Milseoga Uí Mhurchú Teo, Sráid na Trá, An Daingean ☎ 066-915 2644 sean@murphysicecream.ie www.murphysicecream.ie – Open 11am-10pm Mon-Sun)

Restaurant

● Out of the Blue

If Tim Mason had a tenner for everytime the fish cookery in OOTB has been described as "amazing", then he could retire to Dingle and open a little seasonal seafood restaurant. Lucky us that Mr Mason didn't need anything other than a shoestring budget and a dedicated team to open this brilliant, revolutionary, fishy adventure. Amazing it indeed is. They only cook the catch of the day, and they cook it superbly. The wine selection is as adept as the cooking, and OOTB is a totality of delight. (Tim Mason, Waterside, Dingle ☎ 066-915 0811 outoftheblue@ireland.com www.outoftheblue.ie – Open 12.30pm-3pm, 6.30pm-9.30pm Thu-Tue; noon-3pm, 6pm-8.30pm Sun. Closed Nov-Feb. Open Wed high season)

Pies

● Píog Pies

Brid and Steven make some of the country's very best pies, and have been doing so now for five years. The pies exhibit a deft culinary finesse, as well as the smart choice of terrific quality ingredients, so the pies – seafood; Kerry lamb; lentil and root vegetable; free-range chicken and so on – are all equally fine, equally individual and equally delicious. Wonderful. (Brid ni Mhathuna & Steven Neiling, Dingle ☎ 087-794 4036 sales@piogpies.com)

Kenmare

Restaurant

● The Boathouse

Martin McCormack has one of the most jaw-droppingly delightful spaces in Ireland to showcase his fine cooking. Though there are pizzas on offer, the core of the menu leans to Mr McCormack's beloved Spain, and the food is vivid, fun, colourful and deliciously accomplished. (Martin & Montse McCormack, Dromquinna Manor, Kenmare ☎ 064-664 2889 – Open 2pm-9pm)

Bakery and Café

● The Breadcrumb

The Breadcrumb breads are what bread is meant to taste like – distinguished; balanced; rich; satisfying; health-giving. Manuela and her team demonstrate the defining Kenmare standards: stellar. We love to eat in their café as well, where the cooking is ruddy, real and vegetarian. The Breadcrumb is a pivotal address in Kenmare. (Manuela Goeb, O'Shea's House, New Road, Kenmare ☎ 064-664 0645 info@thebreadcrumb.com www.thebreadcrumb.com – Open 8am-6.30pm Mon-Sat, 8.30am-3pm Sun)

Hotel

● Brook Lane Hotel

They make a mean fish pie in Casey's, the bistro of the pretty Brook Lane Hotel. Packed with fresh prawns, smoked fish, mussels and white fish, and topped with creamy potato, it is what a fish pie should be. Their soups are well made also, and salads are fresh and crisp. And that is what is so good about the Brook Lane: it offers exactly what you want, without pretension, without silliness, without nonsense. Despite their relative youth, Dermot and Una have mature heads on their shoulders, and we love the way they do their thing. (Dermot & Una Brennan, Kenmare ☎ 064-664 2077 info@brooklanehotel.com www.brooklanehotel.com)

Tea Shop

● An Cupan Tae

Mary, Mary, Ms O'Leary runs such a sweet tea rooms here at the top of Henry Street. An Cupan Tae is nostalgic in the way Mad Men is nostalgic: with a touch of irony and a heck of a lot of style. They don't cut the crusts off the sandwiches, and you will hardly see a priest sitting at a corner table, but everything else is totally 1963. (Mary O'Leary, 26 Henry Street, Kenmare ☎ 064-664 2001 cupantaekenmare@gmail.com www.cupantaekenmare.com – Open 9am-6pm Mon-Sun, from 10am-5pm off season. Closed Jan-Mar)

Restaurant and Glamping

● Dromquinna Manor

Sally McKenna made an iPhone film about Dromquinna and its glamorous glamping offer when we first visited, so you can see the jaw-dropping location and the wowee! tents and the Boathouse bistro that John and Gwen Brennan have fashioned from the almost-ruins of this beautiful house, on our website. Their work is an astonishing feat of restoration, and respect, and they have created something truly special, something truly optimistic. No wonder so many people want to get married here: it's a house with magic. (John & Gwen Brennan, Kenmare ☎ 064-664 2888 admin@dromquinnamanor.com www.dromquinnamanor.com)

Bakery

● Harrington's Bakery

Kerry

Jerry Harringon's bakery makes very good breads and has been doing so since 1995, using traditional fermentation methods and avoiding the junk that has made modern breads a virtual health hazard. You will find them in many supermarkets and shops in Kerry and also West Cork, and it is fantastic to see the great tradition of regional, specialist baking being carried on by this fine craft bakery. A nice cup of tea, a slice of Harrington's brack, and all is well with the world.(Jerry Harrington, Kenmare ☎ 064-664 1014 harringtonsbread@yahoo.ie www.harringtons.ie)

B&B

● Hawthorn House

Mary and Noel run a cosy, comfy, welcoming B&B, and it's a perfect base for exploring the culinary charms of Kenmare. (Noel & Mary O'Brien, Shelbourne St, Kenmare ☎ 064-6641035 hawthorn@eircom.net www.hawthornhousekenmare.com)

Café

● Jam

The staff in Jam are so good, so charming, so friendly, that were they to tell us that they had nothing but cheese strings and gruel to offer, we would sit down and have cheese strings and gruel. Thankfully, they offer smashing, popular, proper food, and we like to tuck ourselves into this happy warren of rooms and enjoy good breads and soups, nice sausage rolls, good tasty bakes and cakes. "Everything ok?", they ask. Everything is always ok in Jam. (James Mulchrone, 6 Henry Street, Kenmare ☎ 064-664 1591 ✉ info@jam.ie 🖰 www.jam.ie – Open Mon-Sat 8am-6pm. Also in Ballyseeds, Tralee ☎ 066-719 2580 and Old Market Lane, Killarney ☎ 064-663 7716)

local knowledge

Kerry Black Puddings

Kerry black puddings are quite distinctive and, unlike the puddings made in Cork, Kerry puddings tend to be smooth and are usually quite spicy. They are often baked in a tin, like a cake, rather than put into a ring and boiled. Butchers here reserve the chunky, oaty textures preferred in Cork for use in their white puddings. Happily, there are an increasing number of puddings being made – no fewer than two puddings are made in the town of Sneem alone – along with the famed pudding made in Annascaul, the many puddings produced in butcher's shops, and the boudin-style blood puddings made on the Dingle peninsula. Kerry black puddings are thriving.

Ice Cream

● Kenmare Ice Cream

Margaret and Rose started selling their ice cream from a tricycle a few years back, and today you can buy their lovely cool cones on Henry Street and in the shopping centre. Is there a better way to celebrate St Patrick's Day than with a green pistachio KIC cone? No, there ain't. (Margaret McCarthy & Rose Glynn, Henry Street, Kenmare ☎ 086-194 0088)

Smoked Salmon

● Kenmare Select

You will find this superlative smoked salmon in Supervalu in Kenmare, and almost nowhere else, as almost all the production is exported. Hunt it down: it's a beauty – subtle, creamy, saline, clean and delightful. (Cyprien Benoit, Kilmurry, Kenmare ☎ 064-6641162 ✉ info@kenmare-select.com 🖰 www.kenmare-select.com)

Restaurant

● Number Thirty Five

"I would rate it as a Must Eat restaurant in Kenmare" is how PJ McKenna summed up his dinner in No 35, Dermot and Una Brennan's comfortable, welcoming bistro. What did you have, PJ? "Amazingly made slow-cooked pork belly spring roll; simple but amazingly made and presented chicken breast with gravy and roast vegetables, then Malteser surprise with Kenmare ice cream meringue and chocolate sauce in a classic ice cream glass." Must Eat is too right. (Dermot Brennan, 35 Main Street, Kenmare ☎ 064-664 1559 info@no35kenmare.com www.no35kenmare.com – Open 6pm-10pm Wed-Mon)

Restaurant

● Packie's

Martin Hallissey is one of the most genial of cooks, and he cooks the most genial food, food that is simple, tasty, food which enjoys vigorous flavours and textures. His food is neither modern nor traditional, though it has elements of both. Truthfully, it's food that is outside of fashion, and outside of time, so you might have roast duck, or Irish stew, or cod Provencale or seafood sausage with beurre blanc, or zesty Kerry lamb, and it will all be delicious. Service is as genial as the chef and his food. (Martin Hallissey, Henry Street, Kenmare ☎ 064-664 1508 – 6pm-10pm Mon-Sat. Weekends only Nov-Dec. Open one week before Christmas. Closed mid Jan-mid Feb)

Shop

● The Pantry

The Pantry is one of the best wholefood shops, a vital destination for local foods as well as essential wholefoods. It's a tiny shop, and crammed to the roof with things you want and things you need. (Hugo Speykebrood, Henry Street, Kenmare ☎ 064-664 2233 hugokenmare@eircom.net – Open 9am-6pm Mon-Sat, 11am-3pm Sun)

Hotel

● The Park Hotel

Bruce Mulcahy has arrived as head chef at Francis and John Brennan's legendary Park Hotel, and instantly taken the cuisine into the first rank of contemporary Irish cooking. Mr Mulcahy balances the rusticity of a forager with the finesse of an artist, and his food is stunning. Meantime, the staff and management of the hotel demonstrate every day that they have no peers when it comes to a brand of service that is utterly correct and, at the same time, utterly charming, in the most instinctual Kerry way. There is nowhere like The Park. (John & Francis Brennan, Kenmare ☎ 064-664 1200 www.parkkenmare.com)

Wine Importer

● Mary Pawle Wines

Mary and Ivan Pawle run one of the most distinguished bespoke wine companies in Ireland. They focus exclusively on organic and bio-dynamic wines, sourced from a radical band of wine brothers world-wide, and there isn't a dud on their list, a list typified by discrimination, modesty, a polite wildness, and the culture of wine and the enjoyment of wine. The wines share a subtlety, a demureness, that echoes Ms Pawle's own preference for wines that speak quietly, yet echo loudly. (Mary Pawle, Gortamullen, Kenmare ☎ 064-664 1443 www.marypawlewines.com)

Kerry

Gastro Bar

● The Purple Heather

Grainne O'Connell is one of the band of Kenmare Food Heroes, people who not only carved out the town's reputation for good food, but who also maintain it, day after day, through sheer hard work. Something about the room always makes us yearn for classic food when we are here – chicken liver pâté with Cumberland sauce, the mushroom omelette, the cheese platter, the seafood pie. The room is dangerously alluring: it would be all too easy to lose the afternoon in here. (Grainne O'Connell, Henry Street, Kenmare ☎ 064-664 1016 oconnellgrainne@eircom.net – Open 11am-7pm Mon-Sat)

Guesthouse

● Shelburne Lodge

Shelburne is one of the most beautiful places to stay in Ireland. Having distinguished herself as one of Kenmare's greatest cooks when she ran restaurants downtown, Maura Foley now shows herself to be one of the great designers, decorators, and hosts. Shelburne Lodge is sublime in every detail: decor, furniture, art works and

–most especially – the breakfasts, which are the stuff of legend. (Maura & Tom Foley, Killowen, Kenmare ☎ 064-664 1013 ✉ shelburnekenmare@eircom.net 🖱 www.shelburnelodge.com – Open Mar-mid Dec)

Traiteur

● Truffle Pig Fine Foods

PJ and John McKenna had a lovely lunch in Truffle Pig on their last trek through town. Beef and mushroom pie for John, tomato and basil soup for PJ, and they bagged up a bagful of tasty things to take away before they left. The room was full of happy diners, locals and visitors, everyone enjoying the calm clamour of this sweet room. (Andrew & Lindsey Hill, Henry Street, Kenmare ☎ 064-664 2953 ✉ aghill1@msn.com – Open 9.30am-6pm Mon-Sat)

Wine Shop

● Vanilla Grape

Alain Bras stocks an idiosyncratic, intriguing selection of wines in this cute shop. Originally a sommelier and wine lecturer of considerable renown, M. Bras culls wines from 35 regions for his shelves, and the selection is distinguished by his in-depth knowledge of the entire world of wine. An online shop also operates, but a while spent perusing the shelves, wondering how to make up a mixed case, really is a particular delight. (Alain Bras & Christine Arthur, 12 Henry Street, Kenmare ☎ 064-664 0694 ✉ vanillagrape@eircom.net 🖱 www.alainbras.com – Open 8.30am-6pm Mon-Sat)

Chipper

● Wharton's

The McKenna teenagers will argue vehemently with you, should you dare to suggest that there is a better chipper than Wharton's. They will be joined by the massed citizens of Kenmare, who cherish their famous fish and chip shop. Ace grub, and smashing staff who always make a visit fun. (Main Street, Kenmare, ☎ 064-664 2622 ✉ info@whartonskenmare.com)

Restaurant

● Wild Garlic Bistro

After many years of superb cooking and service, it's all change at the Wild Garlic, which readers will have known as Mulcahy's. Bruce Mulcahy retains ownership and has gone to cook in the Park Hotel, while James Coffey has taken up the pans in the very glam room now christened the Wild Garlic Bistro. The menus like to riff on classic pairings, emphasising the search for clean flavours that is their hallmark – ravioli with spinach, ricotta and sage butter; salmon gravadlax with fennel and orange; goat's cheese with walnuts and poached pear; pressed chocolate cake with vanilla ice cream. Smart room, smart cooking. (James Coffey, Henry Street, Kenmare ☎ 064-664 2383 – Open 6pm-10pm Mon-Sun, closed Tue & Wed off-season)

Killarney

Hotel

● Arbutus Hotel

The Arbutus is a calm, sweet, family-run hotel in the centre of town, and it's a place where everyone works very hard to do their best.(Seán & Carol Buckley, College Street, Killarney ☎ 064-663 1037 ✉ stay@arbutuskillarney.com 🖰 www.arbutuskillarney.com)

Restaurant and Craft Shop

● Bricín

Paddy and Johnny do a fine job in Bricín, where there is a comfortable room for eating upstairs, above the craft shop. The cooking is soulful and real – chowder; boxty; pork fillet with sage and apricot – just like the guys themselves. By the way, anything you need to know about Killarney, Paddy and Johnny have the answer. (Paddy & Johnny McGuire, 26 High St, Killarney ☎ 064-663 4902 ✉ bricin@eircom.net 🖰 www.bricin.com – Open 12.30pm-3pm, 6pm-9pm Tue-Sat)

Restaurant

● Chapter 40

Chapter 40 is the avant-garde outpost of Killarney eating. Chef Simon Regan likes to deconstruct his dishes, and then reassemble his ingredients in novel, stylishly imagined, painterly ways on boards, plates and slates. It works, and the ambitions of the kitchen are matched by a confidence and dynamism at front of house that seals the experience. New value menus offer excellent value for money. (Brigid Tangney & Mark Murphy, 40 New Street, Killarney ☎ 064-667 1833 ✉ info@chapter40.ie 🖰 www.chapter40.ie – Open 5pm-10pm Tue-Sat)

Tea Rooms

● Miss Courtney's

Sandra Dunlea is one of the coolest people on planet earth, and Miss Courtney's (not Ms Courtney's, by the way) is her salon of coolness. Ostensibly, it is a tea rooms, where you can have tea, coffee, cakes, and lovely lunches. But in actual fact, it's a tabernacle of style that just blows us away every time we visit. Others have mimicked the Miss Courtney's style, but no one comes near to the awesomeness of the original. (Sandra Dunlea, 8 College Street, Killarney ☎ 087- 610 9500 info@misscourtneys.com, www.misscourtneys.com – Open 10am-6pm Mon-Sat)

Restaurant

● Cucina Italiana

Kerry

Banish the idea of clichéd, red sauce Italian cookery before you walk into Cucina Italiana. Marcello Cesarello sources excellent ingredients, and knows exactly what he wants to do with them: veal parcel with smoked mozzarella; milk-poached cod soup; ravioli with asparagus, mussels and clams; spaghetti with sausage ragu. The room is small, and down a little lane, and whilst prices are relatively high, this is classy cooking. (Marcello Cesarello, 17 St Anthony's Place, Killarney ☎ 064 662 6575 cucinaitaliana@eircom.net – 5.30pm-10.30pm Mon-Sun, closed Tues off season)

Hotel

● The Europe Hotel

With all of their rooms now brought up to spec, the Europe is one mighty big, glamorous proposition. It's huge, yes, but the staff bring the place down to a human scale, and the spa and pool are outstanding. Service is particularly good, and it's always a pleasure to be pulling into the car park at the Europe one more time. (Michael Brennan, Fossa, Killarney ☎ 064-667 1300 reservations@theeurope.com www.theeurope.com)

Restaurant

● Gaby's

Gaby's is one of the longest established Killarney restaurants, and Geert Maes has cooked fine fish and shellfish cookery here for decades. (Geert & Marie Maes, 27 High Street ☎ 064-663 2519 – Open 6pm-10pm Mon-Sat)

Butcher

The German Butcher

The German Butcher has been a constant in our lives ever since we discovered Armin Weise's work in the early 1990's. No one else makes German-style charcuterie with the same level of finesse, the same passionate expertise, as this gifted butcher. Sausages, pâtés and meats are all of benchmark quality, and for us the shop is always the last stop after a trip to Killarney: you fill up the car, then you head home. (Armin Weise, Aghadoe, Killarney ☎ 064-663 3069 info@germanbutchershop.com www.germanbutchershop.com – Open 8am-6pm Mon-Fri, 8am-4.30pm Sat)

Peanut butter

Glór Foods

Peanut butter fans will love Glór peanut butter. What other producer of this preserve would talk about "blending" or the "art of roasting", or even "hot from the oven". The result is a butter that is silky and oily and beautifully textured. Compared to other peanut butters, it's quite liquid. You could imagine dunking a carrot into it, or a stick of celery. They make it plain (our favourite) or flavoured with Belgian Chocolate or with Honey. (Oliver Heffernan, The Old Creamery, Ballyhar, Killarney ☎ 087-3160703 glorfoods@gmail.com www.glorfoods.com)

Café

Jam

The Killarney outpost of James Mulchrone's brilliant food operation enjoys the stellar standards and unbeatable service of the Kenmare original, and the Tralee counterpart. Great for breads and cakes and their signature sausage rolls. (James Mulchrone, Old Market Lane, Killarney ☎ 064-663 1441 info@jam.ie www.jam.ie – Open 8am-5pm Mon-Sat)

made in Kerry

Murphy's Ice Cream

Kerry

Hotel

● Killarney Park Hotel

Any competition to find the best hotel in Ireland will always have Padraig and Janet Treacy's KP up there at the top of the list. The Killarney Park is the most meticulously managed and orchestrated hotel you can imagine, and yet it's also wonderfully soulful and welcoming, a place to which you retreat to find civilised, gracious hospitality. The quality of the cooking in both the park restaurant and the garden bar is outstanding, reflecting the stellar standards that are the signature of the KP. (Padraig & Janet Treacy, Kenmare Place, Killarney ☎ 064-663 5555 ⌂ www.killarneyparkhotel.ie)

Hotel

● The Malton

Kerry

Caroline Byrne simply said "I couldn't fault The Malton, it was superb. I love that they've kept it very old-world and not just the usual bland stuff... I was sorry to have to leave it." The third of Padraig Treacy's Killarney hotels – along with The Ross and The Killarney Park – the Malton is a super destination, with brilliant staff. (Padraig Treacy, Killarney ☎ 064-663 8000 ⌂ www.themalton.com)

Shop

● The Markets

This beautiful shop is simply the coolest artisan speciality store, and Peter Dunleavy has culled the best local produce from the best local producers and put it on the shelves in a funky, fun store that is a radical new arrival in Killarney. (Peter Dunleavy, New Market Lane, High Street, Killarney ☎ 087-637 7508 ✉ peter@killarneymarkets.com ⌂ www.killarneymarkets.com)

Ice Cream Parlour

● Murphy's Ice Cream

Television has made the Murphy brothers extra-famous, but before the cameras arrived they were already famous, as meticulous producers of the most glorious artisan ice creams, and blokes who can also make a pretty spiffing cup of coffee. Sean and Kieran make everyone's life better: that's what Murphy's ice cream does for Ireland. (Séan & Kieran Murphy, 37 Main Street, Killarney ☎ 066-915 2644 ✉ sean@murphysicecream.ie ⌂ www.murphysicecream.ie – Open 11am-10pm Mon-Sun, closes early evening off season)

Restaurant

● Pay As You Please Restaurant

Boy, but the McKennas had a great time in PAYP. The kids thought it was the most radical place they had ever eaten – Elvis movies playing on the walls! the coolest staff! wicked pizzas! – and the adults thought about the irony of Killarney being the home of the first post-modern place to eat in Ireland. For the record, you do pay as you please – the menu has no prices – and you should be very generous because PAYP is one mighty, arty trip and Rob and Barry are cool dudes. Go on, add another tenner. There is nowhere like it. (Robert O'Reilly & Barry McBride, New Market Lane, High Street, Killarney ☎ 086-306 8253 – Open 12.30pm-4pm Thur, 7pm-10pm Fri-Sat, 12.30pm-4pm Sun)

Bar & Restaurant

● Quinlan's Seafood Bar

A groovy, colourful seafood bar that sells the fish caught by the Quinlan family's own boats: now, that's the way to do fish – and chips – and seafood specials. Liam Quinlan's seafood bar would find a happy home in every town in Ireland, and it is another brilliant example of the new thinking and new creativity in Killarney which is transforming the town as a food destination. Watch this one run and run. (Liam Quinlan, 77 High Street, Killarney ☎ 064-662 0666 liam@kerryfish.com www.kerryfish.com – Open from noon, daily)

Hotel

● The Ross

Ciara Treacy's dad, and her Granny, ran The Ross hotel before Ms Treacy took up the reins and continued the family tradition. The Ross is cool school gorgeous, a fabulous piece of design that marries the elements one wants in a hip hotel – great rooms, a great restaurant downstairs in Cellar One with really fine modern food, and there are funky cocktails and nice things to eat in the Lane Café Bar. Great Kerry service brings everything together. (Ciara Treacy, The Ross, Killarney ☎ 064-663 1855 info@theross.ie www.theross.ie)

Bar & Restaurant

● The Smokehouse

The Dunleavys have the eye when it comes to design, when it comes to catching a note of funkiness, and they take their design ethos all the way – you just have to see the bathrooms in The Smokehouse! The staff are as cool as the design, and the food just hits the spot – Dingle prawns; Glenbeigh mussels; Kerry lamb burger; rib-eye with baked potato. (Peter Dunleavy, 8 High Street, Killarney ☎ 087-233 9611 thesmokehousekillarney@gmail.com www.thesmokehouse.ie – Open all day and evening)

Fishmonger

● Spillane's Seafood

Spillane's are specialists in smoked salmon, which can be ordered via their website, but locals also know that if you turn up at their fish processing plant that there is always a great selection of wet fish for sale. (Paudie Spillane, Lackavan, Killarney ☎ 064-663 1320 www.spillaneseafoods.com – Open 9am-6pm Mon-Fri (closed for lunch), 9am-1pm Sat)

Killorglin

Restaurant

● Giovanelli's

Antoinette and Daniele have run a rock-steady operation on Bridge Street over the last five years, winning devotees who like the crisp efficiency of the set up and the calm expertise of the Italian cooking. (Antoinette & Daniele Giovanelli, Lower Bridge Street, Killorglin ☎ 066-979 6640 – Open lunch 12.30pm, dinner 7pm-9pm Tue-Sat)

Deli and Bakery

● Jack's

Jack Healy is a Corkman, from a family of bakers, so we hope the people of Kerry know how fortunate they are to have this great baker working happily away in their Kingdom. Jack and Celine do the best of the best – as well as their breads and cakes and superb deli foods, they have shelves groaning and tumbling with all the good things from the rest of the country. It's a cornucopia, an emporium, a feast, a delight. Of course, he's still a Corkman, like. (Celine & Jack Healy, Lower Bridge Street, Killorglin ☎ 066-976 1132 – Open 8am-7pm Mon-Sat, 8am-5pm Sun)

Restaurant

● Nick's Restaurant

Nick's is a step back in time, to the time of red banquettes, white tablecloths, carpets and fireplaces, bentwood chairs and kindly ladies in charge of service. For which we say: Hurrah! So, decide whether you want to eat in the bar or the restaurant, then order up the classics – prawn and monkfish thermidor; grilled lobster; rack of Kerry lamb with fondant potato; Dover sole with lemon butter sauce; peppered steak with brandy cream sauce. Ageless good times are what Nick's is about. (Nick & Anne Foley, Lwr Bridge St, Killorglin ☎ 066-976 1219 www.nicks.ie – Open 5pm-10.30pm Tue-Sun)

Restaurant

● Sol y Sombra

A tapas bar and music venue in an old deconsecrated Church of Ireland? Only in Kerry, that's for sure. Cliodhna Foley's inspired adventure is so off the wall that it takes your breath away. You can even have your wedding reception here: now, what a day that would be! But, even if you haven't popped the question, the foods and wines in Sol y Sombra are reason to come here, and return here – bacon and egg bechamel croquettes; suckling pig; sausage with apple marmalade. And if you have yet to discover the magical world that is sherry, then now is your chance: the sherries Cliodhna stocks are magnificent examples of one of the world's greatest drinks. (Clíodhna Foley, The Old Church of Ireland, Killorglin ☎ 066-976 2357 www.solysombra.ie – Bar open 5pm, Food served 6pm-10.30pm)

Kerry

Farmhouse Cheese

● Wilma's Killorglin Farmhouse Cheese

Wilma O'Connor's cheese is a local secret in and around Kerry, though you will occasionally see it further afield and, if you do, then snap it up. This is a beautifully produced Gouda and whilst some of the cheeses are flavoured with cumin or cloves, they actually need nothing other than the sweet and tensile cloak of fudgy, condensed milk flavours that characterises the cheese. If you can find the larger wheels of cheese that have enjoyed one or two or more years of ageing, then you have just hit the jackpot. (Wilma O'Connor, Ardmoniel, Killorglin ☎ 066-976 1402 killorglincheese@eircom.net)

Café

Zest Café

The third Lynch family venture in Killorglin is Nicola Lynch's smart café, Zest, and it's very much the contemporary foil to the traditionalism of Nick's. A smart room has smart modern food – salads; pasta; pizzas; focaccia; juices; smoothies; and nice drinks. So, one zest pizza, a zest club sandwich and two energy lift juices. Now, we're motoring. (Nicola Lynch, School Road, Killorglin ☎ 066-979 0303 info@zestcafe.ie www.zestcafe.ie – Open 10am-5pm Mon-Sat. Takeaway service also available.)

Listowel

Kerry

Bistro & Accommodation

Allo's

Armel Whyte and Helen Mullane are professionals, and they cook and serve in the charming bar and restaurant of Allo's with accomplished ease. The bar and bistro is a particularly commodious place, one of the most cleverly realised pieces of salvaged bricolage you will find. Nice cosy rooms upstairs too. (Armel Whyte, 41 Church Street, Listowel ☎ 068-22880 www.allosbarbistro-townhouse.com – Open pub hours, food served noon-9pm Tue-Sat)

Farmhouse Cheese

Béal Lodge Dairy Farm

Kate Carmody has been on a journey ever since she began making cheese as long ago as 1987. A bio-chemist by training, she has in her cheesemaking journey converted her farm to organic status, abjured any GM products, and created three smashing cheeses: a mild and a mature cheddar made with pasteurised milk and, the *primus inter pares*, an aged raw milk cheddar which is an organoleptic joy. Interestingly, Ms Carmody seems to us to keep getting better and better, to keep improving, as time goes by – the journey continues. (Kate Carmody, Asdee, Listowel ☎ 068-41137 cait@eircom.net www.bearorganiccheese.com)

made in Kerry

Valentia Dairy

Deli

● John R's

Home bakery, delicatessen, wine shop, food emporium, café – Pierce Walsh really manages to push all the buttons in John R's and its smart sibling, Café Hanna. You can start the day with a cup of tea and a scone made to Mum's recipe, then have their signature Cornish pasty with some salads for lunch, and buy a nice dinner for the evening with a rhubarb tart as you are on your way out. The shop is elegant and inviting, the cooking is comforting and real. (Pierce Walsh, 70 Church Street, Listowel ☎ 068-21249 ✉ pwalsh@johnrs.com
🖰 www.johnrs.com)

Farmers' Market

● Listowel Farmers' Market

Listowel has one of the best town squares, so turn up, turn up for Curraghchase pork, Piog pies, fresh fish, Toby's olives, Philip's chickens, Salad Bowl treats, Pauline's cakes and much more. (Fridays 10am-1pm
🖰 www.listowelfoodfair.com)

Milltown

Growers

● Hall's Market Garden

Trish and Steve are really super organic growers and so look out for their produce in the Milltown Market on Saturday and in The Markets in Killarney. Their carrots, in particular, have that lovely sandy-soil lightness that is a Kerry characteristic. (Trish & Steve Hall, Milltown ☎ 087-650 0032 ✉ hallsmarketgarden@gmail.com)

Market

● Milltown Organic Market

The weekly market run by Mary O'Riordan in the deconsecrated Old Church is one of the best markets in Ireland. If Tim Burton was a market organiser, he would design all markets to be like Milltown – gothic, fun, alluring, unlikely, and filled with surprises. The producers are top-class Kerry artisans, so bring lots of bags to take home the goodies. And look: isn't that Johnny Depp over there? (Mary O'Riordan, Old Church, Milltown ☎ 066-976 7869 – Open Saturdays 10am-2pm)

Organic Shop

● Milltown Organic Store

The wholefood and organic and gardening emporium in the Old Church is a treasure. (Mary O'Riordan, Old Church, Milltown ☎ 066-976 7869 ✉ info@milltownorganicstore.com 🖱 www.milltownorganicmarket.com – Open 10am-6pm Mon-Fri, 10am-2pm Sat)

Portmagee

Bar, Restaurant & Guesthouse

● The Moorings @ The Bridge Bar

Pan-fried hake with Gubbeen chorizo mash and lemon butter. Now, isn't this just the sort of lip smackin' dinner dish that the hungry traveller wants to find set before him after a long day's journeying out to the Skelligs? Indeed it is, and it's just the sort of thing Patricia and Gerard will set before you in The Moorings. Mr and Mrs Kennedy have made the Moorings a little world unto itself, with the restaurant, bar, gift shop, guest rooms and a self-catering cottage. (Patricia & Gerard Kennedy, Portmagee ☎ 066-947 7108 ✉ moorings@iol.ie 🖱 www.moorings.ie – Restaurant open 6pm-10pm, Bar open noon-9pm. Restaurant closes Oct-Mar)

Sneem

Butcher

● Burns Butchers

Can you believe that little Sneem has not one, but two of the best and best-known black puddings made in Ireland? Kieran Burns is the fourth generation of his family to make their celebrated, baked cake-like pudding, and you can't leave Sneem without stopping at this tiny shop and buying a piece of great culinary art, and culinary history. (Kieran Burns, Sneem ☎ 064-664 5139 ✉ sneemblackpudding@hotmail.com – Open 9am-7pm Mon-Sat)

Farmhouse Cheese

● Derreenaclaurig Farmhouse Cheese

Harry's fine Gouda-style cheese is one of the rarest in Ireland, only sold locally in some shops, sold by Harry himself at local markets during the summer, as well as from the farm. Derreenaclaurig is sweet, mild, clean-tasting cheese, and it's worthwhile hunting down this little treasure if you are touring the Ring of Kerry, and look out particularly for the mature cheeses. (Harry van der Zanden, Derreenaclaurig, Sneem ☎ 064-664 5330)

Butcher

● O'Sullivan's Sneem Black Pudding

Peter O'Sullivan's black pudding is world-class. The O'Sullivan family have been working in Sneem for almost 50 years, and Peter continues the noble tradition of the Kerry black pudding. Remember that these puddings should be heated in the oven, rather than fried, to unveil their full organoleptic majesty. (Peter O'Sullivan, North Square, Sneem ☎ 064-664 5212 sosullivan@sneemblackpudding.ie www.sneemblackpudding.ie)

Kerry

Tralee

Bar & Restaurant

● Cassidy's

Bernard and Geraldine run a good, professional operation here on Abbey Street, and have happily married good food, service and value for several years. (Bernard & Geraldine Cassidy, 16 Abbey Street, Tralee ☎ 066-712 8833)

Cakes

● Cupcakes By Dee

Deirdre Power makes superb, fun, funky cupcakes – yummy carrot; red velvet; fluffy chocolate are just a trio from the selection – and you can buy from the creator at the Saturday Tralee Market and in local shops. Look out for them in Mary Anne's Tearooms, upstairs on Denny Street, and other local cafés. (Deirdre Power, 9 Lios Ard, Tralee www.cupcakesbydee.ie)

Fishmonger

● Duinin Seafoods

Paddy O'Mahony has huge knowledge of the food world, being manager, hotelier, fishmonger and processor. He knows fish at every level of production, which means quality is assured. (Paddy O'Mahony, Market Place, Tralee ☎ 066-712 1026 – Open 9am-6pm Mon-Fri)

Preserves

● Harty's Pepper Jellies

Melanie Harty has the real chef's touch, which is to say that she has a delicate touch. It would be all too easy, making pepper jellies, to let them get fiery and lip-numbingly hot and out of control. But the Harty pepper jellies are subtle and balanced, which means that they add beautiful, mellifluous flavour notes, howsoever you use them in your cooking. You need them in the cupboard, and they add grace and favour, and flavour, to every part of your cooking. (Melanie Harty, 2 Canal Place, The Basin, Tralee ☎ 087-325 8539 info@hartysfoods.com www.hartysfoods.com)

Shop

● Kingdom Food & Wine

Kerry

Pat and Maeve keep on keeping on, doing the good thing day after day, running one of the pivotal Tralee destinations for folk who are hungry for lunch, for people thirsty for good wines, for shoppers hungrily hunting down speciality foods for the evening's dinner. Everything just seems to fit together here in the Kingdom, fashioning a store that is wonderfully curated and orchestrated, all the better to deliver good things to happy customers. (Maeve Duff, Oakpark, Tralee ☎ 066-711 8562 www.kingdomstore.ie – Open from 8am-7pm Mon-Sat)

Butcher's shop

● Aaron O'Connell

A fine local butcher's shop, with a particular, award-winning expertise in that great Kerry signature creation, black and white puddings. (Aaron O'Connell, 22 Upper Castle Street, Tralee ☎ 066-712 6661)

Preserves

● Pickled In Dingle

Strawberry and black pepper jam. Rhubarb vanilla jam. Chilli jam with lemongrass and ginger. Apple clove jelly. Wow, but Marie Charland really pushes the envelope with her creations, and you can get your hands on them, and ask the creator about her vivid creations, at many of the county's Farmers' Markets. (Marie Charland, Ballyluskey, Ballydavid, Tralee ☎ 087-275 9145 mhcharland@hotmail.com)

Restaurant

● Spa Seafoods

Spa Seafoods in The Spa village is a handsome fish shop, seafood deli and a smart seafood café upstairs, so Brendan Walsh is really using all the angles to showcase his family's expertise with fresh and smoked fish. The menus are crisp and concise: Glenbeigh mussels; crab cakes with tartare; smoked haddock and spinach quiche; fresh scampi; seafood platter. A bottle of Martin Codax Albarino with some fish goujons, a hypnotising view out the windows, and what more could one need? (Brendan Walsh, The Spa, Tralee ☎ 066-713 6901 ✉ spa_seafoods@iolfree.ie 🖱 www.spaseafoods.com – Open 12.30pm-5pm, 6pm-9pm Tue-Sun)

Farmers' Market

● Tralee Farmers' Market

It's good to see Tralee catching up with the Farmers' Market phenomenon. Saturday morning in Prince's Quay is the place to get good pies, good pork, lovely plants, excellent breads and baking, cupcakes, salads and sea vegetables and lots more. (Prince's Quay, Tralee, Sat 11am-4pm)

Tuosist

Dairy

● Knockatee Dairy

What other farmhouse cheesemaker produces a cheddar, a Gouda, and two different blue cheeses? You have to go way back in time, to the days of the glorious Maucnaclea Cheeses in West Cork, in the early 1990's, to find a single producer with such a palette of different cheeses. Peter Ireson is led by his instinct when making the Knockatee cheeses, and inspired by a decade of experimenting. His cheeses are always intriguing, quixotic and original, but they are only made in small quantities, so look out especially for the Beara and Gouda Blues, and for the Knockatee Cheddar and Gouda. (Peter Ireson, Lehid Upper, Tuosist ☎ 064-668 4236)

made in Kerry

Beal Lodge Cheddar

Valentia

Ice Cream & Dairy

● Valentia Island Farmhouse Dairy

Unhomogenised milk, buttermilk, yogurts with fruit, sorbets and numerous varieties of ice cream are the proud products that Joe and Caroline Daly make from the milk of their herd of friesians. It would be hard to better the quality of milk from a herd grazing on these windswept, sea salt spattered pastures. The milk and ice creams are pure tasting and delicious, and one senses that a search for purity – they wisely disdain homogenisation, for example – is what animates the Dalys. Don't miss their lovely dairy products, and do try to find the time to visit the ice cream booth at the farm itself. (Joe & Caroline Daly, Kilbeg, Valentia Island ☎ 066-947 6864 valentiaicecream@eircom.net www.valentiadairy.com – Ice-cream Parlour open 11am-7pm Mon-Sun. Closed 1 Sept-31 May)

Kerry

local knowledge

The Kerry Cow

The Kerry Cow is the only breed of dairy cow that is native to Ireland. These dainty cows are black, with white udders, and the breed is thought to date back to Celtic times. The Kerry Cow is well adapted to its environment, a hardy little cow who grows a thick winter coat, and does not have to be housed during the colder months. Kerry cow owners, who include some of Ireland's cheesemakers, praise the cow for its docile nature, its agility, and its easily digestible milk.

County Kildare

Allenwood

Craft Brewery

● Trouble Brewing

When there is Trouble Brewing, it is good news for food lovers. Paul, Stephen and Thom brew from what is little more than a big garage, and they make drinks that enrich your life. Their Dark Arts porter, for example, does just what it says on the tin: there is something fiendishly, wickedly narcotic and illicit about the flavours of this stout, something naughty and wild. We love it. Give us another one! The Or Golden Ale, meantime, has similarly wild hoppy and fruit notes, and a long, consoling aftertaste. You will find the beers in the best pubs, and the bottles of beer in the best wine shops, and do look out for the festival brews the boys fire up for special occasions. Here comes Trouble. (Stephen Clinch ☎ 087-908 6658 📫 info@troublebrewing.ie 📫 stephenclinch@troublebrewing.ie 🖱 www.troublebrewing.ie)

Kildare

Athy

Farmers' Market

● Athy Farmers' Market

The Athy market brings together a lovely collection of dedicted food artisans, each Sunday, and they are joined by a dedicated band of craftspeople, so whether you seek organic carrots or handthrown ceramics, it's all here. (Emily Square, Athy – Open 10am-3pm Sunday

Café

● The Bay Tree Fine Food Co

The Bay Tree specialises in coeliac-friendly cooking, but don't imagine it is simply for people with food intolerances. "I had the best tasting sandwich on the freshest bread here", said a friend, and that is a typical reaction to Michael and Tony's hard work. Everything gleams in this pretty room, which makes it extra welcoming, and the same care is evident in all the cooking. (Michael Smith & Tony Dempsey, 4 Stanhope Street

☎ 059-864 1819 ✉ michael@thebaytree.ie ✉ tony@thebaytree.ie 🖰 www.thebaytree.ie – Open 8am-5pm Mon-Sat, 10am-5pm Sun)

Organic Farmshop

● Castlefarm Shop

Like no one else we know, Jenny and Peter Young understand farming, artisanship, business and media. They are famous farmers, and for all the right reasons: they run a gorgeous farm, run a brilliant farm shop, make beautiful foods, explain their business via their website and via the media, and let people come and see what they are doing. They are, then, the antithesis of the farming model that has left Irish agriculture so intellectually bereft, the model that has divorced farmers from their customers. With Mr and Mrs Young, you can get up-close and personal – Castlefarm isn't just an abstraction of fields and animals, it is a living, working, productive hub of intellectual and social creativity. Castlefarm is a model for every single farm in Ireland. (Jenny & Peter Young, Castlefarm, Narraghmore, Athy ☎ 087-678 5269 ✉ jenny@castlefarmshop.ie 🖰 www.castlefarmshop.ie)

Ballymore Eustace

Organic Dairy Farm

● Ballymore Farm

Ballymore Farm raw milk organic farmhouse butter is the Beluga of Ireland's artisan dairy industry. Richly yellow, wrapped in brown paper, tied up with string, with a neat label with a cute drawing of the Ballymore cows, it summarises everything artisan agriculture is about: the person, the place, the product, the passion. And the perseverance, because of course the Department of Agriculture would be very happy to have no raw milk foods sold in Ireland, even though we know they are healthful, and helpful, and natural. The Harneys also produce delicious milk, and beautiful yogurts, beautiful cream and buttermilk. Milk is a magic liquid: Ballymore Farm foods let you taste that magic. (Mary & Aidan Harney, Alliganstown, Ballymore Eustace ☎ 045-483976 ✉ aidan@ballymorefarm.ie 🖰 www.ballymorefarm.ie)

Restaurant & Gastropub

● Ballymore Inn

What would you get if you synthesised the work of food writers such as Claudia Roden, Deborah Madison, Diana Henry, Sam Clarke, Alice Waters, Skye Gyngell and Marcella Hazan? The answer is: you would get Georgina O'Sullivan's cooking in The Ballymore Inn. For more than fifteen years, Mrs O'Sullivan has been taking the work of people whose food she loves, and refracting it through her own prism. She is the Newton of Irish cooking, and here in the Ballymore Inn, she weaves her influences in the most sincere way imaginable: Dunlavin pork stir-fry with Wexford wild mushrooms, chilli, pak choi and black bean sauce; Duncannon salmon with new potatoes and spinach and chimichurri dressing; West Cork beef fillet with tarragon aioli; pistachio meringue with Kildare raspberries. One of the great Irish food heroes. (Georgina & Barry O'Sullivan, Ballymore Eustace ☎ 045-864 585 ✉ osullivan@ballymoreinn.com 🖱 www.ballymoreinn.com – Open 12.30pm-9pm Mon-Sun)

Ballysax

Organic Chicken

● Ballysax Organic Chicken

Margaret McDonnell produces delicious organic chickens, birds that are a cinch to cook and a joy to eat. Look out for them in good butcher's shop and other stores. Each one will make you two or three meals and a pot of the most delicious, gelatinous stock. (Margaret & Jim McDonnell, Martinstown Rd, Ballysax, The Curragh ☎ 045-442 4735 ✉ magmcdonnell@eircom.net)

Carbury

Farm Shop

● Deirdre and Norman O'Sullivan

Norman and Deirdre are superb organic farmers, and have been stalwarts of the Dublin Food Co-op since the early days back in the 1980's. Beautiful produce, lovingly produced. (Deirdre & Norman O'Sullivan, Carbury ☎ 046-955 3337 ✉ organicveg@eircom.net – Shop open Friday afternoon)

Castledermot

Café

● Mad Hatter Café

Alice Cope's pretty café is the place in Castledermot for freshly made, clean tasting signature dishes, such as her Humpty Dumpty panini, her White Rabbit wrap, the good daily specials or even a BLT (which would have to be a Bill-Lily-Tweedledee, we think). Ms Cope has a purist's patience and a novelist's verve, just the qualities every good cook should have. (Alice Cope, Unit 1, Keenan's Lane, Castledermot – ☎ 085-714 8085 Open 9am-6pm Mon-Sat, 10am-4pm Sun)

made in Kildare

Hadji Bey

Clane

Café

● Zest Café

Kildare

Mark and Alan are fast heading towards a decade as the centre of the culinary culture in Clane. How have they done it? Simple: cook nice, real food, look after the customers (known as Zesters, don't you know), and provide a great service at a good price. Alan's cooking likes to riff on the classics – tempura cod with sweet potato chips; quail with saffron risotto; monkfish with chorizo and calamari; the classic chicken stuffed with goat's cheese. Professional cooking, professional people, splendid service, and a decade of success. (Mark Condron & Alan O'Regan, Unit 6/7, Clane Shopping Centre, Clane ☎ 045-893 222 info@zestcafeandrestaurant.ie www.zestcafeandrestaurant.ie – Open 8.30am-10pm Mon-Sat, 12.30pm-9pm Sun)

Kilcullen

Cafe

● Fallon's of Kilcullen

Brian Fallon is currently president of the Restaurant Association of Ireland, just rewards for a dedicated professional who, with his team, runs a restaurant that is a model of professionalism. Good simple food in the bar, tasty, more elaborate cooking in the restaurant – Silverhill duck with candied beetroot; Kerry prawns with sweet and sour dressing; St Tola goat's cheese tart with pickled pear – and the venue has become very popular for weddings. (Brian Fallon, Main Street, Kilcullen ☎ 045-484681/086-2079958 info@fallonb.ie www.fallonb.ie – Open 12.30pm-10pm Mon-Sun)

Deli & Café

● The Good Food Gallery

"Savage sausage rolls!" Now, wouldn't the promise of a savage sausage roll, made with Jane Russell's pork, bring you to Paul and Sue Carey's deli and café in Kilcullen. In fact, the sausage rolls are so famous that a customer at the Naas market, where Paul and Sue man a stall at the weekends, has christened them the "GFG Savage Sausage Rolls". But the sausage rolls are just one of the carefully cooked and carefully selected foods you will find here, from their own breads and gluten-free breads to choice artisan foods, and there are lots of nice things to both eat here and to take home to make supper effortlessly simple. (Paul & Sue Carey, Main Street ☎ 045-484 551 www.goodfoodgallery.ie – Open 8.30am-6.30pm Mon-Sat)

Butcher

● Nolan's

March 2012, and the Countryside Alliance declares that James and Emma Nolan's shop is the best butcher's shop in Ireland, England, Scotland and Wales. Wow! And there are James and Emma in London getting their gong from the great Clarissa Dickson-Wright, with the praise of the judges ringing in their ears. Of course, the CA award is just the latest accolade won by this outstanding butcher's shop, for Nolan's have won every major award for both their shop and their products. Having their own abattoir means their meat products are superlative, and their creativity is exceptional: their black pudding is an All-Ireland champion, and they picked up 8 Great Taste Awards in 2011 alone for their sausages and puddings. Right across the board, Nolan's is a bright, shining star, with every detail and facet of the shop and what it offers as good as this devoted team can make it. As good as it gets. (James & Emma Nolan, Main Street, Kilcullen ☎ 045-481 229 http://nolansofkilcullen.tripod.com – Open 8am-6pm Mon-Sat)

Sausages

● Jane Russell's Original Irish Sausages

Has any other artisan producer scored so many successes as Jane Russell? Ms Russell has the knack: she simply has to create a new product – most recently, for instance, her venison sausages, or her black pudding – and suddenly everyone is raving about the venison sausages – "deeply tasty" said *The Irish Times* – and the French are handing Ms Russell prizes for the excellence of her pudding. It's a Midas touch, supported by bloody hard work, and it's an enviable record stretching right back to 2004 when these beautiful sausages made their debut. World domination continues apace – you can try Ms Russell's bespoke sausages made for Sinead Hanley's Market Sausage Company at many Dublin markets, for example – and the client list expands week on week. (Jane Russell, Link Business Park, Kilcullen ☎ 045-480100 jane@straightsausages.com www.straightsausages.com)

Kildare

Kildare

Restaurant

● Harte's Bar & Grill

Barry Liscombe really has the *gra* for good food. "Watching my Nan make baked apples with cloves. The smell still makes me emotional", he tweeted to us when we asked about people's earliest food memories. Mr Liscombe oversees an expansive menu in the popular Harte's Bar, but the care and commitment he brings to his work is evident in the cooking. (Barry Liscombe, Market Square, Kildare ☎ 045-533557 info@hartesbar.ie www.hartesbar.ie – Open 4pm-9pm Mon-Thur, 4pm-10pm Fri-Sat, noon-9pm Sun)

Restaurant

● L'Officina

L'Officina knocks any manner of economic sense out of us. We go in, we sit down, we order too many delicious things, then we buy too many delicious things to take away with us, then we get back in the car and head to Cork or on to Dublin, and wonder when we can do it all again. It's completely Pavlovian: the sight and scent of L'Officina sees us acting like crazed mutts and, frankly, we don't care. When a restaurant is so successful at hitting the pleasure points with its artful Italian food, we just want it one more time. (Eileen Dunne & Stefano Crescenzi, Unit 35 Kildare Village, Nurney Road, Kildare ☎ 045-535850 www.dunneandcrescenzi.com – Open 9.30am-7pm Mon-Fri, 9.30am-8pm Sat, 10.30am-7pm Sun)

made in Kildare

Jane Russell's Sausages

Deli

● Mary-Kathryn's Deli

Mary-Kathryn Murphy is cool. She gets it. She knows what's what, like the other cool guys know what's what. She knows not only what good cooking and baking needs, but also what good cooking and baking doesn't need. And she makes it beautiful: everything gets what it needs, and gets a handsome mien as it goes on its way. She is an ascetic aesthetic, and Kildare is lucky to have her. It doesn't matter if you just have a sausage roll and a cup of tea, or some victoria sponge with chocolate icing and a cup of coffee, or bring home some of Johnny's lamb tagine for your dinner: whatever it is that you buy in this little traiteur will be exactly what it should be, could be, and what you want it to be. Decorous deliciousness, and handsome wholesomeness, that's Mary-Kathryn's method. We are impressed. (Mary-Kathryn Murphy, 6 Academy Street, Kildare ☎ 045-530588 marykathryn@campus.ie www.marykathryns.com – Open 8.30am-5pm Mon, 8.30am-6pm Tue-Fri, 8.30am-3pm Sat)

Kildare

Maynooth

Wine Merchant

● Mill Wine Cellar

The Mill is an excellent wine shop with really well-considered bottles on the shelves. They also run wine appreciation classes, and offer a good hamper service. (Berna Hatton, Maynooth ☎ 01-629 1022 info@millwinecellar.ie www.millwinecellar.ie – Open 8am-10pm Mon-Fri, 9am-10pm Sat, 12.30pm-10pm Sun)

Naas

Restaurant

● The Brown Bear

Chef Josef Zammit has worked with some stellar talents during his career, and he is cementing his own reputation as a serious cook now that he heads up the team in the Brown Bear. He can do the straight-ahead stuff for the value menus and for Sunday lunch – spicy chicken wings with blue cheese dressing; haddock in beer batter with chips and mushy peas – but it's with the à la carte that you sense the real ambition – halibut with confit navet and lardo; scallop with sesame purée and soy gel; braised beef cheek with watercress gnocchi; gin-forced rhubarb with buttermilk panna cotta. Do note that they operate a courtesy car at the weekends, so you can explore the excellent wines on the list. (Eugene & Jean Brennan, Two Mile House ☎ 045-883561 thebrownbearpub@hotmail.com www.thebrownbear.ie – Open 6pm-9pm Wed-Fri, 12.30pm-2.30pm, 6pm-9.30pm Sat, 12.30pm-4pm Sun)

Kildare

local knowledge

Irish Butter

Butter in Ireland has been important in every way it is possible for a food product to be important. Part of the folk tradition of Ireland, it has been economically significant, as well as being an essential staple of the Irish diet. Back in history, butter was not simply a condiment, but a foodstuff within itself – it was even termed "white meat". Butter has been used as currency and has been traded, and fabled. It is one of our most significant foods. And, after many years of butter homogenisation, the product is once again being made by Irish farmers and sold from individual Irish farms.

Deli, Café & Hampers

● Harvest Kitchen

Marie Leacy's fine café, wine shop and deli also has a neat sideline as a hamper specialist, but for locals it's an essential destination for morning coffee and for lunchtime soup and great sandwiches. (Marie Leacy, 1 Sallins Road, Naas ☎ 045-881793 ⌚ www.harvestkitchen.ie – Open 9am-5pm Mon-Thu, 9am-6pm Sat)

Artisan Ice Cream

● Missy Moo's Ice Cream

Siobhan has been making the superb Missy Moo ice creams and ice cream cakes for more than six years now, steadily expanding their distribution and bringing the good news of Jaffa Cake-flavoured ice cream to the citizens of Ireland. Ms Woods has a fiendish creativity, and can seemingly transform every sweetie concept into an ice cream – lemon meringue; chocolate fudge brownie; peanut butter blondie. She will run butterscotch sauce through caramel ice cream then fire chocolate fudge squares through it and Voila! Caramel Twirl is born. Look out for the handsome green livery in good stores such as Avoca. (Siobhan Woods, 2 Chapel Lane, Naas ☎ 087-260 3247)

Farmers' Market

● Naas Farmers' Market

A happy porky pig is the symbol that Naas marketeers use on their Facebook page, and it's entirely apt, for you will be happy as a pig in clover after a trip to this wonderful market. Ballymore Farm butter and milk, J&V meats, Gallic Kitchen pies; Seccoto coffee, Sheridan's cheeses and many, many more make for one of the best farmers' markets. (Friary Lane ✉ info@naasfarmersmarket.com ⌚ www.naasfrmersmarket.com – Open Sat 10am-3pm)

Restaurant

● La Vie de Chateaux

VdeC has one of the smartest lunchtime solutions that we know of: their Grandes Assiettes give you one starter and one main course on the same plate, a boon to those who are time-stressed at lunchtime – and a boon to the waiting staff, of course. So you could have a slice of terrine and a piece of steak; salmon rillettes with some sea trout; a salad of sausage and Emmental with steak and chips. There are also cold and warm tartines. In the evening, the menus are almost completly French in orientation – boudin noir and apple tarte tatin; sole

Kildare

meuniere; duck breast with leek and orange sauce; rhum baba, and French cheeses. Daily specials are described on the blackboards. It's a pretty room with a pretty terrace for all those balmy Naas summer evenings, and it's a busy, successful place so you need to book in advance. (Franck Amand, The Harbour, Naas ☎ 045-888 478 ✉ info@viedechateaux.ie 🖱 www.viedechateaux.ie – Open dinner, Mon-Sun)

made in Kildare

Missy Moo's Ice Cream

Traiteur

● VDC@home

This new offshoot of the successful Vie de Chateaux restaurant is café, bakery and traiteur, so you can eat in and then bring dinner home with you. It's colourful and stylish, and don't miss the ice creams. (Franck Amand, 2 Castle Building, Friary Road ☎ 045-889200 ✉ infovdc@home.ie 🖱 http://vdchome.ie)

Kildare

Wine Importer

● The Wine Store/ Tyrrell & Co

When Tomás Clancy of *The Sunday Business Post* was awarding his prize for best wine importer of the year at the start of 2012, he handed the magnum to Simon and Emma Tyrrell of The Wine Store for the third successive year. You will get no argument from wine lovers over Mr Clancy's choice, for the Tyrrells run a superb operation in The Wine Store. They are celebrated in particular for their selection of wines from the Rhone Valley, but the knowledge and discrimination which is their hallmark is evident in every bottle they source and supply – their Spanish wines and sherries are fantastic, their wines from the Loire Valley are beauties, their Burgundies and French regional wines are always delightful. If their wines have a characteristic, it is that they are well-tempered, with even the big Rhone wines exhibiting balance and definition amidst all that umami chewiness. The Wine Store is a treasure. (Simon & Emma Tyrrell, Rathernan, Kilmeague, Naas ☎ 1890-252 624/045-870882 ✉ wine@thewinestore.ie 🖱 www.thewinestore.ie)

Newbridge

Sweeties

● Hadji Bey

The rebirth of the legendary Hadji Bey Turkish Delight in 2010 by the L.C. Confectionery company proved that one of the company's slogans was undoubtedly true. "A good name is worth millions" was one of Hartun Batmazian's favourite aphorisms, and the affection with which the sweets were greeted by people who could never ever have tasted them was extraordinary: the Hadji Bey shop may have closed thirty years before, but the name – and the reputation – lived on. Today, one can enjoy these splendid, aromatic sweeties, in the original rose incarnation, and also in the mix of orange, rose and lemon. Beautifully packaged, they are a sweet that is always a treat. (Harry Gallagher, L.C. Confectionery, Cutlery Road ☎ 045-434 650 leo@urneychocolates.com www.hadjibey.ie)

Fishmonger

● Nick's Fish

Nicholas Lynch's seafood shops are of benchmark quality, so Newbridge got lucky when Mr Lynch opened his second store here. The Newbridge store is notable for having a range of cooked seafood dishes prepared by their chef, in addition to a superb range of fish and shellfish and a useful selection of cookery essentials. (Nicholas Lynch, Moorefield Rd, Newbridge ☎ 045-440 055 www.nicksfish.ie – Open Mon-Fri 9.30am-5.30pm, 5pm Sat)

County Kilkenny

Bennettsbridge

Pottery & Café

● Nicky Mosse Pottery

This is a very pretty shop, and there are good scones and nice coffee as you browse. (Nicholas Mosse, Bennettsbridge ☎ 056-772 7105 sales@nicholasmosse.com www.nicholasmosse.com – Café Open 11am-5pm Mon-Sat, 1.30pm-4pm Sun)

Callan

Bakery

● Keogh's Model Bakery

Breads have been baked in Keogh's for more than a century, with William and his wife, Ann, continuing the proud family tradition. Sacriligeous as it may be, they even bake a Waterford Blaa. (William & Ann Keogh, Bridge Street ☎ 056-772 5254)

Kilkenny

Castlecomer

Café and Crafts

● Jarrow Café

We love Evan and Anna's Jarrow Café. It's such a delightful, calming space, and the cooking is so genuine, so real, so tactile. A dish of Lavistown sausages with roasted vegetables, or their famous chocolate biscuit cake, show that they are expert in savoury and expert in sweet, and we love the freshness of the salads and the lightness of the baking. The Jarrow Café restores you, it's as simple as that. (Anna & Evan Stewart, Castlecomer Discovery Park, Estate Yard, Castlecomer ☎ 056-444 0019 info@discoverypark.ie www.discoverypark.ie – Open 9.30am-5pm)

Cramer's Grove

Ice Cream

● Cramer's Grove Ice Cream

Here's the thing about Nigel and Carol's ice cream: you never forget the first time you tasted it. With us, it was at a market in Carrick-on-Suir many years back, shortly after they had first started to turn their farm milk into ice cream. We were blown away by the Madagascan vanilla, and the brown bread ice cream, stunned by their balance of flavour captured within the pure cloud of ice cold cream. And the memory has never faded. Today, in addition to their ice cream empire, Carol and Nigel also run their Treats café at the McDonagh Junction, with good coffee, nice savoury cooking, and brilliant ice cream treats. Cramer's Grove is a model artisan food company. (Nigel & Carol Harper, Cramer's Grove, Kilkenny ☎ 056-772 2160 ✉ icecream@cramersgrove.com 🖱 www.cramersgrove.com)

made in Kilkenny

Knockdrinna Kilree Goat's Cheese

Kilkenny

Cuffesgrange

Artisan Dairy

● Coolepump Dairy

Look out for the fine plain and flavoured yogurts and excellent milk made by this specialist dairy, which you will find in the best Kilkenny shops. (Ballymack, Cuffesgrange ☎ 086-161 6964 ✉ smaher83@gmail.com

Organic Apple Juice

● Highbank Organic Orchards

Limestone underpins the fertility of the Highbank orchards, allied with organic farming methods which Rod and Julie Calder-Potts have practised here since 1994. The Highbank apple juice is one of the very finest made in Ireland: it has that quality of fleetingness –

"awai" – that Japanese cooks treasure, the sense that when you drink it, it takes you straight to Kilkenny. The juice would have been enough to make the Calder-Potts a treasure for food lovers, but when they perfected their apple syrup, they created one of the defining new Irish artisan foods. Their brand new dry cider and Driver's cider are two more inspired creations. (Julie & Rod Calder-Potts, Cuffesgrange, Kilkenny ☎ 056-772 9918 sales@highbank.ie www.highbankorganicorchards.com)

Apple Juice

● Mosse's Apple Juice

Simon, Tina and Patrick grow excellent apples – amongst other fruits – and make a thirst-slaking juice which is one of the nicest you can buy. Look out for it locally in good shops. (Simon, Tina & Patrick Mosse, Dunedin, Cuffesgrange ☎ 056-772 7790 tmosse@eircom.net)

Cookery School

● Ryeland House

Anne Neary has been teaching the people of Kilkenny to cook for more than twenty years now, and she is a major local celebrity, heard on local radio, and a cook whose books have enjoyed considerable success. Her classes cover the entire gamut of cooking skills, and she works also with another talented Kilkenny cook, Edward Hayden. (Anne Neary, Cuffesgrange ☎ 056-772 9073/086-276 7656 ryelandhouse@gmail.com www.ryelandhousecookery.com)

Gathabawn

Farmhouse Ice Cream

● Gathabawn Farmhouse Ice Cream

William and Anthony Brennan specialise in making bespoke ice creams for restaurants and hotels. You might not realise you're eating their wonderful products, because chefs don't always credit it as being made outside the kitchen - but excellent it will be. They milk their own dairy herd to make the cream for the ice cream, and everything is carefully handmade with the Brennans overseeing each part of the process. (Anthony & William Brennan, Gathabawn, Kilkenny ☎ 086-351 6880 gathabawn@gmail.com)

Gowran

Foodshop

● Glasraí & Goodies

Glasrai & Goodies should really be called Gorgeous Glasrai & Goodies, as that is the term everyone uses to describe Siobhan Lawlor's pretty, essential artisan store: Gorgeous. All the great Kilkenny artisan foods are here, along with delicious baking, fresh salads, local veg, and all the things you need to live the good life. A tabernacle of treats. (Siobhan Lawlor, Main Street, Gowran ☎ 056-773 3799 ✉ siobhan@glasraiandgoodies.com 🖱 www.glassraiandgoodies.com)

local knowledge

Rapeseed Oil

Irish rapeseed oils have stolen the market place both commercially and domestically over the last few years. Their success has been one of the great stories of import substitution in the marketplace. And to a large extent their victory has been won thanks to their healthgiving properties: we all thought olive oil was good for you until we realised that rapeseed oils are actually better for you. Expect to see a range of grande and premier cru oils coming from individual farms and farmers over the next few years.

Graiguenamanagh

Country House

● Ballyogan House

By the banks of the River Barrow, Ballyogan is such a pretty house, so comfortable in its place, so well sited, so well maintained. "The level of hospitality had me smiling all the way: beautiful house and lovely people", says Eamon Barrett of his encounter with this genial gem. The Duries are superb hosts, people who know everything about the area and what is going on there.

They have restored Ballyogan with perfect grace and suitability, directing everything towards a welcoming comfort that makes you feel at home, just as some hot tea and cake, and superb breakfasts, will also mean you won't want to leave. It's not just the house that is in perfect order, mind you: the rolling lawns and mature trees seem as if they too have been arranged with benign care, and gazing out at them from the conservatory is a sublime, calm delight. (Robert & Fran Durie, Graiguenamanagh ☎ 059-972 5969 info@ballyoganhouse.com www.ballyoganhouse.com – Open 1 Apr-31 Oct and for St Patrick's weekend)

Restaurant and B&B

● Waterside

Simple accommodation and clean, simple cooking in a lovely riverside mill is the offer at The Waterside. (Brian & Brigid Roberts, Graiguenamanagh ☎ 059-972 4246 info@watersideguesthouse.com www.watersideguesthouse.com – Open Dinner from 6.30pm. Open seven nights in summer, and Sunday lunch, weekends only in winter)

Inistioge

Guesthouse

● The Inn @ Ballilogue Clochán

"Nestled away on a boreen near The Rower in South Kilkenny, Pat McCarthy's farmhouse renovation is a star" says Eamon Barrett. A collection of old outbuildings have had a magic wand waved over them to create a series of beautiful rooms both vernacular and cutting edge. Exposed stone walls, old dressers and mismatched crockery are mixed with power showers, Barcelona chairs, original art and lovely light fittings. There is tea and lemon cake on arrival and, later, local cheese and oat biscuits to go with a nice bottle of Sauvignon Blanc. The surroundings are sylvan, the garden is perfect, good taste abounds. Next morning, breakfast doesn't miss a beat: fresh orange juice, homemade brown bread, light as a feather pancakes with Greek yoghurt, blueberries and honey, cinnamon French toast with maple syrup. The Inn is simply a stunning achievement. (Pat McCarthy, Ballilogue, The Rower, Inistioge ☎ 051-423857 enquiry@ballilogueclochan.com www.ballilogueclochan.com)

Kilkenny

Shop & Pub

● Bridie's General Store

Part of the Langton group, Bridie's is a small specialist shop selling lots of tasty and unusual foods and gifts, and it is beautifully styled as a gleaming, traditional Irish grocer's. Behind the shop front, it opens out to a gleaming, stunning bar and beer garden. A killer piece of design, by the brilliant David Collins, of course, and only in Kilkenny would you find a Bridie's! (John Street)

Restaurant

● Café Sol

Noel McCarron and his crew do good, straight-ahead cooking in Café Sol, and have been rewarded with many years of success here on William Street. The cooking is open, uncomplicated, edging towards a Med-style sweetness with little savoury bullet-points: herbed crabcakes with wasabi and crème fraiche; Dunmore brill with lime and caper butter; Kilkenny rib-eye with bacon and cheese dauphinoise; iced cassata with cherry compote. Prices are keen, service is fleet and sweet, and the customer focus is never lost. (Noel McCarron, William Street, Kilkenny ☎ 056-7764987 ✉ info@cafesolkilkenny.com 🖱 www.cafesolkilkenny.com – Open 11.30am-9.30pm Mon-Fri, 11.30am-10pm Sat, noon-9pm Sun)

Restaurant

● Campagne

It's always the same at Campagne: "The menus present terrible dilemmas as everything tempts", says Eamon Barrett. Temptation, temptation! So bring on the terrine of foie gras and suckling pig with beetroot purée, let's have another Campagne classic of deep-fried haddock with poached egg and spring onion hollandaise, and what could be better than roasted scallops and chicken wings with a bacon and sweetcorn purée. Garret Byrne's cooking is as rich and colourful as his bright and glamorous dining room, and he likes his food to have a powerful but smooth edge – oxtail soup with watercress cream and Parmesan; roasted partridge with sauté foie gras, savoy cabbage and cep; Sauternes custard with Armagnac prunes and almond tuile. The food has a richness that is considered unfashionable now, but Mr Byrne works a very classic culinary style. Value is keen, but service could loosen up a little. (Garret Byrne & Brid Hannon, 5 The Arches, Gashouse Lane, Kilkenny ☎ 056-777 2858 info@campagne.ie www.campagne.ie – Open 12.30pm-2.30pm Fri-Sat, 12.30pm-3pm Sun, 6pm-10pm Tue-Sat)

Wine Merchant

● Le Caveau

Pascal Rossignol is a polished kind of a guy, and yet there is something about him that is unambiguously feral, something wild. It should come as no surprise, then, that he is a champion of "natural" winemaking, that crossroads of viticulture that is currently the most contentious zone that the wine world has seen in many years. These wines are remarkable, in a very literal sense: you cannot taste them and be unmoved, for they are wild things, and one can see why Pascal Rossignol admires them and sells them. But they aren't the only things he sells, for the tiny Le Caveau is filled with great wines, chosen with fastidious discrimination and amazing knowledge, and sold with great charm by Pascal and Geraldine. A jewel of a place. (Pascal & Geraldine Rossignol, Market Yard, Kilkenny ☎ 056-775 2166 secure@lecaveau.ie www.lecaveau.ie – Open 10.30am-6.30pm Tue-Sat)

Café

● Chez Pierre

Pierre Schneider's nifty little dining room has some nice, laid-back cooking – a bacon tartine for breakfast; potato croquette with green salad at lunch; chicken with tarragon cream for dinner. There are nice puddings to finish off dinner or lunch, and Pierre's is a valuable standby. (Pierre Schneider, 17 Parliament Street, Kilkenny ☎ 056-776 4655 chezpierrerestaurant@hotmail.com – Open 10am-4.30pm Mon-Sat, 7pm-9pm Sat)

Restaurant

● Foodworks

The move to Parliament Street, from Gas House Lane, should bring Peter and Maeve's cooking to a bigger audience, and a bigger audience is what they deserve. Utilising their own rare-breed pork and produce from their polytunnels, they are focused on freshness and provenance. Mr Greany has a confident, sure-handed way with a plate of food, and his finishing notes – almond and sultana dressing with hake; rosemary and balsamic with lamb; red cabbage slaw with their hamburger; green beans and romesco sauce with goat's cheese – reveal a very nuanced, almost musicianly cook. Foodworks has always belonged in the centre of the city. (Peter Greany & Maeve Moore, 7 Parliament Street, Kilkenny ☎ 056-777 7696 foodworkscafe@gmail.com www.foodworks.ie– Open 9am-noon, breakfast, noon-5pm lunch Mon-Sat 5pm-9pm Thu-Sat)

Delicatessen

● The Gourmet Store

Padraig and Irene have added a fab new sit down area at the front of the hugely successful Gourmet Store, one of the city's most popular haunts. As always, says Claire Goodwillie, there are "Huge queues at lunchtime for their pannini and sandwiches, made to order, always good". Claire rhapsodises in particular about the "Pannini with pesto and brie mmmmmm". (Padraig & Irene Lawlor, Main Street, Kilkenny ☎ 056-777 1727 gourmetstore@hotmail.com www.thegourmetstorekilkenny.com – Open 9am-6pm Mon-Sat)

local knowledge

Crafty Kilkenny

Kilkenny is the craft capital of Ireland, so as you eat your way around the county, do check out the many craft artisans whose work mirrors that of the leading food producers. Several of the destinations in this book are also home to wonderful exhibitions of Kilkenny crafts.

Design Shop and Café

● Kilkenny Design Centre

Kathleen Moran is really ringing the changes in the iconic Kilkenny Design Centre. The dining room has been reworked, tasting events have been happening, there is a new coffee shop downstairs, and a food-to-go section has been established. The restaurant has also just begun to open in the evenings, with the menus offering smart modern cooking – duck confit with Inistioge chutney; Mileeven-honey pork belly with new potatoes; Paddy White's rib-eye with crispy potatoes; chocolate fondant with Cramer's Grove ice cream. The Design Centre is once again moving to the very centre of the culture. (Kathleen Moran, Castle Yard, Kilkenny ☎ 056-772 2118 info@kilkennydesign.com www.kilkennydesign.com – Open 10am-6pm Mon-Sat, 11pm-6pm Sun and bank hols)

Farmers' Market

● Kilkenny Farmers' Market

As one might expect in Kilkenny, the Thursday market is quixotic, intriguing, always surprising. Rare plants rub shoulders with hand-made pies and exquisite chocolate bonbons. Eamon's organics tempt you with their vigour, Helen's cheeses with their multifarious magnificence. Lots of excellent producers, lots of excellent foods. (The Market Yard, Kilkenny – Open Thursday morning)

Kilkenny

Hotel

● Kilkenny Ormonde Hotel

"Service is a hallmark of our stay", the travel writer Pol O Conghaile noted when he was in the Kilkenny Ormonde with his family. A cot arrived within minutes of being requested. A car rental return was taken care of by the staff. A baby's sleep suit is washed, dried and returned before you can say "Where The Wild Things Are." Mags, the waitress, wants to send breakfast up to Mrs O Conghaile, earning her a shower of brownie points. And that is the thing about the KO: it has one of the best teams in any Irish hotel, and they look after you. We have focused in the past on chef Mark Gaffney's cooking, but really every member of the crew matches Mr Gaffney's excellence and commitment. Top class. (Mark Gaffney, Ormonde Street, Kilkenny ☎ 056-772 3900 info@kilkennyormonde.com www.kilkennyormonde.com)

Gastro Bar & Tea Rooms

● Marble City Bar & Tea Rooms

There are comfortable tea rooms at the back of the beautiful Marble City bar, part of the Langton group of hostelries, and it's a lovely space in which to take tea. The bar itself serves food throughout the day, and it's good tasty, popular cooking. (The Langton family, 66 High Street, Kilkenny ☎ 056-776 1143 www.langtons.ie – Food served 10am-10pm)

Café

● Café Mocha

"A treasure trove of chocolate and sweet things, almost rococco in its over-the-top cluttered style", writes Claire Goodwillie, a big fan of what Joseph and Laura are doing here in Café Mocha. Lunches are delightful, with good, fresh salads and smart, well-considered hot dishes that just hit the spot. Mocha has proven so successful that evening dining has begun from summer 2012. (Joseph & Laura Delaney, 84 High Street, Kilkenny ☎ 056-777 0074 – Open 9am-6pm Mon-Sat, 11am-6pm Sun, 6pm-9.30pm Fri & Sat)

Delicatessen and Take-away

● Nourish

Crispy savoury tarts, nutty carrot cake – and the best part! – it's all incredibly good value. Italian cook Paolo Ambue also makes home-made breads and huge meringues with raspberry coulis. Home-cooked food to go. (Paolo Ambu, 2 Market Yard, Kilkenny ☎ 056-776 1456 - paolo.ambue@virgilio.it– Open 8.30am-6pm Mon-Wed & Sat, 8.30am-7pm Thu-Fri)

Restaurant

● Rinuccini

The Cavaliere family's Rinuccini feels just right. It is one of those rooms that basks in the restaurantness of a restaurant. Wood panelled, softly lit, elegantly clothed and napped, adorned with the paraphernalia of wine, the rooms feed us an image of Italian restaurants that may be more New York than Turin, but the effect is simply perfect. And the food completes the picture perfectly – ravioli with ricotta and spinach and tomato sauce; prawns with mustard and brandy; fettuccine with polpettine; mussels with tomato, garlic, white wine and chilli. If your boat has come in, then pay a visit to the cellar and enjoy some stratospheric Italian wines, including rare Super Tuscans. (Antonio, Marion & Riccardo Cavaliere, 1 The Parade, Kilkenny ☎ 056-776 1575 info@rinuccini.com www.rinuccini.com – Open noon-3pm Mon-Fri, 5pm-10pm Mon-Sat, noon-3.30pm Sat & Sun, 5pm-9.30pm Sun)

Asian Delicatessen

● Shortis Wong

Is there anything nicer to do in Kilkenny than to saunter down John Street, munching on a hot samosa or a crispy, crumbly spring roll, hot from the counter in Chris and Mary's brilliant Shortis Wong? We don't think there is, just as we don't think there is anything better than hunting through this fabulous food emporium in search of something arcane and exotic. Shortis Wong is one of the great stores, one of the great treats of the South East. Careful not to burn your mouth on that samosa! (Mary Shortis & Chris Wong, John Street, Kilkenny ☎ 056-776 1305 – Open 9am-7pm Mon-Sat)

Artisan Bakery

● A Slice of Heaven

How to describe Mary McEvoy's stunning patisserie? The Miro of Irish baking? The Dali of deliciousness? The Monet of cupcakes? The Kahlo of colour? You really have to stretch for the artistic superlatives to understand Ms McEvoy's incredible work. You could drop this baking into any food loving city and it would be a wow! so how fortunate for Kilkenny that A Slice of Heaven is now open on High Street, and we can all enjoy some of the most outstanding baking in Ireland. Keep an eye out for Mary's demos and workshops and, if the big day is looming, come in for a consultation about the cake from heaven. (Mary McEvoy, 62 High Street, Kilkenny ☎ 087-953 3870 mary@asliceofheaven.ie www.asliceofheaven.ie)

Wine Merchant

● The Wine Centre

The Wine Centre is a pretty extraordinary shop. It's one of those magical places that seems to open out ever expansively, revealing range after range of exciting and exotic wines the further you explore deeper into the store. A great place for spirits and craft beers also, and for newcomers such as Carlow's ginger beer. (Edmond O'Keeffe, 15 John Street, Kilkenny ☎ 056-776 5900 www.thewinecentre.ie – Open 10.30am-10pm Mon-Sat)

Restaurant & Townhouse

● Zuni

"Maria and her team stunned us with the originality, taste and balance of her dishes", a friend wrote in praise of Maria Raftery's amazing 7-course Savour Kilkenny festival dinner. It was a dazzling series of riffs on favoured Kilkenny ingredients:Goatsbridge trout Scotch eggs; Mary Walsh's chicken confit with sweetbreads in a pie; Knockdrinna goat's cheese spring rolls with pumpkin hummus; Donald Russell beef with foie gras nuggets; halibut with samphire and lemon verbena; a mojito jelly; Ballymoney venison with chestnut mousse, and all this before a giddy trove of Zuni Sweet Shop desserts, incuding salted toffee lolly, blackcurrant and stout jelly, passionfruit iceberg and lots more giggly, gimmee-more fun. Ms Raftery continues to blossom as a cook, continues to learn, and the more she learns the more she seems to enjoy herself. (Paul & Paula Byrne, 26 Patrick Street, Kilkenny ☎ 056-772 3999 info@zuni.ie www.zuni.ie – Open 12.30pm-2.30pm, 6.30pm-10pm Mon-Sat; 1pm-3pm, 6pm-9pm Sun)

Kilmacow

Bakery

● Harney's Bakery

It may reside in County Kilkenny, but one of the specialities of Harney's bakery is their version of the Traditional Waterford Blaa. (Denis Harney, Kilmacow ☎ 051-885118)

Lavistown

Farmhouse Sausages, Burgers & Study Centre

● Lavistown Farmhouse

Olivia Goodwillie is one of the great figures of Irish artisan foods. She has an artist's eye and an artisan's heart, which explains why her Lavistown sausages are so good.

Her foods are pure things, made to be as good and as distinctive as they can be. We have a crackpot theory about how a farmhouse cheese reflects the character of its maker, and Mrs Goodwillie's sausages reflect her character – impish; humorous; smart, with a note of irony. Other bangers are commercial compromises, but Lavistown are little porky works of art: Mrs Goodwillie can do nothing else. (Olivia Goodwillie, Lavistown ☎ 056-776 5145 courses@lavistownhouse.ie www.lavistownhouse.ie)

local knowledge

Trail Kilkenny

County Kilkenny leads the way when it comes to presenting an integrated tour of its leading food artisans, specialist shops and restaurants. The Taste of Kilkenny Food Trail will lead you unerringly to great bakers, cookery schools, cafés and farm shops. And they even have the GPS co-ordinates to ensure you don't get lost as you eat your way around the county.

Piltown

Apple Juice

● The Little Apple Co.

Look out for the fine Little Apple Co apple juices and fresh apples at Farmers' Markets locally. (Mark, Philip & John Little, Clonmore House, Piltown ☎ 051-387109)

Kilkenny

Honey

● Mileeven

Eilis Gough is one of Kilkenny's food pioneers, first producing the Mileeven honeys twenty five years ago. Today, it is the second generation of the family, Sarah Gough, who is powering the company, having introduced a new range of flavoured honeys under the Sarah's Honey title. The Mileeven honeys, jams and cakes have always been distinguishd by a fastidious attention to detail, and a winning aesthetic: the foods look good even before you taste them, and they taste better than they look. A model, specialist food company. (Sarah & Eilis Gough, Owning Hill, Piltown ☎ 051-643368 mileeven@indigo.ie www.mileevenfinefoods.com)

Shellumsrath

Free-Range Poultry

● Kilkenny Free Range

Mary and Tony Walsh produce excellent Shellumsrath chickens and geese, supplying them mainly to good restaurants, but private customers are also catered for, especially with their Xmas geese. Proper poultry is hard to find, so these are valuable and quite delicious. (Mary & Tony Walsh, Shellumsrath ☎ 056-776 3426 www.kilkennyfreerange.com)

Stoneyford

Farmhouse Cheese, Pork, Preserves, Café

● Knockdrinna Farmhouse Cheese & Lavistown Farmhouse Cheese

Seven years is all it took for Helen Finnegan to go from being a wannabe cheesemaker to winning the accolade of Supreme Champion at the 2011 British Cheese Awards for her Knockdrinna Kilree goat's cheese. The scale of her achievement is extraordinary, as extraordinary as the purity and creativity of her farmhouse cheeses. She makes cheeses with goat's milk, with sheep's milk and with cow's milk, and from them all she extracts a refulgent depth of flavour that dances alongside floral, herbal, mineral and nutty flavour notes. Her skill is to maintain the unique character of each of the Knockdrinna cheeses, and she has also performed a great public service in continuing the production of Kilkenny's legendary Lavistown cheese. Helen Finnegan is one of the most accomplished artisan producers of her generation. (Helen Finnegan, Stoneyford ☎ 056-772 8446 hlanders@esatclear.ie www.knockdrinna.com)

Farm Shop

● Knockdrinna Farm Shop

In Helen Finnegan's shop, you can see all of County Kilkenny. Well, the parts that you can eat, anyhow, for this little shop and tearoom is packed with all the bounties of one of the most dynamic food counties in the country. Alongside Mrs Finnegan's own award-winning cheeses and her most delicious pork products and home baking, there are Coolepump yogurts and milk, Dunedin cordial, Mosses apple juice, Lavistown sausages, to name just a few locals, along with some Wicklow blow-ins – Coolattin Cheddar; Kingfisher tea; Wicklow veg. In our notes we scribbled down that "It's the shop where you want to buy everything" and, reader, we did just that. Helen Finnegan is a woman who takes every venture she embarks on to new heights. (Helen Finnegan, Stoneyford ☎ 056-772 8446 hlanders@esatclear.ie www.knockdrinna.com – Open 10am-6pm Tue-Sat)

Thomastown

Café

● The Blackberry Café

County Kilkenny is home to many mighty food mavens – fish smokers, cheesemakers, chocolatiers, cooks, bakers, teachers, milk maids – powerful, creative women who spearhead the local food culture. Jackie Hoyne is one of the foremost of these creative women, and her lovely Blackberry Café is a showcase both for her own skills and for the fruits of the Kilkenny artisan food culture in which she is a major player. She spent a long time working in banking in the UK, hankering to get back home and open her own place. When she did, in late 2007, she opened one of the sweetest destinations you will find, a gorgeously restored building with glorious food, food that is simple, but utterly pure and true, food that is deeply rooted, and thereby deeply satisfying. A favourite place in a favourite county. (Jackie Moyne, Market Street, Thomastown ☎ 087-053 7858)

Kilkenny

Trout Farm

● Goatsbridge Premium Irish Trout

When Mags and Ger Kirwan launched their Goatsbridge Irish Trout Caviar, Mrs Kirwan explained her modus operandi: "Be brave when all around you are fearful", Mrs Kirwan said, echoing the sagely Warren Buffet, and explaining the seemingly bonkers idea of launching a unique, expensive, trout caviar at a time of unprecedented recession. Is Goatsbridge trout caviar the right product at the right time? There is no doubt about it: Goatsbridge is on its way to becoming an iconic Irish artisan food, like Milleens cheese, or O'Hara's stout, or Clonakilty Black Pudding, the food that broke the mould. You will remember the first time you ate it, and where you were, and who served it to you, and who was with you, a food that acts as a portal to the memory of pleasure. Mags and Ger continue to produce their beautiful Goatsbridge trout, another benchmark product from a dynamic couple. (Margaret & Gerard Kirwan, Thomastown ☎ 086-818 8340/086 254 4906 info@goatsbridgetrout.ie www.goatsbridgetrout.ie)

made in Kilkenny

Goatsbridge Trout

Farm Produce

● Kylemore Farm produce

Martin Lyng rears excellent beef and lamb, and sells these fine meats at local Farmers' Markets. Look out for Martin's Xmas turkeys. (Martin Lyng, The Rower, Thomastown ☎ 051-423647)

Country House

● Mount Juliet

Nothing cheers a critic more than a crew who are determinedly working to be their best. That, after all, is what we mean by 'The Best In Ireland' – people determined to do their best, be their best, achieve their best. And in Mount Juliet, manager William Kirby and his cheffing trio – Cormac Rowe, Ken Harker and John Kelly – are determined to give us the best that they've got. In the past, we had simply sidelined Mount Juliet as a plush hideaway for golfers with too much money. And it is plush, and grand. And there are people in golf sweaters – at breakfast time! Ouch! But that doesn't matter, because what counts here is a place determined to reach out to its local community through sourcing the best Kilkenny ingredients, a place that is ingenious and creative and very, very beautiful, and where the staff work extra hard. 'A breath of fresh air and fresh thinking', said *The Irish Times*. They also have more grey squirrels than we have ever seen in our lives. (William Kirby, Thomastown ☎ 056-777 3000 info@mountjuliet.ie www.mountjuliet.ie)

Restaurant

● Sol Bistro

A characterful room in Thomastown is home to the second Café Sol branch. The cooking has the character and colour of the Med, with local touches – Goatsbridge smoked trout salad with dill and caper cream; Knockdrinna goat's cheese with wild mushrooms in a tart; orange and almond polenta cake. Keen prices and good vegetarian options. (Noel McCarron, Thomastown ☎ 056-775 4945 info@cafesolkilkenny.com www.cafesolkilkenny.com – Open noon-4pm, 5pm-close Mon-Fri, noon-close Sat & Sun)

Chocolates

● Truffle Fairy

The Truffle Fairy has really taken wing in the last while. Mary Teehan's confidence as a chocolatier and the increasing success of her enterprise have chimed together to make for one of the leading artists in her field. We use the term artist deliberately, because as part of the Savour Kilkenny Festival in late 2011, Mary actually made a number of chocolate canvases which were installed in a gallery in Thomastown. They were bold and crazy and brilliant and, in reality, they were simply large scale examples of what Ms Teehan does in microcosm with every chocolate truffle she makes. Chocolate art, yes indeed. (Mary Teehan, Thomastown ☎ 056-779 3375 mary@trufflefairy.com www.trufflefairy.com)

Wine Academy

● Wine Academy Ireland

Mary Gaynor and her team run courses in wine appreciation from basic introductory courses to advanced certificate and specialist training levels. The Wine Academy is the longest-established wine educator in Ireland. (Mary Gaynor, The Quay, Thomastown ☎ 056-772 4894 marygaynor99@eircom.net www.wineacademy.ie)

Kilkenny

Tullaroan

Bakery

● Oldtown Hill Farmhouse Bakery

Standards are high amongst artisan producers in Kilkenny, and Oldtown Hill Bakery is a defining example of what we mean by high standards. The bakery uses locally milled flour, they use fresh milk from their own dairy farm, they employ skilled bakers, no junk is permitted, the breads and cakes share the most beautiful appearance, the packaging is top notch, and all of this care, concern and concentration make for breads and cakes that define artisanship. Joy and James just have the instinct for good baking, and thankfully Oldtown Hill breads and cakes are available from North Dublin down to Waterford. And don't miss their terrific Dolly's Donuts, and the beautiful Dolly's Donut van. (Joy & James Moore, Oldtown Hill, Tullaroan ☎ 056-776 9263 ✉ oldtownhill@mail.com)

made in Kilkenny

Highbank Orchard Syrup

Urlingford

Rapeseed Oil

● Second Nature Oils

Kitty Colchester's organic rapeseed oils, sold under the Second Nature label, have supplanted high-end extra virgin olive oils in our kitchen. Other Irish rapeseed oils are used for cooking, but Kitty's is the oil for salads, for dressing cooked vegetables, for drizzling over pastas. The oils are floral and lush, and organic production means none of the bad stuff – the hexane solvents, the anti-frothing agents, the chemical fungicides, insecticides, herbicides and synthetic fertilisers, and any trace of genetically modified seed – are allowed. We like the green freshness of the plain oil, but there are flavourd oils also – chili, rosemary, lemon, mandarin, and garlic.They are in every good shop, and should be in every good kitchen. Vital. (Kitty Colchester, Drumeen Farm, The Islands, Urlingford ☎ 087-9265423 ✉ info@secondnatureoils.com 🖱 www.secondnatureoils.com)

County Laois

Abbeyleix

Bakery & Café

● The Gallic Kitchen

We go all the way back with Sarah Webb's Gallic Kitchen, back to the late 1980's when Ms Webb began baking, just as we began writing guide books. She has sustained us through all those years, by being brilliant, creative, dynamic, original and dedicated. She has been a muse for our books, as we reflect on her work, and she has been a constant companion in our kitchen. We make the detour off the N7/N8 into Abbeyleix every time we drive the road, because Gallic Kitchen food sustains you in a way few other bakers and cooks can: one bite of the twin-barrelled sausage rolls, with a cup of tea, and you are ready to face the world. Sarah Webb has been one of the great players in Ireland's food culture over more than two decades, and she is still moving forward (witness the hot food stall at the Temple Bar Market), she is still holding herself to the very highest standards. She is an inspiration. (Sarah Webb, Main Street, Abbeyleix ☎ 086-605 8208 🖰 www.laois.gallickitchen.com – Open 10am-6pm Mon-Sun. Also at Temple Bar & Farmleigh markets amongst others.)

Jams, Preserves & Relishes

● G's Gourmet Jams

Thirty six saucepans! That's what you might see at any given time on any given day in the little factory where Helen Gee and her team make their jams, relishes and chutneys. Bubble, bubble, bubble, thirty six times over. Pan after pan, pan after pan, bubbling away on the stove, just like you remember your granny making her jam, stirring the pot, the scent of sugar, the scent of fruit, the intoxication of the preserving process, the age-less and age-old practice, bubbling away, day after day. Of course, it is this very simplicity that makes Helen's jams special, the simplicity that focuses on the communion of farm-fresh fruit and sugar, and nothing else. (Helen & Clive Gee, Ballypickas, Abbeyleix ☎ 057-873 1058 ✉ gsgourmetjams@eircom.net 🖰 www.gsgourmetjams.ie)

Laois

Ballacolla

Farmhouse Cheese

● Abbey Organic Cheese Co.

Pat Hyland is best known as a stallholder at the Saturday Temple Bar market, where he has sold his own Paddy Jack cheeses, and a range of European cheeses, for many years now. It's fully two decades since Pat made the leap from farmer to cheesemaker, and then marketeer, and his enthusiasm and banter are as vivid as ever. (Pat Hyland, Cuffsborough, Ballacolla ☎ 057-873 8599 ✉ abbeycheese@eircom.net)

Ballickmoyler

Country House & Organic Farm

● Coolanowle Country House Health Spa

The Mulhall family are part of the New Agricultural Economy. Several years back, they switched from chemicalised farming to organic farming. Then they pioneered selling their amazing organic meats from their farm through Farmers' Markets, sold from their gleaming vans. In late 2010 they opened their own Farm Shop at their farm at Cooleanowle. Bernadine runs a smashing B&B in the house, and there are guest cottages. The Mulhalls are ahead of the posse, they are ahead of the curve, and they are flourishing, because they know and understand one simple truth, as espoused by the legendary Wendell Berry: "Eating is an agricultural act". (Eddie & Bernadine Mulhall, Ballickmoyler ☎ 059-862 5176 ✉ coolanowle@eircom.net 🖱 www.coolanowle.com)

Laois

Ballyfin

Hotel

● Ballyfin

The great Aileesh Carew and the great Fred Cordonnier run front-of-house and run the kitchen at super-swish Ballyfin. It's grand, but it's not stuffy, thanks to an excellent team who confidently know their way. (Aileesh Carew, Ballyfin ☎ 057 875 5866 🖱 www.ballyfin.com)

Killenard

Hotel

● The Heritage/Sol Oriens

What you will recall about the Heritage, after you have crossed over the hotel's threshold and driven back into the real world, is the pitch-perfect level of service that the staff at the hotel deliver, as to the manner born. There may be elements of the complex that you can cavil at, but rest assured that the staff will silence your misgivings about golf courses or blingy design or whatever. They are a wholly exceptional crew, from the concierges – the best! – to the receptionists to the staff in the bars and restaurants, to the invisible workers who bring your children bedtime biscuits and milk. The team make The Heritage, and they make it special. (Struan Craig, Killenard ☎ 057-864 5500 info@theheritage.com www.theheritage.com)

Mountrath

Cakes and Café

● The Cosy Cafe

A pretty cup cake, a nice cup of Java Republic coffee, and all is well with the world in Sinead's cosy café. Cosy it is, and a vital Mountrath address for warming home cooking. (Sinead Hanlon, The Square, Mountrath ☎ 057-875 6211 - shinohano@hotmail.com – Open 8am-6.30pm Mon-Sat, 8am-3pm Sun)

Country House

● Roundwood House

"It's still a family environment and our guests seem to like that", Hannah Flynn told *The Irish Times*. Thank heavens for family continuity, for new generations who are happily carrying on the pioneering work of their parents. Roundwood expresses the perfection of imperfection, the beauty of something aged, something organic. And now, blessed with the energy of Hannah and her husband, Paddy, Roundwood is poised for the future, the family environment intact, ready for the next 300 years. (Hannah & Paddy Flynn, Mountrath ☎ 057-873 2120 info@roundwoodhouse.com www.roundwoodhouse.com)

Portlaoise

Wholefoods

The Fruit'n'Nut Place

Fruit'n'Nut is a very fine wholefood shop and a key Portlaoise address. (The Wellwood family, 1 Lyster Square, Portlaoise ☎ 057-862 2239 – Open 9.30am-6pm Mon-Sat)

Town House

Ivyleigh House

Tradition is one of those terms the Irish aren't really comfortable with. Talk about traditional food, for instance, and they imagine some fossilised culinary relic of times past, rather than a contemporary food culture infused with knowledge of the past. Similarly, when it comes to design, the Irish reckon you have either got to be modern, or live in an ancient mausoleum. Dinah Campion's lovely house, Ivyleigh, proves that this dichotomy is false. The style here is traditional, but is infused with a modern eye that emphasises lightness and brightness. The cooking, at breakfast, is traditional, which is to say it takes the best of the past and shares it with the best of the present – delicious cooking, but modern and light. Mrs Campion, in this way, creates a masterly synthesis in Ivyleigh, making for a place of good-mannered civility, understated charm, an alliance of the personal with the professional that is terrifically successful. Ivyleigh House is the star of Portlaoise. (Dinah Campion, Bank Place, Portlaoise ☎ 057-862 2081 info@ivyleigh.com www.ivyleigh.com)

Restaurant

The Kingfisher

The Kingfisher is a rock-steady Indian restaurant, which also offers a valuable home delivery sevice of its complete menu. (Khurshid (GooGee) Anwar, Main Street, Portlaoise ☎ 057-866 2500 inquiries@kingfisherrestaurant.com www.kingfisherrestaurant.com – Open noon-2pm Wed-Fri, 5.30pm-11.30pm Mon-Sun)

Granola

Paddy's O'Granola

Patrick O'Connell has shown himself to be a very adept businessman over the last couple of years as Paddy's

O'Granola has grown from a simple student start-up into a major commercial brand with an accompanying high profile. It must be all that granola he's having for breakfast! (Patrick O'Connell, Cullahill, Portlaoise ☎ 086-397 6215 paddy@granola.ie www.granola.ie)

Restaurant

Seasons Bistro

Kevin Hennessy is a perspicacious, professional restaurateur, and he moves where his audience want to go, in recent times introducing more casual dishes to the Season's menu. So, there are burgers, lasagne and steak sandwich for lunch, and rosemary lamb shank and fillet steak and goat's cheese and mushroom wellington for dinner. The prices and the dishes are approachable, the professionalism is paramount. (Kevin Hennessy, 24a Market Square, Portlaoise ☎ 057-868 0809 seasonsportlaoise@gmail.com www.seasonsbistro.ie – Open 12.30pm-2.30pm, 6.30pm to late Tue-Sun)

Rathdowney

Ice Cream

Rossmore Farmhouse Ice Cream

Killa Vanilla. Deadly Buzz. Fudgey Wudgey. Aubrey and Rebecca Stanley can sure come up with the groovy names for their farmhouse ice creams, made with the milk of their own herd. Look out for their super old-style ice cream cart at festivals, and Dubliners can get a taste of the ices at O'Connell's restaurant in Donnybrook. (Rebecca & Aubrey Stanley, Errill, Rathdowney ☎ 0505-44294/087-967 1430 dairy@rossmorefarm.ie www.rossmorefarm.ie)

Laois

Stradbally

Piemontese Beef

Irish Piemontese Beef

We first tried Piemontese beef at Electric Picnic, shortly after Michael and Mary Fennelly and John Commins – who farms his cattle in County Tipperary – began to make it available to Irish customers. The beef has a

major USP: it is lower in fat, cholesterol and calories than beef from other breeds, but is lower even than chicken or salmon. But, truth be told, that isn't the USP that counts. The Piemontese beef also has the USP that really counts: it is delicious. It takes a little bit of careful cooking, but if you handle it delicately, then it will reward you with a tremendous sweet, herbaceous flavour. We loved it. You will find it at the Newbarn farm shop in Ashbourne, Co Meath, on Saturdays and the meat can be ordered from their site, which also details other stockists. (Mary & Michael Fennelly, Stradbally 087 913 5349 info@irishpiemontesebeef.ie
🖱 www.irishpiemontesebeef.ie)

Organic Cake and Pancake Mixes

● Sowan's Organic

Sowan's are vital kitchen esentials. We don't know quite how they make it seem so simple to have a loaf of bread, a plate of pancakes or a tasty sweet cake on the table in no-time-at-all, but that is just what they do. Whiz, fold, pour, bake: it's done. And not only is it done, but what you have just made is completely natural, completely pure, completely organic. With a bag of Sowan's, everyone is a baker, a patissier, a pancake maker. (Don Brown, Stradbally ☎ 086-805 8115 📫 info@sowansorganic.ie
🖱 www.sowansorganic.ie)

Country Market

● Stradbally Country Market

Sally McKenna has yet to put the memory of the event behind her. It is Electric Picnic 2011. The girls and guys from the Stradbally Country Market have mounted a mighty stall at the festival, selling beautiful foods, wonderful local vegetables, terrific baking, the best bowl of porridge at the Picnic, and lots more besides. Sally buys some Scotch eggs to take home, having been told by John McKenna that they are Scotch eggs for the Gods. Packing up, Sally forgets the eggs, and leaves them in the prep kitchen of the Theatre of Food. All the way home, she is thinking of those Stradbally Scotch eggs. Mrs McKenna has yet to get over the shock of discovering that the eggs were left in Stradbally. Don't make Sally's mistake: shop at the Stradbally market and get a Garda escort to get those Scotch eggs safely home to your house and your lunch table. (St Patrick's Hall, Stradbally – Open Saturdays 10am-12.30pm)

County Leitrim

Carrick-on-Shannon

Boxty Producer

Boxty Bakers

Stephen Hennessy is making boxty a radical deal. The traditional potato cake has always been a regional rarity, with considerable local debate about how it should be made. Mr Hennessy wants the world to embrace boxty, so he has cooked it, sliced it and packaged it, and even made a boxty with bacon pieces. They are a Godsend, especially in a house with teenagers, who can fry them up with eggs and whatnot and stave the eternal hunger pangs. The packaging is excellent, the flavour is divine, and boxty is – surely – destined for world domination. (Stephen Hennessy, Dublin Road, Carrick-on-Shannon ☎ 071-965 0700 🖱 www.boxtybakers.ie)

Farmers' Market

Market Yard Farmers' Market

A beautiful market yard and a beautiful collection of local growers and producers is the winning combination in Carrick-on-Shannon. Organic meats, farmhouse cheeses in perfect condition, local organic vegetables and lots of breads, baking, flowers and fresh fish. Get there early on Thursdays, and then have a cup of tea in the Yard itself to sustain you. (Market Yard, Carrick-on-Shannon 🖱 www.themarketyardcentre.com – Open Thurs 10am-3pm)

Gastropub

The Oarsman

Shaun Hanna heads up the Oarsman kitchen in Ronan and Conor Maher's pioneering gastropub, and his food is powerful, well-considered and delicious, working themes and variations in dishes such as rare-breed saddleback pork, where the belly and neck are slow-cooked, the fillet is roasted and the whole is beautifully served with a great turnip gratin. His judgement is just as apt with the Sheerin's lamb tasting plate, where he roasts the rump and confits the shoulder and matches it with an unctuous potato gratin and a smart rhubarb and rosemary chutney. This is super, no-nonsense food from a great team, from the terrific house breads all the way to excellent puddings, and the value is excellent for such finely sourced foods. The Maher brothers saw, before almost anyone else, how the rural Irish pub could be reborn and re-energised, and their success is one of the most heartening success stories in Irish food. (Ronan & Conor Maher, Bridge Street, Carrick-on-Shannon ☎ 071-962 1733 info@theoarsman.com www.theoarsman.com – Food served noon-9pm Tue-Sat. Open till 9.30pm Fri & Sat)

local knowledge

Boxty

Boxty is a regional potato dish, a speciality of the counties Cavan, Leitrim, Longford and parts of Fermanagh, where it's called a 'hurley'. Two types are generally made: pan boxty and boiled boxty. And as well as these there are regional variations, so you might hear tell of dumpling boxty, or baked boxty loaf. Boiled boxty is a mix of cooked and raw potatoes, that undergoes a further boiling. Because of the different cooking processes this type of boxty can taste like a dumpling, or a gnocchi. Pan boxty is a simpler presentation of grated, unrinsed potato. Both types are then traditionally fried, often using the residual fat and cooking juices of a piece of bacon that will form part of the meal. Traditionally, Boxty was only made at Hallowe'en, though you can now buy it throughout the year.

Dromahair

Farmhouse Cheesemonger

● Cheese Etc

Trevor and Myra's Cheese Etc has long been one of the finest market stalls in Ireland, for they are both expert and accomplished curators of Irish farmhouse cheeses, and a fount of knowledge on that endless, arcane and absorbing subject. Find them at Carrick-on-Shannon, Manorhamilton and Sligo, and prepare to feast on a prodigious display of great artisan cheeses. (Trevor & Myra Irvine, Main Street, Dromahair ☎ 086-265 4675 ✉ cheeseetc@eircom.net. Also at the following markets: Carrick-on-Shannon Thur 10am-2pm, Manorhamilton Fri 10am-2pm, IT College Sligo Sat 9am-1pm)

Dromod

Bakery

● Dromod Homemade Boxty

Look out for Timmy's boxty in shops and supermarkets in the county, along with his breads, fadge and pancakes. The colourful red and yellow label will alert you to this fine example of one of the great traditional foods of the North West. (Timmy Faughnan, Station Road, Dromod ☎ 071-963 8535)

Drumshanbo

Smokehouse

● Carraig na Breac Smokehouse

The name means "Rock of the trout", an aptly poetic title for this specialist smokehouse, whose products can be found in good shops on the west coast. Peter and Niamh smoke bacon, duck and chicken, using a traditional kiln, and they have a light touch with the smoking, using organic oak, apple and beech wood. (Peter & Niamh Curry, The Food Hub ☎ 071-964 0522)

Bakery

● Jinny's Bakery

Jinny's is one of the great Irish bakeries. Sinead and Pascal's breads are so vivid with flavour, so beautifully controlled in their crust and crumb, that they deliver untold pleasure to the eater. Just try a slice of that Irish Stout Bread and succumb to its tartness, its subdued sweetness, its classy confidence. Like the best artisans, Sinead and Pascal have gotten better and better through their first decade of baking, and the growth in their confidence has been exponential. You will find the breads in good shops in the North West, and don't miss them: Jinny's is a treasure. (Sinead McGuire & Pascal Gillard, Carrick Road, Drumshanbo ☎ 071-964 1033 ✉ sinead@jinnysbakery.com 🖱 www.jinnysbakery.com)

Jamestown

Restaurant

● The Cottage

At The Cottage they cook food that makes you want to clear your plate. Not because that's what your mammy always told you to do, but because it is simply too good to leave behind: the breads, most especially the slices of dark, sweet walnut and treacle loaf, and the accompaniments of sundried tomato paste and a basil pesto that is lush, deeply green and fresh as you like; buttery scallops served with style on a sweet potato purée that was warm with spice; a feta and spinach filo parcel with an intensely flavoured minestrone velouté. Here, too, is food to make you smile: enter the sexed-up crispy pancake that was A.B.F. - Anything But Findus - a deep-fried parcel of spiced vegetables served with a delectable mango chutney and cracking little bowl of dahl. The vegetable accompaniments include spuds two ways, both properly mashed and in fried chunk form, along with parsnip, and dressed with a lightly curried sauce. What Sham has done for crispy pancakes, it seems he was repeating for curry chips. Fair play to you, Sham - a Malaysian chef, using Irish ingredients, cooked with a broadly Asian accent but with always an eye to Irish sensibilities - which explains why the dessert menu, in addition to its brownie with sweet chilli ice cream - which gently challenges with the promise of being both hot and cold at once - also includes an elegant riff on that Irish mammy special, the apple tart. Welcome to The Cottage folks, where East meets West of Ireland. (Sham Hanifa, Jamestown ☎ 071-962 5933 ✉ info@cottagerestaurant.ie 🖱 www.cottagerestaurant.ie – Open 6pm-10pm Thurs-Sun, noon-4pm Sun)

Kinlough

Restaurant with Rooms

● The Courthouse

Piero Melis is a great cook. 'Went there with a friend and stayed overnight, and was really wowed! by Piero's cooking', reported a friend. '[There was] a nice twist on many 'standard' dishes that elevated them to something unique, interesting and memorable. You don't have to re-invent the wheel to produce something stimulating!' We couldn't agree more. Our last dinner in The

Courthouse was outstanding, as Mr Melis wove his way carefully and colourfully around a series of beautiful creations – sea urchins with garlic, chilli and olive oil; a cracking aubergine parmigiana; king prawns with brandy sauce and pea purée; Thornhill duck with spinach and wild mushroom sauce; a fine seafood and chicken paella; penne with smoked salmon and vodka. The focus in the Courtyard is on making certain that every dish is vibrant with flavour, and it makes for great eating; eating that more and more people seem to be discovering as the room was really buzzing all around our table, with happy folk enjoying special food. Make sure to stay overnight, and enjoy the Iselis wines from Sardinia. (Piero Melis, Main Street, Kinlough ☎ 071-984 2391 thecourthouserest@eircom.net www.thecourthouserest.com – Restaurant open 6pm-9.30pm,'till 10pm high summer), noon-2.30pm Sun)

Rossinver

Organic Centre

● The Organic Centre

"Skills For Life" is what the Organic Centre promises, and is what the Organic Centre delivers. Spend a day or more at one of the many courses here – discovering wild foods; making stone walls; understanding nutrition, maybe come for their Potato Day, or the Apple Day – and you come away feeling not just empowered, but distinctly wiser. Something in your head and your heart will have been skilled up by the wise instructors and lecturers, the feeling that the natural world is your ally, your companion, your collaborator. The Organic Centre is a portal into understanding the rhythms of the world we live in, and when you step out of the portal at the end of the course, the world will look differently to you. It will look better, friendlier. The most recent course we did was on discovering wild herbs, conducted by expert tea blender and herb authority Joerg Muller, and it was a fabulous experience, a brilliant blend of Goethian science and natural exploration, with a great lunch sandwiched into the middle of the day, So, skill up. (Hans Wieland, Rossinver ☎ 071-985 4338 organiccentre@eircom.net www.theorganiccentre.ie – Shop open 10am-5pm every day, except bank holidays)

County Limerick

Adare

Farmer Cooks

● Adare Farm Foods

Tommy Relihan and his family know what Irish farming is all about: creating a brand that links the farm and the foods. Their cows produce milk which they sell as Adare Farm milk, and as sorbets and ice creams. Their Angus cattle produce superb eating, and are sold along with their lamb via their farm shop in the Limerick market, where they spit-roast their pigs every Saturday. They feature the pig-on-a-spit at events and parties, and wheel out their ice cream cart when the sun shines. So, everything about Adare Farm says: Adare Farm Foods, productive, creative, imaginative, offering pleasure, creating solutions. Brilliant, and a model for Irish farming, going forward, as the pundits say on the radio. (Tommy Relihan, Adare ☎ 087-296 2626 ✉ info@adarefarm.ie 🖱 www.adarefarm.ie)

Restaurant

● White Sage

Tony and Bobbie Schwarz have fashioned a huge success story in White Sage, tearing through the recession on an offer that showcases his superb cooking and her terrific service. Mr Schwarz is ambitious and talented, his cooking is nuanced, and he has learnt with the best. His food inclines to the ageless French techniques – ragouts; veloutés; rillettes; foie gras terrines – but there is an earthiness in this food that comes from the quality of the ingredients and the pedigree of the providers of those ingredients. So, the spinach velouté with a prawn and chicken sausage also has wild nettles; the daube of beef has the tartness of Guinness; the menus revel in offal and game dishes; duck confit has Champagne rhubarb and ginger, and that rhubarb returns in a sweet tart with a walnut and almond crumble. The setting – in a gorgeous thatched cottage in Ireland's prettiest village – simply could not be more idyllic, and value is very keen. (Tony & Bobbie Schwarz, Main Street, Adare ☎ 061-396004/087 9450254 ✉ info@whitesagerestaurant.com 🖱 www.whitesagerestaurant.com – Open 6pm-9.30pm Tue-Sat)

Restaurant

● The Wild Geese

The Italian term 'sprezzatura' is used to describe someone who does difficult things with quiet confidence and seeming nonchalance. 'Studied carelessness' is how the *OED* defines it, which doesn't seem quite right, however. 'Concealed effort' seems rather better, and that would be a good way to describe David Foley's cooking in the Wild Geese. Mr Foley's cooking is complicated, and yet, the dish will conceal the effort: where some chef's food screams 'Pay attention!', David Foley's dishes simply say: 'Enjoy'. It's masterly, and it's delicious, of course, full of little surprises like deep-fried leeks with scallops and black pudding, or the saffron in the sauce with monkfish, or the curried crust with baked Bluebell Falls goat's cheese. The room is equally sprezzatura – intimate, romantic – and the final part of the sprezzatura is Julie Randles' service, which is simply the art of the hostess. (David Foley & Julie Randles, Rose Cottage, Main Street, Adare ☎ 061-396451 ✉ wildgeese@indigo.ie 🖱 www.thewild-geese.com – Open 6.30pm-10pm Tue-Sat, 12.30pm-3pm Sun)

Annacotty

Restaurant

● Copper & Spice

Bryan and Seema Conroy's cooking is cultured and globetrotting. Whilst menus that range from Asia to the Pacific and on to India would normally have food lovers running away, this couple have always demonstrated a rare ability to focus on the culinary culture of the dish – Japanese gyoza; sheekh kebab; vegetarian thali – and to bring it home safely and surely. Keen prices and good service complete the story of one of Limerick's stars. (Bryan & Seema Conroy, The Mill Bar, Annacotty Village ☎ 061-338791 ✉ copperandspice@eircom.net 🖱 www.copperandspice.com – Open 5pm-10.30pm Mon-Sat, 2pm-10pm Sun)

Coffee Roaster

● Ponaire Coffee

Ponaire is one of the cult brands in Irish speciality food. Tommy and Jennifer have been working steadily, steadily since they started roasting coffee beans back in 2006, first opening their Annacotty shop beside the roastery, then opening a super outlet at the hip Limerick Milk Market, all the while infiltrating their coffees into cool restaurants and hip shops throughout the country. One image we love tells you everything: people circumnavigating the Newport Roundabout near to the Annacotty roastery get the scent from the beans that Jennifer is roasting, and promptly make that detour to stop at the shop and get that Ponaire hit: worth the detour or what! The various blends all demonstrate subtlety and delicacy, and we know it's ridiculous to say it, but these are feminine coffees, and they remind us of an old joke about pianists from the 19th century: Liszt may have conquered Europe, but Chopin seduced Europe. Ponaire coffees are Chopinesque. (Thomas & Jennifer Ryan, Unit E1 Annacotty Business Park, Annacotty ☎ Roastery 061-339799 ☎ Coffee Shop 061-339801 info@ponaire.ie www.ponaire.ie – Roastery & Deli open Mon-Fri, Milk Market open 11am-4pm Fri & Sun, 7am-4pm Sat)

made in Limerick

Ponaire Coffee

Ballingarry

Artisan Producer

● The Green Apron

Theresa Storey is a truly gifted artisan. In the same way that some people get music, or some people get the sea, she gets food. She just gets it. Her chutneys and preserves are benchmark productions, mellifluous creations that float on flavour, not least the chocolate and raspberry jam which is one of the best things we have tasted in recent times. There is a long family history of artisanship, and Theresa's children are already making waves as cooks and food lovers, so the future is secure for West Limerick. You can source this brilliant produce at the Milk Market and at the Ballingarry market, and Theresa – a trained botanist – also runs many courses on gardening and growing. (Theresa Storey, Derryclough, Ballingarry ☎ 069-68524 storeytd@tinet.ie storeytd@thegreenapron.ie http://.thegreenapron.ie/wordpress – Open in the Milk Market and various Festivals)

Restaurant & Country House

● The Mustard Seed

We have described Dan Mullane as 'a poet of the aesthetic world, a man whose grasp of design, comfort and style is matched by few others in Ireland'. That's true – only people like Paddy Foyle and Ken Buggy have the sort of crazy, meticulous, inspired eye that Mr Mullane has when it comes to shaping a room, a house, a garden. His brilliance makes Echo Lodge, where his Mustard Seed restaurant is housed, into one of the most pleasing houses to stay in anywhere in Ireland. But being a master of design is meaningless without the hospitality that truly animates a room, a restaurant, a house, and, guess what? Dan Mullane is as inspired a host, as he is a designer. In fact, he is even better as a host, than he is as a designer. For more than 25 years he has been greeting, meeting, and making welcome, and he does it today with the freshness, the zest, the spontaneous wit and natural charm, that first marked him out as someone special all those years ago. "The Mustard Seed and Dan Mullane are charm itself", says Aoife Cox. (Dan Mullane, Echo Lodge, Ballingarry ☎ 069-68508 ✉ mustard@indigo.ie 🖱 www.mustardseed.ie – Open all year, except first two weeks in Feb)

Drumcollogher

Bakery

● Brudair's Bakery

Brudair's is one of the towns two local bakeries, and you will find their fine breads in local shops – we greatly enjoyed the malt and barley bread recently. If you're feeling brave, then do ask locals to tell you the story about Mr Brudair and Christy Ring and the Munster Final. (Church Street, Dromcollogher ☎ 063-83051)

Organic College & Market

● Organic College & Market

Farming has become the new tech in Ireland, so courses in the agricultural colleges are hugely oversubscribed. If you can manage to get a place on one of the organic courses at Drumcollogher, lucky you, for you will learn all you need to know about respect for the land and for nature, and about yourself. (Drumcollogher ☎ 063-83604 ✉ oifig@organiccollege.com 🖱 www.organiccollege.com)

Bakery

● Twomey's Bakery

Lucky Drumcollogher has managed to hold onto its pair of small bakeries, and Twomey's prodce a fine range of breads that you will find in local shops. (Pat Twomey, Church Street, Dromcollogher ☎ 063-83084 ✉ twomeysbakery@eircom.net 🖱 www.twomeysbakery.com)

Hospital

Smoothies and Juices

● Wild Orchard

We love the Wild Orchard smoothies, juices and lemonades, proper drinks that you can give to the kids, and enjoy yourself when you need a shot of energy. The company also distributes a range of other Irish artisan food products. (Diarmuid Crowley, Enterprise Centre, Hospital ☎ 061-383930 ✉ diarmuid@wildorchard.ie 🖱 www.wildorchard.ie)

Kilcornan

Preserves

● Nature's Bounty

Colette O'Farrell hs turned her capacious hands to running Miss Marples' tea shop in the city, but lovers of her singular Nature's Bounty preserves needn't worry: her bespoke, foraged fruit business is continuing in all its glory. These are some of the best preserves you can buy. (Colette O'Farrell, Cowpark, Kilcornan ☎ 061-393942)

Farmhouse B&B, Rare Breed Pork Products

● Rigney's Farmhouse Bed and Breakfast

Caroline Rigney is one of the finest artisans in County Limerick. There is a pristine quality to her work, from the rearing of rare breed animals to the production and sale of these special meats, a skill and application which is wholly singular and inspiring. It amazes us that her produce isn't on the menus of every single good restaurant and hotel in Limerick, for no other speciality products speak so loudly of the county. But, whilst we wait for the restaurateurs to catch up, the rest of us can enjoy these fabulous foods thanks to Mrs Rigney's beautiful farm shop: a trip here to load up the cool box with these amazing meats is a trip to savour. And, of course, should you stay in Mrs Rigney's fine B&B, you will have these amazing sausages, puddings and bacon for your breakfast. (Caroline Rigney, Curraghchase, Kilcornan ☎ 087-283 4754 info@rigneysfarm.com www.rigneysfarm.com – Farmshop open 10am-6pm)

Killonan

Artisan Confectionery

● Pandora Bell

Nicole Dunphy sources superb confectionery and brands it beautifully under the Pandora Bell label. It's all as pretty as a picture, and quite delicious. (Nicole Dunphy, Killonan, Ballysimon ☎ 086-824 1823 hello@pandorabell.ie www.pandorabell.ie)

Limerick City

Café

● Café Noir

Pat O'Sullivan knows food. He was reared in the businesss in the days when kitchens had to master every discipline, and it shows in the care and consideration of the foods cooked and sold in the city's four Café Noir outlets. Good breads, good salads, good quiches, good sausage rolls, good cakes, good coffee, good tapas, good pies, good wines. Mr O'Sullivan and his crew make it look easy, but to run an outfit of this scale takes real discipline, and a very clear focus, which comes from Mr O'Sullivan's modest desire to "serve the simple menus on offer in Parisian cafés". They get there with gas in the tank, and the four outlets are amongst the stars of the city. (Pat O'Sullivan, Robert Street, Limerick ☎ 061-411222 Castletroy; O'Connell Street; University of Limerick www.cafenoir.ie – Open 8am-5.30pm Mon-Sat)

Restaurant

● Copper & Spice

The original C&S manages the same brilliant culinary feat as their Annacotty branch, managing to synchronise a pan-Asian globe-trotting menu offer into something delicious, authentic and particularly satisfying. Value for money is excellent, and the service is always assured and polite. (Bryan & Seema Conroy, 2 Cornmarket Row, Limerick ☎ 061-313620 copperandspice@eircom.net www.copperandspice.com – Open 5pm-10.30pm Mon-Sun)

Restaurant

● Cornstore

Maura Baxter's menu for the 2012 Limerick Love Gourmet Week was a masterclass in menu writing: scallops with potato cake, pancetta, and Longueville cider beurre blanc; skillet of Carrigaholt mussels with white wine, garlic and herb cream; bouillabaisse with monkfish, prawns, red snapper, mussels and toasted loaf; beef Rossini with potato rosti and red wine jus; vodka and black pepper strawberry pavlova. These were just some of the dishes on offer, and their sense of history, their sense of balance, is simply delightful. Put this food in a lovely space – which the Cornstore has in spades – add in some of the smartest children's food you can find, and you have a success story. (Maura Baxter, 19 Thomas Street, Limerick ☎ 061-609 000 limerick@cornstore.com www.cornstorelimerick.com – Open noon-4pm Mon-Sun, 5pm-10pm Mon-Thur, 4pm-10pm Fri & Sat, 5pm-9.30pm Sun)

Restaurant

● La Cucina

Take a slice of margarita and a slice of pepperoni pizza. Introduce five pasta dishes – penne all'arrabbiata; cannelloni with goat's cheese and spinach; bucatini with peas and mushrooms; spaghetti carbonara; and spaghetti bolognaise. Now, make everything distinctive, make everything delicious, and make everything perfect, as perfect as it can be. If you can do this, then you can do what Bruno and Lor do in the little La Cucina: they make everything as perfect as it can be. And they do it calmly, charmingly and, given the expertise evident in every dish, they do it pretty cheaply as well. When John McKenna had a quick, solo lunch here one afternoon – spinach and ricotta ravioli, then a hit of espresso – his notes read: 'Attention to detail is immense, staff superb, Bru & Lor as cool a couple as you get in Irish food.' When he came back with all the family – that's the five pasta dishes – the same was true, as the attention to detail of each pasta was inspiring – the carbonara clinging to the pasta, the cannelloni fresh and light, the bucatini perfect and woodsy, the arrabbiata light and hot, the spag bol perfection itself. La Cucina is some place. (Bruno & Lorraine Fanneran, 5 University Court, Castletroy ☎ 061-333980 ✉ eat@realitalianfoodies.com 🖱 www.realitalianfoodies.com – 10am-9.30pm Mon-Fri, noon-9.30pm Sat)

made in Limerick

Real Italian Foodies

Pub

● The Curragower Bar

The cooking in the Curragower, one of Limerick's most famous pubs, is a treat: unfussy, hearty, homey and delicious. It's a perfect example of a menu that only does a few things, and does them well. Their chowder is the creamiest soup chock-full of salmon, prawns and white fish with little chunks of potato, and comes with deliciously soft and wholesome brown bread. The scampi are proper breaded prawns, lightly fried and served prettily on a pile of crunchy, colourful salad. The fishcakes are crispy, and soft on the inside, served with a cool, fresh mint cream dressing. Apple and toffee crumble, served with a choice of cream, ice cream or home-made custard, is served pie-slice style. There is a talented cook at work in the Curragower, with a real feel for food and a light touch. (Cian Bourke, Clancy's Strand, Limerick ☎ 061-321788 🖱 www.curragower.com – Food served noon-7pm Wed-Sun)

Fishmonger

● René Cusack

Cusack's has been trading since 1910, at which time Michael Cusack's business was known as the Grimsby Fish Stores, and today Paul Cusack has been at the helm since 1985. Mr Cusack will describe the experience of buying and selling fish as "a cultural thing", so as a fishmonger and shopkeeper he goes the extra mile – the Cusack stores are beautifully maintained, service is fleet and knowledgeable, the long thread of history adding in a back story to the simple matter of buying something nice for your dinner. An essential address. (Paul Cusack, St Alfonsus Street, Limerick ☎ 061-440054 – Open 9am-5.30pm Mon-Sat. Also at The Limerick Milk Market ☎ 061-317566 – Open 10am-6pm Tue-Sat)

Café

● Ducartes at the Hunt Museum

A pretty café in a pretty room with a beautiful location by the river is reason enough to include the Hunt Museum in any itinerary of the city. (Hunt Museum, Rutland Street, Limerick ☎ 061-312662 ⌂ www.huntmuseum.com – Open 10am-5pm Mon-Sat, 2pm-5pm Sun)

Wine Shop

● Fine Wines

The Fine Wines empire is centred in Limerick, where there are almost a dozen stores arrayed around the city, but the empire extends from Tralee right up to Galway on the west coast and Malahide on the east coast. Lots of good wines and pretty much everything else you could want to drink from a dynamic company with more than two decades' of experience. (Ralph Parkes, Vintage House, 48 Roches Street, Limerick ☎ 061-417784 ✉ info@finewines.ie ⌂ www.finewines.ie – Open 10.30am-10pm Mon-Sun)

Butcher

● Jim Flavin

Flavin's is a legendary butchers, which is quite an accolade when you consider how many talented butchers the city has. With beef from their own farm at Grange, fattened on a wheat and maize diet grown on the farm itself, you can't find better beef, and their sausages are award winners many times over. Carmel Flavin heads up the second store at the Greenpark shopping centre, where you find the same brilliant range as the original Castletroy store, and the shops also have a very good fish and vegetable range. (Jim & Carmel Flavin, Dublin Road, Castletroy, Limerick ☎ 061-331977. Also at Greenpark, Limerick ☎ 061-609404 ✉ jimflavinbutchers@gmail.com ⌂ www.jimflavinbutchers.ie – Open 7am-7pm Mon-Sat)

Restaurant

● Freddy's Bistro

Liz Phelan and Caroline Kerley run a great show in Freddy's, and they have done so for many years. Like other great sister 'n' sister teams – think of Cork's Farmgate, or Jacque's – they seem effortlessly professional, utterly in control, calm, confident and capable. They source and cook lovely food, and they don't mess about with it, so flavours are true and clean and the dishes are classic combinations: mushroom risotto with Parmesan; chicken with herb stuffing and red wine sauce; crab linguini with white wine sauce; sticky toffee pudding with vanilla ice cream. Fine cooking and excellent service. (Liz Phelan, Theatre Lane, Lower Glentworth Street ☎ 061-418 749 www.freddysbistro.com – Open from 5.30pm-late Tue-Sat)

Restaurant

● The French Table

"Thomas and Deirdre Fialon's hearts are in it", the travel writer Pol O Conghaile wrote after a visit to The French Table. True indeed, but along with their hearts we should add that their bodies and souls are in it too. They are a super-dedicated, super-hardworking pair, he cooking his acclaimed creations in the kitchen, she running the room with alert mastery. The cooking plays with a very straight bat: French onion soup; escargots with garlic and herb butter; beef sirloin with dauphinoise potatoes; duck a l'orange; tarte du jour. The dishes may be classic, but the creativity and professionalism in their cooking is palpable, and the sense of welcome is genuine, so one feels like a lucky, honoured guest at this French Table. (Thomas & Deirdre Fialon, 1 Steamboat Quay, Limerick ☎ 061-609 274 frenchtable@yahoo.co.uk www.frenchtable.ie – Open Lunch from noon Tue-Fri, Dinner from 6pm Tue-Sun)

Butcher

● Garrett's Speciality Butchers

With two shops in Limerick, Garrett Landers can now make even more people excellent, accomplished cooks. His charcuterie is prepped and prepared, and Mr Landers thinks more like a chef than a cook: he does the work, the prep, the marinading, the flavouring, the trussing, so you don't have to. All you have to do is fry or roast and then take all the acclaim for being a great cook. So, beginner cooks should beat a path to these shops, and let Mr Landers and his team take the strain out of getting dinner perfect, every time. (Garrett Landers, Unit 16 Racefield Shopping Centre, Dooradoyle ☎ 061-305734, Unit 3 Castletroy Centre ☎ 061-216127 info@garretts.ie www.garretts.ie – Open 7am-7pm Mon-Fri, 7am-6pm Sat)

Artisan Producer

● Gingergirl

Hand-chopped. Hand-made. Hand-filled. Hand-written. Hand-tied. Hand-delivered. Helen Keown is the archetype of the modern artisan, inasmuch as her foods are all directed and orchestrated by her, from the moment when the ingredients are first selected and first sliced to the moment when she hands you the jar at the farmers' market in UL. The process explains how Ms Keown seems to be able to capture the essence of her ingredients along with their flavours, so the marmalade offers sunshine, the apricot preserve makes you think of the downy flesh, the onion marmalade has both earthiness and that straining-for-sunshine, the crab apple jelly has the sense of autumn. Call it alchemy, and call it hand-made, and call it hand-some. (Helen Keown, Sunnyside, Rosbrien, Punches Cross, Limerick ☎ 087-611 6360 ✉ helen@gingergirl.ie 🖱 www.gingergirl.ie)

Restaurant

● Hampton's

A Robata barbecue grill and meats sourced from legendary Limerick butcher Noel O'Connor, who joins a cast list of other stellar suppliers, gives Hampton's the sort of dream team coalition that any restaurant wants. It's a glam room, and whilst the menus offer choices other than grill specialities – indeed their kid's menus and vegetarian choices are terrific, and there are good salads and pastas – it's the grills that call loudest: knife 'n' fork ribs; lamb chops with champ; T-bone with creamed potatoes; burger with fries; peppered pork fillet with pepper sauce. (Ronan Branigan, Henry Street, Limerick ☎ 061-609325 ✉ info@hamptonsgrill.ie 🖱 www.hamptonsgrill.ie – Open noon-10.30pm Mon-Sun)

Delicatessen

● Ivan's of Caherdavin

Ivan's is a Limerick legend, a beautiful big store with everything from a coffee-and-sandwich-to-go to a catering service and wedding cake and wedding flowers offer. It gets mighty busy at lunchtime, so get there early. (Ivan Cremins, Caherdavin, Limerick ☎ 061-455766 ✉ sales@ivanslimerick.ie 🖱 www.ivanslimerick.ie – Open 7am-10pm Mon-Sun)

Restaurant

● Jasmine Palace

The Jasmine Palace is the original of the Tsang family's group of restaurants, which includes several brands of ethnic eateries in Limerick and elsewhere. It's big and popular and fun, and the Cantonese specialities are the ones to go for. (Tsang family, O'Connell Mall, O'Connell Street, Limerick ☎ 061-412484 info@jasminepalacerestaurant.com www.jasminepalacerestaurant.com – Open 4pm-11pm Mon-Thu, 12.30pm-11.30pm Fri & Sat, 12.30pm-10.30pm Sun)

local knowledge

The Milk Market

The re-birth and re-invention of Limerick's classic Milk Market has been the most significant public act of confidence in market trading, artisanship and speciality food in modern Ireland. Combining the traditional Friday flea maket, the Saturday food market and the Sunday Riverside markets under the handsome hood of the Milk Market has been an inspired move, giving Limerick something akin to Cork's English Market, and heading in directions where Dublin has feared to tread. The market trustees are in no doubt as to where they are headed: they want the leading market venue in Ireland. They are well on their way with this mix of shops and stalls. To see how far they have come, just look at the unforgettable images captured by the photographer Gerry Andrews of people trading at the market in the 1970's. The following are the major shops in the Market:

● **Adare Farm Shop** Tommy Relihan roasts a pig on a spit on Saturdays, and sells superb farm produce from their farm in Adare. (☎ 087-2962626) ● **Bon Appetit Creperie** Good crepes and eats from Sebastian and Kasia, and lots of superb French foods. (☎ 061-634666) ● **Café Lazio** Roberto fries the fish and chips and also makes good pizzas. (☎ 061-317 919) ● **Country Choice** Peter Ward is a legendary figure in Ireland's artisan food culture. One bite of anything he sells will explain his status. (☎ 067-32596) ● **Rene Cusack** The great West Coast fish merchants have superlative fish and shellfish. (☎ 061-317566)● **Green Acres Cheese & Coffee** Mari is one of the veterans of the Milk Market from the old days, and she has great cheeses and delicious teas and toasties. ● **Anne Lloyd's Market Kitchen** Anne cooks and prepares everything she sells and you can both eat in at the Kitchen or take the foods away. (☎ 087-988 5759) ● **Polonia Food Market** Polish breads and other Eastern European specialities. ● **Ponaire Coffee** Tommy and Jennifer are coffee legends, and you can get their great brews and their great beans. ● **Sallymills Cakes** Nora and David are artist bakers: just try that award-winning carrot loaf cake. (☎ 061-318924)

The Saturday and Sunday markets bring a joyful band of stallholders to communion with the shopkeepers. Many of them are amongst the most creative and dynamic market traders in Ireland, including ● **The Green Apron** ● **Piog Pies** ● **The Real Olive Co.** ● **Killowen Orchard** ● **Kilshanny Cheese** ● **On The Wildside** ● **Green Saffron** ● **Rose Cottage Farm** ● **The Mushroom Man** ● **Flying Cheese Brigade** (Cornmarket Row, Limerick www.milkmarketlimerick.ie – Open 10am-4pm Fri, 8am-4pm Sat, 11am-4pm Sun)

Tea Room

● Miss Marples Tea Rooms

Colette O'Farrell has branched out from her superb Nature's Bounty business to offer a vintage tea rooms in the Racefield Centre, working with Jane Harris. As one would expect from these dynamic women, good things are brought from the garden and the hedgerow and transformed into deliciousness – organic elderflower cordial; meringues with rumtopf; aspargus and pea soup; plum crumble; home-made blackcurrant ripple ice cream; lovely soda breads; delicious teas. The only mystery here is how can you stop eating everything. (Jane Harris & Colette O'Farrell, Racefield, Father Russell Road ☎ 089-421 9889 missmarpleslimerick@gmail.com – Open 9am-5pm Mon-Fri, 10am-5pm Sat)

Restaurant

● Mortell's

Tasty wild fish, caught in Irish seas, prepped by the chef and cooked simply is the secret of Brian and Maggie's deli and restaurant. It's a simple space, but the focus is very sharp, and Mr Mortell's methods remind us of the Fishy Fishy school of getting it right: pristine fish treated with respect at every stage of the process until it gets onto your plate. They also serve nice breakfasts should you be in town early, but don't miss the fish. (Brian & Maggie Mortell, 49 Roches Street ☎ 061-415457 mortb@eircom.net www.mortellcatering.com Open 8.30am-4.30pm Mon-Sat)

Butcher

● O'Connell's Butchers

O'Connell's is the oldest butcher's shop in Limerick and, under the stewardship of Paul Craughan, its standards have never been higher. Mr Craughan is a competitive butcher, aiming to make every creation – his sausages, his hams, his lamb torpedoes – a competition winner, and many of his signature inventions have gathered the gold medals at the competitions. O'Connell's is a real butcher's shop, so come here for great meats, great advice and great service. Just look for their handsome butcher's bike at the door. (Paul Craughan, Little Catherine Street, Limerick ☎ 061-414 819 poconnells@gmail.com – Open 8.30am-5.30pm Mon-Fri, 7.30am-5.30pm Sat)

Butcher

● Pat O'Connor's Butchers

Noel O'Connor emphasises that in order to be a good butcher, you also need to be a good stockman back on the farm. His beef shows the qualities of a butcher who is both good stockman and good butcher: Aoife Cox tried Noel's fillet of beef and found it "nothing short of stunning". Incredibly, Noel is the 5th generation of his family to serve in the trade. (Noel O'Connor, 43 William Street, Limerick ☎ 061-419 224)

Deli

● Olio & Farina

Susan Mulvill's shop is super pretty and packed with beautiful Italian foods that you can enjoy in the caffé. O&F marries integrity with that gutsy Italian aesthetic that is so inimitable, so even for the space of an espresso you can inhale that bottega bohemianism. (Susan Mulvihill, 2 Little Catherine Street, Limerick ☎ 061-319133 ✉ limerick@olioefarina.com 🖱 www.olioefarina.com – Open 9am-8pm Mon-Sat, 11am-6pm Sun)

Butcher's Shop

● Michael O'Loughlin

Good meats, good helpful service, and everything you might need from gamebirds to Birdhill beef is what you will find in Michael's shop. (Michael O'Loughlin, Upper William Street, Limerick ☎ 061-414102 – Open 8am-6pm Mon-Sat)

Hotel & Restaurant

● One Pery Square

Patricia Coughlan's boutique hotel has set the standard that every other Limerick hotelier has been chasing, ever since Ms Roberts opened the doors to this most elegant Georgian house. Piece by piece, she has organically and patiently extended the scope of the hotel, adding in a garden, a wine shop, wine evenings and classes, in addition to the spa and Brasserie One restaurant. There are some kitchen changes as we write, and we look forward to seeing the new culinary focus in the Brasserie. Ms Coughlan's achievement in One Pery Square has been only mighty: she is a major figure in Irish food and hospitality. (Patricia Coughlan, 1 Pery Square, Limerick ☎ 061-402402 🖱 www.oneperysquare.com – Open 6pm-9pm Tue-Sat (till 9.30pm Fri & Sat)

Restaurant

● The River Bistro

Few chefs are as closely associated with a single city as Diarmuid O'Callaghan is with Limerick. He made his name cooking in the Green Onion Café back in the day, when it was Limerick's hottest hot spot. Then a spell in the kitchen of the Market Brasserie followed, before he and his wife, Carmel, got the keys to the smart little River Bistro, and they haven't looked back since they opened their doors. Mr O'Callaghan's menus have always been diverse – tandoori lamb; fillet of salmon with orzo; duck spring roll – but his signature style is to bring a gutsiness to these influences, so belly pork with prawns will be finished with crispy tripe, duck rillettes will ground a dish of seabass, bacon jam anchors monkfish, and a potato farl with smoked salmon and crabmeat is just right. (Diarmuid O'Callaghan, 4 George's Quay, Limerick ☎ 061-400990 riverbistro@eircom.net www.theriverbistro.com – Open 6pm-10pm Tue-Sat)

Fish & Game

● John Sadlier

It's almost forty years since John Sadlier took over the running of this Limerick institution from his parents. Today, it's an excellent fish shop, always reliable, with great service and advice. (John Sadlier, Roches Street, Limerick ☎ 061-414232 john.sadlier@hotmail.com – Open 8.30am-5.45pm Tue-Sat)

Café

● The Sage Café

Mike and Siobhan keep it all simple and good in the city's perennially busy Sage Café – the cooking shows that this Sage is, indeed, wise. There are nice things for breakfast, nice things for lunch, nice things to drink, and the room is charming and ever-delightful. So, let's meet for a chat and a glass of wine and enjoy some good risotti, maybe a chicken pie, or some smart pastas and, of course, the legendary carrot cake. (Mike & Siobhan Hogan, 67-68 Catherine Street, Limerick ☎ 061-409458 www.thesagecafe.com – Open 9am-5pm Mon-Sat)

Bakery

● Sallymills Artisan Cakes & Desserts

David and Norah are moving quickly with their artisan bakery, which now operates a shop at the Limerick Milk Market. They have earned a stellar reputation as bakers of sublime cakes, particularly wedding cakes, but the new shop lets them embrace savoury cooking as well as the gorgeous sweet things – scrambled eggs on Sallymills brown bread; blue cheese, spinach and pecan quiche; chorizo and chick pea salad. (David & Norah McCaffrey, Ballysimon Road, Limerick ☎ 061-318924 www.sallymillsbakery.com – Pastry shop in the Limerick Milk Market, Fri, Sat & Sun, UL Farmers' Market Tue)

Hotel & Restaurant

● The Savoy Hotel

"Service in the Savoy under Ronan Branigan's stewardship is what 5 star should be all about", says Aoife Cox, a delighted guest at Limerick's happening Savoy Hotel. That standard of service pulls everything together here – the quality of the public rooms and the bedrooms, the excellence of the breakfasts, and the quality of the food served in both their Market Square Brasserie and in the next door Hampton's Grill. The food in the Brasserie is very carefully sourced – Donald Russell beef; Marsh Daisy chicken; Carrigaholt crab – and the Savoy is where the action is. (Ronan Branigan, Henry Street, Limerick ☎ 061-448700 reservations@savoylimerick.com www.savoylimerick.com)

Hotel & Restaurant

● The Strand Hotel

Tom Flavin has been making waves with his work in the River Restaurant in Limerick's Strand Hotel. His ambition is palpable, and it's as broad as his culinary palette, which runs from rustic Irish – rib-eye steak with crisp onion rings – through Mediterranean – salmon with tomato and olive salsa – through to Asian – tempura vegetable spring roll with Asian-style vegetables and Oriental dressing. There is finesse and energy in the cooking, and service is fleet and polite. Mr Flavin also makes a very fine range of his dressings, sauces and relishes which are sold under the Secret Ingredient label, and you should have a cache of these in the suitcase as you check out of the Strand. (Sean Lally, Ennis Road, Limerick ☎ 061-421 800 hello@strandlimerick.ie www.strandhotellimerick.ie)

Artisan Market

● The UL Market

Blimey! Back when John McKenna was a law student, the student diet was Erin packet soups and fortifying sandwiches made with Galtee cheese. And now it has come to this: on campus farmers' markets with mouth-watering, fresh, sustainable, delicious, artisanal foods produced by gifted, creative producers. Blimey! Young people today... (University of Limerick ☎ 061-202700 – Open noon-5.30pm Tue)

Café

● The Wild Onion Bakeshop

The only thing consoling us about the closure of the Wild Onion in Limerick is the fact that Bob and Ruth are baking at the Wild Onion Bakeshop. The 'Onion

local knowledge

Brawn and White Meat

Limerick butchers often offer the now rare, traditional cuts of pork and ham – specifically brawn (made from pig's head) and salted pork fat, known locally as "white meat".

has been a staple of our Guides, and we look forward to the Bakeshop taking up that role. Meantime, can we have some corn bread with cheddar cheese and chillis, some cranberry and raisin scones, some walnut and blue cheese bread, and some Brookies. Oh, and some blueberry cupcakes with blueberry buttercream icing. That will do nicely. (Bob & Ruth Di Girolamo, Ennis Road, Limerick ☎ 061-325 555 eat@wildonioncafe.com www.wildonioncafe.com – Open 8am-4pm Wed-Fri, 9am-2pm Sat, 9am-noon Sun)

Wine Shop

● The Wine Buff

The Limerick Wine Buff has served the people of the city well since opening its doors in the millennium year, and Mike O'Mara's shop and his selection and service are not just as fine as ever, they just get better and better. Essential for food and wine lovers. (Mike O'Mara, 17 Mallow Street, Limerick ☎ 061-313392 www.thewinebuff.com – Open 10.30am-7pm Mon-Sat, 10.30am-8pm Fri)

Newcastle West

Butcher's Shop

● Burke's Family Butchers

Pretty Newcastle West has the most charming butcher's in Burke's, and look out in particular for their traditional salted bacon, a speciality of the area that you will also find in other butcher's shops in the town. In particular, look for the aged, salted bacon fat known as "white meat", West Limerick's answer to Lardo de Colonoatta. The gentlemen will be delighted to give you detailed instructions as to the correct ways to use it, and they will tell you proudly that "they come all the way down from Mullingar for it!". (Bob Burke, The Square, Newcastlewest ☎ 069-20158)

County Longford

Longford

Aughnacliffe

Artisan Chocolates

● ChocOneill

Jamie and Beatrice are really fine chocolatiers, and their work has both an artistic and a conceptual verve that marks ChocOneill out from the crowd. Their ingredients are sourced with meticulous attention to detail, whether it is Irish honey or the best vanilla or a single bean chocolate, and those ingredients then meet exacting artistic standards, so everything from a simple truffle to the grooviest Easter egg will simply blow your mind. Their move to Longford hasn't stopped them being stalwarts of the Naas Saturday markets, so east coasters can get their lovable chocolates there each week whilst folk in and around Aughnacliffe can visit the atelier to buy these pieces of edible art, but do phone in advance to let them know that you are coming. (Jamie & Beatrice O'Neill, The Hollow, Dunbeggan, Aughnacliffe ☎ 086-212 8067 ✉ info@choconeill.ie 🖱 www.choconeill.ie – Open by appointment)

Longford

Restaurant

● Aubergine Gallery Café

Stephen and Linda do a fantastic job upstairs in the Aubergine, balancing their funky food riffs with their solid-sender standards, and keeping everyone happy all the while. You could walk up the stairs and have potato and leek soup, and slow-braised lamb shoulder with smoked bacon mash, and then some pavlova. Or, on the same night, it could be smoked haddock and spinach risotto with curry foam, and then stir-fried beef with noodle salad, with peanuts, chilli and coriander. Getting that balance right is what they do so well in the Aubergine, and it explains their continuing success. (Stephen & Linda Devlin, 1st Floor, The White House, 17 Ballymahon Street ☎ 043-334 8633 ✉ stephendevlin@hotmail.com – Open noon-4pm Tue-Sat, 6pm-9.30pm Fri & Sat, 2pm-7pm Sun)

Longford

Butcher's Shop

Herterich's Butchers

Herterich's is a standard bearer in Longford town, and has gotten better – and bigger – over the years. Excellent meats, excellent deli goods. (Louis Herterich, 38 Ballymahon Street, Longford ☎ 043-334 6597 herterich@tinet.ie – Open 8am-6pm Mon-Sat)

Market

Longford Farmers' Market

Longford has a lovely little market in the square on Friday mornings. See you there for O'Halleran's eggs, Kinneden organic vegetables; lots of nice home baking and local jams and chutneys and fresh fish and, of course, the craic. (Market Square, Fridays 9.30am-2pm)

Chocolate Shop and Café

Torc Café and Food Hall

Is the chocolate fountain the true symbol of Torc Café? Overflowing, tumbling, cascading with goodness, fun and indulgence? Well, yes, that will do nicely to describe Ruth McGarry-Quinn's excellent food hall and café, where you will discover delicious breakfasts, scrummy lunches, and beautiful foods-to-buy. It's a bright, happy, cheering room, and one is always happy to be pushing open the door to be greeted by the aromas of coffee, chocolate and the scent of sweet things. (Ruth McGarry-Quinn, New Street, Longford ☎ 043-334 8277 info@torccafe.com www.torccafe.com – Open 9.30am-5.15pm Mon-Sat, 9.30am-7pm Fri)

Restaurant & Country House

Viewmount House

We predicted some time back that Gary O'Hanlon was one of the coming stars of modern Irish food, and that he would soon be known to a national audience, thanks not just to his superb cooking in Viewmount, but also thanks to the level-headed and passionate way in which he sees his work, his suppliers, his calling, his crew. The business of celebrity has already started for Mr O'Hanlon – the awards, the telly, the public appearances – but what is interesting is how he uses these chances to tell his story. He stays on message, and he talks about his work to build a community of suppliers, and to build an audience who understand what he is trying to do in

Viewmount, in Longford. So far, so good: Viewmount is one rockin' restaurant, and Mr O'Hanlon turns the produce of his suppliers into culinary gold, with a style of food that is generous, earthy and agrestic – salt-fried 28-day sirloin with truffled Crozier Blue; Finnebrogue venison with Yorke's swede and Valrhona chocolate sauce; his signature anise-cured Thornhill duck confit. Beryl Kearney runs the room with complete assurance, and Viewmount is a sure-fire success story. The house also offers excellent accommodation, so make a night of it. (Beryl & James Kearney, Gary O'Hanlon, Dublin Road, Longford ☎ 043-334 1919 info@viewmounthouse.com www.viewmounthouse.com – 6.30pm-9.30pm Wed-Sat, 1pm-4.30pm Sun)

local knowledge

Batch Loaves

There is a subtle difference to the white yeasted bread made in Ireland and that made in the UK. The Irish loaf was and still today is baked in a batch or a brick, whereby dough is placed side by side and baked almost as a single loaf.

The result is that the Irish white loaf has no crust on the side.

We learned this from *Ireland's Traditional Foods* **by Cathal Cowan and Regina Sexton. This book remain an invaluable resource of information on traditional foods and drinks, and is the product of an enormous amount of scholarly work by both authors.**

County Louth

Louth

Annagassan

Fish Smoker

Coastguard Seafoods

Terry Butterly is a fish processor whose smoked salmon is held in particularly high regard, especially by chefs. Look out for the sides of smoked salmon with its Coastguard Seafoods logo on the cover. (Terry Butterly, Harbour Road, Annagassan ☎ 042-937 2527)

Ardee

Curry Sauces

Aruna Sauces

Sarajit's sauces are really, really good, and Sarah is really, really good at selling them. The Aruna sauces started out as a spin-off from the couple's Fuchsia House restaurant, and have blossomed into a business all on their own. They are vastly superior to anything coming out of the UK in a jar, and you can literally make a superb curry in mere minutes. A high-quality food that gives you a high-quality life. (Sarah Nic Lochlainn & Sarajit Chanda, Fuchsia House Restaurant, Dundalk Road ☎ 086-3819073 sarah@aruna.ie www.aruna.ie)

Butchers and Delicatessen

Callaghan's Butchers and Deli

Peter Callagahan is the business. His skills have won him numerous butchery and charcuterie competitions, and his business is based on sourcing the finest stock from local farms and then treating it with respect, dry-ageing the beef for between three and four weeks until it is perfect. It's a vital store in Ardee, and whilst Mr Callaghan is continuing a proud, skilled family tradition, he is also improving and perfecting that tradition all the time. (Peter Callaghan, 58 Market Street ☎ 041-685 3253 www.callaghansbutchersardee.com – Open 9am-6pm Mon-Thu, 9am-7pm Fri, 9am-6.30pm Sat)

Restaurant

Fuchsia House

Whilst Fuchsia House has a richly deserved reputation as a destination for exciting Asian cooking, Sarah and Sanjit also offer a most appealing Made in Louth menu – Coastguard smoked salmon with Caffrey's brown bread; Ardee lamb cutlets with potato rosti; selection of four County Louth cheeses. It's a typically inspired idea from this inspiring couple. But, if your hunger wants to wander further afield, then the ethnic cooking is ace – Ma Aruna's chicken curry; Bengali fish curry; Kerala prawn curry. As one would expect, there is a superb menu for children, so everyone who comes to Fuchsia House is properly looked after. (Sarah Nic Lochlain & Sarajit Chanda, Dundalk Road, Ardee ☎ 041-685 8432 sarah@fuchsiahouse.ie www.fuchsiahouse.ie – Open noon-3pm, 6pm-11pm Tue-Sat, noon-9pm Sun & bank holiday Mons)

Blackrock

Sauces & Dressings

Bia Blasta

Clare McEntegart's company makes extremely fine sauces, relishes, dressings and dips. They are earthy, tactile, and extremely useful, and have hauled in a big catch of food awards over the last few years. (Clare McEntegart, Blackrock ☎ 087-123 0001 info@biablasta.com www.biablasta.com)

Carlingford Peninsula

Bar & Restaurant

Fitzpatrick's Bar & Restaurant

Danny Fitzpatrick and his team have been doing the good thing in Jenkinstown for nigh on two decades, running a pristine operation that works because they are so customer focused. Everything is ship-shape and sharply defined here because the team care so much about their work, and from the second you arrive at Fitzpatrick's, you are taken care of. The cooking delivers solidly rendered versions of culinary classics, from that Saturday night special you have been thinking about to just-right food for the kids. (Danny & Dympna

Fitzpatrick, Rockmarshall, Jenkinstown ☎ 042-937 6193 admin@fitzpatricks-restaurant.ie www.fitzpatricks-restaurant.ie – Open 12.30pm-9pm Tue-Wed, 12.30pm-9.30pm Thur, 12.30pm-10pm Fri & Sat, 12.30pm-3.30pm, 5.30pm-9pm Sun)

Delicatessen

Food For Thought

TJ is one of the local food lovers who is a player at the monthly Carlingford producers' market, held in the Foy Centre, so if you can't make it to Dundalk Street to the shop, you can find him there. But you should make it to FFT, for it's a superb deli, a centrepiece for local foods – Big Red Kitchen, Lily's Teas, Dunany Flour, Aruna sauces, Derrycama Oils, Oliesto dressings, and many more. As well as all the great foods and wines, FFT is home to true, honest cooking – great signature sandwiches, lovely platters, excellent pizzas. Ace. (Tom Hayes, Trinity Mews, Dundalk Street, Carlingford ☎ 042-938 3838 tjhayes@iol.ie – Open 9am-7pm Mon-Sat, 10am-7pm Sun)

Louth

Guesthouse with Restaurant

Ghan House

'As invigorated as ever!', writes Paul Carroll. There are a lot of people in Irish hospitality who would love to be able to say that about their work. So, what is Mr Carroll's secret? What is it about running the lovely Ghan House that so invigorates him? Doing a better job, every day, is the answer. This crew never rest on their efforts, or even their laurels. They are always searching for ways to get better, like introducing a great value midweek tasting menu, so that more people can get a chance to sample Robert Read's fine, fine cooking – 18-hour Kettyle short ribs of beef; belly of Fermanagh pork with Carlingford crab; wild Wicklow venison with beetroot jelly; lemon tart with frozen Limencello yogurt. With the kitchen powering ahead, Mr Carroll just makes sure to take care of the beautiful gardens, and the beautiful house, and in Ghan House he has created a shrine to hospitality in Carlingford, one of the most beautiful villages in the country. (Paul Carroll, Carlingford ☎ 042-937 3682 ghanhouse@eircom.net www.ghanhouse.com – Open lunch by arrangement, dinner 7pm-9.30pm. Sunday lunch. Booking essential for lunch and dinner)

Bistro

Kingfisher Bistro

Siblings Mark and Claire have been a mainstay of Carlingford eating for many years now, and they work extra hard, serving dinner seven nights, as well as Sunday lunch. Mark's cooking riffs on the classics – duck confit with noodle cake; salmon with tomato fish velouté; john dory with spriing onion risotto. It's a homely, welcoming place, with many admirers. (Claire & Mark Woods, Darcy McGee Court, Dundalk Street, Carlingford ☎ 042-937 3716 www.kingfisherbistro.com – Open 6.30pm-9pm Tue-Sun, 12.30pm-3pm Sun)

Louth

made in Louth

Glebe Brethan Cheese

Pub

The Anchor Bar/PJ O'Hare's

Known locally as PJ's, this busy, bustling, atmospheric pub has a fine reputation for its cooking, and wisely uses ingredients sourced from the locality. So, some local oysters, a bowl of Carlingford chowder, a good steak from Savage's butchers, and lots of craic. (Michael & Bernadette Heaney, Whitestown, Carlingford ☎ 042-937 3730)

Bistro and Accommodation

The Oystercatcher Bistro

How many cooks and restaurateurs deserve the accolade "legendary"? Not many, but Harry and Marian Jordan do. They were amongst the first people to put Carlingford on the map, decades ago, and now they are back cooking in the town, smart as ever, keen as ever. "We are loving it", Harry says of his return to the pots and pans, whilst Marian manages the room. "Simple bistro fare", is what they do, except with this couple simple doesn't mean straightforward – who else makes a black pudding and muesli mousse, a dish Harry first invented almost thirty years ago, and there are exotics like cataplana, boar stew, megrim with samfaina sauce, and barley risotto with Parmesan and teriyaki. Legendary it surely is. (Harry & Marian Jordan, Market Square, Carlingford ☎ 042-937 3989 theoystercatcher@eircom.net www.theoystercatcher.ie – Open 6pm-9.30pm Mon-Sat, 4pm-8pm Sun)

Castlebellingham

Farmhouse Cheese

● Bellingham Blue

Peter and Anita make one of the most iconic cheese types, a raw milk blue cheese that unifies the richness of Irish pasture milk with the savour and rusticity of the blue veining that pock marks the canvas of the Bellingham cheeses. Peter also makes the Boyne Valley Blue, using raw goats' milk. (Peter & Anita Thomas, Mansfieldtown, Castlebellingham ☎ 042-937 2343 ✉ glydefarm@eircom.net)

Louth

Rapeseed Oil

● Derrycama Farm

Carol and Patrick Rooney make a very fine rapeseed oil at Derrycama. Their rapeseed oil is grown, pressed, filtered and bottled at the farm, and in addition to its multiple health benefits, the oil is delicious. There are flavoured varieties, but we like the lean, limber taste of the pure oil the best. Look for it in good shops throughout the county and throughout the country. (Patrick & Carol Rooney, Castlebellingham ☎ 087-822 3875 ✉ info@rapeseedoil.ie 🖱 www.rapeseed-oil.ie)

Drogheda

Restaurant

● Borzalino Restaurant

Dom and Filomena run a popular, family-friendly place in Borzalino, and the locals love it. (Dominic & Filomena Borza, 20 Loughboy, Mell, Drogheda ☎ 041-984 5444 🖱 www.borzalinorestaurant.com – Open 5pm-10.30pm Wed-Mon. Closed Tue)

Organic Flour

● Dunany Flour

Andrew and Leonie grow and grind wholemeal wheat, spelt and rye flours, all organically certified, all wrapped in handsome brown paper bags, and you need these beautiful flours in your larder and in your life. Look for them in good local shops and in many wholefood shops. (Andrew & Leonie Workman, Dunany, Togher, Drogheda ☎ 041-685 2242 ✉ leoniew@eircom.net)

Wine Bar

D'Vine

Sonia and Damien have fashioned a real success story in D'Vine, and if you can put it down to one thing, then it has to be the aesthetic that they bring to every detail of their wine bar and restaurant. Ms Micallef has the DNA needed to make that aesthetic work, with a mixture of French and Italian blood, and a design and fashion background. Mix those together and you have pretty much the perfect restaurateur. So, a mixture of tapas to share, some fine wines, and a little spot of music on their gorgeous terrace after dinner: that will do nicely. (Sonia Micallef & Damien Leddy, Distillery House, Dyer Street, Drogheda ☎ 041-980 0440 http://www.facebook.com/Dvinewinebar)

made in Louth

Aruna Sauces

Restaurant

Eastern Seaboard Bar & Grill

Hear that? The sound of a distant but distinct 'na na na na nah!'? That'll be the sound of Drogheda residents and boy, but do they have good reason for a touch of smugness. They have the chic, smart Eastern Seaboard Bar and Grill on their doorstep and - sorry 'n' all - but you don't. What's more, in 2011, they added Brown Hound - arguably the prettiest bakery in the country - and the far from ordinary Mo's To Go takeaway to their good food tally. All three are thanks to husband and wife team, Reuven Diaz and Jeni Glasgow - we'd christen them Smart and Smarter but that would belie the fact that this is a marriage of equal, and different, talents - he the master in the kitchen, she with the razor sharp eye for design. Whoever supposes it folly to start a business (or three) in the midst of a recession - not to mention siting a hip, sophisticated eatery in the incongruous surroundings of a housing estate on the outskirts of Drogheda - will have at least a couple of weeks to reconsider their position when they find that that is how long it will take to get a buzzy Friday or Saturday night table at Eastern Seaboard. A legend in the making. (Jenni Glasgow & Reuven Diaz, 1 Bryanstown Centre, Dublin Road, Drogheda ☎ 041-980 2570 ✉ info@easternseaboard.ie 🖱 www.easternseaboard.ie – Food served noon-10pm daily, till 8pm Sun)

Fishmonger

The Fish Cart

Patrick's shop is an excellent place for sourcing fresh fish and shellfish. (Patrick Kirwan, 55 Lawrence Street, Drogheda ☎ 041-983 0622 ✉ – Open 8am-6pm Mon-Sat)

Pizzeria

La Pizzeria

Jian Carlo, the pizza maker in La Pizzeria, is famously moody. He may be grumpy, but his thin-crusted pizzas will make you very happy. So, enjoy the ageless room – Chianti fiascos! gingham tablecloths! – and when your pizza has made you all happy, smile at him, melt his heart. (Jian Carlo, 38 Peter Street, Drogheda ☎ 041-983 4208 Open from 5pm, except Wed)

Restaurant with Rooms

Scholars Townhouse Hotel

Scholars is kind-of old style, in terms of design, and service, and food, which we rather like. (Glenn McGowan, King Street, Drogheda ☎ 041-983 5410 ✉ info@scholarshotel.com 🖱 www.scholarshotel.com)

Restaurant and Café

Stockwell Artisan Foods

Artisan Attitude is what Gwen and Orlaith demonstrate in the two excellent Stockwells – the deli-café on Stockwell Street, and the café-restaurant on Mayoralty Street. The girls not only have a nous for food, they have a nous for food that is healthful, energising and honest, whether you are having no more than a cup of coffee and one of their (legendary, quickly sold out) scones for breakfast, or buying something good and wholesome to bring home for your dinner later in the day. Stockwell provides a mighty, valuable service for the town, so head here and sample that Artisan Attitude. (Gwen Fearon & Orlaith Callaghan, 1 Stockwell Street, Drogheda ☎ 041-981 0892 ✉ info@stockwellartisanfoods.ie 🖱 www.stockwellartisanfoods.ie – Open 8am-5pm Mon-Sat. Also at 1 Mayoralty Street, Drogheda)

Coffee House

Traders Coffee House

"For the first 9 months I lived in Drogheda, I couldn't

get a really good cup of coffee. And then Traders came along, thank GOD. This little coffee shop is just like the ones I used to love in LA: they offer a perfectly-brewed cup of coffee, delicious pastries and cakes and beautiful, handcrafted sandwiches". That's the wonderful Clare, who blogs as "An American in Ireland", expressing perfectly the reaction of locals to Niamh and Eoin's groundbreaking Traders. Others use just one term to sum up the shop's impact: "Finally!". Yes, finally Drogheda has a place where coffee becomes the narcotic we all want, and how wonderful that it should be Ariosa coffee, roasted in County Meath. Everything in Traders is as good as it can be, as good as they can make it. (Niamh Fagan & Eoin Holmes, 1 Laurence Street, Drogheda ✉ tradersdrogheda@aol.ie – Open 8am-6pm Mon-Sat)

made in Louth

Bellingham Blue

Dundalk

Wine Shop

● Callan's Wine Shop

Callan's has a really fine range of wines for sale, and Niall Callan is a young man with a deep passion for his favourite wines. (Niall Callan, Park Street, Dundalk ☎ 042-933 4382 ✉ info@callans.ie – Open 10.30am-11.30pm Mon-Sat, 12.30pm-11pm Sun)

Farmers' Market

● Dundalk Farmers' Market

Friday morning in the square is the place to be to get all the County Louth goodies. (Peter Thomas ☎ 087-277 8538, Market Square Fri 10am-3pm)

Coffee Roasters

● Green Bean

Green Bean have a camp on both sides of the border, as they also have a café in Banbridge. The roasting is carried out in Dundalk, and their standards have won them a devoted following, particularly in the trade, and private customers can order the coffees through their website. (Pat & Deirdre Grant, Coe's Road ☎ 042-933 2417 🖱 www.greenbeanroasters.com)

Louth

Food Hall

McAteer's The Food Hall

A high, wide, colourful and handsome food hall is the big draw at the popular McAteer's, which combines shop, bakery, deli and restaurant all under one roof, a la New York. A cup of Suki tea, a MayRose cup cake, and good service from friendly staff, along with everything you might need. (Jerome & Bobby McAteer, 15 Clanbrassil Street ☎ 042-932 6420 www.mcateersthefoodhouse.com)

Fishmonger

Johnny Morgan

The Morgan family are famous fish people in County Louth, and this sparkling shop is one of the best places to buy fish. (Colm Morgan, 7 Eimer Court, Market Square, Dundalk ☎ 042-932 7977 – Open 9am-5.30pm Tue-Fri, 9am-3pm Sat)

Restaurant

No. 32

Susan Heraghty has always had a brilliance for knowing just what people want. Plates for sharing? Enjoy that spatch-cocked chicken. Some nice burgers? Roast lamb burger with hummus and mint for me. A quick plate for dinner? Duck confit with Puy lentil cassoulet for you and pork medallions with spinach and mash for me. It's all terribly clever and well considered, and it explains why No 32 is both so enduring and so popular. (Susan Heraghty, 32 Chapel Street, Dundalk ☎ 042-933 1113 info@no32.ie www.no32.ie – Open from 5.30pm Mon-Sat)

Wine Shop

Quintessential Wines

Seamus Daly's shop is fun. Indeed, you can tell from his Facebook scribblings, even before you walk in the door of the colourful little shop near to the train station, that here is a witty, humorous man who enjoys his calling. The wines are excellent, the service is excellent, the Facebook page is one of the very best: how does he find so many funny cartoons about wine? (Seamus Daly, 9 Dublin Road, Drogheda ☎ 087-274 5204/041-983 0960 sales@quintessentialwines.ie www.quintessentialwines.ie – Open 11am-8pm Mon-Sat, till 9pm Thu & Fri)

Dunleer

Farmhouse Cheese

● Glebe Brethan Cheese

"Every field in it holds special memories for me", David Tiernan has said of his farm at Dunleer, where he is the fourth generation of Tiernans to mind the fields and mind the cows. "It is in my blood", David explained to Marie-Claire Digby in *The Irish Times*. This connection may go some way to explaining why Glebe Brethan has such an iconic status as an Irish cheese. Made in 45kg wheels from the raw milk of Montbeliarde cows, it is a stunning cheese, but the quality of the cheese alone doesn't explain Mr Tiernan's status in Irish food. There is something so honest, so elemental, so dignified about the man and what he does and what he makes and the way he does it that simply stuns people. Mr Tiernan has a moral force and, like Myrtle Allen's work at Ballymaloe, it is an explosive power. Taste Glebe Brethan, and taste that power. (David Tiernan, Glebe House, Dunleer ☎ 041-685 1157 dtiernan@iol.ie www.glebebrethan.com)

Louth

Termonfeckin

Farm Shop

● McEvoy's Farm Shop

David McEvoy's shop has a particular reputation for Christmas turkeys, but all of the meat and fowl this farmer and butcher produces is of fine quality. Chickens are reared to 80 days, pork is free-range from Middle White pigs, lamb is dry-aged for three weeks, beef is dry-aged for three weeks and they make good sausages. (David McEvoy, Nunneryland, Termonfeckin ☎ 041-988 1242 – Open 9am-6pm Mon-Sat)

County Mayo

Achill

Hotel & Restaurant

Achill Cliff House Hotel

Teresa McNamara's little hotel is a sweet, welcoming place and Ms McNamara works hard at her cooking. The menus read rather straight ahead – garlic mushrooms; deep-fried brie; duck with ginger and orange sauce – but the cooking is lively and flavourful, and extremely enjoyable, especially if you have built up an appetite from a day on the surf or hiking the cliffs. The location is brilliant if you want to golf, cycle and surf, and the McNamaras offer true hospitality, and some amazing views of Keel beach and the Minaun cliffs. (McNamara family, Keel ☎ 098-43400 info@achillcliff.com www.achillcliff.com)

Mayo

Fish Farm

Achill Island Turbot

When we first visited Michael Flanagan's turbot farm, it completely blew us away. "So, this is what the future of fish farming looks like", we mumbled with amazement, looking at the pristine fish in their pristine aquatic environment, which is on land and indoors! Later that evening, we ate the fish, and we were blown away for the second time that day: the taste of the future! AIT is a visionary venture: you have seen nothing like this. (Michael Flanagan, Bunacurry Business Park, Achill ☎ 098-47023 info@achillislandturbot.ie www.achillislandturbot.ie)

Café

The Beehive

Our good friend Judy Enright summed up eating in Patricia and Michael's The Beehive in a single, appreciative line, when writing in *The Boston Irish Reporter*: " Lunch at the Beehive on Achill Island: chicken, mozzarella, and roasted red pepper panini with garlic mayonnaise – yum!". Yum it is at this classic Achill destination, where for more than two decades now the Joyces have done the good thing not only with food and service, but also with shopping: their craft shop is an excellent stop but one, of course, that should only be browsed in when you have a full, happy tummy. They can take care of that for you. (Patricia & Michael Joyce, Keel, Achill Island ☎ 098-43018 joycesbeehive@msn.com – Open 9.30am-6pm Mon-Sun. Closed Nov-Feb)

made in Mayo

Achill Island Lamb

Guesthouse

Bervie

Philosophy. Don't you just love a house where the first category on their website – even before you get to the accommodation and the food – is "philosophy". Ah, little Bervie, an old coast guard station dating from 1932, a place where you step from the garden through a little wicket gate, and there you are on the beach at Keel strand. If this is philosophy, then it is epicurianism, pure and simple, the simple and modest life, the untroubled soul, flecked with sea salt and sand and sunshine. Bervie makes you a child all over again. Elizabeth cooks whilst John pulls the corks, and the food, like the philosophy, is simple and true, the foods of the area cooked in the way that suits them best. Don't miss the unique Achill lamb, which enjoys a distinctive pré-sale taste that deserves to have its own geographical label, for it is as distinctive as Connemara lamb, but more saline, more succulent. The food, the comfort, the calm rooms, all chime as sweetly as good philosophy. Bervie creates a synthesis for your soul. (John & Elizabeth Barrett, Keel, Achill Island ☎ 098-43114 john.barrett.bervie@gmail.com www.bervieachill.com – Open May-Oct)

Surf School, Bicycle Hire, Coffee, Ice cream & Chocolate

Blackfield

Surf school. Café. Fashion atelier. And double-decker bus. Gerry Brannigan's Blackfield really has the lot, and this sort of left-field adventure is just what you dream of finding on Achill. Lovely coffees will bring you back to life after the waves have smashed your body and your resolve. Blackfield is a member of the Great Greenway Adventures group. (Gerry & Sabrine Brannigan, Closh-reid, Achill Island ☎ 098-43590 info@blackfield.com www.blackfield.com – Open Easter until Oct, 10.30am-5.30pm Mon-Sat, 11am-5pm Sun)

Mayo

Butcher

● Calvey's Master Butchers

Their own Farm. Their own abattoir. Their own butcher's shop. Calvey's pushes all the right buttons when it comes to getting the unique taste of Achill lamb straight to your plate. If you haven't tasted Achill organic lamb and Achill mountain lamb, then we suggest you get in the car right now and head west: this meat really is that good. Grainne Calvey also offers beef and other meats, but the Achill lamb is worth the detour. (Grainne Calvey, Keel, Achill Island ☎ 087-290 8129 www.calveysofachill.com – Open 9am-6pm)

Restaurant

● Calvey's Restaurant

Mayo

Six-hour braised Achill lamb shank, served with mash. Grilled Achill lamb with rosemary potatoes and wild mint jelly. Yes, yes, we know there are other things to eat in Maeve Calvey's restaurant, but to be able to eat Achill lamb from the producers on Achill Island is some sort of special treat. Okay, so go back the following night to Calvey's and have the fish and shellfish which form their other signature dishes, but trust us: once tasted, you will never, ever forget the taste of that Achill lamb. (Maeve Calvey, Keel, Achill Island ☎ 098-43158 www.calveysofachill.com – Open 11.30am-5pm, 5.30pm-9.30pm Mon-Sun)

Restaurant

● The Chalet & Keem Bay Fish Products

Gerry Hassett has almost thirty years' experience as a fish smoker, focusing on organic salmon, mackerel and kippers. With Julie, Gerry also operates The Chalet, which incredibly has half-a-century of service to Achill. Unmissable destinations when visiting Achill. (Gerry & Julie Hassett, Keel, Achill Island ☎ 098-43157 – Open May-Nov 6pm-9pm Mon-Sun, sometimes open from noon during July and August)

Ballinrobe

Cakes

● Devour Bakery

"The best pastry chef I know, and I know some good ones", is how Gary O'Hanlon from Viewmount House in Longford first introduced us to Yvonne Murphy. Yvonne makes perfectly beautiful and deliciously edible cakes and goodies, and has followed her dream to open a bakery in County Mayo. Her cakes are the stuff of dreams, so artful and imaginative, alluring and wow! (Yvonne Murphy, 3 Church Lane, Ballinrobe ☎ 094-952 1626 🖱 www.devourbakery.net)

Ballina

Fish Smokery & Delicatessen

● Clarke's Salmon Smokery

The Clarke brothers run benchmark shops in both Ballina and Westport. For decades the family have been famous for their smoked salmon, but in fact that expertise runs through every aspect of a model modern fish business, so their prepared fish dishes and their deli fish concoctions are just as fine as their wet fish and their smoked fish. You simply won't find a more customer-focused business than Clarke's, which makes shopping in the Mayo stores a particular treat, everytime. (Kevin, John, Peter & Dara Clarke, O'Rahilly Street, Ballina ☎ 096-21022 ✉ info@clarkes.ie 🖱 www.clarkes.ie – Open 9am-6pm Mon-Sat. Also at Peter Street, Westport, Co Mayo)

Mayo

Butcher, Bakery, Deli & Café

● Heffernan's Fine Foods

Heffernan's seems to be a business blessed with eternal youth. It's actually more than 50 years old – established in 1961 by John Heffernan – and yet it is as hip-to-the-trip as anywhere in the West, and these days the West can mount some pretty spectacular addresses to shop and eat. Like so many other Mayo destinations, Heffernan's reinvented itself a few years back, adding a spiffing deli and café whilst continuing the butchery business, which is founded on Mayo meats, coming direct from their own abattoir, where Anthony Heffernan oversees everything. Many people today talk about farm to fork, but Heffernan's is the real deal: there is care evident at every juncture here, from Bridie's brown bread to your supper striploin. Another vital slice of the great County Mayo renaissance. (Geraldine & Anthony Heffernan, 4 Market Square, Ballina ☎ 096-21218 🖱 www.heffernansfinefoods.ie – Open 9am-6pm Mon-Sat)

Restaurant with Rooms

The Ice House

Set hard by the banks of the River Moy, the Ice House is visually stunning when you glimpse it first: a piece of rigorous, angular design that is every bit as jaw-dropping as the views down-river at this idyllic location. Inside this temple of stylishness, manager Dara Cruise has a fine team working alongside him. The kitchen crew works with good west coast ingredients such as the local Clarke's salmon from Ballina, Bluebell Fall's goat's cheese from County Clare, Dromoland estate venison, Glasan Farm beef, and leaves from the local Blas Glas organic farm, and they fashion smart, polished plates from breakfast through to their smart bar bites – Clarke's smoked haddock fish fingers in poppy seed beer batter with hand-cut chips. (Dara Cruise, The Quay, Ballina ☎ 096-23500 ✉ chill@theicehouse.ie 🖰 www.theicehouse.ie)

Mayo

Restaurant

Market Kitchen

"I can tell you very quickly and simply that I had one of the best meals of the year so far up in Market Kitchen in Ballina last week", writes our man out West. "They have moved to a new premises, and the food really was stunning, particularly considering the price. It seems to be very much a team-based effort in the kitchen, but what a team: they really have a great system going there." Susan and Kieran certainly have the good system going here, upstairs at Murphy Bros. and the cooking is rockin': mushrooms à la crème; organic salmon with a leek, prawn and cheese pie; chump of lamb with polenta fried feta; Elphin pork belly with black pudding potatoes; chocolate ganache pudding with pistachio ice cream. Great value for money, and there is terrific energy in the MK. (Susan Walshe & Kieran Sweeney, Clare Street, Ballina ☎ 096-78538 ✉ themarketkitchen@gmail.com 🖰 www.marketkitchen.ie – Open 3pm-late Tue-Sat, 2pm-9pm Sun, open bank holiday Mons)

Ballycastle

Coffee House

Mary's Bakery

Mary's is such a sweet, old-style bakery and café, unpretentious, welcoming, and blessed with good cooking and good baking that is agelessly enjoyable. (Mary Munnelly, Main Street, Ballycastle ☎ 096-43361 – Open 10am-6pm Mon-Sun, with more limited hours off season)

Shop and Bar

● Polke's

Our guide books don't do bars, so when we make an exception - like Polke's – then you know we are deadly serious when we say that this is an unmissable pub. It's a darling wee place, with a wee shop at the front, and that wee dram on the counter has your name on it. (Brian Polke, Main Street, Ballycastle ☎ 096-43016)

Country House

● Stella Maris

There is a Proustian quality to Frances Kelly's cooking, a lingering of detail in every aspect of a dish, a search for definition that goes far beyond what is normal in the food world, a search for detail that will unearth the goddess in every bite. Several years back, we wrote this: "Every single dish we ate on a recent family visit to Stella Maris was perfect in every detail. Not fussy perfect, or pretentious perfect, or obsessive perfect. Just perfect in and of itself...". Like the best female cooks, Ms Kelly knows where perfection lies, and she knows that it's not in demonstrating ego, but rather in its opposite: lose yourself in your work, and perfection arrives with your vanishing. The food is the hallmark of the modest Stella Maris, a bright Mayo star where Terence McSweeney's service complements Ms Kelly's culinary magic. (Terence McSweeney & Frances Kelly, Ballycastle ☎ 096-43322 www.stellamarisireland.com)

Castlebar

Bakery

● Cherry Blossom Bakery

Simon and Siobhan like to share the love with their Cherry Blossom loaves: "Pure joy in every bite", says the label on their sour dough loaf, and it underscores their care with a sign that reads: "Made with love." The bakery has bloomed since they started in December 2010, and the loaves are now a feature of many of the best West coast shops. (Simon & Siobhan Stenson, Ballyvary ☎ 094 9038 302 www.cherryblossombakery.ie)

Café

Café Rua

Café Rua is the original McMahon family stronghold, opened originally by mum Ann McMahon, and now run by daughter Colleen McMahon. Mrs McMahon taught her children how to cook when they were youngsters, and they learnt well. They explained to Maria Moynihan in *The Farmer's Journal* that "Café Rua was Mum's child, and she raised it and passed it on to us, so we have a responsibility". What an extraordinary way to express how family businesses work, and what an insight into what makes Café Rua so brilliant: the Café is, in effect, another member of the family. Interestingly, Café Rua is so friendly, and the cooking so welcoming and soulful, that you too will feel like a family member when you eat here. Café Rua is home, and we don't know anywhere else like it. (Colleen & Aran McMahon, New Antrim Street, Castlebar ☎ 094-902 3376 ✉ aran@iol.ie 🖱 www.caferua.com – Open 9am-6pm Mon-Sat)

Mayo

Deli & Café

Rua

Aran McMahon is a player. His work with his team in the beautiful Rua demonstrates a simple truth: to cook well is to eat well is to live well, and you must live as well as you can manage, and help others to live as well as they can, thanks to your guidance. The people of Castlebar live better because of RUA, not just because of what McMahon and his team do and what they cook and what they sell, but also because of the way they do it, their sense of style, their confidence, their nous. Rua makes Castlebar cosmopolitan, and that is one of the great feats of magic in Irish food. This is an unmissable destination, and an all-round feel good place from one of the best players in Irish food. (Aran McMahon, Spencer Street, Castlebar ☎ 094-928 6072 🖱 www.caferua.com ✉ aran@iol.ie – Open 9am-6pm Mon-Sat)

Butter makers

Cuinneog

It was as long ago now as 1990 that Tom and Sheila Butler established Cuinneog, making both country butter and buttermilk at a time which wouldn't have seemed especially propitious for a small scale dairy product in the West of Ireland. But Cuinneog's excellence found a market, and the butter and buttermilk have thrived, finding an audience both in Ireland and the UK. You will find Cuinneog in both speciality shops and supermarkets. (Seamus Mulligan, Shraheens, Balla, Castlebar ☎ 094-903 1425 ✉ info@cuinneog.com 🖱 www.cuinneog.com)

Claremorris

General Store

● The Food Store

Niall Heffernan's brilliant store is a model of what a dedicated local food store should be. It is an expert butcher's shop, and it is also a traiteur where those excellent meats are transformed into food-to-go dishes. It is a dedicated bakery. And it is a benchmark general food store, so whatever you need for whatever you want to cook or to eat is here for you, and it is served by staff who are dedicated and customer-focused. A one-stop shop with all the answers to your culinary queries. The Food Store delivers solutions, charmingly. (Niall Heffernan, Ballyhaunis Road, Claremorris ☎ 094-936 2091 ✉ info@thefoodstore.net – Open 7.45am-6.30pm Mon-Thu, 7.45am-7pm Fri-Sat. Also at Silverbridge Shopping Centre ☎ 094-937 7788 – Open 9am-6.30pm Mon-Thur & Sat, 9am-8.30pm Fri)

Cong

Hotel

● Lisloughrey Lodge

Chef Jonathan Keane made quite a splash cooking in Westport before taking up the kitchen reins at the lovely Lisloughrey Lodge. He is a talent, he is a forager, he is ambitious, and he is modest and conscious of what he still has to learn, and we suspect he will become quite a player over the next few years as his star ascends. He has been joined in Lisloughrey by Jorg Demerer, one of the best managers in the business, so this team is aiming for the stars. Mr Keane's food is cheffy in execution – he serves pate on an ice cream stick, he pairs chocolate with olives, and chocolate with black pudding – but it eats clean and lovely and the earthy touches in turf-smoked scallops, or home-salted cod, or nettle risotto, or shellfish porridge, or a samphire butter with john dory, all show a chef in touch with his roots. (Niall Kerins, The Quay, Cong ☎ 094-954 5400 ✉ reception@lisloughreylodge.com 🖱 www.lisloughreylodge.com)

Louisburgh

Café

● Hudson's Pantry

There has always been something sunshiney about Richard and Trish Hudson. Even when they were in the far-from-sunshiney confines of Navan, in deepest County Meath, they always seemed as if they were channelling a better source of light than everyone else, and Richard's cooking has always enjoyed a tropical energy, with a need to locate his culinary palette in the lands where the lemon trees grow. That fusion of influences, from Mediterranean Europe and Northern Africa, leads to dishes that will put you in mind of Diana Henry and Claudia Roden: zarzuela; Greek lamb; saffron risotto with scallops; calamari with harissa. The room is simple, as it should be, and they advertise "the best crispy chicken wings that you have ever tasted". Reason enough to head way out west. (Richard & Tricia Hudson, Long Street, Louisburgh ☎ 098-23747 – Open 1pm-8pm Tue-Sat)

Mulranny

Hotel

● The Mulranny Park Hotel

Before we talk about chef Ollie O'Regan's beautiful cooking in the lovely Mulranny Park, we must take a little detour to mention that the brown bread cooked in the hotel by Helen is one of the best breads we have encountered in recent years. Stop by the hotel, pull up a lunchtime chair in the bar, order a bowl of chowder and brown bread, and you will enjoy one of the best lunches in the West. In the beautiful Nephin restaurant, Ollie O'Regan has been building his team and his talent since the hotel opened, and his cooking is marvellously sure, due in no small part to the fine ingredients from great producers who now surround the hotel. He does wonders with Gerry Hassett's smoked Clare Island salmon, transforms Sean Kelly's Mayo lamb into a taste masterpiece, makes a dish of Clew Bay scallops with glazed pork belly that is so good you would get up in the middle of the night to eat it, and his sympathetic treatment of the superb Curraun Blue trout served with roast ceps is grandstanding cooking. The Nephin is one of the happiest dining rooms we know, and superb service completes one of the Best of the West. Dermot Madigan and his team are an inspiring and inspired bunch, and their wonderful Greenway initiative is one of the most brilliant innovations in Irish hospitality. (Dermot Madigan, Mulranny, Westport ☎ 098-36000 www.mulrannyparkhotel.ie – Bar lunch served 12.30pm-9pm. Restaurant open 9.30am-9pm Mon-Sun)

Trout Farm

● Curraun Blue Trout Farm

We visited Tom and Tom's trout farm on a blustery Mayo afternoon, and the vivacity of the fish was a joy to behold: chuck in a handful of feed and the fish were leppin' out of the lake. Later that day, we ate the fish in the Nephin Restaurant, beautifully paired with spinach, broad beans and asparagus, and the texture and taste of the trout was a revelation: where so much farmed fish tastes flabby, the Curraun trout were sprightly, textured and utterly delicious. Don't miss this superb fish when in Mayo. (Tom & Tom Dougherty, Doughil, Mulranny ☎ 087-285 8758 curraunblue@eircom.net)

Mayo

Newport

Relishes

● A Taste of Days Gone By

Patti Moss really understands food. Her preserves are unusual by Irish standards – apple jam; banana butter; William's pear jam – but there is nothing token about the flavours, which are enlivening, distinctive and hugely satisfying. The range has expanded to include salad dressings and seafood sauces, and everything Ms Moss makes has freshness, exuberance and polish. (Patti Moss, Furnace, Newport ☎ 087-753 8055 ctmoss1@eircom.net www.pattishomemadejam.com)

Seafood

● Croagh Patrick Seafoods

Padraig Gannon rears beautiful oysters – both native and Pacific – on the north shore of Clew Bay, as well as excellent mussels and clams. You will find this glorious seafood in Clarke's fish shop in Westport as well as in the SuperValu. (The Gannon family, Roslaher, Newport ☎ 087-249 7570 info@croaghpatrickseafoods.ie www.croaghpatrickseafoods.ie)

Butcher

Kelly's Butchers

Sean Kelly is one of the most famous food personalities in Ireland, and he has been one of the most tireless champions on behalf of County Mayo and its food culture. He inspires people in two ways – firstly, by virtue of the superb quality of his meat products and his prize-winning charcuterie creations (this is a man who can make a wedding cake out of black pudding). Secondly, he inspires by example, for he is hard-working and enthusiastic and up-for-it. If he had only been a politician, the country would be in safe hands. Those hands, instead, have dedicated themselves to hard work and creativity, improving the quality of life for everyone who gets to sample the superlative produce of Kelly's butchers. (Sean, Seamus, Kenneth & Cormac Kelly, Main Street, Newport ☎ 098-41149 info@kellybutchers.com www.kellysbutchers.com – Open 9am-7pm Mon-Thur, 8am-8pm Fri & Sat)

Country House

Newport House

Newport is one of the great Irish country houses. It is grand, serene, majestic, aristocratic, with cooking that matches all of these attributes, classic cuisine that is led by magnificent local ingredients. Despite its grandeur, it has few airs, but many graces, and staying and eating here is a very special experience. The bar, incidentally, is one of our favourite places in which to have an aperitif. (Kieran Thompson, Newport ☎ 098-41222 www.newporthouse.ie)

Westport

Restaurant

An Port Mor

Frankie Mallon is one of those chefs who gets it. He knows what is good, he knows what works. He learnt well from good chefs and teachers like Guy Savoy and

Paul Rankin, and in the narrow warren of rooms that is An Port Mor, he shows that he knows what people want. There is nothing extraneous in his cooking, so everything is designed to hit the spot, like classics such as cod with a fine herb crust and a white wine, cream and chive sauce, or the great Achill sea trout with Clew Bay mussels. His food has the rigour of Martin Shanahan and the logic of Maura Foley, and you see it in his pairing of ingredients, like Glebe Brethan cheese with Inishturk crab in a light, satisfying tart, or his signature starter of pot-roasted pig's cheeks with Kelly's black pudding and apple and vanilla sauce. This is rocksteady food, the right food in the right place in the right town from the right chef. (Frankie Mallon, Brewery Place, Bridge Street, ☎ 098-26730 www.anportmor.com – Open 6pm-10pm Tue-Sun)

Wine Merchant

● Cabot & Co

Mayo

Liam Cabot never does the obvious. He wants to find the best Blau Frankisch. He has to have the most up-and-coming producer of Spatburgunder. He will search and search until he gets the best Gruner Veltliner that money can buy. He seems to operate at a tangent from the conventional wine world: where everyone else wants to be Mozart, he wants to be John Cage. But his obliquity is a rare gift, and his searches yield stunning wines: just try that Spatburgunder from Friedrich Becker and you will say "Why can't they make wines of this quality in Burgundy". His wine list hasn't got a dud bottle, irrespective of the price point. The day you discover the wines of Cabot & Co is one of the best days of your life. (Liam & Sinead Cabot, 4 Cloghan, Westport ☎ 098-37000 sales@cabotandco.com www.cabotandco.com)

Restaurant

● Carrowholly Cheese

Andrew has been making his Carrowholly cheese since 1999, using raw cow's milk to fashion seriously delicious gouda-style cheeses that are florid, floral and nutty. The plain Carrowholly shares the market stalls with flavoured versions - the sublime nettle; classic cumin; garlic and chive, and black pepper. The Old Russet Carrowholly is aged from between six and nine months, and is recognisable from its rich red-coloured rind. Mr Pelham-Byrne is a true artisan, keeping production small, selling most of his cheeses himself at farmers' markets, enriching the culinary culture of County Mayo. Look out also for an oak-smoked Carrowholly, sold at the markets in Westport, Castlebar and Foxford. Fantastic. (Andrew Pelham-Byrne, Carrowholly, Westport ☎ 098-28813 carrowhollycheese@gmail.com www.carrowhollycheese.ie)

made in Mayo

Cuinneog Country Butter

Fishmonger & Delicatessen

Clarke's Seafood Delicatessen

Peter Street is the Westport home of the legendary Ballina fish smokers and fishmongers. It's a superb deli as well, and the Clarkes know how to look after you. (John, Dara, Kevin & Peter Clarke, Peter Street, Westport ☎ 098-24379 info@clarkes.ie www.clarkes.ie – Open 9am-6pm Mon-Sat)

Mayo

Hotel & Restaurant

Knockranny House Hotel

So there is poor old Seamus Commons, having to cook for a big band of starred chefs from Europe who are having a tour of Mayo: a daunting challenge, for there is no species of human more critical, and self-critical, than a starry chef. So, Seamus fires out the food, helped by his team who match their boss all the way – the tasting of prawns; the seared scallops with chorizo aioli; the sea bass with fennel doughnut; the lobster with samphire and gold leaf; the foie gras with cardamon jelly; the tasting of lamb with Kelly's black pudding; the lemon meringue with almonds. And what does the La Fougere team get from the starry chefs for all their hard work...? Well, a standing ovation, actually, and a lot of puzzlement from the chefs as to why Mr Commons isn't showered with stars and sharing stages with René and Ferran and Heston. Because that is where Mr Commons belongs: he is one of the great contemporary Irish talents, and the good news is that he continues to innovate, and continues to get better. The food in Knockranny has been pared back slightly, and is all the better for it: an unmissable destination. (Adrian & Ger Noonan, Westport ☎ 098-28600 www.khh.ie)

Seaweed Products

● Lotide Fine Foods

Everything Seamus Moran turns his hand to, he makes delicious. Seaweed pastas? Fab. Seaweed sausages? Fab. Seaweed puddings? Fab. Mr Moran simply has that touch, he has that balance, that nous, and it's the mark of a great cook, and of a great innovator. We love all the Lotide products, for they crackle and fizz with flavour, they make cooking sheer fun. (Seamus & Carmel Moran, Moyna, Kilmeena, Westport ☎ 098-42616 ✉ info@lo-tide.com 🖱 www.lo-tide.com)

Chocolate Shop

● Marlene's Chocolate Haven

If Marlene's shop is a Chocolate Haven, then that must make Marlene a Chocolate Maven. So, visit the Maven in the Haven for the legendary hot chocolate, great mochas, delicious scones, and loads of chocolate treats. (Marlene, Limecourt, James Street, Westport ☎ 098-24564 ✉ info@chocolatehaven.net 🖱 www.chocolate-haven.net – Open 9am-6pm Mon-Sat. Closed Wed off season)

Mayo

Butcher's Shop and Café

● Kate McCormack & Sons

Kate McCormack's is a legendary butcher's shop in Westport, with a history stretching back over six generations, and a stellar reputation amongst local food lovers and local chefs. It's an archetypal shop, white-tiled, with butcher's hooks and just the right feeling and ambience. Just beside the shop you will find McCormack's coffee shop, which is a lovely space in which to take tea and cakes, and nice simple lunches, whilst you enjoy the paintings in the gallery. (John McCormack, Bridge Street ☎ 098-25619 ✉ john.a.mccormack5@gmail.com 🖱 www.katemccormackandsons.ie)

Honey

● Murrevagh Honey

Look out for the fine, hand-harvested honey produced by the apiary managed by James and Derek. You will find it in the Mulranny market, and in Kelly's butchers in Newport. (James McDermott & Derek Norton, Murrevagh, Mulranny, Westport ☎ 086-816 3382 ✉ jmcdermott47@gmail.com – Sold when available, in the Mulranny Market and Kelly's butchers)

Restaurant

● Pantry and Corkscrew

A charming café with an impressive art collection, the décor in P&C is nicely à la mode, all sagey green and mis-matched furniture, with lots of young families and lunching ladies making for a lively, homey spot. They serve an amazing burger of sage and cheddar infused organic beef, with their own ketchup and hand-cut chips, and you would walk to Westport just for this. The savoury cooking is deftly delicious and smartly sourced – Kelly's bangers with mash; McCormack's steak; rustic salmon fish fingers; Turkistan chickpea burger; chicken and prawn with bacon chimmi-churri. Lovely room, lovely wines, lovely place. (Janice O'Rourke & Dermott Flynn, The Octagon, Westport ☎ 098-26977 – Open noon-3.30pm, 5.30pm-10pm Wed-Sun)

Restaurant

● Quay Cottage

Kirstin McDonagh is back in Westport's iconic Quay Cottage, a fact that will delight food lovers who recall the Cottage with much fondness from its days as a trail-blazer in Westport's culinary scene. Michel Nagy runs the kitchen, Pascale Soual runs the front of house, and the characterful room and the characterful cooking are right on song: seafood taster plate; confit duck tartlette; monkfish wrapped in smoked pork belly; cod with langoustine bisque; rib-eye with confit shallots; Kelly's pork platter; orange and whiskey steamed pudding. (Kirstin McDonagh, The Quay, Westport ☎ 098-50692 🖰 www.quaycottage.com – Open 6pm-10pm Tue-Sat)

Restaurant

● Sage

"I return to Sage with both excitement and confidence each time", confides a food-loving friend, and that lovely mixture of anticipation and surety is just the right way to describe the pleasures of Sarah and Davide's lovely, simple Sage restaurant. This is a him 'n' her place such as you might find in a little Italian country village, where he does the kitchen and she does the service, and they have been blessed with great success over the last couple of years. The food is simple, and true, thanks to very dedicated cooking from Mr Dannaloia, who takes every ingredient from scratch and works his magic by cleverly counterpointing his main ingredients with sharp savoury notes, like a caper and anchovy mayo with calamari, or the fresh vibrancy of spinach and ricotta in hand-made ravioli, or the sweet unctuousness of their signature dish of slow-cooked pork belly with beans. There is something very loving about the food, something modest and artisanal, with respect and attention carefully lavished on every piece of bread, every plate of food, which makes it especially delightful to eat. Great service, and great value too. (Sarah Hudson & Davide Dannaloia, 10 High Street, Westport ☎ 098-56700 – Open 5.30pm-close Tue-Sat)

made in Mayo

Lotide Seaweed Sausages

Restaurant

Sol Rio

"I set out to find them, wondering if they could really be *that* good. And they were". That's Marie-Claire Digby of *The Irish Times* writing about her quest to find, and her discovery of, Jose Barroso's legendary pasteis de nata, the egg-custard pastries Jose makes for the deli in Sol Rio, the hugely popular restaurant the couple run on Bridge Street. Jose has a sure touch with the pasteis, and with everything else on the menu, in both the ground floor café and the first floor restaurant. He sources carefully, so everything is imbued with taste and integrity, from the pastas and pizzas to the farmer's style chicken, and there is a lovely menu for children. (Sinead Lambert & Jose Barroso, Bridge Street, Westport ☎ 098-28944 info@solrio.ie www.solrio.ie – Open noon-3pm, 6pm-10pm Tue-Sun)

Country Market

Westport Country Market

The Westport market is a legend amongst Country Markets, one of the first established, and still one of the best. Get there early. (Town Hall, Westport, Thursday, 8.30am-1pm)

Farmers' Market

Westport Food & Craft Market

Saturday morning on the Mall beside the river brings the artisans and craftspeople out with all their delicious and delightful things. See you there at 9am, sharp! (The Mall Sat 9am-5pm)

Hotel

Westport Plaza Hotel

Joe and Anne Corcoran's hotel is one of those destinations where things are always done correctly. The greeting, the service, the cooking, the housekeeping all sync beautifully here, and the professionalism of the staff gladdens the heart. The Corcorans have a very clear vision of creating and keeping a happy workforce as the means by which you create happy guests in an hotel, and they have made this simple, sympathetic philosophy work, both in the Plaza itself and in its larger, adjacent sister hotel, the Castlecourt. There is such an evident sense of commitment from the staff here that it strikes you the very second you walk through the door – nothing is too much trouble, anything you need to know they know already, or will find out for you. This is just the spirit you want to discover when staying in a resort hotel in a holiday town like pretty Newport, and manager John Clesham and his crew come up trumps. Nice cooking in Restaurant Merlot – Angus beef with horseradish mash; Newport lamb with piperade – completes the picture. (Joe Corcoran, Castlebar Street, Westport ☎ 098-51166 info@westportplazahotel.ie www.westportplazahotel.ie)

Mayo

local knowledge

The Kelly Kettle

Many people are surprised to hear that the legendary Kelly Kettle is actually made in Ireland, yet it has been made in Ireland by four generations of the Kelly family. "Camping equipment for wilderness survival, emergency preparedness or disaster kits" it says on the website – and we have to add from personal experience it is absolutely essential for a family picnic day out on the beach. (Patrick & Seamus Kelly, Newtown Cloghans, Knockmore PO, Ballina ☎ 096-22250 – Office hours 9.30am-5.30pm GMT Mon-Fri www.kellykettle.com

County Meath

Ashbourne

Coffee

Ariosa Coffee Roasting Boutique

Coffee standards in Ireland continue to ascend faster than any other sector of speciality food, apart from the craft brewing ferment currently tearing through the country. Michael Kelly's Ariosa company has been one of the instigators of that improvement, for he is a driven, perfectionist bloke, the sort of quiet revolutionary who makes things happen, who spurs changes, whose standards lift all boats. His Saturday stall at the Temple Bar Market has a permanent queue, and when you get that perfect hit of coffee, you know why people wait so patiently. Excellent online ordering means these precious beans can be yours wherever you are. (Michel Kelly, Racehill, Ashbourne ☎ 01-835 3078 info@ariosacoffee.com www.ariosacoffee.com)

Chocolate Shop

Chez Emily

The County Dublin-based chocolatiers cross the border to bring their delights to Ashbourne. There is nothing nicer than a chocolate shop, and Emily's is amongst the very best. (Helena Hemeryck & Ferdinand Vandaele, Main Street, Ashbourne ☎ 01-835 2252 info@chezemily.ie www.chezemily.ie – Open 10am-6pm Mon-Sat)

Butcher

Hugh Maguire

Hugh Maguire is one of the great butchers. He's not one of the greats because he has won numerous awards – which he has, of course – or because he is a player in the Craft Butcher's organisation – which he is, of course. He is one of the greats because he knows what makes a butcher's shop great – the bacon; the sausages; the puddings; the beef. And he has never forgotten that making sure those simple details are as good as they can be is what keeps you going, is what keeps you special, is what keeps the customers coming back. He looks after the pennies and the pounds, of course, look after

Meath

themselves. The shop is smart, the staff are terrific, the bacon, the sausages, the puddings, the beef are as good as it gets. (Hugh Maguire, Unit 3-4 Ashbourne Town Centre ☎ 01-849 9919 hughmaguirebutchers@eircom.net – Open 8am-7pm Mon-Wed, 8am-8pm Thur, 8am-9pm Fri, 8am-6pm Sat)

Farm Shop & Restaurant

Newbarn Farm

William and Yvonne Ruiter run a farm shop, a restaurant and an open farm which the children can explore whilst you try out some nice cooking in the Donkey Shed Restaurant. They sell their own produce as well as locally sourced foods, and wisely use their own produce in the restaurant, along with Piemontese beef from County Laois and fish from Nick's in the town. A stroganoff with Piemontese beef; a Newbarn pork pie with shredded pork shoulder; and Kathy Sheridan in *The Irish Times* says you should try the warm seafood platter and the scones, which are made to a Delia Smith recipe. Is Newbarn the smart way for all farms to be, or what? On Saturdays, look out for the superb Piemontese beef sold at the market. (William & Yvonne Ruiter, Ashbourne ☎ 01-849 9337 info@newbarnfarm.ie www.newbarnfarm.ie)

Meath

Fishmonger

Nick's Fish

Nicholas Lynch's fish empire is an iceberg. What you see jutting out from the water – the smart shops at Ashbourne and Newbridge with their terrific selection of fish and smartly chosen foods and wines – are just the visible parts of a smart, successful piscine business that has been trading for almost 30 years. Behind the public facade are the five fishing boats that Nick deals with, so this is a boat-to-shop business. And, in Newbridge, there is a full-time chef working behind the scenes to prepare their fish cakes, chowders, lasagnes and fish pies, which are sold in both shops. This is the way to source, select and cook fish, with skill, knowledge and discrimination. "I stand over what we offer", says Nick, and it's no surprise the stores have both won awards for the excellence of their offer and the skill of their staff. If you need a live lobster, some sushi, or a expertly deboned fillet of hake, then Nick's your man. (Nicholas Lynch, 9 Town Centre, Ashbourne ☎ 01-835 3555 www.nicksfish.ie – Open 10am-6pm Mon-Fri, 10am-5pm Sat)

Athboy

Farmers' Market

Athboy Stables Farmers' Market

The 200-year-old site where the Athboy market takes place was restored by the locals, as part of an RTE television programme, bringing back into use an area that was both a stables and a piggery in its prime. How apt to have a good farmers' market in this place, with great traders selling good foods and crafts. The network of markets in Meath is slowly extending, and there are now outposts in Enfield, Trim, Oldcastle, Duleek and at Sheridan's in Carnaross. (Kells Road, Athboy ☎ 087-817 3325 athboystables@gmail.com www.athboyfarmersmarket.ie – Open 11am-2pm Sunday)

Butcher

Brogan's Butchers

Niall Brogan's shop seems inconsequential – there are thousands of other shops that look just like this – but Brogan's is actually rather special. Mr Brogan knows his stuff, but he is modest, so he doesn't shout about it. He just does his best, and that is what the lucky customer gets: the best. (Niall Brogan, Main Street, Athboy ☎ 046-943 2122 brogansbutchers@hotmail.com – Open 9am-6pm Mon-Sat)

Meath

Ballivor

Fudge

Man of Aran Fudge

Tomás's fudge is almost hallucinogenic, it's so vivaciously colourful. So, it's easy to spot at the farmers' markets. (Tomás Póil, Station House, Ballivor ☎ 086-256 6542 info@manofaranfudge.ie www.manofaranfudge.ie)

Carnaross

Restaurant

The Forge

Pauric and Irene have been doing the good thing in Carnaross for more than a decade now, cooking with good ingredients and doing it simply: seatrout with spinach and lemon butter; chicken supreme with smoked bacon and creamed potato; Glebe Brethan cheese croquette with tarragon tomato sauce. Pauric also bakes for local shops and holds cookery courses throughout the year, as well as teaching local school kids about healthy growing and cooking. (Pauric & Irene White, Pottlereagh, Carnaross ☎ 046-924 5003 www.theforgerestaurant.ie – Open 5pm-9.30pm Tue-Sat, 12.30pm-3pm Sun)

Cheese Warehouse

● Sheridan's Cheesemongers

The Sheridan brothers, Kevin and Seamus, are amongst the most respected people in the world of Irish food. They are players – food players, political players, intellectual players, social players – in addition to being the best cheesemongers Ireland has ever had, and makers of the world's greatest crackers. They are also fun – we have been in the audience as Seamus Sheridan has reduced an entire tent full of people to helpless tears of laughter, talking about jam, and the GAA, and Protestant food. The brothers conduit the culture they have absorbed, there is milk in their blood, and they are Yin and Yang, interacting opposites, fire and water. There is an air of improvisation about them which leads interesting people to be drawn to them: they have always had the coolest staff imaginable in their shops. Their annual food fair hooley at their headquarters in Meath is one of the best food days in the culinary calendar. Kevin Sheridan says: "People just need to think about food". Kevin Sheridan has said that if he didn't sell cheese, he would be a gardener. Seamus Sheridan has said that if he didn't sell cheese, he would be a park attendant in St Stephen's Green. No interest in working for Goldman Sachs, then. (Kevin Sheridan, Virginia Road Station, Carnaross ☎ 086-852 0334 www.sheridanscheesemongers.com)

Clonee

Garden Centre Cafe

● Garden Works

The Garden Works centres, in Clonee and Malahide, have a fine reputation for their food, as well as their gardening essentials. (Piercetown, Dunboyne, Clonee ☎ 01-825 5375 info@gardenworks.ie www.gardenworks.ie – Open 10am-6pm Mon-Sat, 11am-6pm Sun & bank hols)

Kells

Mobile Kitchen

Boolies Farm Canteen

A "Farm Canteen" sounds like an oxymoron – aren't canteens the very definition of greasy fast food? But Boolies is something else, a smart, compact mobile food canteen fed by its own 28-acre holding where Danny and Ruth rear Dexter beef, pigs, chickens, ducks and bees. There is an orchard and a polytunnel. So, what you get with Boolies is as far removed from canteen junk as you can imagine. John Rogan smokes their bacon, they use meats from the award-winning Thomas Doherty, they do a spiced chicken and yogurt flatbread that will knock your socks off, they have reinstated the much-missed faggot to the menu, and Boolies is re-writing the book on canteen cooking. (Danny King & Ruth McGuinness, The Boolies, Balrath, Kells ☎ 086-385 7788 www.thebooliesfarmcanteen.com – Athboy Farmers' Market and various festivals)

Butcher

Thomas Doherty

You might see Thomas Doherty spit roasting a pig at a local food fair, or setting out his stall at Sheridan's annual food jamboree, signs that this is no ordinary butcher. Mr Doherty has won many awards for his sausages and puddings, which is always a good sign, and he is a real craftsman, as you can see from everything displayed in the shop. Excellent. (Tommy Doherty, 6 Canon Street, Kells ☎ 046-924 1398)

Farmers' Market

Kells Farmers' Market

Kells has both a country market, on Fridays, and a weekly farmers' market, on Saturday. (Saturday, 10am-2pm, FBD Insurance Ground, Kells)

Soft cheese, buttermilk, cream, cheesecakes

Kilbeg Dairy Delights

Kieran and Jane's delights really are conquering the country. A few years ago and Kilbeg products were hard to find. Today, they enjoy shelf space all over the country, even in our little local store in deepest West Cork. How have they done it? Quality, authenticity, deliciousness, whether you are trying a Moodie

Smoothie or their excellent quark. Like the best dairy farmers, they understand the magic of milk, and they can summon that magic into superb dairy products. A model, modern Irish dairy enterprise. (Jane & Kieran Cassidy, Horath, Carlanstown, Kells ☎ 046-924 4687 info@kilbegdairydelights.ie www.kilbegdairydelights.ie)

Farm Shop

Ryan's Farm

Jim Ryan is another dynamic Meath farmer taking his foods direct to the public, via a farm shop at the farm at Ballinlough, open 4 days a week, and at farmers' Markets in Trim and Dublin. They offer lamb, 4-week-aged beef, pork from James McDonald, free-range chicken and bacon smoked by the brilliant John Rogan. Head out here to Ballinlough, and get a taste of the farming future and look out for Jim's smart, bright van. (Jim & Pamela Ryan, Ballinlough, Kells ☎ 087-991 0833 www.ryansfarm.com Shop open Wed-Sat 9am-5pm)

Meath

local knowledge

Irish Farmhouse Cheese

"Historical record reveals that a significant farmhouse cheese-making tradition existed in Ireland until well into the sixteenth and seventeenth centuries. However, by the seventeenth century the cheese-making tradition declined due to changing economic developments" – Regina Sexton and Cathal Cowan writing in *Ireland's Traditional Foods*. **Thankfully the cheesemaking tradition re-emerged in 1968, when Milleens Cheese began to be made in West Cork. It has since flourished, though none of the cheeses made today have any historical links to cheeses of the past. Many of the cheeses sold in Ireland undergo the affinage process (we prefer to use the term "minded") in Sheridan's cheese rooms in County Meath.**

Restaurant

Vanilla Pod Restaurant

Maybe it's because it is an independent, stand-alone restaurant, albeit one housed in the Headford Arms Hotel, that gives the Vanilla Pod its energy, its ambition.

They really try here, and it shows in the cooking and the wines and the service, and their longevity, with more than a decade of service to the town. The food is modern, bistro cuisine, which suits the room and the customers – Thai chicken wings; salmon with spinach in puff pastry; squash and sage risotto; Vanilla Pod burger with bacon and cheddar. (Olivia Duff, Kells ☎ 046-924 0084 info@headfordarms.ie www.headfordarms.ie – Open 5pm-10pm Mon-Thur, 5pm-11pm Fri & Sat, 12.30pm-9.30pm Sun)

Laytown

Farmers' Market and Ecology Centre

Sonairte National Ecology Centre

The gardens at the Sonairte education centre have been organically certified for more than 25 years now. The core of the project is a 2.2-acre walled garden, south-facing and fertile, providing food for the Mustard Seed café in the centre as well as other markets. They run many splendid courses, and have a monthly market. (The Ninch, Laytown ☎ 041-982 7572 www.sonairte.ie)

Meath

Navan

Hotel & Restaurant

Bellinter House

Bellinter is a true style icon, one of the great pieces of architectural restoration, and one of the most beautiful places to stay in Ireland. They have the most fantastic pool in the country, superbly professional staff, and luxury that knows just what luxury is. It's a real treat, and you're worth it. (Jay Bourke, Navan ☎ 046-903 0900 info@bellinterhouse.com www.bellinterhouse.com – Eden Restaurant serves breakfast and dinner. Food served in Drawing Room and Bellinter Bar all day)

Chipper

Hyland's Traditional Fish & Chips

Hyland's is a legendary chipper, despite being a relative newcomer to the trade, having opened late in 2011. It's not unknown for them to literally sell out everything in the shop, and when *The Irish Times* ran its reader competition to discover the nation's best chip shops,

Hyland's was the runner-up, praised for chips that were "perfectly crispy yet fluffy on the inside", and one correspondent named them "the best chips I have ever tasted". Fresh fish that is battered right in front of you, County Meath beef burgers and homemade relishes completes the picture. Hyland's is no ordinary chipper, so make that detour to Watergate Street. (Ian & Maggie Hyland, 4 Watergate Street, Navan)

Bar

Ryan's Bar

Ryan's is a very popular bar, but they take their food seriously, and are game enough to travel to Kinsale to represent County Meath in the All-Ireland seafood chowder competition. (Michael & Anne Ryan, 22 Trimgate Street, Navan ☎ 046-902 1154 – Morning coffee served, and bar food served noon-3pm Mon-Fri)

Coffee House

Trader's Coffee House

Having conquered Drogheda with their coffee and their coffee culture, Niamh Fagan and Eoin Holmes have set up in the lovely Solstice Arts Centre. A GB5 La Marzocco machine and great Ariosa beans will be the centrepiece of the Trader's offer, and these guys really do things the right way, so a trip to Traders is always a thrill. (Niamh Fagan and Eoin Holmes, Solstice Arts Centre, Railway Street, Navan ☎ 046-909 2305 www.solsticeartscentre.com)

Meath

made in Meath

Burke's Farm Ice Cream

Ratoath

Cookery School

Fairyhouse Food & Wine School

At the amazing Sheridan's food festival in 2012, Billie O'Shea of the Fairyhouse school was part of an exhibition featuring Dexter beef, where she showed how to slow cook the cheaper cuts of meat, as well as quick stir-fry recipes and barbecue ideas. Now, is that the sort of woman you want to teach you to cook, or what? A woman who knows how to slow cook

Dexter beef has our hearts as well as our stomachs. "We have a passion for food", they say, and they sure do. Lots of lovely courses, and great instructors will see you up there in culinary heaven before you know it. (Billie O'Shea, Ratoath ☎ 01-689 6476 info@fairyhousecookeryschool.com www.fairyhousecookeryschool.com)

Slane

Farmhouse Goat's Cheese

● Boyne Valley Blue

BVB is one of the newest Irish farmhouse cheeses, a collaboration between goat farmer Michael Finegan and cheesemaker Peter Thomas who makes Bellingham Blue in County Louth. Like Bellingham, Boyne Valley is a raw milk blue cheese, and it is already a cult cheese: there is even a blue cheese salad with candied walnuts, wine-poached pear, pickled red onion and parsnip and carrot crisps on the menu at WJ Kavanagh's, Dublin's impossibly hipster eatery. Mr Finegan is already a well-known face on the artisan circuit, and his fine cheese is going to make him very famous indeed. Don't miss it. (Michael Finegan, Mullagha Farm, Slane ☎ 086-384 4162 welovegoatscheese@mullaghafarm.ie)

Patisserie and Delicatessen

● George's Patisserie and Delicatessen

George Heise has been feeding the good people of Slane with excellent breads and buns and cakes for more than a decade now. In recent years, the baking business has developed a second strand, working out of farmers' markets in the greater Dublin area between Wednesdays and Sundays, bringing the mischbrot and the California rye bread to the capital, and George is a major player in the essential Saturday Dublin Food Co-op. (George Heise, Chapel Street, Slane ☎ 041-982 4493 reservations@georgespatisserie.com www.georgespatisserie.com – Open 9am-5pm Mon, 9am-6pm Tue-Sat)

Community Farming Collective

● Slane Food Circle

This visionary venture is the brainchild of local farmer Des Crinion and other like-minded folk who wanted a community food store that sold local foods. So, step in and find Rebekka McGinn's breads, Dave Moore's pork, Ariosa coffee, Dunany flour, Derrycama oils, Norman Kenny's organic veg, Des's sheep's milk cheese, John McDonnell's beef and lamb, Stackallen apple juice and much more. Brilliant, and a template to be copied throughout the country. (Des Crinion, Stackallen, Slane ☎ 087-225 8060 www.slanefoodcircle.com)

made in Meath

Ariosa Coffee

Country House & Restaurant

● Tankardstown House

Brian and Patricia Conroy's country house offers accommodation both in the house itself and in courtyard apartments. It's a handsome set-up – Catherine Cleary in *The Irish Times* described it as "a little corner of Meath that is Provence" – and with two restaurants and a shop set amidst 80 acres it's a pretty world unto itself. (Brian & Patricia Conroy, Slane ☎ 041-982 4621 www.tankardstown.ie)

Meath

Free-Range Tamworth Pigs

● The Whole Hoggs

"They could not be in a nicer place", Peter Whelan says of the 59 acres in Rathmaiden which his Tamworth pigs ramble and rootle around, overlooking the Hill of Slane. Tamworths were known originally as The Irish Grazer, and they are handsome animals, who make for super bacon. The Whole Hoggs is a most promising enterprise, and with a farm shop and delivery service, it's easy to get this happy pork into your life. (Peter Whelan ☎ 041-982 0659 info@thewholehoggs.com www.thewholehoggs.com)

Stamullen

Strawberry Farm

● Clarke's Fruit Farm

Clarke's is a mighty fruit-growing enterprise, and a model fruit-growing enterprise with no less than fifty acres of strawberries, raspberries, blackberries and blueberries. Their picking methods and fastidious care in the tunnels yield excellent fruit, and we don't know of a more efficient, market-focused farm business. Their fruit is also made into jams, with the jam making carried out by Follain of West Cork. There is a farm shop where you can buy the fruit and the jams. Clarke's is one of the most dynamic farming enterprises we have ever seen. (Pat & Mary Clarke, Clinstown, Stamullen ☎ 01-841 3262 www.clarkefreshfruit.ie)

Jams, Chutneys & baked goods

Big Red Kitchen

Nicola has turned her jam making hobby into a prospering business making jams, chutneys and preserves over the last two years, and their quality has seen them travel as far as Bandon's iconic URRU store and Kilkenny's Gourmet Food Store. They are lovely confections of sweet fruit, and it's delightful to see this little enterprise making its way into people's kitchens. (Nicola Smyth, Rivendell House, Stamullen ☎ 086-150 8462 nicola@bigredkitchen.ie www.bigredkitchen.ie)

made in Meath

Boyne Valley Blue

Tara

Ice Cream

Burke's Farm Ice Cream

The quality of John and Bernie Burke's ice cream can be measured by the quality of their stockists – Avoca; Sheridan's; Bombay Pantry; Eastern Seaboard; Farmgate; Cinnamon Cottage; Waterfall farmshop, to name just a handful. It's proper order: these ice creams and sorbets are superb, with iconoclastic combinations built on a foundation of superb Jersey cow milk. So, a liquorice ice for you, an apple crumble for me, and everyone's happy. (Bernadette & John Burke, Corbalton, Tara ☎ 087-953 2656 burkesfarmicecream@eircom.net www.burkesfarmicecream.com)

Farmhouse Cheese

Gleann Gabhra Goat's Cheese

Dominic Grayson has described the milk he produces from his herd of 140 goats as "medicine without a prescription", a wonderful summation of the health benefits of goat's milk. Putting theory into practice, Dominic and Fionnuala sell a non-homogenised goat's milk, Bainne Ur, and make a mild goat's milk cheddar-style cheese, Tara Bán. They also make ice cream and fudge with the milk. Whilst the Graysons stress the health benefits of goat's milk – and anyone wasting their money on soya milk should really be exploring goat's milk products – don't overlook the fine tastes of both the milk and the cheese: healthful, yes, but delicious too. (Dominic & Fionnuala Grayson, Baile Mhae, Teamhair, Tara ☎ 046-902 6817 dfgrayson1@eircom.net www.gleanngabhra.com)

made in Meath

Killbeg Dairy Delights

Meath

County Monaghan

Ballybay

Farmers' Market

Ballybay Farmers' Market

There is a nice little market in Ballybay each Friday. Look out in particular for produce from the local Camphill community amongst lots of nice local stuff. (Ballybay Square & Riverdale Car Park – Open 10am-noon Fri)

Carrickmacross

Restaurant

Courthouse Restaurant

Conor Mee and Charlotte Carr are two of the stars of cooking and service in the borderlands region, having acted as mainstays in the Nuremore Hotel and in Rosso, in Dundalk, where Mr Mee made a mighty reputation. In Carrickmacross they have the lovely, stone-walled space of the Courthouse to show their stuff, and their creativity and confidence is bang on song, with delightful, delicious concoctions such as Annagassan crab with cocktail sauce and toasts; Mulberry Meadow farm salad with chicken; duck with duck fat chips and orange gravy; lamb's liver and sweetbreads; rhubarb baked Alaska. A class act, for sure. (Conor Mee & Charlotte Carr, 1 Monaghan Street ☎ 042-969 2848 info@courthouserestaurant.ie www.courthouserestaurant.ie – Open 12.15pm-2.30pm Mon & Wed-Sat, 5.30pm-9.30pm Mon & Wed-Sat, open till 10pm Fri & Sat, 12.15pm-4pm, 4pm-9pm Sun. Closed Tue)

Hotel & Restaurant

Nuremore Hotel

The Nuremore is a comfortable, relaxed hotel, surrounded by beautiful grounds and a golf course, and it's a destination where the Gilhooley family have always maintained very high standards with food and service throughout many years of service. (Suzanne Gilhooley, Carrickmacross ☎ 042-966 1853 info@nuremore.com www.nuremore.com)

Silverhill Ducks

Clones

Country House

Hilton Park

Fred and Joanna are the ninth generation of the Madden clan to occupy the mighty Hilton Park. The house is beautiful, gargantuan and serene, and Fred's professional cheffing background allied with the superlative produce of their gardens and polytunnels is just the combination for special food that tastes of the earth. (Fred & Joanna Madden, Scotshouse, Clones ☎ 047-56007 mail@hiltonpark.ie www.hiltonpark.ie)

Clontibret

Organic Grower

Mulberry Meadow Farm

The brilliant Gearoid Lynch of Cavan's Olde Post Inn and Conor Mee's Courthouse Restaurant are two local stars who have the great good fortune to be supplied with vegetables and salad leaves by Marty of Mulberry Meadow. "Their produce is truly excellent – we hope they will be as successful as Gold River Farm in Wicklow", says Gearoid. "Our only ingredients are the healthy soil, the sun, water, love and attention", says Marty Brennan. What more could a good organic grower possibly need? Meet Marty at the Monaghan market each week, and sign up for his box scheme. (Marty Brennan, Clontibret ☎ 087-096 3943)

Emyvale

Farmshop and Ducks

Silver Hill Foods

Here is a lovely tribute, by the very talented team at Mulberry Gardens restaurant in Dublin, to the excellence of Silverhill Ducks: "It always makes us proud when a product produced here in Ireland is regarded as the very best in world, and without doubt that can be said of the duck produced by Ronnie & Lyla Steele on Silverhill Farm, Co. Monaghan. Ronnie and Lyla started rearing ducks over 50 years ago and today supply some of the very best restaurants all over the globe. In fact about 90% of what they produce is exported, so we are lucky to be able source it for Mulberry Garden every once in a while. As the flavour speaks for itself, John will simply be pan roasting it and serving it medium to rare. John's salt-baked beetroot is back on the menu as an accompaniment with the duck: John is using the basis of ancient cooking techniques as he covers the beetroot entirely in salt, spices, orange zest and egg whites. This way of cooking brings out an incredibly intense and earthy flavour. In addition to the beetroot, the duck will be served with wild leek hand picked from the head of Howth, lentils and cabernet sauvignon vinegar". Delightful, and richly deserved, because Silverhill ducks are delicious. Travellers should note that there is a very cute shop selling the Silverhill duck in many forms just at the northern end of Emyvale. Do they have the Mandarin pancakes you need for classic Peking duck? Indeed they do. (Stuart Steele, Emyvale ☎ 047-87124 ✉ silverhill@eircom.net 🖱 www.silverhillfoods.com – Farmshop open 11am-6pm Mon-Sat)

County Offaly

Ballinahown

Honey

● Meadowsweet Apiaries & Farm Shop

Andrew McGuinness is a superb apiarist, and his honeys are a showcase for the floral diversity of the county. You can get these superlative honeys – and lots more bee-keeping equipment – at his farmshop, where there are also fresh eggs, fresh vegetables, and lots of ingenious beeswax products. (Andrew McGuinness, Doon, Ballinahown ☎ 086-884 4938 andrew@meadowsweetfarmshop.com www.meadowsweetfarmshop.com – Shop open Fri-Sat 9am-6pm)

Banagher

Artisan Bakery

● Coolfin Gardens Organic Bakery

Jonas and Layla bake lovely breads, breads with excellent crust and crumb, breads that sustain the body and improve the mind. Slowly, steadily, organically, Coolfinn has become a major player in the artisan bread arena, and the sight of their stall at farmers' markets is always the promise of a treat. The last time we bought the breads – at the Galway market – they seemed to us to have simply gotten better and better. (Jonas Hein & Layla O'Brien, Coolfin House, Banagher ☎ 087-204 5593 coolfingardens@gmail.com)

Birr

Tea Room

● Emma's Cafe & Deli

Emma's is excellent, stylish and a don't-miss stop for good coffee and smart sandwiches. There are also lots of nice tempting things to buy on the shelves of a lovely destination in this lovely town. (Adrian Shine & Debbie Kenny, 31 Main Street, Birr ☎ 057-912 5678 – Open 9am-6pm Mon-Sat, 11am-6pm Sun)

Organic Dairy Products

Mossfield Organic Farm

Mossfield milk has made it down to us here in West Cork, along with Ralph Haslam's buttermilk and yogurts, and we are waiting for first sight of Mossfield butter and the newest Mossfield Slieve Bloom, a cheddar-style cheese. Mossfield, in other words, is slowly conquering the country, these brilliant organic dairy farm products are appearing on the shelves of more good food stores and wholefood shops, and that is just fine by us, for the Mossfield foods are exceptional organic dairy products, foods that seem hard-wired into the rich limestone pastures of County Offaly. Brilliant. (Ralph Haslam, Clareen, Birr ☎ 057-913 1002 info@mossfield.ie www.mossfield.ie)

Organic Store

The Organic Store

The Organic Store is a peach. It's packed with everything you want, and it's also packed with everything you need. Jonathan Haslam's shop is also one of those special stores that celebrates the locality, that celebrates the best Offaly foods, so get your Clanwood beef and your Mossfield yogurts and your Lough Boora vegetables and your Coolfin breads here. The OS is one of the best shops in Ireland, beyond a doubt, and one of the most fun places to shop. Don't miss it when in Birr. (Jonathan Haslam, Main Street, Birr ☎ 057-912 5881 organicstorebirr@gmail.com – Open 10am-6.30pm Mon-Sat)

Pork Charcuterie

Prue & Simon's

Every once in a while you will come across a Prue & Simon's sausage, and it will stop you in your tracks. "Now that", you will say to yourself, "is the way a pork sausage is meant to be, and is meant to taste". This brilliant mother and son team concoct the most sublime sausages, the sweetest bacon, the best black and white puddings. Mrs Rudd has always seemed to us to be a cook of rare discrimination and her talent, allied with Simon's seemingly inexhaustible energy, makes Prue & Simon's an archetypal artisan company. So, get some of those pepper and thyme sausages, and prepare to be stopped in your tracks. (Prue & Simon Rudd, Busherstown, Moneygall, Birr ☎ 0505-45206 prue@prueandsimons.com www.prueandsimons.com)

Cloghan

Organic Soup

Clanwood Farm

In our last Food Guide, Clanwood Farm merited a short entry, mainly about Orla Clancy's organic soups. Since then, Mrs Clancy has become a superstar, the Beyoncé of Offaly organics. She has won Electric Picnic awards for her brilliant Organic Kitchen, she has won prizes as businesswoman, as farmer, and she has become a go-to girl for the media. Proper order. Mrs Clancy is a dynamo, and a classic example of just how dynamic women can be in agriculture. We have a crackpot theory about how the solution to Ireland's agriculture problems is to have women running all the farms. When people tell us it wouldn't work, we just say: what about Orla Clancy and Clanwood Farm and that beautiful beef and those wonderful soups and those delicious eggs and the amazing Organic Kitchen? Hmmm. Maybe the theory isn't so crackpot after all. Look out for the Organic Kitchen at the best music and cultural festivals, and get that unique Offaly Burger made entirely of Offaly ingredients. (Orla & Sean Clancy, Cush, Cloghan ☎ 087-649 4477 clanwoodfarm@eircom.net www.clanwoodfarm.ie)

Organic Farm

Lough Boora Farm

One of the best things we have eaten in recent times was Jess Murphy's Lough Boora Farm Plate, in Kai restaurant, in Galway. There were sweet, golden beets. There was pickled cucumber. There were ribbons of carrots, there were tiny fresh salad leaves, and a smashing beetroot dip. The plate said everything one could need to know about how a smart cook interacts with a smart organic grower, and how the lucky customer is the happy person who gets the benefit of an alliance made in culinary heaven. Tony Garahy's Lough Boora Farm is a major organic player, as supplier to shops, restaurants and via his box scheme. His fine, healthy soil produces the most beautiful vegetables, and they are nothing but sheer goodness, sheer health. Mr Garahy also produces a most beautiful calendar each year, which showcases his vegetables as art. Quite right, too. (Tony Garahy, Cloghan ☎ 057-934 5005 loughboorafarm@eircom.net)

Coolnagrower

Organic Farm

Philip Dreaper

Philip Dreaper is one of the mighty Offaly organic masters, his produce a statement of the art of organics and agriculture. His label is a statement of goodness, so look out for the Coolnagrower logo in good shops. (Philip Dreaper, Coolnagrower, Fortal, Birr ☎ 057-912 1562 ✉ philip@coolnagrower.ie 🖱 www.coolnagrower.ie)

Killeigh

Organic Dairy

Glenisk Organic Dairy

The Cleary family's Glenisk is the biggest organic dairy brand in Ireland, but their scale doesn't mean that they sit still, and every few months seems to bring a new innovation with their yogurt portfolio, most recently a new brand of yogurts with fruit. Top class. (Vincent Cleary, Newtown, Killeigh ☎ 057-934 4000 ✉ info@glenisk.com 🖱 www.glenisk.com)

Free-Range Beef

Quarrymount Free-Range Meats

Ray Dunne's enterprising beef business takes the meat from his herd and sells it via several farmers' markets each week – Killeigh; Limerick; Killaloe; Dublin – as well as offering a home delivery system, for customers who order on-line. Ray also sells beef sausages – a rarity away from Northern Ireland – and good chickens. Quarrymount won a special merit award at the 2012 farmers' market championship in Enniscorthy. (Ray Dunne, Killeigh ☎ 086-833 1006 ✉ raydunne@freerangemeats.ie 🖱 www.freerangemeats.ie)

Portarlington

Blueberries

Derryvilla Farm

If you have never had a taste of Derryvilla Blueberry Tonic, then you haven't lived. One sip, and you will think you have the energy of Thor and the agility of Spider Man. Not bad for a simple concoction of blueberry fruit, and John and Belinda's smart creativity. (John & Belinda Seager, Derryvilla, Portarlington ☎ 057-864 2882/087 246 6643 ✉ info@derryvillablueberries.com 🖱 www.derryvillablueberries.com)

Sugarcraft

● Sweet Creations

Miriam Pearson's cakes are OMG! amazing. The sugarcraft work is stunning, but what we like most is the fact that her cake characters and her cakes are impish and fun, and not just perfect and cold. Sublime sugarcraft. (Miriam Pearson, Pinewood, Cushina, Portarlington ☎ 086-405 1555 ✉ miriam@sweetcreations.ie 🖱 www.sweetcreations.ie)

made in Offaly

Mossfield Organic Farm

Tullamore

Farm Produce

● The Farmer's Gate

The FG is a an excellent place for sourcing local speciality foods from Offaly, and from further afield. Look out for such goodies as Pigs on the Green sausages, Dina's Country Kitchen relishes and Donegal Rapeseed Oil. (The Tan Yard, Tullamore)

Beef & Lamb

● Farm Factory Direct

The County Offaly lamb and Hereford beef prepared and sold by Ivor and Margaret in FFD is sublime. The meat is beautifully prepared, and is truly epicurean: earthy, herbaceous, umami, and quite wonderful. (Ivor & Margaret Deverell, Kilcruttin Business Park, Tullamore ☎ 057-932 9405 ✉ info@farmfactorydirect.ie 🖱 www.farmfactorydirect.ie)

Beef and Lamb

● Hanlon's

Hanlon's is a delightful, colourful, much-loved traditional butcher's shop on Patrick Street. (Michael Hanlon, Patrick Street, Tullamore ☎ 057-935 1534 – Open 8am-6pm Mon-Sat)

Craft Bakery

O'Donoghue's Bakery

O'Donoghue's is a good bakery and bakes good breads. Cathal O'Donoghue understands the central truth about baking – quality bread needs time. Take away that time – as large-scale bakeries do – and what you produce is nothing more than "water standing upright". O'Donoghue's breads get all the time they need, which makes them well worth your time. (Cathal O'Donoghue, Kilcruttin Centre, Tullamore ☎ 057-932 1411 bread@odonoghuesbakery.ie)

Tamworth Pork

Pigs on the Green

Fergus Dunne used to run a splendid wholefood shop in Tullamore, before switching his focus to beautiful Tamworth pigs and the luscious produce they bestow. Today, Fergus and Sandra make superb black pudding sausages; gorgeous pork sausages; delicious Italian sausages; and spicy chilli sausages. They cure lovely streaky and back bacon, sell loins and neck of pork and, rumour has it, a Pigs on the Green pancetta is on the way. We picked up our supplies in Morton's in Galway, but look out for their colourful pink and green label in other shops, including The Farmer's Gate in Tullamore, and on the menu in good Midlands restaurants. Wonderful stuff, and a dynamic new adventure. (Fergus & Sandra Dunne, Tullamore ☎ 087-314 6824 fergusjdunne@gmail.com)

Butcher

Tormey's Butchers

The Tormey family are benchmark butchers who run benchmark butcher's shops, and their beautiful Tullamore store may be the most handsome of their trio of shops. Their beef is rightly celebrated, but the skill, knowledge and culture of butchering is evident in every piece of meat they produce and prepare. (Tormey family, Bridge Street, Tullamore ☎ 057-932 1426 info@crtormeys.ie www.crtormeys.ie – Open 9am-6pm Tue-Sat)

Offaly

made in Offaly

Glenisk Organic Dairy

County Roscommon

Athlone

Organic & Holistic Farm

● Hillside Farm

Helen and Sean rear organic beef and lamb which they offer for sale as whole, half or quarter carcases. They also offer allotments for people who want to dig their own dinner as well as many courses, from herb growing to Nordic walking, which is the one we want to do. (Helen & Sean Butler, Tavanagh, Brideswell, Athlone ☎ 090-968 3709 ✉ info@hillsidefarm.ie 🖱 www.hillsidefarm.ie)

Boyle

Farmers' Market

● Boyle Farmers' Market

A beautiful market with pretty stalls in the beautiful location of the grounds of King House, the Boyle market is a smasher. They maintain an excellent website and are good Facebookers, so you know what is going on. Best of all is the produce – Tulsk fruit; local organic vegetables; gorgeous sourdough bread from Mayo; fresh eggs; venison pies; local honeys; organic meats; Fred's fresh fish; Ballycross juices; home baking, and lots, lots more. Fab. (King House, Main Street, Boyle ✉ unabhan2@eircom.net, Saturday 10am-2pm)

Castlemine

Farm Shop

● Castlemine Farm

When we gave the Allen brothers of Castlemine Farm our Farmer of the Year award at the end of 2011, we wrote this to explain why they deserved the gong: "The Allen brothers have shown a revolutionary way for Irish farmers to work. They have a new shop in Roscommon, they have a brilliant range of cooked pies using their own beef, and the Castlemine Farm produce is outstanding.

Derek and Brendan aren't just farmers: they are Players". If only every Irish farmer wanted to be a player, then Ireland would be the mightiest agricultural nation in the world. Derek and Brendan's one-two act – Derek is the public face, Brendan stays down on the farm on those limestoney pastures – is one of the best double acts Irish agriculture has ever seen, so as they have built their business and their farm shop and delivery service, they have also built their profile. They are visionaries, they are funny, they are wise, they are gifted. They are Players. (Derek & Brendan Allen, Castlemine ☎ 090-662 9886/087 2231202 ✉ info@castleminefarm.ie) ✇ www.castleminefarm.ie – Open 10am-6pm Fri & Sat)

local knowledge

Roscommon Lamb

Roscommon is the lamb capital of Ireland, the county with the highest output of lambs, and each year they organise a Lamb Festival to celebrate the fact. There are lamb barbecues, there is sheep shearing, wool crafts and sheepdog trials. In fact the county even boasts its very own breed, the Roscommon Long Wool Sheep which was first recognised in the 1870s. The Roscommon sheep was a large, white-faced breed that lost ground to smaller, more manageable sheep, and is only now becoming popular again as a specialist rare breed.

Roscommon

Food and Wine Shop

● Gleeson's Artisan Food & Wine Shop

This gorgeous shop is the second part of Mary and Eamonn Gleeson's Roscommon empire, perfectly syncing with their townhouse and restaurant. The shop has all you need: great artisan foods, their own breads and cooked meats, food to go, beautiful lunchtime things to eat. Vital. (Mary & Eamonn Gleeson, The Manse, Market Square, Roscommon ☎ 090-662 6954 ✉ info@gleesonstownhouse.com ✇ www.gleesonstownhouse.com – Open 7am-9pm Mon-Sun)

Townhouse & Restaurant

Gleeson's Townhouse & Manse Restaurant

When you have been in business for just over twenty years, serving good country cooking in a solid manse house at the centre of the square in Roscommon town, you are sure doing something right. That's what Mary and Eamonn Gleeson have achieved in their townhouse, restaurant and food emporium, and it is a mighty achievement. In fact, to be honest, we don't know how they manage to achieve all they do, running what is in effect a small hotel, cooking from breakfast to dinner, and selling superb, carefully curated artisan foods in their shop, along with great cooked foods-to-go. The really impressive thing about Mary and Eamonn, however, is the constant desire to improve: they could coast by on the fact that they are the best in town, but they don't. They are hungry to be better, even after two decades, and that is both laudable, and touching. Gleeson's is the pivotal point, indeed the pinnacle, for Roscommon's food culture. And do note that Roscommon is the lamb capital of Ireland and, appropriately, has an annual lamb festival, when Gleessons prepares special lamb dishes. (Mary & Eamonn Gleeson, The Manse, Market Square, Roscommon ☎ 090-662 6954 info@gleesonstownhouse.com www.gleesonstownhouse.com – Open daily for breakfast, lunch and dinner)

made in Roscommon

Galway Hooker

Craft Brewery

The Hooker Brewery

Aidan Murphy – who makes Galway Hooker with his cousin, Ronan Brennan – is deeply serious. You can't make a pale ale as fine as Galway Hooker – it is one of the iconic drinks of modern Irish craft brewing – without being deeply serious. Mr Murphy has the degree in food science from UCC. He has the Master's in brewing and distilling from Heriot-Watt University. He has brewed in the Isle of Man, and in San Francisco. Hooker was established in 2006, and right from the out the drink was fashioned with food in mind. When we first tried the beer, it fair blew us away, and one moment we treasure especially was a glass of Hooker drunk sitting at the bar of The Oarsman, in Carrick-on-Shannon, on a summer's afternoon. It was one of those moments when time stopped. Galway Hooker didn't conquer us, it seduced us. Hooker is one of the high points of the Irish craft beer revolution. Do not miss it. (Aidan Murphy & Ronan Brennan, Racecourse Road, Roscommon ☎ Aidan Murphy 087-776 2823 ✉ aidan@galwayhooker.ie ☎ Ronan Brennan 087-236 6186 ✉ ronan@galwayhooker.ie 🖱 www.galwayhooker.ie)

Bakery

● Molloy's Bakery

Molloy's bake everything from scones to three tiered wedding cakes, and you will find their baking in many local shops, as well as their own retail shop and café. They have been baking for fully ninety years, and in recent times the bakery has continued to grow. There are nice lunch treats in their café, including Castlemine Farm produce. (Mark Molloy, Galway Road, Abbeytown, Roscommon ☎ 090-662 5940 ✉ info@molloysbakery.ie 🖱 www.molloysbakery.ie)

Organic Shop

● Tattie Hoaker

Tattie Hoaker is both an excellent, surprising, helpful organic shop and a distributor of organics throughout the region. It's a great store, a place where everything exudes sheer health and goodness. (Aidan Gillan & Maureen Brosnan, 14 Goff Street, Roscommon ☎ 090-663 0492 – Open 10am-6pm Mon-Sat)

County Sligo

Ballymote

Country House

● Temple House

Roderick and Helena have devoted themselves to the maintenance and preservation of handsome old Temple House, a gargantuan slice of living history. The house is particularly beloved by sportsmen, but stay for a day or so and let it insinuate itself into your blood. Look out especially for their annual festivals. (Roderick & Helena Perceval, Ballymote, Sligo ☎ 071-918 3329 ✉ mail2007@templehouse.ie 🖱 www.templehouse.ie)

Castlebaldwin

Guesthouse & Restaurant

● Cromleach Lodge

Christy and Moira have been welcoming guests to Ballindoon since 1978, and after almost 35 years they are as keen and as professional as ever. (Christy & Moira Tighe, Ballindoon, Castlebaldwin, Boyle ☎ 071-916 5155 🖱 www.cromleach.com)

Collooney

Artisan Foods & Café

● The Village Food Fare

The Village is a smashing arrival into Sligo, and is notable for the presence of Sligo's superb Gourmet Parlour, and also for having a wonderful store with lots of great Irish artisan foods such as Castlemine Farm produce from Roscommon, Gilligan meats, Linnala ice cream and loads more besides. Don't miss all the lovely crafts upstairs as well. (Maggie Heylin, Collooney Roundabout, Collooney ☎ 087-939 7650 – Open 9am-6.30pm Mon-Fri, 9am-6pm Sat, noon-6pm Sun)

local knowledge

Kilcullen's Hot Sea Water Baths

Kilcullen's seaweed baths is 100 years old. A century of service, a century spent harnessing the goodness of seaweeds and sea water for the benefit of our collective health. There are other seaweed baths, but there are no seaweed baths like Kilcullen's, with its traditional steam boxes, its traditional big baths, its fresh, tangy, kelpy, sea salty seaweeds. A visit here is one of life's great pleasures.

Enniscrone ☎ 096-36238 seaweedbaths@gmail.com www.kilcullenseaweedbaths.com – Open 10am-9pm Jun-Aug, noon-8pm off season

Grange

Honey

● Knocknarea Honey

Keith Clarke is – in real life – a boat skipper, but for our purposes he is really an apiarist, producing the very fine Knocknarea Honey. Look out for it in good local shops. (Keith Clarke, Moneygold, Grange ☎ 071-914 2738 keithclarke2@eircom.net)

Rathlee

Sea Vegetables

● Carraig Fhada Seaweed

Sea vegetables and everything to do with them have become very fashionable lately, but long before they were fashionable Frank Melvin was collecting and drying them out on the Long Rock. Mr Melvin is the link between the ancient practices and the modern practices, he is the constant between sea vegetables as a daily staple and sea vegetables as a lifestyle attribute. His vegetables are fantastic, and you will find them in the best wholefood shops. (Frank Melvin, Cabra, Rathlee, Easky ☎ 096-49042 carraigseaweed@eircom.net)

Riverstown

Country House

Coopershill

There is something about Coopershill which is artfully smart. You could take one look at this big 18th-century pile and feel sorry for the owners – the maintenance! the heating bills! the roof! the damp! But your sympathies would be misplaced, for the house is actually uber-green, and has major environmental awards patting them on the back for their wood-burning stove, their rain-water harvesting, their wetland drainage system. They have a tidy business selling their superb venison, another award-winning venture. And when you stay and eat dinner, they can virtually count how many metres many of the ingredients you will be enjoying will have travelled to reach your plate: 50 metres for the vegetables? 200 metres for the venison? Some of it will be even closer. Country houses used to be worlds unto themselves, and Simon and Chrtistine run Coopershill in just that fashion: self-sufficient people in a supremely self-sufficient place. It's a gorgeous house, and Christine's cooking is amongst the best you will find, a beautifully rendered country cuisine. (Simon O'Hara, Riverstown ☎ 071-916 5108 📫 reservations@coopershill.com 🖱 www.coopershill.com)

Sligo

Country Grocer

Cosgrove's

"Cosgroves is fab", says Aoife Cox after a visit to Sligo's venerable grocer's shop. "I wanted to wrap it up and relocate it to the capital, just so I could visit more often". Sorry Aoife: Cosgrove's ain't going nowhere, as it is one of those classic addresses that defines Sligo. It's the most gorgeous, traditional grocer's shop, complete with patient, polite service that makes you feel special every time you shop here. Brilliant. (Cosgrove family, Market Street, Sligo ☎ 071-914 2809 🖱 www.cosgrovesdeli.com – Open 9.30am-7pm Mon-Sat)

Pub

Foley's Bar

Foley's, says Aoife Cox, "is one of those small but crammed-to-the-rafters kind of places. The confection er's side of things is regular newsagent's stuff - bottles of Fanta, bags of Tayto and Wrigley's spearmint gum - but the main business is the off-licence. They had an impressive range of whiskeys and whiskies, including at least one from Japan, and the wine selection ran the gamut from Sutter Home to Louis Jadot Puligny-Montrachet. I spotted, amongst other notables, Trimbach Riesling, Museum Rioja and some Chateau Ksara from Lebanon. The lady behind the counter wondered if I was looking for anything in particular - 'if you want anything, just ask - we probably have it,' said she, and I believed her". (18 Castle Street, Sligo ☎ 071-913 8900)

Food-To-Go

● The Gourmet Parlour

"We don't compromise", Catherine Farrell will tell you as a way to explain the success and the longevity of the GP. "Everything is homemade - if we make a ham sandwich the ham is boiled in house, the mayo is home-made with free-range eggs". When Aoife Cox paid a visit, the Gourmet Parlour rendered her helpless: "Within seconds - seconds, I tell you - I succumbed to the charms of apple tart, homemade blackcurrant jam and a spinach and mushroom pie. The lure of authentic and honest baking was simply irresistible". It has been that way ever since the girls first featured in our books back in 1991: authentic and honest. See also the new GP in Collooney. (Catherine Farrell & Annette Burke, Bridge Street, Sligo ☎ 071-914 4617 ✉ info@gourmetparlour.com 🖱 www.gourmetparlour.com – Open 9am-6pm Mon-Sat)

Bar & Restaurant

● Hargadon's

Joe Grogan and Miriam Harte and their team run a superbly managed organisation in the legendary Hargadon's Bar, one of Ireland's best-known pubs. Their reputation today is founded on cracking food and superb value – they grabbed the Good Value Award in Ireland at the *Food & Wine* awards – and even their evening menu dishes come in at under ten euro. But the dishes aren't inexpensive because of low-quality ingredients: in fact, their sourcing is superb – Silverhill duck; Burren smoked salmon; Clarke's meats; Charlie Kelly's shellfish. Great wines from their own wine shop complete a happy picture. (Joe Grogan & Miriam Harte, 4 O'Connell Street, Sligo ☎ 071-915 3709 🖱 www.hargadons.com – Open noon-3.30pm Mon-Sat, 4pm-9pm Tue-Sat)

Wine Shop

Hargadon's Wine Shop

The star of Hargadon's wine shop is, of course, their own wines from their Languedoc vineyards, Terra Monti, which produces a range of whites, reds and rosés. France has the best representation in the shop, but they have culled wines from all of the viticultural world. Do look also for their own French olive oil. Hargadon's have also opened a sister shop at Cabinteely, in south County Dublin. (Joe Grogan, Johnston Court Shopping Mall, Sligo ☎ 071-915 3709 info@hargadons.com www.hargadons.com – Open 10.30am-6pm Mon-Wed & Sat 10.30am-7.30pm Thu & Fri)

Delicatessen

Kate's Kitchen

"The impossibly well-stocked Kate's Kitchen", is how Aoife Cox described Kate, Beth and Jane's magnificent emporium. "All the classic artisan brands are here", says Aoife, "Sheridan's, Ummera, Gubbeen, Janet's Country Fayre, they were all there, along with Natasha's kale crunchies, and far cheaper than you'll get them in Dublin. It is exactly the kind of place where you would expect to find the most up-to-the-minute artisan brands". (Kate, Beth & Jane O'Hara, 3 Castle Street, Sligo ☎ 071-914 3022 kateskitchensligo@gmail.com www.kateskitchensligo.ie – Open 8.45am-6.15pm Mon-Sat)

made in Meath

Carraig Fhada Seaweed

Café

Lyon's Café

Gary Stafford knows food. He understands what good cooking requires, he minds his dishes, he shepherds them and mentors them to be as good as they can be. And the result for the devoted customers in Lyons Café is delicious, authentic food, food with trueness and goodness, food that zings with health and energy. We have compared Mr Stafford's work with Avoca, and that's not just the self-service set-up the places share: it's more a comparison of people trying so hard to be their best, to do their best, and to do it day in, day out. Like Avoca, Lyons Café has a bright, cheery atmosphere, the sound of happy customers enjoying today's vegetable tagine, or a steak and cheese sandwich, or a proper burger with couscous. "Everything made for taste" we noted one day: Lyons Café – Made For Taste. The staff, of course, are top notch. (Gary Stafford, Lyon's Department Store, Quay Street, Sligo ☎ 071-914 2969 info@garystafford.com www.garystafford.com – Open 9am-6pm Mon-Fri, 8.30am-6pm Sat)

Café & Wine Bar

Ósta Café & Wine Bar

Brid Torrades brings it all back home, sourcing from the gifted artisans and suppliers who live and work near to Sligo, and her zeal for the local extends even to breakfast, where her foods come from within a 30-mile radius. She has always been the most perspicacious, committed restaurateur, and her tenure in our guides stretches back to our very first book. Ever since those early days, her love for fresh local foods has only gotten deeper, and that zeal is evident in every bite of Osta's dishes. Lovely. (Brid Torrades, Unit 2, Weir View House, Stephen Street, Sligo ☎ 071-914 4639 ostacafe@gmail.com www.osta.ie – Open 8am-7pm Mon-Wed, 8am-8pm Thu-Sat)

Restaurant

The Silver Apple

Tamar Adler's great cookery book is entitled *An Everlasting Meal*, and is subtitled: "Cooking with economy and grace". Both titles suit Louise Kennedy and Stephen Gault's food in The Silver Apple. The Silver Apple is up the stairs, above Rafferty's bar, for whom Ms Kennedy also supplies the food – chicken wings, panini, big burgers, good coffees – and she also has a lovely range of her pâtés and preserves for sale in Kate's Kitchen, in the centre of town. Upstairs in the bistro, Ms Kennedy showcases the classics – Killybegs smokies; Lissadell mussels; chicken chasseur; moules frites; Cumberland sausages and mash; Catalan fish stew – to which she brings her own spin, her grace and economy. The menus and wine list are adroit and what is here is what is needed, with nothing superfluous, just an artful understanding of the value of good food, and its economy and grace. (Louise Kennedy, Gateway Bar, Lord Edward Street, Sligo ☎ 071-914 6770 silverapplesligo@gmail.com www.silverapple.ie – Open 5pm-10pm Wed-Sun. Open 7 nights July & Aug)

Farmers' Market

Sligo Farmers' Market

Sligo has developed a cracking market, so look out for Irish organic meats, Bluebell Farm organic nettle pesto; J&M's veggie treats; eggs from Ballysadare; Trevor's cheeses; Organic Centre plants; Kinneden organic vegetables; Shanvaus honeys; Gerry's fish, and lots more. Just smashing. (Sligo IT Sports Field Car Park, Saturday 9am-1pm)

Restaurant & Cookery School

Source

Source is a hugely ambitious project – cookery school; restaurant; wine bar – all in one handsome three-storey building on the corner of John Street. Eithna O'Sullivan heads up the school, the restaurant has a commendable policy of local sourcing and uses the best Sligo ingredients, and offers a really lovely room in which to eat. And, given that owners Ray and Eileen Monahan have their own wines from their vineyard in the Languedoc, then a glass of Terra Monti La Perrine is going to be rather special upstairs in the wine bar. Service is uniformly excellent. (Ray & Eileen Monahan, Joe Grogan, 1 John Street, Sligo ☎ 071-914 7605 📫 info@sourcesligo.ie 🖱 www.sourcesligo.ie – Restaurant open 9.30am-9.30pm Mon-Sat, 1pm-9.30pm Sun. Wine Bar from 3pm Wed-Sun)

Wholefood Shop

Tir na nOg

Tir na nOg is the shop that instigated the food movement in the North West, back in the 1980's, when there was nothing but a disjointed gaggle of people with ideas and ambitions up here. They brought those ideas, ambitions – and their produce – to Tir na nOg, and the shop sold it and supported it, and put the town on the map for food. Their achievement has been immense, and we would like to see Eurotoques reward them with a special prize for all that hard, inspired work. (Mary & Norah McDonnell, Grattan Street, Sligo ☎ 071-916 2752 – Open 9am-6pm Mon-Sat)

Wine Merchant

The Wine Buff

Tom and Linda's shop is now on Tobergal Lane, and they offer the top-class array of wines sourced by the

Wine Buff consortium, along with all the paraphernalia needed to get the most from the wonderful world of wine. (Tom & Linda Ryall, Tobergal House, Tobergal Lane, Sligo ☎ 071-914 0020 📫 tom@thewinebuff.com 🖱 www.thewinebuff.com – Open 10.30am-7pm Tue-Fri, 10.30am-6pm Sat)

Strandhill

Café

● Shells

Shells is where the surfer dudes and all the hipsters head to in Strandhill for good baking and excellent drinks. The room has a cool bricolage feel that feels just right, one of those spaces you hoped you would find, a little food lover's archetype. (Myles & Jane Chambers, Strandhill ☎ 071-9122938 📫 eat@shellscafe.com 🖱 www.shellscafe.com – Open 9.30am-5pm Mon-Thur, 9.30am-6pm Fri-Sun)

County Tipperary

Tipperary

Ballymacarbry

Beef

Omega Beef Direct

Joe Condon is a smart guy, and he very early latched onto the fact that Ireland needed to return to its traditional beef breeds – Galloway; Moiled; Dexter; Kerry; Droimeann – in order to get the best beef from the pastures and from the hills. He rears happy, hairy organic Galloways on "a rambling tract of hill land" near Ballymacarbry, and his beef is of superb quality – umami; herbaceous; tactile; full of deep chocolatey, coffee-type flavour notes. The delivery service is as brilliant as the meats themselves and the butchery, which is handled by the legendary Michael McGrath of Lismore, could not be better. A visionary venture in every way, Omega Beef is both alpha, and omega. (Joe & Eileen Condon, Clashavaugha, Ballymacarbry ☎ 087-273 5447 omegabeefdirect@gmail.com www.omegabeefdirect.ie)

Borrisokane

Organic Farmer

Michael Seymour

Michael Seymour farms 125 organic acres in Borrisokane, home to Angus beef and Texel sheep. We like the confident branding of the farm – "A Seymour Organic Farm " – a confident, dramatic gesture which reflects Mr Seymour's wise, holistic, almost poetic approach to farming. And, like everyone else, we love these organic meats and their live, refulgent flavours and sweetness, the way the beef and lamb conveys its sense of place. When the meat is ready Michael brings it to the markets at Nenagh and Ennis, but you can also buy it at the farm itself and via a box delivery system. Wonderful farming, wonderful produce. (Michael & Olive Seymour, Finnoe Road, Borrisokane ☎ 067-27182 www.sheepwalkfarm.com)

Cahir

Orchard

The Apple Farm

Con Traas is the finest farmer of his generation. His work in The Apple Farm confounds most every notion of modern Irish farming: his work is singular, distinctive, regional, terroir-based, and profitable. He has turned his face against the blandness of commodity farming, sought out a new way of thinking about agriculture, and new practices to make it work. Goddammit, Traas makes farming sexy! Give this man a television series and he could do for Irish farming what Professor Brian Cox has done for physics and astronomy. His produce is superlative, and he is in control of every aspect of his production and supply chain. People don't come to the Apple Farm to shop: in truth, they make a pilgrimage to salve their souls, to get a feel of what an ideal farm looks like, and feels like. They know when they get here that this is how farms and farming should be, and they want to be reassured that there are farms that are brilliant, health-giving and inspiring. The Apple Farm is that farm. The Apple Farm inspires, it feeds your soul as well as your body. (Con Traas, Moorstown, Cahir ☎ 052-744 1459 con@theapplefarm.com www.theapplefarm.com)

Organic Products

Ballybrado

Julia Finke has brought a new focus to the venerable Ballybrado brand, repackaging many products and introducing a very fine – and award-winning – children's muesli, which is one of the smartest new products we have come across in recent times. The new generation is bringing an exciting dynamic to this great firm. (Julia Finke, Ballybrado House, Cahir ☎ 052-746 6206 ballybradoltd@eircom.net www.ballybrado.com)

Farmers' Market

Cahir Farmers' Market

The Cahir market is heading up on a decade of doing the good thing at the Craft Granary, and its success and longevity is explained by the wonderful mix of stalls that you find here: fresh fish, local spuds, good pies, farm chickens, gourmet pâtés, farmhouse cheeses, fresh fruit juices, the lot. Splendid. (Craft Granary near the Square, Cahir, 9am-1pm Sat)

Tipperary

Potatoes & Apples & Farm Produce

● O'Brien's Farm Shop

Pat O'Brien grows a fine potato and, like everyone else, we detour off the motorway to call to the shop to buy those potatoes, and eggs, and honey, and cabbage, and pork meat, and all the good things Mr O'Brien produces. Car filled, we head south once again, happy as Larry. (Pat O'Brien, Outrath, New Inn, Cahir ☎ 052-746 2282 – Honesty box at farm)

Café & Deli

● The River House

The River House is where we stop every time we are passing through Cahir and, it seems, we are not alone. Mel Gibson – yes, that Mel Gibson – stopped in for lunch when recceing movie locations in summer 2012. Mad Max 4 in Cahir? We like the idea. And we like the professionalism of the River House, a restaurant that manages to cope equally well with the tourists visiting Cahir Castle as well as individual eaters like ourselves. (Jennifer Bailey, 1 Castle Street, Cahir ☎ 052-744 1951 riverhousecahir@gmail.com www.riverhouse.ie – Open 8.30am-5pm Mon-Sun, Open till 9.30pm Thur-Sat, till 7pm Sun)

Baking

● Tasty Treats

We first met Rhona and Corinna at Electric Picnic, where they sold every morsel they had baked with such care and brought to the festival, to ravenous music heads. At the end, reader, there was not so much as a crumb remaining: now, that's baking, that's a Tasty Treat. (Rhona Boyle & Corinna Dooley, Cahir ☎ 087-783 0079)

Carrick-on-Suir

Wine Merchant

● Approach Trade

You may have never heard of Approach Trade, but the chances are that you will, in some good restaurant or in a good wine shop, have had a happy encounter with one of the Spanish wines which Rafael Alvarez imports. Mr Alvarez has superb taste, utter discrimination, and he knows his winemakers, he knows the stars, he knows the regions. Simply beautiful wines. (Rafael Alvarez, Mill River Pk, Carrick-on-Suir ☎ 051-640164 ✉ info@approachwines.com 🖱 www.approachwines.com)

Farmers' Market

● Carrick-on-Suir Farmers' Market

Get to the Heritage Centre early for the choice stuff, on Friday mornings. (Heritage Centre, Friday 10am-2pm)

Cashel

Hotel & Restaurant

● Bailey's Hotel

Bailey's is a very comfortable hotel, but it's most singular merit is the excellent staff who animate the hotel. This crew always over-deliver for their guests, and they are charming about it all the while. (Phil Delaney, Cashel ☎ 062-61937 ✉ info@baileyshotelcashel.com 🖱 www.baileyshotelcashel.com)

Café

● Café Hans

Here's a few specials from the blackboard on one day of service at Café Hans: lamb shanks with colcannon; fishcakes with crab and mussel butter served with chard and rocket salad and chorizo and roast pepper cous cous; hake with warm Spanish new potatoes. Look at the cadence of those dishes, look at their rhythm, look at how one ingredient provides the harmony – the warm potatoes; the chard and rocket; the colcannon. What lovely cooking Steffie Matthiae produces, and what a powerhouse of success this café has been from the day it opened. Café Hans is one of the glories of 'Tipp. (Hansie & Steffie Matthiae, Moor Lane, Cashel ☎ 062-63660 – Open noon-5.30pm Tue-Sat)

Restaurant

● Chez Hans

Cork's Ballymaloe House has a few years start on Chez Hans, having opened in 1964 whilst Hans opened in 1968, but these two institutions have been the most consistent and creative places to eat during their long history of serving the people of Ireland. Jason and Louise are the second generation, and they have chosen both to follow and yet to contemporise the classic cook ing which made the restaurant's reputation – lobster with lemon butter sauce; O'Dwyer's spring lamb with ratatouille; Kilmore scallops with salsa verde; silverside of beef with mustard greens and lovage; vanilla bean rice pudding. Hans is not inexpensive, yet you will be thankful for every cent you spend on this glorious food. Service is textbook good. (Jason & Louise Matthiae, Moor Lane, Cashel ☎ 062-61177 🖱 www.chezhans.net – Open 6pm-9.30pm Tue-Sat)

Sheep's Milk Cheese & Milk

● Crozier Dairy Products

Henry Clifton-Browne is becoming quite a media player these days, with a raft of media appearances focusing on his farming activities. The decision to start bottling Crozier sheep's milk should see Henry featuring in an awful lot more programmes, for this is a genuine and significant innovation. Crozier Blue cheese, meantime, continues its seemingly effortless progress as one of the most interesting and distinctive of Irish farmhouse cheeses, its taste profile coalescing all the disparate elements of the cheese into a gorgeous unity of flavour. (Henry Clifton-Browne, Ballinamona, Cashel ☎ 062-61120 📫 cliftonbrowne@eircom.net 🖱 www.cashelblue.com/crozier.htm)

Sausages & Puddings

● Una O'Dwyer Fine Foods

Una O'Dwyer has built her portfolio and her profile patiently over the last five years. Her range of speciality sausages has expanded organically, so you can now enjoy black pudding and thyme, or sweet chilli pork, or Cumberland or sundried tomato and basil, in addition to her traditional sausages. Her puddings are delicious and, as with the sausages, they are steadily becoming more and more available. Ms O'Dwyer has an impish creativity and as a female craft butcher she brings a different, welcome perspective to the traditional arts. (Una O'Dwyer, Cashel ☎ 062-65889)

Bakery and Café

● The Spearman

Do you know that feeling when the guy in the queue ahead of you orders what you were going to order, and it turns out that he gets the last one available because there has been a mad rush on the dish, because everyone else has been ordering it as well? That happened to us last time in The Spearman, and we were gutted. We could taste that chicken and broccoli gratin! We were ready to receive it and, then, heartbreak! Mind you, we made do with a fine steak sandwich. Next time, we shall turn up at the lovely Spearman's even earlier for lunch. No more disappointments for us. (Elaine & JD Spearman, 97 Main Street, Cashel ☎ 062-61143 spearmansbakery@gmail.com www.spearmanstearoom.com – Open 8.45am-5pm Mon-Sat)

Clogheen

Farmhouse Cheese

Bay Lough Farmhouse Cheese

Dick and Anne are two of the wisest, most sagacious farmers and individuals we know. And you know what? You can taste that wisdom, that sagacity, in their excellent Bay Lough cheeses: this cheese doesn't jump out of its skin trying to impress you. Instead, it is slow to unfurl its flavour profile, it is patient with you as you wait for the clean, lactic canvas and the mustardy-mushroomy flavours to bubble through. As this is cider country, you should pair Bay Lough with a glass of artisan cider, or maybe with a bottle of Knockmealdown Porter. Have a bite, have a sip. Wait. Don't worry: that Baylough bite is coming your way, sure as night follows day. (Dick & Anne Keating, Clogheen ☎ 052-746 5275)

Restaurant and Accommodation

The Old Convent

Writing about The Old Convent, Eamon Barrett signed off by saying: "And finally, a lovely goodbye". After all that had gone before – two extraordinary meals courtesy of the tasting menu dinner and a scrumptious breakfast, and a day relaxing and enjoying the comforts of this fine, fine house – and Dermot and Christine Gannon even manage "A lovely goodbye". Ahhh. Doesn't that do your heart good? But it's true: everything in The Old Convent is heartfelt – the welcome, the care, the cooking, even the goodbye. This explains how TOC has been such a success, because after leaving the first thing you want to do is to return. And you want to return to enjoy again that extraordinary cooking, an eight-course symphony that pays tribute to the great artisans from whom Mr Gannon sources his ingredients. His food is the Golden

Mean of the Golden Vale, a thing of rare beauty perfectly in symmetry, in proportion and in harmony. (Dermot & Christine Gannon, Clogheen ☎ 052-616 5565 info@theoldconvent.ie www.theoldconvent.ie – Open for dinner at 8pm Wed-Sun, with different hours during low season)

Tipperary

made in Tipperary

Crozier Blue

Clonmel

Restaurant

Befani's Mediterranean Restaurant

Adrian and Fulvio have given Clonmel what the town always wantd: a casual, all-day room in which you can nibble or nosh as much or as little as you like, enjoying a good vibe, good value and good service. You can collate a collection of tapas, you can have Slaney lamb shank with white beans or a sirloin steak with fries, and to make a night of it you can even opt to stay in one of their simple rooms in the townhouse. Efficient, professional, reliable and enduring. (Fulvio Bonfiglio & Adrian Ryan, 6 Sarsfield Street, Clonmel ☎ 052-617 7893 info@befani.com www.befani.com – Open 8am-11am Mon-Sun, 12.30pm-2.30pm 5.30pm-9.30pm Mon-Sun)

Farmers' Market

Clonmel Farmers' Market

A flight of top-class artisans are here on Saturday mornings to delight you with their tasty wares. (St Peter & Paul's Primary School, beside Oakville Shopping Centre. Saturdays, 10am-2pm)

Cookies

The Cookie Jar

Cate's giant cookies are the bee's knees. They are the old-fashioned style of American cookie, wholesome, satisfying, domestic, all conjuring up images of floury hands and aprons and big glass jars with beckoning cookies resting inside. The good news is that Cate is slowly taking over the cookie world, so look out for one of Cate's jars on a counter in your good deli or coffee shop. (Cate McCarthy, Poulmucka, Clonmel ☎ 052-613 5448 info@thecookiejar.ie www.thecookiejar.ie)

Bakery & Cafe

Hickey's Bakery & Café

A Spirit Store. A Fancy Bakery. Those are the descriptive titles on the shop of J. Hickey, just inside the walls of Clonmel, and Nuala Hickey's bread shop and café could not be better titled, for just a single slice of their legendary barm brack will lift your spirits. For the uninitiated, for the barm brack ingénue, barm brack is not just a traditional fruit loaf. Barm brack is a cultural totem. It is something worth arguing about, and maybe even worth fighting about. Barm brack is not just an historical creation, it is history itself. And so, it is worthy of the big questions: is it heretical to make barm brack scones? (Nuala has made these). Is it permissible to toast barm brack? Butter or no butter? Tea or coffee with the brack? Should ladies wear a hat? Questions, questions, and you can find happy answers to them all at Hickey's beautiful tea rooms, the St Peter's of barm brack. Do note that you can order the brack online, and that the bakery also has many, many more delicious things for sale. (Nuala Hickey, West Gate, Clonmel ☎ 052-612 1587 hickey.nuala@gmail.com www.hickeysbakery.com – Cafe Open 9am-6pm Mon-Sat)

Wholefood Shop

The Honeypot

A busy wholefood shop with lots of good things to discover, including Wine Buff wines. (The Honey Pot, 14 Abbey Street, Clonmel ☎ 052-612 1457 thehoneypot@hotmail.com – Open 9.30am-6pm Mon-Sat)

Crisps

O'Donnells Crisps

"My, but they are worthy of your attention" Aoife Cox wrote after her first taste of Ed O'Donnell's crisps. And indeed they are. Using potatoes from the family farm at Seskin, Mr O'Donnell flavours them with Apple Farm cider vinegar, and Mount Callan cheddar. In a world where snack foods are a by-word for the most chemicalised gunk imaginable, the O'Donnell crisps are clean-tasting and satisfying. Once tasted, you will never eat a a bag of the brand leaders again, and we expect Mr O'Donnell to be the brand leader sometime soon. (Ed O'Donnell, Seskin Farm, Kilsheelan, Clonmel ☎ 052-6139016 info@odonnellscrisps.com www.odonnellscrisps.com)

Wine Warehouse

● Red Nose Wine

Gary Gubbins proves that in today's wine world, it is as importent to be a Social Media Master as it is to be a Master of Wine. Facebooker, tweeter, blogger, columnist, Mr Gubbins gets the message of his wines out there, telling the story, foregrounding the culture, humanising the wines by introducing us to the people who make them, and he is a superb communicator, right up there with the best social media masters. His wines are as interesting as his writings and musings, and Red Nose is on top of its game. (Gary Gubbins, Clonmel Business Park ☎ 052-618 2939 - info@rednosewine.com 🖱 www.rednosewine.com – Open 2pm-6pm Tues, 11am-7pm Wed-Sat)

Tipperary

Farmshop

● Rosie's Farmshop

Rosie and Liam Casey opened their terrific farm shop in 2011, after Rosie had completed a course at the Organic College in Drumcollogher. The shop is a real smasher, packed with good things, especially fine organic meats and lots of the best artisan foods from Tipp and the surrounding counties. And, after you have filled all your bags, there is space to take some coffee and have a chat with the boss. Excellent. (Rosie Casey, Poulmucka, Clonmel ☎ 052-613 7764 📪 info@rosiesfarmshop.ie 🖱 www.rosiesfarmshop.ie – Open 9.30am-6pm Mon-Fri, 9.30am-5pm Sat)

Craft Butcher

● James Whelan Butchers

Pat Whelan has likely become the most famous butcher in Ireland over the last two or three years. He has written a book, become a media staple, become a media columnist, been one of the big players in the dynamic Tipperary Food Producers conclave and, crucially, moved beyond the confines of Clonmel to Monkstown, in south Dublin, where James Whelan Butchers shares part of the space in Avoca's latest, ground-breaking food store. In addition, he has developed the online ordering aspect of the shop, so boxes of James Whelan meats now head to all corners of the country. It's all based, of course, on outstanding Angus beef from their own farm, and meticulous care at farming and food preparation, and Pat Whelan never forgets that. The shops are exemplary, the service standards are exemplary, and Mr Whelan is always driving standards higher, higher, higher. (Pat Whelan, Oakville Shopping Centre, Clonmel ☎ 052-612 2927 www.jameswhelanbutchers.com – Open 8am-6pm Mon-Wed & Sat, 8am-6.30pm Thu, 8am-7pm Fri)

made in Tipperary

James Whelan Butchers

Wine Shop

The Wine Buff

The Honey Pot location on Abbey Street is actually the third location the WB has enjoyed in Clonmel. It's well worth following this fine selection of wines around the town. (The Honey Pot, Abbey Street, Clonmel ☎ 052-612 1457 clonmel@thewinebuff.com www.thewinebuff.com – Open 10.30am-5.30pm Mon-Sat)

Cloughjordan

Community Farm

Cloughjordan Community Farm

The Cloughjordan Community Farm is interesting. It's a COA – Community Owned Agriculture system – rather than the more conventional CSA – Community Supported Agriculture. This means that the members own the land, rather than the farmer owning the land, and they pay the farmers to produce for them, and then have a subscription system. Very clever indeed, and a model for other communities. (www.cloughjordancommunity-farm.ie)

Cookery School

Cloughjordan House

Sarah Baker seems to have managed to put herself at the centre of Cloughjordan activities over the last couple of years. A mix of her cookery classes at the Cloughjordan House cookery school, cookery demos, classes for schools, running a 400-year-old house where guests can stay and playing host to festivals and gatherings and dinners has revealed a woman with dynamic energy. How does she do it all? We don't know, but we're glad she does. (Sarah Baker, Cloughjordan House, Cloughjordan ☎ 087-9690824 www.sarahbaker.ie)

Tipperary

Artisan Bakery

● Cloughjordan Woodfired Bakery

Joe Fitzmaurice decided he wanted to live in the country after many years as part of the successful family team behind Dublin's Blazing Salads. So, he moved to Cloughjordan and built a wood-fired sourdough bakery. As you do. The breads use long fermentation – no less than 18 hours for the sourdough breads – and the baking is done in an Alan Scott-designed masonry oven, also known as "black ovens". The fuel used comes from beech trees felled from the local Knocknacree Woods, and this is a mighty enterprise just getting underway. (Joe & Julie Fitzmaurice ☎ 087 994 6768 ✉ cloughwoodfiredbakery@gmail.com 🖱 www.cloughjordanwoodfiredbakery.com

local knowledge

Barm Brack

Probably named from the ***barm*****, drawn off the yeast in the making of malt, there is also speculation that the name comes from the Irish** ***bairgain breac*****, meaning speckled cake. The town of Clonmel is famed for its brack baking.**

Dundrum

Meat Processor

● Crowe's Farm

The Crowe brothers are on a roll these days. In the pork and bacon world, they are major, major players, their products smartly branded, and newly packaged as we write. The brothers understand the cardinal rule about artisan foods: it's all about them, their work, their farm, their values, their need to be players, their hunger to be better, their ability to communicate to the customer that a packet of Crowe's bacon is not a packet of bacon: it is a packet of Crowe's Bacon, and behind it is a century of farming, and five years of organic practices, and a decade of expert charcuterie. It's mega-delicious, outstanding produce, as you would expect from a happy farm and happy farmers. (TJ, Ned & John Paul Crowe, Dundrum ☎ 062-71137/087-824 7394 ✉ info@crowe-farm.ie 🖱 www.crowefarm.ie)

Emly

Patés

● Knockara Pâtés

Maria makes fine pâtés using duck livers, chicken livers, smoked salmon and pork, along with very fine terrines, sauces and flavoured butters and she sells them at farmers' markets between Ennis and Cahir. Lovely work, and we bet yours don't last beyond lunchtime. (Maria Mulcahy, Emly ☎ 062-57339 ✉ knockarapates@gmail.com)

Tipperary

Fethard

Farmhouse Cheese

● Cashel Blue Cheese

We gave a little speech to open the new Cashel Blue cheese production unit in summer 2011. Seeing the grand, enormous new building, and recalling our first ever visit to the farm back in 1989, seemed to offer an enormous contrast between Cashel Blue then and Cashel Blue now. Except, it didn't, really. Cashel is still made on the farm – the new unit was built on a prized pasture – and is still made from the milk of their herd, by the same team who have been making it for yonks. Bigger, yes, but unchanged. The Cashel Blue expansion is an example of retro-innovation: get bigger by adhering to the same things that made you special in the first place, but just increase the scale. Our little speech was all about Seamus Sheridan's story about the Italian buyers who loved Cashel Blue and who asked if they could buy "10 types of Cashel Blues". "But ye don't understand", said Seamus: "There is only ONE Cashel Blue." (Sarah Furno, Beechmount, Fethard ☎ 052-613 1151 ✉ info@cashelblue.com 🖱 www.cashelblue.com)

Golden

Café

● Lily Mai's Café

Feargal and Frances changed direction with their Lily Mai a while back, making the restaurant into a café, making it more informal, more relaxed, and the result has been an exponential growth in the business. In addition to the original café in Golden, there are now very fine Lily Mai cafés in Bunratty and at the Dove Hill Design and Garden centres in Carrick-on-Suir. The cafés and shops work because they are very real – real food, real service, real engagement with the customer. In Golden, Linda Coleman-Poyntz cooks some lovely food – Annascaul black and white pudding crostini with gooseberries; walnut-crusted chicken breast with potato and rocket salad; Moroccan lamb with couscous; pork chops with nutmeg potato gratin. Breads and puddings are tactile and true, and Lily Mai is shaping up to become the Avoca of the South West. (Frances Fogarty, Feargal Ó Cinnéide, Thomastown, Golden ☎ 062-72847 lilymaiscafe@gmail.com www.lilymais.com Also at Dove Hill Design Centre, Carrick-on Suir, Dove Hill Garden Centre, and Bunratty Village Mills, Bunratty, Co Clare – All open for coffee, lunch and dinner)

made in Tipperary

Cashel Blue

Kilgarvan Quay

Restaurant

Brocka-on-the-Water

There is no other restaurant in Ireland like Brocka. You might find places like it in rural France – we ate in something similar to Brocka thirty years ago when holidaying in France, that is to say a private house where you could go to eat food grown and cooked by the owners and where the cooking was intriguingly unorthodox. For that is the Brocka prescription – country food in a private country house where the menu is hand-written, where they don't take credit cards, where the design is utterly unlike any other restaurant. Anne Gernon's cooking ranges between dishes that are now Brocka classics – the Cooleeney cheese croquettes with chutney; the baked seabass with hollandaise; the pork medallions with plum and clove sauce; the benchmark meringues – and Anne's imaginative riffs, such as a starter of roll mop herrings with goat's cheese, capers and garlic, or Tipperary organic lamb with aubergine and pesto. Puddings are just as granny would have made – crumbles, meringues, ice creams, fresh fruits. Delightful. (Anthony & Anne Gernon, Nancy Burns, Kilgarvan Quay, Ballinderry ☎ 067-22038 – Open 7pm-10pm Mon-Sat. Reservations only)

Lorragh

Free-Range Pork

● Old Farm Pork

Keeping rare-breed pigs in Ireland is – along with sourdough bread baking and craft brewing – the hippest thing you can possibly do. Margaret and Alfie got there early, and have been rearing their lovely saddlebacks for more than five years now. The media has caught up with them over the last year or so, and they have become staples of the farming supplements and the colour sections – the Good Life with Saddlebacks. Their superb pork and bacon should be a staple of your dinner table, so get in touch with them for the delivery service and get the good life in your diet. (Margaret O'Farrell & Alfie McCaffrey, Lorrha ☎ 086-810 0125 🖱 www.oldfarm.ie)

Tipperary

Nenagh

Café

● Cinnamon Alley Café

Bounteous and colourful are the words that come to mind when you first see the food in Marie Nagle's Cinnamon Alley. And it's not just those wowee! puddings and desserts and cakes: the savoury food is generous, comforting and really well considered, from that first cup of Palombini coffee to a bowl of tomato and basil soup with brown bread for lunch. And then some of those magic desserts, of course. (Marie Nagle, Hanley's Place, Sarsfield Street ☎ 067-33923 – Open 9am-5.30pm Tue-Sat)

Country Shop

● Country Choice

Peter Ward has done what no one else has ever managed in Ireland: he made shopkeeping into an art form, founded on expertise, graft and craft, and a deep-rootedness that lets him see the nonsense in the country and the culture very clearly. There is a sense of outrage in Mr Ward, an impatience for all the gombeenism and sleeveenism that is all around him in the political, culinary and cultural fields. He would have made a great politician, except he wouldn't, of course, for he wouldn't make the compromises. Country Choice, his Nenagh shop, and its Limerick Milk Market outlet, are singular places, unique places, embodiments of the culture of

Irish food in all its local glory. Peter Ward works too hard but, as a cattle dealer's son from Meath, work is in the blood. (Peter & Mary Ward, 25 Kenyon Street, Nenagh ☎ 067-32596 peter@countrychoice.ie www.countrychoice.ie – Open 9am-5pm Mon-Sat, coffee shop closes at 5pm)

Tipperary

made in Tipperary

Cooleeney Cheese

Bar & Restaurant

The Fairways Bar & Orchard Restaurant

First time we heard about Geoff Jones's cooking, it was when a friend sent a wee note raving about the soup they had enjoyed at lunchtime in the bar. If you pay attention to the soup, then you are a focused chef, and Mr Jones is just that. His cooking is notable for a particular love of fish – sourced from Rene Cusack's – but his skill and imagination runs throughout the menus, and he can jump from bacon and cabbage to a sizzling fajita to a dish of trout with mustard and spring onion beurre blanc without a jot of self-consciousness. A nice blazing fire and a rustic ambience counterpoint ambitious contemporary cooking. (Geoff Jones & Joan McGowan, Kilruane ☎ 067-41444 www.thefairwaysbar.ie – Open Mon-Sun for lunch and dinner)

Craft Butcher

Hackett's

A classic butcher's shop, in the old style. Old-style service, old-style skills, old-style quality. Those things never go out of fashion, you know. (Michael Hackett, 94 Silver Street, Nenagh ☎ 067-31340 – Open 9am-6pm Mon-Fri, closed Wed, 8.30am-5.30pm Sat)

Craft Butcher

Hanlon's

Hanlon's is a top-class butcher's shop, a handsome store for sourcing excellent meats and meat products prepared by a crack team. It's the sort of store that emphasises and exemplifies the strength-in-depth in terms of retail excellence in a town like Nenagh. (Gregory & Michael Hanlon, 14 Kenyon Street, Nenagh ☎ 067-41299 greghanlon@eircom.netv– Open 8am-6pm Mon-Sat, 8am-7pm Fri)

Craft Butcher

Larkin's Bar & Restaurant

Larkin's is known as a traditional pub which is a destination for music sessions, but Cormac and Maura Boyle also properly look after the food in the bar. They do classics like bacon and cabbage, sausages and champ, beef and Guinness casserole, but the dishes aren't a clichéd rendition: they are freshly made and freshly imagined and endlessly enjoyable. (Cormac & Maura Boyle, Portroe, Nenagh ☎ 067-23232 info@larkins.ie www.larkins.ie – Open pub hours. Food served 10.30am-9.45pm Mon-Sat, noon-9.45pm Sun with more limited hours off season)

Tipperary

local knowledge

Pork and Bacon

It was commonplace to keep a pig in Ireland, to such an extent that historically it was treated almost like a domestic animal, with many stories of pigs living in comparative luxury by the home hearth. Bacon became the most popular meat in the country, and was widely made through the necessity of preserving the meat. Recent times have seen a revival in pig keeping and consequent improvement of the pork meat available. Rare breeds are now prized, and curing methods are once again studied and enjoyed. Artisan bacon and sausages, so rare just a decade ago, are now widely available through markets and via farm deliveries.

Chocolates

Lough Derg Chocolates

Malachy and Elaine turned to chocolate making having lost jobs in the downturn, but the growth of Lough Derg Chocolates since they debuted in late 2011 has been virtually explosive. They have gotten the whole thing right: the distinctiveness of the chocolates; the design and packaging; the awards for their know-how and energy; the route to market through markets and then on into shops. And, as the song says, they've only just begun, so watch these guys go. (Malachy & Elaine Dorris, Newtown, Nenagh ☎ 087-968 3534 info@loughdergchocolates.ie www.loughdergchocolates.ie)

Tippearay

Home Baking

Mag's Home Baking

Mags Bergin bakes lovely healthy loaves and pastries, and Mag's is real home baking with that true, natural, domestic, home-made taste. Mags, you might say, does it so you don't have to. (Mags Bergin, Shesheraghkeale, Limerick Rd, Nenagh ☎ 067-33958 neelisa@eircom.net)

Farmers' Market

Nenagh Farmers' Market

Nenagh Market is a beauty, one of those special town markets that fuses farmers' market with country market. Top class. (Teach and Leinn, Kenyon Street, Nenagh, Sat 10am-2pm)

Café

The Pantry

Grainne Moylan and her team have been doing the good thing for twenty years now in The Pantry. You survive that long by having a natural instinct for food, and by knowing what people like to eat, and the sort of place in which they like to eat it. And that is the secret of The Pantry: everything here tempts, everything here is tempting – look at that blackboard, and you are suddenly famished for a bowl of beef stew with champ. Look at those home-cooked hams on the counter and you want slices of them with mustard and fresh salads and a brown scone and butter. Look at those tarts and you want a little apple tart and a nice cup of tea. We can resist anything, of course, except temptation. Grainne and her crew know that about us, and only too well. (Grainne Moylan, Quentin's Way, Nenagh ☎ 067-31237 info@thepantrycafe.ie www.thepantrycafe.ie – Open 8.30am-6pm Mon-Sat)

Resturant

The Peppermill

Mairead and Robert have built a rock-steady, hugely popular local restaurant in The Peppermill, since opening more than a decade ago. There is a wine bar with a tapas menu downstairs, and the restaurant is on the first floor. Cooking and serving modern, European-style food is their ambition, but the European accents are underscored by local staples such as Inch House black pudding and Union Hall fish and shellfish and Tipperary meats. Splendid, graceful service pulls all the elements together. (Mairead & Robert Gill, Kenyon Street, Nenagh ☎ 067-34598 ✉ info@thepeppermill.ie 🖰 www.thepeppermill.ie – Open 5pm-10pm Tue-Fri, 4pm-10pm Sat & Sun)

Bakery Cafés

● Quigley's

When the judges were handing Margaret O'Connor of Quigley's Bakery the Tipperary Business Woman of the Year award in mid-2012, they noted that Ms O'Connor had grown the business from one outlet in 1988, when she joined the company, to no fewer than 16 outlets across nine different counties in Ireland by 2012. Ms O'Connor's achievement is genuinely phenomenal. Other food businesses grow that fast by franchising and, in the process, they destroy their reputations and wreak havoc on the values that made them attractive to people in the first place. Ms O'Conor is different: she knows that Quigley's Bakery and the Café Q outlets rely on the fact that there is a high-quality bakery producing high quality breads and pastries in Nenagh, and she has held steadfast to that. Her success is a model example of doing something right, and doing it your own way. Just as importantly, she knows the value of team work. We expect to see her on every Women in Business panel for the next decade, explaining that One True Thing, explaining how conventional wisdom is bunk, and how her wisdom works. The cafés, of course, are only excellent. (Margaret O'Connor, Lisbunny Business Park, Nenagh, branches at: 9 Kenyon Street, Nenagh ☎ 067-36445 also ● Athlone Town Centre, Co Westmeath ☎ 090-647 7017 ● Roscrea Shopping Centre, Roscrea, Co Tipperary ☎ 050-523313 ● Liberty Square, Thurles, Co Tipperary ☎ 050-424397 ● Patrick St, Tullamore, Co Offaly ☎ 057-936 0353 ● MacDonagh Junction, Kilkenny ☎ 056-772 2606 ● Cruises Street, Limerick ☎ 061-411050 ● Crescent Shopping Centre, Dooradoyle, Limerick ☎ 061-228688 ● Parkway Shopping Centre, Limerick ☎ 061-418407 ● Douglas Shopping Centre, Cork ☎ 021-489 9481 ● Shamrock Plaza, Carlow ✉ quigleysbakery@eircom.net 🖰 www.quigleys.ie)

Relishes

The Scullery

Florrie Purcell has more than twenty five products in the Scullery range now, vital preserves, relishes and glazes that make your life richer, better, tastier. Her individual plum puddings are one of the most inspired artisan products of recent years, and have been a tumultuous success, but every jar she makes shows care, skill and creativity. (Florrie Purcell, 7 Springfort Industrial Park, Limerick Road, Nenagh ☎ 086-174 4402 ✉ florrie@thescullery.ie)

Roscrea

Ice Creams & Sorbets

Boulabán Ice Cream

Kate and Michael's Boulabán ice cream picked up an Irish Restaurant Award prize for best artisan product in 2012, proof of just how fine the Boulabán ices are. The milk of their Holstein-Friesian herd is the start of the process, the ice cream is made on the farm the same day as milking, and their own wild creativity in concocting flavours then showcases this good milk to perfection. You will find the tubs in local shops and in good restaurants. (Kate & Michael Cantwell, Boulabán, Roscrea ☎ 0505-43430 ✉ kmcantwell@eircom.net 🖱 www.boulabanefarm.ie)

Templemore

Artisan Beer

White Gypsy Brewery

Cuilán Loughnane is to Irish craft brewing as Myrtle Allen is to Irish food: the hero of the locality. Like Mrs Allen, Mr Loughnane's perspective is distinctly – and deliberately – limited. He wants local beers for local folk, the way things used to be, the way things used to be half a century ago, when Perry's in Rathdowney made a Tipperary ale for Tipperary locals. His signature and his influence are all over the shop. He has made contract beers for many other brewers, popping up here and there – The Brook Lodge; Metalman; Messrs Maguire – and he got his start in brewing in Tipp, when he bagged a job at Dwan's in Thurles, after returning from Canada.

As he works, you can almost feel his brain fizzing with ideas, plans, ambitions: the alchemist in his lab in total control, thinking about smoked beers, thinking about Tipperary ruby ales, thinking about barrel-aged porters, about winter ales and pilsners, the world of beer brought back home to Templemore. (Cuilán Loughnane, 14 Priory Place, Templemore ☎ 086-172 4520 ⁘ www.whitegypsy.ie)

Tipperary

Terryglass

Gastropub

● The Derg Inn

"The decor is... well, everything", said *The New York Times*, before going on to praise the cooking in Mick and Joyce Soden's famous pub. The Derg is a local hero, and as a destination it works because everything in it works – the bricolage style, the friendly service, the tasty cooking, the good drinks, the teeming atmosphere on the weekends and on the music nights. A key destination in this lovely village. (Joyce & Mick Soden, Terryglass ☎ 067-22037 ✉ derginn@eircom.net ⁘ www.derginn.ie – Food served 11am-10pm Mon-Sun)

Thurles

Artisan Cheese maker

● Cooleeney Cheese

There is something very interesting about Cooleeney, which makes it different from other artisan cheese producers. Jim and Breda Maher produce a kaleidoscope of cheeses on their farm, exploring the panorama of possibilities that milk offers: cow's milk and goat's milk, raw milk and pasteurised; young and mature; plain and seasoned; large cheeses and small cheeses and logs of cheese and wheels of cheese; farm milk and bought-in milk. And they exploit all these possibilities, brilliantly, in a range of cheeses that are distinguished by being so diverse, yet of such uniform excellence and individual distinctiveness. A parallel comparison exists outside of cheesemaking – in the world of baking, brewing and distilling, where Irish Distillers, or Arbutus Breads, or Franciscan Well Brewery all produce a range of products. But such a broad range is rare amongst cheesemakers, who often make only a single version of their cheese. Cooleeney is the most heterogeneous cheese company in these islands, and one of the glories of contemporary Irish agriculture. (Jim & Breda Maher, Moyne, Thurles ☎ 0504-45112 info@cooleeney.com www.cooleeney.com

Preserves

Crossogue Preserves

Like the best Irish artisan foods, Veronica Molloy's Crossogue Preserves manage to be both wonderfully agrestic - tactile, humming with sweetness and nectary resonance, satisfyingly true - whilst also being wonderfully adroit - the flavours of the preserves always conjoined in happy harmony, a perfect marriage of tastes and textures born out of every pot. It's no easy thing to manage this culinary double-act, but Crossogue Preserves achieve it every time. A jar of Crossogue makes your life better. (Veronica Molloy, Ballycahill, Thurles ☎ 0504-54416 info@crossoguepreserves.com www.crossoguepreserves.com)

Country House & Restaurant

Inch House

The Egan family are amongst the most dynamic of the food pioneers who have created the wave of artisans and restaurateurs that now characterise Tipperary. John and Nora Egan opened their house to guests in 1989, adding the restaurant five years later, so there is nearly a quarter century of service from the family to their community. Whilst Nora Egan has ceded the day-to-day running of the house to her daughter, Mairin, she has developed a parallel career as the creator of Inch House black pudding, a wonderful artisan pudding which won a bronze award at the Concours International du Meilleur Boudin competition in France in 2011. Mairin, meanwhile, runs this fine house and restaurant with the confidence that comes of family experience, and both the house and the restaurant are places of quiet excellence. (Mairin & Nora Egan, Thurles ☎ 0504-51261 mairin@inchhouse.ie www.inchhouse.ie – Restaurant open 6pm-9pm Tue-Sat)

Beef

Irish Piemontese Beef

John Commins, in alliance with County Laois farmer Michael Fennelly, rears Piemontese beef. The beef has a major USP: it is lower in fat, cholesterol and calories than beef from other breeds, and is lower even than chicken or salmon. But, truth be told, that isn't the USP that counts. The Piemontese beef also has the USP that really counts: it is delicious. It takes a little bit of careful cooking, but if you handle it delicately, then it will reward you with a tremendous sweet, herbaceous flavour. We love it. You will find it at the Newbarn farm shop in Ashbourne, Co Meath, on Saturdays and the meat can be ordered from the site, which also details other stockists. (John Commins, Two Mile Borris, Thurles & Michael Fennelly, Stradbally, Co Laois ☎ 087-9135349 info@irishpiemontesebeef.ie www.irishpiemontesebeef.ie)

Restaurant

Mitchel House

Chef Brendan Sheridan does some rather funky riffing on classic dishes in Michael O'Dwyer's Mitchel House restaurant: he adds a slice of St Tola goat's cheese to Caesar salad; he adds smoked chicken to roasted mushrooms; his Barbarie duck comes with white cabbage; he makes a white onion jam for sirloin steak, and puts a beetroot purée with monkfish. Overall, his cooking leans to strong savoury notes, so this is satisfying, umami cooking, and value is very good indeed. It's your destination in Thurles. (Michael O'Dwyer, Mitchel Street, Thurles ☎ 0504-90776 mitchelhouse@eircom.net www.mitchelhouse.ie – Open 5pm-9.30pm Wed-Sat, 12.30pm-2.30pm, 5pm-8pm Sun)

Farmers' Market

Thurles Farmers' Market

Saturday mornings at the greyhound track brings together a small but very classy bunch of artisans who together make for a fine farmers' market. (Saturday 9.30am-1pm)

local knowledge

Tipperary Apples

Alongside Armagh, in Northern Ireland, Tipperary is known as the Orchard of Ireland. There are 70 varieties of native Irish apple trees, preserved for us thanks to the patient work of Seed Savers and The Orchard Trust.

Bakery

● The Tipperary Kitchen

Chocolate biscuit cake. Get it wrong in the making, and it is the cake that sits there, uneaten, unloved. Get it right in the making, and it vanishes faster than an Irish summer. Anne Marie Walsh's chocolate biscuit cake vanishes so fast in our house that it seems to disappear rather than just be eaten. It's a beauty, and it shows the sure touch of this fine baker, who also makes excellent breads, lovely spotted dog, fine meringues. Look for the Tipp Kitchen products in good local shops. (Anne Marie Walsh, Holycross Village, Thurles ☎ 0504-43257 📫 holycrossstores@eircom.net)

Tipperary Town

Soups & sauces

● Browne's Soups

Sarah and Michael have been making the good soups – and latterly, the good sauces – for the people of Ireland for a decade now, and their success is down to the old truisms: high quality, hard work, good promotion via the Tipperary Producers group and at big events like the Ploughing Championship, and a true sense of value and values conveyed by the brand, which is to say that it's all about the Browne family, working hard. Their packaging is as vibrant and cultured as their soups, and it's wonderful to see these classy foods so widely available. (Sarah & Michael Browne, Clonmel Road, Tipperary town ☎ 062-82090 📫 info@msbrowne.com 🖱 www.msbrowne.com)

Café

● The French Quarter Café

The French Quarter is part of the Tipperary Excel arts and culture centre, and Anne-marie and Loic put the culture firmly on the plate in the café. Along with Loic's Brittany specialities – French tarts, pear and almond tart – there are nice soups, quiches and wraps. Good service pulls the whole show together and the relaxed vibe is thanks to the fact that almost everyone in the room is a regular, enjoying the best cup of coffee in town. (Anne-marie Ryan & Loic L'Herrou, Mitchell Street, Tipperary ☎ 062-82592 – Open 9.30am-5.30pm Mon-Fri, 10am-5.30pm Sat)

County Waterford

Ardmore

Restaurant

Cliff House Hotel

He is larger-than-life, is Martin Kajuiter, both literally – he is toweringly tall – and figuratively – he is a huge presence. His work is closer to artist-painter than chef. His concern for textures ranges from the ruddy to the ethereal. His concern for the scents of a dish is paramount, but the secret of his brilliance is his ability to understand the possibilities inherent in the simplest things – herbs, flowers, carrots, cabbage, and to re-contextualise these simple things in the most thrilling way imaginable. The hotel has the good fortune to have a manager, Adriaan Bartels, who is as accomplished as his chef. The rooms are sublimely impressive, regardless of whether you're in the most basic room or glamming it up in the duplex Terrace Suites, and there's no escaping the setting, on the cliffside overlooking the stunning Ardmore Bay. Cliff House is a modern Irish classic. (Adriaan Bartels, Ardmore ☎ 024-87800 info@thecliffhousehotel.com www.thecliffhousehotel.com – Restaurant open noon-3pm, 6.30pm-9pm Mon-Sun – residents only Fri & Sat)

Restaurant

White Horses

Before Cliff House, Ardmore already had a shining destination restaurant in the lovely White Horses, a homely, jolly place to visit where the cooking is hearty and satisfying, where everyone from teenager to granny will find something to please from an imaginative and clever menu and where there will be the most sumptuous cakes and desserts to finish off. The cakes alone, we assure you, are worth the trip, and you will leave dreaming of their bounteous delight. A really special, simple and smashing destination in sunny Ardmore. (Christine Power & Geraldine Flavin, Main Street, Ardmore ☎ 024-94040 whitehorses@eircom.net – Open 11am-11pm Tue-Sun, with more limited hours off season)

Waterford

Ballyduff

Organic Eggs & Meat

Glenmore Organics

"Some of the finest eggs laid on the Oul' Sod" is how Joe McNamee describes Seamus and Christine's beautiful organic eggs, the produce of happy hens on happy pastures. You can also buy Glenmore beef and lamb, direct from the producers, and at their market stalls. (Christine & Seamus Hyland, Ballyduff Upper ☎ 058-60412)

Ballymacarbry

Country House

Glasha Farmhouse

Most of the people who stay at Glasha are frequent visitors, returning one more time for Olive O'Gorman's great hospitality, returning one more time to this beautiful area, so beloved of hillwalkers and hikers. But, no matter how often you have stayed, you will still be blown away by the transformation of the Glasha dining room when you sit down to dinner on your next visit. What was once a comfortable but domestic space is now a super-cool room of poised elegance, with a patio door out onto the walled courtyard. So, after a big afternoon hike in the hills, peel off the Osprey backpack and ditch the Meindls, and bring on the Comeragh lamb with rosemary, the striploin with creamed mushrooms, and the good red wine. (Olive O'Gorman, Ballymacarbry ☎ 052-613 6108 glasha@eircom.net www.glashafarmhouse.com)

Country House & Restaurant

Hanora's Cottage

Its location is idyllic, and how hill walkers must love it when they come in sight of Hanora's Cottage at the end of a long day hiking the byways of Ballymacarbry. It's both nicely smart and nicely informal, and the breakfasts – before you head off on that hike – are amongst the best prepared anywhere in the country. The perfect beginning to the day, then, and the perfect ending to the day. (Eoin, Judith & Mary Wall, Nire Valley, Ballymacarbry ☎ 052-6136134 hanorascottage@eircom.net www.hanorascottage.com)

Butlerstown

Free-range Meats Farmshop

Pine Grove Farm

Along with sourdough breadmaking and beer brewing, the passion to breed and rare speciality pork is one of the defining tropes of Irish artisanship, as we write this book. Ronan and Joy's Pine Grove Farm is a quintessential example: gorgeous pork, fresh chickens, farmers' market stall, pig on a spit. Lovely sausages, fresh eggs, lovely black puddings, breakfast blaas, all just pure darling, the way a farm should be, the way farmers should sell their wares. Catch Ronan and Joy at the Waterford markets, and book them for your big birthday. (Carmel & Ronan Joy, Whitfield, Butlerstown ☎ 051-399804 www.pinegrovefarm.eu – Open 4pm-7pm Thur-Sat)

local knowledge

Waterford Blaa

Look out for the soft floury white rolls that are Waterford Blaa. Larger and softer than a bap and noticeably square in shape, they are said to have derived from croissants, brought to Waterford in the late seventeenth century.

Cappoquin

Bakery and Coffee Shop

Barron's Bakery

Barron's is one of Waterford's finest traditional bakeries, with breads and blaas all made in their classic, traditional Scotch oven, with the bread allowed lots of time to develop and ferment, and with the final result offering nothing but sheer goodness. Esther and Joe Barron's bakery is simply wonderful, an archetype of what an Irish artisan company could be, should be, and can be. Their beautiful history of the bakery and the Barron family, *Our Daily Bread*, is an outstanding local history, and the bakery's importance to the pretty town of Cappoquin cannot be overstated. (Esther & Joe Barron, Cappoquin ☎ 058-54045 barronsbakery@eircom.net www.barronsbakery.ie – Open 9am-5.30pm Mon-Sat)

Apple Juice

Crinnaghtaun Apple Juice

David and Julia's apples and apple juice are ace. The apples, happily, are a mainstay of our local supermarket and, as we tear our hair out pushing aside bags of apples from Chile and Brazil and New Zealand and Italy, suddenly, a bag of Irish apples from Crinnaghtaun will hove into view: sold! Julia's apple juices are brilliant, packed with health. (Julia & David Keane, Cappoquin ☎ 058-54258 ✉ sales@irishjuiceco.com 🖱 www.irishapplejuice.com)

Waterford

Farmhouse Cheese

Knockalara Farmhouse Cheese

Knockalara is one of the few sheep's milk cheeses made in Ireland, and it's a real beauty. Wolfgang and Agnes have fashioned both the classic Knockalara and the fresher Dromana range of cheeses for more than twenty years, and the experience shows: these cheeses are expert and professional, but not at the cost of quirkiness or complexity: the cheeses have rivers of taste and tongue-teasing textures, especially the mature and hard versions of the cheese. A cow's milk cheese – Comeragh – is also produced, and Agnes and Wolfgang always have other experiments going on in the dairy. They are also great marketeers, and this is the ideal place at which to buy the Knocaklara cheeses, as you can sample them at a variety of ages. Wonderful artisans, wonderful cheesemakers. (Wolfgang & Agnes Schliebitz, Knockalara, Cappoquin ☎ 024-96326 ✉ wschliebitz@eircom.net)

Country House

Richmond House

The McKennas had driven from West Cork and when we arrived at Richmond, we sat down in the drawing room and had fresh, warm scones and handmade jam and a pot of tea. The fire blazed away, the comfort was as palpable as the sense of welcome. Was there ever such a happy bunch of travellers, so happy to have arrived at their destination, in such a happy place as Richmond House? Out of such precious, unexpected moments, moments of thoughtfulness and generosity, spring a lifetime's worth of happy recollections, and that is exactly what Paul and Claire Deevy specialise in, in this lovely country house. They are elemental, thoughtful people. They and their team look after you, and make sure you have everything you could possibly need, from the tea and scones on arrival to Paul's lovely country cooking at dinner and then their delicious breakfasts to set you up for the day. Richmond is a special place, a place where time takes its time. (Paul & Claire Deevy, Cappoquin ☎ 058-54278 info@richmondhouse.net www.richmondhouse.net – Open for Dinner for non-residents 7pm-9pm Mon-Sun, closed Sun off season)

made in Waterford

Flahavan's Oats

Dungarvan

Shop

Country Store

Conor Lannen's Country Store summons lots of local heroes – Knockanore cheese, Baldwin's ice cream; Crinnaghtaun apple juice; Powersfield House cooked meals and cakes; Barron's breads – and allies these to a great list of kitchen essentials and staples in a store that is one of the landmark addresses of Dungarvan. (Conor Lannen, 3 Shopping Arcade, Mitchell Street, Dungarvan ☎ 058-43061 www.thecountrystore.ie – Open 8am-6pm Mon-Sat)

Craft Brewer

Dungarvan Brewing Company

Cormac and Tom fashion three of the most beautiful, bottle-conditioned ales and stouts you have ever drunk. From a little brewery in a little industrial estate, they brew up magic: the fresh and hoppy Helvic Gold, the powerful, refulgent Black Rock stout – "Could bring tears to the eyes of older drinkers" wrote John Wilson in *The Irish Times* – and the mighty Copper Coast red ale. It is no exaggeration to say that these beers improve the quality of your life. We think of them as health drinks – the produce of pure ingredients, clean water, and a coruscating creativity that conspire to make you feel good, and to do you good. The DBC is one of the most important artisan companies. (Cormac O'Dwyer & Tom Dalton, Westgate Business Park, Dungarvan ☎ 058-2400 www.dungarvanbrewingcompany.com)

Farmers' Market

Dungarvan Farmers' Market

Dungarvan has a lovely square, and in that square you will find the lovely Dungarvan farmers' market, on Thursday mornings. (Gratton Square, Thursday mornings. Contact Síobhan La Touche, ☎ 086-394 0564 contact@dungarvanfarmersmarket.com www.dungarvanfarmersmarket.com – Open 9am-2pm Thursdays)

Country Lodge

Gortnadiha Lodge

Eileen Harty is a great hostess, a fount of energy and knowledge, and she makes a mighty breakfast for her guests at Gortnadiha. (Eileen Harty, Ring, Dungarvan ☎ 058-46142 info@gortnadihalodge.com www.gortnadihalodge.com)

Waterford

made in Waterford

Metalman Pale Ale

Restaurant

Nude Food

Now, just say you have a had a busy morning shopping at the Dungarvan market and the hunger is upon you. What to do? Nip into Nude Food, and let Louise Clark rustle up her Spanish eggs – Ballinamult eggs with roasted tomatoes and peppers, served with sourdough bread. Ah! Isn't that the thing! And that is the thing with Ms Clark: she knows what we want to eat. She understands appetite, and how to satisfy it, and this gift makes her a true cook. What's more, the Nude Food principle applies all day, so when the hunger strikes at lunch, then it's JD Power's pork belly with couscous, and if the hunger strikes on a weekend evening then it's sirloin with dauphinoise potatoes and portobello mushrooms. Ms Clark is the business, and Nude Food is a star. (Louise Clark, 86 O'Connell Street, Dungarvan ☎ 058-24594 nudefoodireland@gmail.com www.nudefood.ie – Open 9.15am-6pm Mon-Wed, 9.15am-9.30pm Thu-Sat. Open Sun during summer months and three weeks before Christmas)

Butcher

John David Power

JD Power's is one of the mainstays of Dungarvan's food culture, a peerless butcher's shop, with some of the nicest pork and bacon you have ever tasted. (John David Power, 57 Main Street, Dungarvan ☎ 058-42339 – Open 9am-5.50pm)

Country House

Powersfield House

Eunice Power is becoming a legend. It's not just her superlative recipe writing in *The Irish Times* that is doing it, though her sublime baking recipes are must-cook! good. And it's not just her beautiful B&B, Powersfield House, or her celebrated catering company, or her role as a cookery teacher at the Tannery cookery school. It is, indeed, all of these things. We just ask: how does she do it? But Mrs Power does it with gas in the tank, it seems. Endlessly capable, effortlessly preparing beautiful food, right at the centre of the dynamic Waterford food culture, a powerhouse, a sport of nature. (Eunice Power, Ballinamuck West, Dungarvan ☎ 058-45594 eunice@eunicepower.com www.eunicepower.com)

Café & Bar

Quealy's Café Bar

Andrew Quealy runs a nice, hip business here, just off the square. The blackboard specials are tasty and well-cooked and the bar has a nice vibe. (Andrew Quealy, 82 O'Connell Street, Dungarvan West, Dungarvan ☎ 058-24555 info@quealys.com – Quealy's Bar open noon-3pm, 5pm-9pm Wed-Sun)

Restaurant

The Tannery

"Even in restaurants as exceptional as The Tannery, there are times when things transcend to a higher level", says Eamon Barrett. Tell us about the Nirvana Plateau, Eamon: "Carpaccio of lamb breast, broccoli and broad beans was a dish of exquisite beauty and taste. As delicate as a cloud it was the epitomy of good cooking. Cannelloni of veal cheek with glazed carrots and Madeira butter was a superb dish. Roast monkfish on the bone with salt-baked celeriac and shellfish cream only just overshadows crispy Parmesan rolls with wild garlic mash and slow-cooked shallots. A chocolate honeycomb cake was gorgeous, whilst yogurt pannacotta with biscotti and blood orange sorbet is pretty as a picture." Paul Flynn's cooking has become simpler, more direct, more focused on his garden, his seasons, his suppliers. He knows how to please people, and that is what this great, sexy restaurant does: it pleases people in the most elemental, profound and unforgettble ways. (Paul & Maire Flynn, 10 Quay Street, Dungarvan ☎ 058-45420 info@tannery.ie www.tannery.ie – Open 12.30pm-2.30pm Tue-Fri & Sun, 6pm-9.30pm Tue-Sat)

Waterford

Townhouse & Cookery School

● Tannery Townhouse & Cookery School

There is a quirky picture behind the main cooking station at the Cookery School: it's the rear end of a pig. It alerts you to the fact that this experience is going to be different. Cheeky, memorable, full of style. The Cookery School is built around a number of cooking stations, and an adjacent dining room. It gets serious in here, and it gets fun. Dancing has been known to break out late on in the evenings. Then what better than to retire to the elegant rooms, where a breakfast of fresh baked buns are delivered to your door each morning. (Paul & Maire Flynn, 10 Quay Street, Dungarvan ☎ 058-45420 info@tannery.ie www.tannery.ie)

Dunhill

Beverages

● Dunhill Castle Sparkling Spirit

Dunhill Castle sparkling spirit mixes Irish spirit at 13% vol with the juice of unfermented apples. The taste is clean and lively and nicely surprising, with the alliance between the spirit and the juice very well balanced. Serve it nice and cool and get that good, fresh hit. (Donal Lehane, Irish Artisan Beverages, Eco Park, Dunhill ☎ 051-396625 www.irishartisanbeverages.com)

Pâtés

● Healy's of Waterford

Elizabeth and Michael produce some very fine pâtés, which you will find in local stores. There is a classic chicken liver pâté, and a really good smoked salmon pâté, just the thing to get the dinner off to a good start. (Elizabeth Healy, Dunhill Rural Ecopark, Ballyphilip, Dunhill ☎ 086-8136770 ✉ khealy99@yahoo.com)

Artisan Chutneys

● Tastefully Yours

We would walk a country mile for a great piccalilli, and the best piccalilli we have tasted in donkey's years is made by Norbert Thul and Audrea Hassett's company, Tastefully Yours, from Dunhill. The TY piccalilli is one of the best new speciality products, but then everything this talented pair fashion is beautifully made, the flavours are always crisply focused, sharp and enlivening, and they are also beautifully packaged. There is a neat shop and tearoom also at Dunhill Ecopark where they sell the complete TY range along with fresh breads and cakes, and look for them also at farmers' markets. (Norbert Thul, Audrea Hassett, Dunhill Rural Ecopark, Ballyphilip, Dunhill ☎ 051-396590 ✉ tastefullyyours@live.com)

Dunmore East

Restaurant

● Azzurro at The Ship

Azzurro is one of three restaurants in Waterford owned by the Cavaliere family, and Azzurro hits the mark with super pizzas, pastas, and some really good fish cooking. Calamari with saffron aioli is a great seaside starter to begin with, or maybe try a plate of tapas from the blackboard. A big pot of moules frites with garlic crostino or a thin and crispy pizza rustica with chorizo, ham and mushrooms are both super dishes. There's always a great buzz of locals and tourists in here and Azzurro is very well managed. (Adriano Cavaliere, Dock Road, Dunmore East ☎ 051-383 141 ✉ info@azzurro.ie 🖱 www.azzurro.ie – Open Mon-Sun. Open for midweek lunch daily from May-Sept)

Traiteur & Café

● The Lemon Tree

Joan Power enjoys a double-first in her culinary makeup: not only does her work exhibit the purity that comes from a Ballymaloe School background, but she was also born into the business, with her folks running the

Candlelight Inn. So, The Lemon Tree is both a café, and a weekend evening restaurant during the summer season. It is both a shop, and a catering company. Joan Power cooks, and she also teaches cookery. You can come for breakfast, or an 8-course tasting menu dinner. There is food to eat in house, and food to take away for dinner or for the freezer. Her cooking swerves towards a natural sweetness – crumbed cod with chive champ and oven-roasted tomatoes; daube of their own beef with leek champ; 6-hour belly pork with chorizo potato cake; bread and butter pudding – and menus show a vivid imagination: celeriac, dilisk and potato gratin with sole; leeks, nettles and Knockdrinna goat's cheese in cabbage rolls; nori and coconut broth with shellfish. The Lemon Tree is blossoming. (Joan Power, Dunmore East ☎ 051-383164 lemontreecatering@eircom.net www.lemontreecatering.ie – Open 9am-8pm Mon-Thur, 9am-9.30pm Fri & Sat, 10am-4pm Sun)

Waterford

Bar

The Spinnaker Bar

Niall Edmondson's superbly run village bar offers dependable and impressive bar food in an authentic setting in the beautiful village of Dunmore East. Fish and chips is super fresh hake with crispy batter, some good chips and mushy peas, a seafood pie is bursting with fish, lamb burger on a Waterford blaa with Ballymaloe relish is a nice twist. There is a strong emphasis on local sourcing and a good selection of desserts to keep the family very happy after a day on the beach. (Niall & Maria Edmondson, Dunmore East ☎ 051-383133 info@thespinnakerbar.com www.thespinnakerbar.com – Open pub hours, food served May-Sept)

Fenor

Restaurant

The Copper Hen

Eugene Long's solid, creative hand at the stove ensures a satisfying evening at The Copper Hen, in Fenor, just outside Tramore. Mr Long presents dishes that are his versions of classic combinations - sirloin of beef with shoestring potatoes and garlic butter; confit duck with red cabbage and marsala - and the execution is classic too, with everything hitting just the right note as flavours synchronise, textures complement and tastes bring delight. The room is pleasant, service is friendly and you only have to go downstairs to Mother McHugh's pub for after dinner drinks. (Eugene Long & Sinead Frisby, Above Mother McHugh's Pub, Fenor ☎ 051-30300 ✉ thecopperhen@gmail.com 🖱 www.thecopperhen.ie – Open 5.30pm-10pm Thu-Sat, 12.30pm-4.30pm Sun)

local knowledge

WWW

WWW equals West Waterford Weekend, an association of The Cliff House, The Tannery and O'Brien's Chop House. Three great addresses to eat and stay over a weekend.

Waterford

Ferrybank

Boutique Hotel

● Athenaeum Hotel

The Athenaeum is a stylish boutique hotel, but whilst the mode is modern, the service is old school – friendly, correct, helpful, informed. (Stan & Mailo Power, Christendom, Waterford ☎ 051-833999 ✉ info@athenaeumhousehotel.com 🖱 www.athenaeumhousehotel.com)

Kilmacthomas

Porridge & Oat Products

● Flahavan's

John Flahavan and his family run one of the best Irish food companies. You might think there is little that one can do with oats other than to make porridge, but Flahavan's don't let that sort of thinking hold them back. They are continually spinning new and smart and innovative ideas into the market, and they think about oats the way the best dairy farms think about milk: as a magic substance that can be utilised in multiple forms. Don't dare to go camping without their portable porridge pots, don't try to go for a hike without one of their oat bars, and don't try to start the day without a bowl of Flahavan's to rev up your engine. A model Irish food company. (John Flahavan, Kilnagrange Mills, Kilmacthomas ☎ 051-294107 ✉ oatmail@flahavans.com 🖱 www.flahavans.com)

Knockanore

Farmhouse Ice Cream

Baldwin's Ice Cream

Farm-fresh milk from his own herd is Thomas Baldwin's ice cream secret, and the canvas of great Waterford milk is the basis for really superb ice creams. Thomas then adds a palette of flavours – honeycomb; vanilla; strawberry and so on – that make for really satisfying eating. Mr Baldwin is a purist at heart, so the classic ices really deliver the promise of rich milk and cream blended into icy deliciousness. Find the ices in good shops, and look out for Mr Baldwin's ice cream cart at festivals and shows. (Thomas Baldwin, Kileenagh ☎ 086-322 0932 thomas@baldwinsicecream.com www.baldwineicecream.com)

Waterford

Farmhouse Cheese

Knockanore Cheese

Eamon Lonergan has a quarter century of cheesemaking in his portfolio, and a pedigree herd of Friesian cows whose milk makes the Knockanore cheeses. The Knockanore cheeses are cheddar in style, aged for at least six months, and over time the range has expanded to include an oakwood smoked cheese, and cheeses flavoured with pepper and chives, garlic and chives and garlic and herbs, and there is also a crushed chilli cheese which is a Gold medal winner. (Eamonn Lonergan, Ballyneety, Knockanore ☎ 024-97275 www.knockanorecheese.com)

Lismòre

Butcher

Michael McGrath

McGrath's is one of the great Irish butchers, and one of the great Irish butchers shops. The shop is a little miracle of time preserved – it could be 1938 in here, it could be 1960, it might even be 2013 – and it is a treat just to walk into the store and see tradition proudly preserved. We love the fact that there is actually very little meat on display. So, you ask for what you would like, or for what they recommend, and they fetch it and prepare it for you. That's service. (Michael McGrath, Main Street, Lismore ☎ 058-54350 – Open 7am-6pm Mon-Sat)

Restaurant

O'Brien Chop House

"Robust" It's such a good, chewy word, isn't it? Justin Green, a man who knows a bon mot when he finds one, describes the Chop House food as "Traditional robust Irish food. Sourced locally, served simply". That's what they do in the Chop House, where that gifted young cook, Robbie Krawczyk, has charge of the kitchens – Kilmore Quay scallops with Caherbeg black pudding; saddleback pork chop with sage and garlic butter; McGrath's hangar steak with baked bone marrow; blackberry and autumn raspberry mess; lemon posset with ginger shortbread. Our last dinner was one of the brightest eating highlights of the year, and yet one senses that for the Chop House crew, this gig is only starting, and that something special, unique and wild lies ahead. (Justin & Jenny Green, Main Street, Lismore ☎ 058-53810 info@obrienchophouse.ie www.obrienchophouse.ie – Open 12.30pm-9.30pm Mon-Sat, open from 11.30am Sun)

Waterford

Home Store, Café & Bakery

The Summerhouse

Head to the rere of the pretty Summerhouse store, past all the covetable lifestyle wannahaves, and you will find a cosy, tidy café where Gael and Owen make some totally delicious things to eat. The baking draws in folk for coffee and teas and good tarts and cakes, but don't overlook the careful preparation of lunchtime specials like local sausages with mash, or chicken stroganoff. The care that blesses the cooking is immediately evident, and there is a precise, much-loved aesthetic in every element of the Summerhouse. (Gael & Owen Byrne, Main Street, Lismore ☎ 058-54148 info@thesummerhouse.ie www.thesummerhouse.ie – Cafe open 10am-5.30pm Tue-Sat)

Lemybrien

Mountain Lamb

Comeragh Mountain Lamb

William Drohan's terrific mountain lamb is principally supplied straight to chefs and restaurants, but you can buy a whole or a half lamb, prepared, via their site, and the meat is for sale at Ardkeen Stores. The meat has won some serious food prizes, and the flavours are beautifully sweet and herbaceous. (William Drohan & Aidan Dunwoody, Lemybrien ☎ 086-858 3605 www.comeraghmountainlamb.ie)

Portlaw

Farmhouse Cheese

● Triskel Farmhouse Cheeses

Waterford

Anna Leveque's Triskel cheeses are nuanced, delicate and subtle, and that subtlety reflects the classic Gallic-style forms of the cheeses morphed with Irish milk, and filtered through Ms Leveque's own signature style of cheesemaking. Anna works with raw goat's milk and cow's milk, not just because of the flavour profile, but because she believes it is both more natural, and safer. She has made a mighty reputation for her Triskel cheeses in double-quick time, and the story has only begun on a talented, distinctive cheesemaker. (Anna Leveque, Killowen Orchard, Portlaw ☎ 086-074 4534 triskelcheese@hotmail.com)

Tramore

Cake Shop

● Cáca Milis

Alison does some nice baking here in the simple, informal Cáca Milis, whether you are hunting down a vanilla slice with a cup of coffee or a wedding cake for your nuptials. (Alison Hutchinson, The Cross, Tramore ☎ 051-390936 www.caca-milis.ie – Open 9.30am-4.30pm Mon-Wed, 9.30am-5pm Thur-Sat, 11.30am-2.30pm Sun)

Health Bars

● Chia Bia

Chia is an ancient seed that is packed with Omega-3, anti-oxidants, fibre and protein, and has been used by indigenous South American tribes for thousands of years. Chia Bia sell the seed – salvia hispanica – in both whole form and milled: you will find it widely available, and can order online. (Barrie Rogers & Ray Owens, Tramore ☎ 051-393685 info@chiabia.com www.chiabia.com)

Fish and Chips

Dooley's Fish and Chips

With two locations in Tramore and one in Waterford City, the Dooley family claim 'The best fish and chips in the South East', which is confident talk, and backed up by the fact that they featured in *The Irish Times* readers' poll of the best chippers in the country. The fish, from local supplier M.J. Flanagan, is super fresh, the batter is dry and crispy and the chips leave you scraping the end of the box for those little crunchy bits. And whatever you order, get them to throw in a couple of those mini battered sausages with that tempura-like batter: you'll have scoffed them before you even make it to the car! (Dooley family, Main Street, Tramore ☎ 051-381529. Also at Strand Road (☎ 051-381012) and Park Road, Waterford (☎ 051-390100) contactus@doolys.ie www.doolys.ie – Open noon-10pm Mon-Sun)

Restaurant

The Market Street Restaurant

When Michael Mee makes a chicken liver pâté, he makes sure that the chicken livers are from Mary Walsh's superb free-range fowl. And if he wraps a chicken breast in bacon and serves it with a wholegrain mustard cream, then it is Mrs Walsh's chicken once again. That's the sort of perspicacious cook he is, and his classic touch brings home timeless food – Atlantic salmon with white wine cream; rump of Comeragh lamb with red wine; black sole with lemon and parsley butter. How lovely to see a cook so proud to use good cream and butter in his sauces, and with the confidence to cook in such a classical style. (Michael Mee, 2 Market Street, Tramore ☎ 051-338495 info@themarketst.com www.themarketst.com – Open 5pm-10pm Wed-Thur, 12.30pm-3.30pm, 5pm-10pm Fri-Sun

Waterford

Shop

Ardkeen Stores

The Jephson family's super supermarket is one of the treasures of the county and the country. Last time we shopped here, virtually everything we bought came from the counties of Waterford and Cork, with just a little bit of our money going further north, thanks to a superb

Sheridan's duck confit, which was produced in Cavan. Few food miles, superlative Irish produce, and a magical experience, thanks to brilliant staff. It seems ridiculous, but everything sold here is good. In particular, look out for the foods of the season, like Mairead Halley's fantastic fruits - her greengages are amazing - or the San Marzano tomatoes which Currids of Grantstown grow exclusively for Ardkeen. Irish apples arrive in from O'Dwyers of Piltown, and there is a great array of vegetables from Tom Cleary of Wellingtonbridge, a grower also highly praised by Michael Quinn of Waterford Castle. In a perfect food retailing world, every supermarket would be like Ardkeen. (Kevin Jephson, Ardkeen Shopping Centre, Dunmore Road, Waterford City ☎ 051-874620 ✉ QualityFood@ardkeen.com 🖱 www.ardkeen.com – Open 8am-9pm Mon-Sat, 9am-6pm Sun & hols)

Waterford

Producers' Market

● Ardkeen Producers' Market

The brilliant Ardkeen Stores can do the magic both inside – their store is incomparable – and outside, when they host their fortnightly farmers' market. South east stars like Indulge Bakery, Pine Grove farm, Boho Kitchen, Crough Farm venison and Merrigan Farm potatoes amongst others join a colourful bunch of artists and artisans. (Seamus Doyle ✉ market@ardkeen.com 🖱 www.ardkeen.com – Open 10am-2pm on the second and fourth Sun of every month)

Restaurant

● L'Atmosphere

Saturday night, and the atmosphere in L'Atmosphere is electric, with the punters squeezed in sardine-style – it's so tight in here, says Eamon Barrett, that you almost need a shoe horn to get people in and out of their tables at weekends – but no one cares because it's Saturday night and Arnaud is cooking, and you are going to have a hectic, happy time. Arnaud Mary's food is big and gutsy – 6-hour leg of lamb; cote de boeuf; cassoulet of duck confit and Toulouse sausage; tartiflette Savoyarde; chocolate meringue soufflé with chocolate sauce – and what he doesn't know about extracting flavour from every bit of every beast he prepares and cooks isn't worth knowing. "Authentic" is the term they stress that they are seeking to achieve with the food, the ambience, the room, the service, the value, and they get there with gas in the tank. (Arnaud Mary & Patrice Garreau, 19 Henrietta Street, Waterford ☎ 051-858426 restaurant.latmosphere@gmail.com www.restaurant-latmosphere.com – Open 12.30pm-2.30pm Mon-Fri, 5.30pm-late Mon-Sun)

Deli & Coffee Shop

Berfranks

Frank and Bernadette's café and deli is one of those places that has a hearth feel to it: it draws you towards it, it draws you in, just as you are drawn to the warmth of the fire in the hearth. You want to sit there of a morning with Java Republic coffee and a bowl of Flahavan's porridge. You want to meet a mate to share gossip and a toasted special. You want to have a quiet moment with a glass of white and some delicious Dunhill paté. Berfranks delivers all these hearth moments, and Bernadette and Frank do it with smiling grace, with winning nonchalance. (Frank & Bernadette Treyvaud, 82 The Quay, Waterford ☎ 086-844 6460/087-985 6791 befranks@gmail.com www.befranks.ie)

Waterford

made in Waterford

Dungarvan Stout

Restaurant

Bodega!

Bodega! is great. All of it. The style. The cooking. The service. The wines. The craic. The sense of fun. The lack of pretension. The good times. It's a maverick place run by two maverick brothers, Cormac and Donagh Cronin, who have steered it stealthily now for more than a decade, and the brothers are great restaurateurs, people who know how to source their foods – Waterford blaa from M&D Bakery, Triskel goat's cheese, Crowe farm pork – people who know how to write menus and wine lists, people who understand how to fill a room with the promise of good times, and how to deliver that night after night. Chef Shannon Ni Neill is knocking out some fantastic cooking, and Bodega really is a star. (Donagh & Cormac Cronin, 54 John Street, Waterford ☎ 051-844177 info@bodegawaterford.com www.bodegawaterford.com – Open noon-5pm Mon-Fri, 5.30pm-10pm Mon-Wed, 5.30pm-10.30pm Thu-Sat)

Restaurant

La Boheme

Eric Theze's cooking has been getting better and better in La Boheme. "A recent meal was outstanding", writes Eamon Barrett, "the highlight being a beautiful piece of sea bass cooked very simply with a beurre blanc, a truly glorious piece of fish". But then, virtually every other dish matched this triumph: Dunhill venison sliced sliver thin served with whipped goat's cheese is a beautifully adroit starter, Fenor Farm pork belly with Puy lentils and pear is gutsy and fine, a chocolate fondant for pudding is executed to perfection. M. Theze is letting his food be more natural and in doing so, is succeeding much, much more. His fish cookery, in particular, is frequently sublime, especially their signature lobster dish, with the lobster claw served as a salad, which is unbeatable. The whole experience is helped by the glamour of the room, which is the basement of the Chamber of Commerce building on Georges Street, and fine service seals the deal. (Christine & Eric Theze, 2 George's Street, Waterford ☎ 051-875645 ✉ labohemerestaurant@eircom.net 🖱 www.labohemerestaurant.ie – Open 5.30pm-late Tue-Sat)

Bar and Whiskey Blender

Downe's Bar

Don't miss Downe's own blend of whiskey, No.9, when you drop into this 250-year-old pub for a dram. (8-10 Thomas Street, Waterford ☎ 051-874 118)

Restaurant

Espresso

Espresso is the place for pastas and pizzas, and part of the Cavaliere family trio of Waterford restaurants. (Adriano Cavaliere, Parnell Street, Waterford ☎ 051-874141 ✉ info@espresso.ie 🖱 www.espresso.ie – Open 12.30pm-2.30pm, 5pm-late Mon-Sat, 1pm-9pm Sun)

Wholefood Shop

Full of Beans

FoB are excellent wholefood shops, with all the requisites for heathful cooking and baking. (Frances & Barry Coffey, Georges Court, Waterford City Centre, ☎ 051-843653 – Open 9.30am-5.30pm Mon-Sat. Also Full of Beans 2, Ardkeen Shopping Centre, ☎ 051-844644 ✉ fullofbeanswaterford@gmail.com)

Café Bar

Geoff's Café Bar

Geoff's is Waterford's best and coolest bar, eschewing trends by offering surroundings that make nobody feel under- or over- dressed, playing music that's always ahead of the curve and serving food that is simple and satisfying. Deep-fried calamari, fresh crab, good pasta dishes and humungous burgers – no wonder it's always busy. (9 John Street, Waterford ☎ 051-874 787 – Open noon-9pm Mon-Sat, 1pm-7pm Sun)

Sushi

Glorious Sushi

Tatyana's sushi is very fine indeed, and it is as good to look at as to eat. The pretty boxes include Rainbow Mix, California Roll, and a range of assorted boxes which show her panorama of ingredients – eel; prawns; tofu; pickled vegetables; grilled peppers; smoked salmon; sea vegetables, umeboshi plums. There is no better, more energising lunch than a tray of sushi, so seek them out in local stores, including Ardkeen. (Tetyana Zhemerdyey, Unit 5B, Six Cross Road Business Park, Waterford ☎ 087-2975156 info@glorioussushi.com www.glorioussushi.com)

Café

Granary @ Waterford Treasures Museum

With Waterford's fantastic Museum of Treasures having moved home to the newly renovated Bishop's Palace on the Mall, Peter Fowler's operation has grown to take over the entire ground floor of the Granary building in Waterford City. Which is just as well since the queues at lunchtime were getting a bit long! This is exactly the kind of food you hope to find in every town but rarely do - a couple of daily hot specials augmented by some really good savouries, salads, soups and a mouth-watering selection of desserts. The coffee is excellent, the staff know your name and it's no wonder that those queues continue. (Peter Fowler, Waterford Museum of Treasures, Hanover Street, Waterford ☎ 051-854428 – Open 8am-5pm Mon-Sat)

Bakery

Hickey's Bakery

Hickey's are esteemed producers of the wonderful Waterford blaa, the most singular regional bread in Ireland,

and their sterling work in continuing the tradition deservedly won them a Eurotoques award. (Brian Hickey, 59 Barrack St, Waterford 051-375388)

Shop

Jay Bees

The traditional bakery at this little service station is home to some of the best baking you will find in Waterford. The Amish Mennonite community who provide the baking – in addition to some lovely, practical wooden garden furniture from the adjacent Ideal Woodcrafts – make superb carrot cake, tarts, scones, cinnamon rolls and more. At Christmas, don't miss the mince pies. The commununity also sell at the Waterford Saturday market at Broad Street and John Roberts Square. (Campus Station, Ballinakina, Woodstown ☎ 051-382305 – Open 8am-7pm Mon-Fri, 8.30am-7pm Sat)

Butcher

Tom Kearney's Family Butchers

The Kearney family's traditional butcher's shop is the place for meat lovers. The quality and consistency of the meat from their own farm is peerless, and everything else they sell matches that quality. (Tom Kearney, 37a John Street, Waterford ☎ 051-874434 tkearney@gmail.com – Open 8.30am-6pm Mon-Sat)

Craft Beer

Metalman Brewing

Grainne Walsh has an IT background, and when she worked at Amazon she liked the way they would work out different approaches, how the managers would take responsibility. "You learn how to do", she says. Do what? Everything. She describes herself as a tweaker, that old Steve Jobs thing – keep at it, keep at it, keep at it. Having travelled and worked abroad, she was dismayed by the lack of good beer in Ireland, so she decided to do something about it with her partner, Tim: they would create some brews – Metalman Pale Ale; Windjammer; Alternator – then they would build a brewery, Metalman Brewery. As you do. She's going to be a star, we know it. Taste those Metalman brews, and you will know it too. (Grainne Walshe & Tim Barber, 14 Tycor Business Centre, Tycor, Waterford ☎ 087-250 9638 info@metalmanbrewing.com www.metalmanbrewing.com)

Butcher & Catering

● Jack Molloy & Son

The Molloy name is synonymous with meat in Waterford city, and the family have been trading for more than seventy years. In addition to a popular catering service Molloys produce pre-cooked bacon ribs, which you will find sold at the shop and through selected supermarkets. (Jack Molloy, 60 Barrack Street, Waterford ☎ 051-35552 ✉ jack@jackmolloy.com 🖱 www.jackmolloy.com 🖱 www.molloyribs.com)

Craft Butcher & Good Food Deli

● Billy Murphy

It's not unheard of for many people in Waterford to travel across the city to the suburb of Lisduggan to visit Billy Murphy Butchers. The shop is sparkling clean and bright, there are awards everywhere and a great team of trained butchers are on hand to advise and counsel and sell you something delicious for dinner. (Billy Murphy, Waterford Shopping Centre, Waterford ☎ 051-376061 ✉ contact@billymurphy.ie 🖱 www.billymurphy.ie – Open 8am-6pm Mon-Thur & Sat, 8am-8pm Fri)

Bakery

● M&D Bakery

M and D are Michael and Dermot, and in addition to their legendary Waterford blaa, the Walsh brothers produce an excellent array of breads which you will find in good local shops and supermarkets. (Michael & Dermot Walsh, 34 Mount Sion Avenue, Waterford ☎ 051-378080 ✉ mdbakery@eircom.net)

Butcher

● O'Flynn's Butcher's

The queue reaches out the door at weekend mornings at O'Flynn's, as meat-loving Waterfordians line up to buy beef from the family's own farm. (Bernard O'Flynn, 17 Georges Street ☎ 051-874409 – Open 8.30am-6pm Tue-Thu, 8am-7pm Fri, 8am-4.40pm Sat)

Restaurant

● La Palma on the Mall

Where Espresso is the punky sister, and Azzurro the cosmopolitan brother, of the Cavaliere family's trio of restaurants, La Palma is more the paternal uncle of the trio. The setting is formal, but unpretentious, the food mixes Italian staples with Irish favourites. (Dario Cavaliere, 20 The Mall, Waterford. ☎ 051-879823 info@lapalma.ie www.lapalma.ie – Open 5.30pm-10.30pm Mon-Sat)

Café

The Park Lodge Café

The beautiful Park Lodge Café at the entrance to The People's Park in Waterford City is a fantastic spot for that Sunday morning coffee and a lazy time mulling over the papers. There's a great array of savouries and sweet things and the café is always buzzing with families just in from the playground or joggers just in from a run around the park. (People's Park, Waterford ☎ 051-874874)

Thai Restaurant

Sabai

Catherine and Seamus Heffernan are locals who came back to the city and ran Tuk Tuk Thai before opening in the beautiful Derrynane House. The kitchen, under the direction of Em-Orn, mixes Thai and Vietnamese classics and, if you are still in your back-packing days and looking for chilli heat, they will spice it up for you. (Catherine & Seamus Heffernan, Derrynane House, 19 The Mall, Waterford ☎ 051-858002 info@sabai.ie www.sabai.ie – Open 12.30pm-2.30pm, 5.30pm-10pm Tue-Fri, 5.30pm-10pm Sat, 1pm-5pm, 5pm-9pm Sun)

Country House & Restaurant

Waterford Castle

The interesting thing about the cooking in Waterford Castle, says Eamon Barrett, is the alchemy created between Michael Quinn – classic chef, grounded in simplicity and good ingredients – and David Quinn, his deputy, who is pushing towards his own version of a Martin Kajuiter/Mickael Viljanen approach to cooking. Either one of these cooks on their own would be interesting, but the collaboration between their respective schools of cooking is where the magic happens, and the food here has never been better. Leslie Williams concurs, and notes that in the 'Castle "the attention to detail on the food for breakfast was also really good with everything from fish of the day to blueberry pancakes to local sausages". Waterford Castle is a powerhouse right now, so don't miss it. (Michael Quinn, The Island, Ballinakill, Waterford ☎ 051-878203 📫 info@waterfordcastle.com 🖱 www.waterfordcastle.com – Open 6.30pm-9pm Mon-Sun)

Café

● Waterford Crystal Visitors Centre

If crystal is your thing you should not miss a visit to the beautiful new Waterford Crystal Showroom and visitor centre, now located on the Mall in Waterford City. But even if cut glass isn't for you, the café is definitely a good stopping point. The display of cakes and sweet things is almost overwhelming – their red velvet cupcakes are delicious – and they make a brilliant hot chocolate. (House of Waterford Crystal, The Mall, Waterford City ☎ 051-317000 🖱 www.waterfordvisitorcentre.com)

Wine Shop

● World Wide Wines

It's a challenge to keep a fine wine and liquor store open during a recession, but Declan and Claire Brady's enthusiasm and love for their product makes them a true destination wine store. WWW is also a fantastic stockist of premium vodkas like Skyy, Kettle One, Grey Goose, keeps the top-flight gins like Tanqueray 10, Sipsmith and Hendricks and houses an envious collection of Scotch and Irish whiskey, along with an amazing collection of wines. Only brilliant. (Declan & Claire Brady, Cove Centre, Dunmore Road, Waterford ☎ 051-878798 🖱 worldwidewines@eircom.net – Open noon-10pm Mon-Fri, 11am-10pm Sat, 12.30pm-10pm Sun)

local knowledge

Oats

Oats are now recognised as an indigenous right-on product that is an absolute superfood. But this wasn't always so. Back in the 1700s when oats began to be milled at Kilmacthomas, they were a meal for the penitential and the poor. Barley and wheat and the much-loved potato were all considered superior. Oats were used to stave off dire need, feeding both humans and animals. The only culinary kudos for the oat was their use in the making of blood puddings.

County Westmeath

Athlone

Farmers' Market

Athlone Farmers' Market

A farmers' market, in Market Square. Now, that's just where it should be, and you should be there too. (Market Square, Athlone, Saturday 9am-2pm)

Restaurant

The Left Bank Bistro

There wasn't much happening in Athlone when Annie and Mary opened the Left Bank in 1995. But these two mighty women made things happen, with the brilliance of their cooking and the brilliance of their service and today, as they head towards two decades of delicious cooking and professional élan, their creative juices are undimmed, their enthusiasm as alive as ever. The cooking here has always been honest, delicious, and hip: hoi sin ribs with Asian slaw; veal schnitzel with Parmesan and sage crust; smoked black pudding with wholegrain mustard. Value, service, charm and culinary art all entangle here, in a magical piece of left bank theory and practice. (Annie McNamara & Mary McCullagh, Fry Place, Athlone ☎ 090-649 4446 info@leftbankbistro.com www.leftbankbistro.com – Open 10.30am-9.30pm. Lunch served noon-5pm, dinner served 5.30pm-close Tue-Sat)

Restaurant

The Olive Grove

Garry and Gael's Olive Grove has a fab riverside location, hard by the river, and for many years now this charming, unpretentious, good-times restaurant – they have some great gigs here – has been one of the key destinations in the town. The cooking is modern, international and fun: ham hock terrine with sauce gribiche; hake with saffron risotto cake; Gilligan farm burger with Beechlawn organic leaves. Great service, great vibe. (Garry Hughes & Gael Bradbury, Custume Pier, Athlone ☎ 090-647 6946 www.theolivegrove.ie – Open noon-4.30pm, 5.30pm-10pm Mon-Sat, noon-9pm Sun)

Westmeath

Restaurant

Thyme

If you need a masterclass in sourcing artisan ingredients, then John Coffey is your man: confit of Fergus Dunne's free-range Tamworth pork; Cured organic Clare Island salmon; carpaccio of Beechlawn organic beetroot; McCarthy's black pudding and smoked bacon potato cake; Castlemine Farm rib-eye steak; Friendly Farmer chicken rillette; fillet of Kilmore Quay cod; buttermik pannacotta with Beechlawn organic beetroot. Mr Coffey brings a studious and modest attitude to these stellar ingredients, and he has a way of putting just the right things on the plate, and no more – twice-baked goat's cheese soufflé with beetroot carpaccio; slow-braised pork belly with black pudding croquettes; pork confit with celeriac remoulade; chicken rillette with pickled vegetables. Thyme is an exciting kitchen, an exciting place. (John Coffey, Custume Place ☎ 090-647 8850 ✉ info@thymerestaurant.ie 🖱 www.thymerestaurant.ie)

Westmeath

Colinstown

Country House

Lough Bishop House

Lily. Patricia. Gwen. Hilda. Viola. Sweetheart. Go on, have a guess? Who are we talking about? We are talking about the Irish Moiled cows and heifers who you might meet at Helen and Christopher's idyllic Lough Bishop House. Along with Irish Draught horses, Helen and Chris breed Irish Moiled cattle and, along with Jersey and Kerry cows, they are surely the most beautiful things munching in a field near to you. That's the thing about the Kellys: everything they do has an aesthetic edge, so the cows aren't just gorgeous, they even have sweet, Edwardian-style names – a cow named Hilda! This is typical of Lough Bishop, a gorgeous place, and the ultimate Irish agri-tourismo. Lough Bishop is a true demonstration farm, for it demonstrates how farming can be a cultural and aesthetic practice, and how a farm can be an idyll, a place where time is brought back to agricultural time. There's nowhere like Lough Bishop, and the Kellys are outstanding ambassadors for Irish farming and Irish hospitality.(Helen & Christopher Kelly, Derrynagarra, Colinstown ☎ 044-966 1313 ✉ enquiries@loughbishophouse.com 🖱 www.loughbishophouse.com)

Glasson

Bar & Restaurant

● The Fatted Calf

"The Fatted Calf is brilliant, providing one of the best family meals we've had anywhere. It's an example of how things could be done. And that's not just in small villages... but also in big cities where so few good food places are so family-friendly". We are quoting Catherine Cleary's encomium from *The Irish Times* because it perfectly summarises Feargal and Fiona's achievement here in the Fatted Calf. This bar and restaurant gives you what you want, but it gives it to you better than you had hoped. Ms Cleary and her family had a perfect meal, after a long family car ride when a bad meal would have been an epic disaster. But the FC delivers, modestly, deliciously, always focused on the customer, always focused on the food – you would drive here just for the bar snacks – and you would walk here for the Skeaghanore duck with roast pineapple, or the dried beef and smoked beetroot salad or the buttermilk chicken with tarragon aioli. (Feargal & Fiona O'Donnell, Glasson ☎ 090-648 5208 ✉ feargal@thefattedcalf.ie 🖱 www.thefattedcalf.ie – Open 12.30pm-9pm Tue-Wed, 12.30pm-9.30pm Thu-Sat, 12.30pm-8.30pm Sun)

Westmeath

Bar & Restaurant

● Grogan's of Glasson

Grogan's is a popular and professional pub with tasty food on offer at lunch and dinner. (Miriam & Moira Grogan, Glasson ☎ 090-648 5158 ✉ grogansofglasson@hotmail.com 🖱 www.grogansofglasson.com – Open 9am-noon, noon-5pm, 5pm-9pm Mon-Sat, 9am-11.30pm, 12.30pm-3.30pm, 4.30pm-8pm Sun)

Restaurant with Rooms

● Wineport Lodge

Ray Byrne is one of the great hoteliers of his generation, and he is also one of the most creative, inventive and disciplined. We have followed his career in our books since long before Wineport was ever created, and he has always been the most perspicacious, forward-looking operator. In Wineport, he and Jane English marshal a superb team, and so everything in this glorious water side getaway is as good as it can be, as good as they can make it, not least the superb modern Irish cooking of chef Cathal Moran which is amongst the best cooking to be found in the Midlands. Mr Moran has a sure touch, no matter how international his canvas: rabbit and sweet potato tagine with baba ghanoush and flatbreads; pork belly with turnip and savoy cabbage; gratin of smoked trout thermidor; St Tola goat's cheese fondant with smoked almonds. Lovely cooking, and great service. (Ray Byrne & Jane English, Glasson, Athlone ☎ 090-643 9010 lodge@wineport.ie www.wineport.ie – Open 5.30pm-9.30pm Mon-Sat, 2pm-4.30pm, 5pm-9.30pm Sun)

Kilbeggan

Oats

● Kilbeggan Organic Oats

Ever since he launched his Kilbeggan organic oats, Pat Lalor has become quietly famous. His fame rests on a simple story about his oats that he tells very simply and, once you have heard it, you will never forget it. We won't spoil the story for you – Mr Lalor is bound to be coming your way some day soon – so we will just say that we are devotees of these sublime porridge oats. They are the simplest food but, thanks to Mr Lalor's philosophy and his culture, they amongst the most profound. We build our days with them: without the morning's bowl of Kilbeggan, we wouldn't know where to begin. A bright star in the artisan firmament. (Pat Lalor, Ballard Organic Farm, Kilbeggan ☎ 087-255 7679 www.kilbegganorganicfoods.com)

Mullingar

Organic Fruit and Vegetables

● Casey's Natural Produce

Mick Casey sells his organic produce at markets in Mullingar, Athlone and Collinstown, so his weekends are pretty much tied up. Mick also operates a box delivery system, and supplements the produce of the farm at Gaybrook with whatever imported produce he needs. So, sign up for that box scheme and get these good veggies into your life. (Michael Casey, Gaybrook, Mullingar ☎ 087-226 0841 info@caseysnaturalproduce.ie www.caseysnaturalproduce.ie)

Café

Gallery 29

The Gray sisters offer nice, true cooking three days of the week in their pretty café. (Ann & Emily Gray, 29 Oliver Plunkett Street, Mullingar ☎ 044-934 9449 – Open 9am-5.30pm Thurs-Sat)

Bakery

Lilliput Loaf Company

Louis Peppard's baking works two ways: he bakes traditional Irish breads – boxty; griddle potato farls; soda breads – in addition to baking artisan breads from Europe. Louis and his team set up their fireplace, with traditional implements, and bake their breads at markets and festivals, and it is a mighty sight to see their set up. Quite brilliant. (Louis Peppard, Unit 2, Mullingar Enterprise Technology & Innovation Centre, Mullingar ☎ 087-251 9439 lilliputloaf@gmail.com)

Westmeath

Organic Farm and Allotments

Lough Owel Organic Farm

Joe Brady is yet another of those dynamic farmers who have taken their destiny into their own hands, taken control of the family farm, and opened up farm shops, farmers' market stalls, delivery services, allotments, farm open days, demonstrations and speciality animal breeding. So, look out for Joe's silver and green Citroen van, visit the shop, meet the man at the markets and get yourself a good organic Westmeath Angus beef burger. (Joe Brady, Tullaghan, Mullingar ☎ 044-934 1649 joebrady.farm@yahoo.ie owelorganic.wordpress.com)

Farmers' Market

Mullingar Farmers' Market

Sunday morning beside Penney's is the place to be for all the good Midlands' produce. (The Fairgreen car park, Mullingar 10.30am-2pm, Sun)

Restaurant & Takeaway

Oscar's

Busy, boisterous and bustling is the modus operandi of Oscar's. It's professional, it's fun, they have a big take-away food business as well as the restaurant side and the cooking is tasty all the way: excellent steaks; good chick en wings; duck confit; hot, tasty pizzas; nice bruschetta; baby back ribs; chicken noodle salad. (Noel Kennedy & Tony Maloney, 21 Oliver Plunkett Street, Mullingar ☎ 044-934 4909 – Open 6pm-9.30pm Mon-Wed, 6pm-10pm Thu & Sat, 12.30pm-2.15pm, 6pm-8.15pm Sun)

Butcher

C. R. Tormey & Sons

The Tormey family opened our eyes to the magnificence of Irish beef. It was many years ago now when we first met James Tormey and his dad, at Crookedwood House, near to Mullingar, and listened, gobsmacked, as father and son explained just how they achieved the standards of beef production that characterised the family's three butcher's shops. It was inspiring stuff, and even more inspiring to see the skills and knowledge that make for great butchering being passed from generation to generation. Those skills, and that experience, are evident in every piece of meat one buys from the family's three shops. Of course, being experts, they don't shout about their expertise: they just quietly look after customers who admire them and respect them and trust them. So, go to Tormey's, and get your eyes opened.(James Tormey, Harbour Place, Mullingar ☎ 044-934 5433 www.crtormeys.ie – Open 8am-6pm Mon-Sat, 'till 8pm on Thur & Fri)

made in Westmeath

Kilbeggan Organic Oats

Wine Importer

Wines Direct

A lot of the people who feature in this guide established their businesses in the early 1990's, and now have fully two decades of experience, expertise and – if you are Paddy Keogh and his team at Wines Direct – you still have the enthusiasm of an ingénue, despite twenty years at the wine press. But, there is nothing artless or innocent about Wines Direct: these guys are professionals to their fingertips and, for the consumer, the organisation works like clockwork: brilliant list; brilliant offers; brilliant innovations; brilliant service and delivery. Mr Keogh's newest idea, the Wine Explorers Club, is one of his best: a monthly delivery of new discoveries culled from around the globe, pitched at different price levels. This is the equivalent of being out there in the vineyards with Paddy and his producers, picking up the marl, feeling the breezes, watching the arc of the sun on the aspect of the vineyard, tasting from the barrique, feeling the culture of the vine. Fantastic. (Paddy Keogh, 49 Lough Sheever Corporate Park, Mullingar ☎ 1890-579 579/044-934 0634 sales@winesdirect.ie www.winesdirect.ie)

Multyfarnham

Bar, Restaurant & Accommodation

● Weir's Bar & Restaurant

"Weir's Bar & Restaurant: Get There Early". That's what it should say on Pat and Una's website, especially for Sunday lunch when this smart gastro-pub will be heaving with locals culled from miles around to enjoy good, rock-steady cooking – potato skins and bacon; chicken with roast potato, gravy and stuffing; Silverhill duck with orange sauce. The really clever thing about Weir's is the judgement shown in the creation of the menus and the execution of the cooking: they know what they can do best, and they don't try to do anything else. And they look after everyone, so the kid's food is smart too. So, the signature fisherman's platter, the Angus sirloin steak, and a couple of bottles of Howling Gale Ale, and all is well. (Una & Pat Weir, Multyfarnham, Mullingar ☎ 044-937 1111 weirs@eircom.net www.weirsmultyfarnham.ie – Open 12.30pm-8.30pm Wed-Sat, 12.30pm-6pm Sun)

Westmeath

Rathowen

Fish Smoker

● Corrylane Smoked Foods

John Rogan is a splendid, inquisitive, experimental fish smoker, who has in recent years branched out and started smoking bacon and sausages, in addition to mackerel, salmon and trout. Look out for the products locally and and at farmer's markets, and enjoy their somewhat feral, somewhat wild smoky flavours. (John Rogan, Corry Lane, Rathowen ☎ 043-667 6264 corrylanesmoked@eircom.net)

County Wexford

Arthurstown

Country House & Restaurant

● Dunbrody Country House

Kevin Dundon is one of the best-known chefs in Ireland, but his fame rests on his professional and astute cooking in the lovely Dunbrody House, more than just TV appearances and endorsements. Eamon Barrett described Mr Dundon's cooking as "perfectly pitched", and so it is, a fine, modern Irish cuisine. (Kevin & Catherine Dundon, Arthurstown ☎ 051-389600 info@dunbrodyhouse.com www.dunbrodyhouse.com)

Bridgestown

Apple Juice & Farm Shop

● Ballycross Apple Farm

Ballycross is a brilliant example of how a farm can become a multi-platform destination. You can visit the von Engelbrechtens to buy their apples, their pumpkins and their splendid apple and vegetable juices. You can come for an ice cream, or to enjoy some waffles. You can walk on farm trails and meet their animals. You can buy a gift in the farm shop, and turn up when Santa pays a visit. It's quite brilliant, and terrific fun. And the juices, pressed by the traditional rack and cloth method, are first class. (The von Engelbrechten family, Bridgestown ☎ 053-913 5160 info@ballycross.com www.ballycross.com – Farmshop open Aug-Feb, 2pm-6pm Sat & Sun)

Broadway

Prepared Foods

● Zanna Cookhouse

"Lovely Food for Lovely People". Ah, boy, wish we had thought of that slogan first to describe Owen and Lorna's excellent Zanna. But these guys are the sort of people who come up with the smart ideas all on their own, and since they started baking in 2007 they have been unstoppable, expanding from their kitchen into a working complex, expanding from farmers' markets into retail, expanding their range from savoury to sweet baking and soup making, and grabbing Bord Bia entrepreneur prizes along the way. Sourcing from other south-east artisans means the Zanna foods taste true and real: these guys have their feet in the earth, even though their success has been nothing but stellar. (Owen, Lorna & David Mullins, St Iberius, Broadway ☎ 053-913 1714 owen@zannacookhouse.ie www.zannacookhouse.ie)

Bunclody

Home Bakery

● Sugar and Spice

Mary's home bakery is the kind of specialist, domestic-style bakery that used to be a fixture of every town in Ireland, but which have largely disappeared. Happily, Sugar & Spice is still with us, vibrant as ever, a vital part of the town, providing a modest, polite, assured service for its customers from breakfast 'til lunchtime, for afternoon tea and morning coffee, with special cakes and bakes to take away and make your life better. Happy, maternal service makes Sugar & Spice a wee treasure. (Pat & Mary O'Neill, Main Street, Bunclody ☎ 053-937 6388 sugar_spice@eircom.net – Open 8am-6pm Mon-Fri, 8am-5pm Sat)

Wexford

Carne

Seafood Bar

● The Lobster Pot Seafood Bar

The Hearne family's bar and restaurant is one of the best-known destinations in the South-East. But it's not just a tourist staple, because the cooking is consistent and unpretentious, fresh and flavourful, and the rooms are terrifically atmospheric: there is nothing quite like a late-afternoon drink in these little tabernacles of delight. (Ciaran & Anne Hearne, Carne ☎ 053-913 1110 – Bar open noon-8.45pm Mon-Sun. À la Carte Restaurant menu 6pm-9pm Tue-Sat & 12.30pm-8.30pm Sun. In winter closes 7.30pm on Sun)

Duncannon

Restaurant and Accommodation

Aldridge Lodge

Billy and Joanne made the news in the spring of 2012, when they announced the surprise birth of a daughter, Kaitlin, whom the couple had not been expecting. For the rest of the time, however, this couple attract media attention because of good cooking and the excellent value they offer, both for food and for accommodation. Aldridge is one of the best destinations in the South-East, and Mr Whitty's cooking is creatively based on his own produce and the produce of other members of his family. Mr Whitty, following the birth – on Friday 13th! – returned home to cook a full service, and the following Monday he won the Restaurant's Association award for best Wexford restaurant. Quite a weekend. (Billy Whitty & Joanne Harding, Duncannon ☎ 051-389116 info@aldridgelodge.com www.aldridgelodge.com – Open 7pm-9.30pm Wed-Sat, 1pm-7pm Sun)

Enniscorthy

Wexford

Country House

Ballinkeele House

Sky-high standards, and impeccable attention to detail, are the keynotes of John and Margaret Maher's fine country house, Ballinkeele. The Mahers are expert at making everything sync together - the food is local and agrestic in flavour, exactly the country house cooking you were hoping to enjoy as you drove to the house. The rooms are magnificently maintained, with just the right period detail, and the Mahers are splendid hosts. (John & Margaret Maher, Enniscorthy ☎ 053-913 8105 john@ballinkeele.ie www.ballinkeele.ie – Open Feb-end Oct)

Flour

Ballyminane Mills

A traditional water-powered mill, which uses French burr stones to grind the wheat from Ballyhamilton Farms to make Uncle Aidan's Flour, means Ballyminane is something of a treasure. Uncle Aidan's flour is very fine indeed, as slow grinding means the wheat germ remains intact, something that modern industrialised milling removes. There is also an operational saw mill. John Murphy stresses the authenticity of this method of working, both in the milling process, and in the resulting flavour and character of Uncle Aidan's flour. It's a beauty. (John Murphy, Ballindaggin, Enniscorthy ☎ 053-925 5162 info@uncleaidansflour.com www.ballyminanemills.com)

Farmhouse Cheese

● Carrigbyrne Farmhouse Cheese

Paddy and Juliet made their first cheeses as long ago now as March 1982, and their achievement in creating and maintaining the iconic St Killian is a mighty one, for they are pioneers as well as perfectionists. At its best – and it is a delicate little soul, so it needs a careful, practised minder – St Killian is one of the glories of Irish farmhouse cheesemaking: tensely lactic, beautifully balanced between salinity and creaminess, extraordinarily satisfying. They also produce the fine St Brendan brie and the Emerald Irish brie. When he isn't farming and making cheese, Mr Berridge is busy with a host of other experiments, from anaerobic digestion systems to green energy, to new cheese ideas. (Paddy & Juliet Berridge, Adamstown, Enniscorthy ☎ 053-924 0560 info@carrigbyrne.ie www.carrigbyrne.ie)

Wexford

Farmers' Market

● Enniscorthy Farmers' Market

The Wexford markets – Enniscorthy; Gorey; New Ross and Wexford – are truly excellent, both in the range of stalls and the professional management and orchestration of the markets. Bring the baskets to the sqaure in Enniscorthy on Saturday morning for all the good things from the good people. (Abbey Square, Enniscorthy www.wexfordfarmersmarkets.com – Open Saturday 9am-2pm)

Ice-Cream

● Featherbed Farm Foods

Brothers Paul and Simon have fused their farming and culinary backgrounds to create Featherbed ice creams, and they have fashioned a classic range – vanilla; strawberry; rocky road; chocolate and chocolate cookie; summer fruits; roasted banana. Look out for them in the farm shop and look out especially for their handsome ice cream cart at destinations such as Mount

Usher and other festivals. (Paul & Simon Cooper, Featherbed Lane, Oylegate, Enniscorthy ☎ 053-917 7581 ✉ info@featherbedfarm.ie 🖱 www.featherbedfarm.ie)

Yogurt

● Killowen Yogurts

Beautifully re-branded not so long ago, Nicholas Dunne's yogurts have been careful to stress that they are the product of one farm, and one family. This gives them not just integrity, but their brilliant, complex flavours. These are really lovely yogurts, slightly sharper in their lactic bite than other farm yogurts, and always brilliantly distinctive and hugely enjoyable. (Nicholas & Judith Dunne, The Beeches, Courtnacuddy, Enniscorthy ☎ 053-924 4819 ✉ killowenfoods@eircom.net 🖱 www.killowen.ie)

Hotel and Spa

● Monart

Monart got it right when it opened, and continues to get its alliance of relaxation and invigoration just right, whilst improving with age. 'Monart confounds your expectations, and therein lies its success', says Eamon Barrett. 'It's a glitzy, glamorous place, a modern extension added onto a lovely old building, with electric gates to enter - all of these things make you expect the worst of Celtic Tiger 'We have built it and therefore it will be brilliant' excess. In fact, nothing could be further from the truth. At its core are wonderful staff, who love hospitality to their fingertips - if you've been before they know what room you were in, they welcome you back, and they mean it. The architecture is wonderful, curved wings spanning out into the woods from the main building and as the grounds have matured the calmness that is inherent at Monart has just increased. Everything is kept spick and span and even if you are not the type of person who likes to spend a weekend in a robe you will still find much to enjoy at Monart.' (Liam Griffin, The Still, Enniscorthy ☎ 053-923 0999 🖱 www.monart.ie)

Ferns

Craft Bakery & Coffee Shop

● Nóirín's Bakehouse

NB: Nota Bene Nóirín's Bakehouse, for this is a classy bakery and bakehouse and café, the café located just off the Main Street in Gorey. The expertise right across the spectrum of their baking, from brown soda bread to Mars attacks to parsnip and sweet potato quiche, is truly impressive, and their consistency has seen them build a large network of outlets in addition to their own retailing at farmers' markets. (Nóirín & Vincent Kearney, Newtown, Ferns ☎ 053-936 7335 info@noirins.ie www.noirins.ie)

Dry Cure Bacon

● O'Neill Foods

Pat O'Neill has a background in the commercial bacon-curing trade, but he developed his own dry-cure recipe and set out his own stall a few years ago. His bacons and hams are delicious, with that lovely salty-sweet taste and firm texture. The awards have deservedly followed, and you will find the O'Neill bacons all down the east coast, including some of the leading Dublin stores, and Pat himself sells at the Wexford markets. (Pat O'Neill, Bolinadrum, Ferns ☎ 087-677 9803 oneillfoods@eircom.net www.oneillfoods.ie)

Gorey

Farmers' Market

● Gorey Farmers' Market

The Community School is the place to be to enjoy the produce from the wonderful community of growers and producers who sell in the Wexford markets. (Gorey Community School www.wexfordfarmersmarkets.com – Open 9am-2pm Sat)

Café & Delicatessen

● Partridge's

Christian Pauritsch hasn't stopped moving since he opened Partridge's back in 2007. What was once a small café and shop has effectively tripled in size, and the newest innovation has been the creation of their own bakery. There is so much going on here – shop; deli; bakery; café; gallery space – that you have to ask: what don't they do? And the answer is: if they don't do it today, chances are they will be doing it tomorrow. Truly dynamic, whether you just want to buy a bag of good tea or have a calm, relaxing weekend dinner of Wicklow lamb with garlic and rosemary mash. A real Wexford star. (Christian Pauritsch, 93 Main Street, Gorey ☎ 053-948 4040 ✉ info@partridges.ie 🖱 www.partridges.ie – Shop open 9am-5pm, Café open 9am-6pm)

Artisan Preserves

● Wild About

Fiona Falconer is a docoumentary producer turned foraging artisan, and she makes a range of products using wild and native ingredients. "We grow most of our own produce, what we don't grow ourselves we source from neighbouring farms, we very much believe in local economy, without it, the people have no power and the land has no voice" she writes, and indeed she writes very well. Her Facebook page is a blast. Using permaculture and picking seasonally, Fiona's preserves utilise wild berries and greens, and she has already won a number of awards. You can find her preserves at the Marlay Park Market and People's Park Markets in Dublin. (Fiona Falconer, Tus Nua, Gorey ☎ 086-812 2952 ✉ info@wildabout.ie 🖱 www.wildabout.ie)

local knowledge

White Pudding

White pudding in Ireland used to be associated with the killing and butchering of the pig. Then, surplus puddings were distributed amongst neighbouring farms, making this both a ritualistic and community-spirited food. A sociable food. A Festival is called for, we think.

Wexford

Kerlogue

Cookery School & Catering Service

● Phelim Byrne

Caterer, teacher, cookery writer, wedding caterer, buffet organiser, and restaurateur at Wexford Golf Club's Séasúir bistro, Phelim Byrne is one busy guy. His appetite for work is matched only by his ability to do a zillion and one things well, for this guy is a real pro, whether you want someone to cook for your daughter's confirmation, throw a wedding in your garden or learn how to cook Thai food. (Phelim Byrne, Wexford Enterprise Centre, Strandfield Business Park, Kerlogue, Rosslare Road, Wexford ☎ 053-918 4995 ✉ info@phelimbyrne.ie 🖱 www.phelimbyrne.ie)

Killinick

Farm Shop

● Karoo Farm Shop

Karoo is the food shop and tea room of your dreams. Chocka-mocka with good things, and with delicious things to eat both here and to take away, Karoo positively invites an orgy of spending in the shop, followed by a trip to the tea room for a bowl of chunky vegetable soup and then a steak pitta with mushrooms and melted brie. Mignon Fochessati has an aesthetic that blesses everything in this quixotic, choice destination: stop by and let it bless your little head. (Mignon Fochessati, Killinick ☎ 053-915 8585 ✉ info@karoo.ie – Open 9am-6pm Mon-Sat, 11am-5pm Sun)

made in Wexford

Stable Diet

Kilmore Quay

Wexford

Artisan Baker

● Hanna's Artisan Baking

"Spices are the soul of food", says Hanna-Mari, so her sweetbread pastry has a touch of cardamon, and she loves vanilla and cinnamon and all the good things that make her baking zesty and distinct. Her cakes are incredible creations – look at those mini-Christmas cakes! look at those chocolate whoopie pies!– and here is a baker who we are going to be hearing a lot about. (Hanna-Mari Bates, Sarshill, Kilmore ☎ 086-199 2740 ✉ hannasartisanbaking@gmail.com)

Restaurant

● The Silver Fox

Shane and Gopal have been cooking good food for over twenty years in Kilmore Quay, testament to their quality and consistency in a place where other restaurants come and go like ships in the night. Fish and shellfish should be your choice – Dublin Bay scampi; sole meuniere; herb-crusted cod – but there is also Slaney lamb, duck confit and sirloin. Set menus are excellent value. (Shane Carroll & Gopal Kawander, Kilmore Quay ☎ 053-912 9888 ✉ info@thesilverfox.ie 🖱 www.thesilverfox.ie – Open from 12.30pm Mon-Sun)

New Ross

Farmers' Market

New Ross Farmers' Market

Saturday morning at the Quay is home to one of Wexford's splendid, splendidly organised markets. (The Quay, New Ross www.wexfordfarmersmarkets.com – Open 9am-2pm Sat)

Café & Wholefood Shop

In A Nutshell and Café Nutshell

"They really make an effort" is what the professionals say about Patsy and Philip's Café Nutshell. The Nutshell is the cream of the New Ross crop: "Just plain brilliant" is what *The Irish Independent* said a few years back, and that holds true today as the Rogers hold true to their mantra of honest sourcing and honest cooking. Their lovely soups include to-die-for broccoli with cheese, they have a winning way with solid hitters like lamb stew and chicken curry, and the baking sets a benchmark for sandwiches and wraps that are imaginative, precisely finished, and for toothsome, comforting desserts that are just as delicious as everything else. The care and energy visited on the food in Café Nutshell gladdens the heart, and the determination to make food that is nourishing, wholesome and rooted is inspiring in both intention and execution. (Philip & Patsy Rogers, 18 South Street, New Ross ☎ 051-422777 inanutshell8@gmail.com – Cafe open 9am-5pm, Deli/shop open 9am-6pm Tue-Sat)

made in Wexford

Killowen Yogurts

Farm Produce

Tinnock Farm Produce

We would walk a country mile for John and Peggy's fresh country butter and fresh buttermilk, and load up with their beef, lamb and eggs whilst we are at it. Lovely produce from the farm, and available at the Wexford markets and in Dun Laoghaire on Sundays. (John Murphy & Peggy Gaffney, Tinnock, Campile, New Ross ☎ 087-417 0506/087-220 3300 tinnockfarm@live.ie)

Rosslare

Resort Hotel

●Kelly's Resort Hotel & Beaches Restaurant

'I am a host to everyone who stays', Bill Kelly told an interviewer a few years back. 'I like to talk to them, to greet them and welcome them. It's the way we've always done it.' Talk to them, greet them, welcome them. That's a trinity of imperatives ready to stand alongside Michael Pollan's great mantra about food: 'Eat food. Not too much. Mainly plants.' Like Pollan's aphoristic haiku, Bill Kelly's few words reveal exactly why and how Kelly's Hotel is the best hotel in Ireland, and the best-loved hotel in Ireland: people welcome you, they greet you, they talk to you. That's hospitality, that's hotel keeping, and Bill Kelly has no peers as an hotelier. His family-run hotel is one of the glories of modern Ireland, a destination with a unique aesthetic, a place where a talented team do their best, every day. The cooking, the art collection, the wines, the comfort, all take place within the context of an hotel where you are greeted, made welcome and chatted to. So simple, so profound, so perfect. (Bill Kelly, Rosslare ☎ 053-913 2114 ✉ info@kellys.ie 🖱 www.kellys.ie – Closed early Dec-late Feb)

Wexford

Restaurant

●Beaches Restaurant

Eugene Callaghan was always going to get to the top. Right from the day he won the Roux brothers' scholarship when working alongside Paul Rankin in Belfast's Roscoff restaurant, when that restaurant was at its zenith, Mr Callaghan's unique style was always going to get him the gig that suited him best.After La Marine, in Kelly's Hotel, he succeeded Jim Ahearne in Beaches, the hotel dining room. He has always had the gift of being able to make every dish he cooks seem definitive, authoritative, complete. He knows food, he knows cooking, and he knows it in a way that is different to any other Irish chef. His food is about food, in the way Maurice Ravel's music, for example, is about music: it is knowing, but so supremely controlled that you don't see the back-story. But his cooking ushers in the whole history of contemporary cooking. He guards the canon, he is keeper of the secrets. (Eugene Callaghan & Bill Kelly, Rosslare ☎ 053-913 2114 ✉ info@kellys.ie 🖱 www.kellys.ie)

Bistro

● La Marine

Ronan Dunne runs the kitchens in Kelly's fine La Marine bistro, and he has a sure hand with the savoury cooking that has made this one of the best destinations in the South East: black pudding and apple tarte tatin; seafood and saffron chowder; veal liver with champ; chicken with ceps and mushrooms; cinnamon gateau. The room is lovely and boisterous and youthful, and it's always holiday time in La Marine. (Eugene Callaghan & Bill Kelly, Rosslare ☎ 053-913 2114 ✉ info@kellys.ie 🖱 www.kellys.ie – Open 12.30pm-2.15pm, Snack Menu 12.30pm-5pm, 6.30pm-9pm Mon-Sun. Closed early Dec-late Feb)

Saltmills

Fishmonger

● Suzie & Patrick Whelan

Look for the sign saying "Fresh Fish" between Arthurstown and Wexford, then stop to buy some of the freshest fish you have ever enjoyed from Suzie and Patrick's van. Smashing fish and shellfish, lovely fishcakes, and if you aren't driving the R733, look out for the van at Ferrybank, Tramore and Kildare. (Suzie & Patrick Whelan, Curraghmore, Saltmills ☎ 051-562158 – Open 9am-5.30pm Thur-Fri)

Wexford

Restaurant

● La Dolce Vita

When Eamon Barrett writes that 'I think La Dolce Vita is singular, a unique and authentic Italian experience', then you know that Roberto Pons and his team are truly doing the good thing. In fact, they have been doing the good thing since opening in 2003 after moving south from Dublin, where they had run a great and authentic Italian restaurant, Il Ristorante, in Dalkey in the early 1990's, and where Mr Pons showed his devotion to the food of his birthplace, Liguria. That devotion is alive and well today, and has fashioned the most devoted clientele imaginable, so that only two issues need concern you when it comes to LDV: how long will you have to wait to get a table? And, would it seem rude to order everything on the menu? Believe us, you will want to try the rose veal liver with onions – one of the signature dishes of Il Ristorante – and the sausages with lentils, the lamb chops with roasted garlic, the superlative pasta dishes, the perfect risottos, the beautiful desserts. Ah, la dolce vita! (Roberto & Celine Pons, 6-7 Trimmer's Lane, Selskar, Wexford ☎ 053-917 0806 – Open 9am-5.30pm Mon-Thur, 9.30am-9.30pm Fri & Sat)

Wine Merchant & Delicatessen

● Greenacres

Architectural gem, wine store, food store, art gallery, and bistro: Greenacres is a world unto itself, a place that celebrates the culture of design, painting, wine and food. That's the sort of universe we like, so once you have torn yourself away from the wine shop and deli, head straight into the Greenacres Bistro, where they serve an all-day menu of cheese and meat platters, a lunch menu, and an evening menu. Suppliers are good – Meyler's fish; Doyle's butchers, Hereford beef – and the cooking wisely leans towards simplicity. (James & Paula O'Connor, Selskar, Wexford ☎ 053-912 2975 info@greenacres.ie www.greenacres.ie – Shop open 9.30am-6pm Mon-Sat, noon-5pm Sun. Bistro open from noon Mon-Sat)

Wexford

Wine Merchant & Delicatessen

● Kate's Farm Shop

Kate's is a magnificent emporium, a warren of rooms packed with everything you need, good foods collated and collected from the region and presented in pristine condition, with little notes telling you where everything has emanated from. So, join the never-ending throng of shoppers and get hold of all the good local gear. (Kate & Ollie O'Mahony, New Line Road, Wexford ☎ 053-918 4823 oliverom@eircom.net – Open 9am-6pm Mon-Sat, 11am-5.30pm Sun)

Restaurant

● Le Tire Bouchon

It's a brave restaurant that uses terms such as "fine dining" and draws inspiration from the French classics in our laid-back, informal eating era, but Kevin Carley and Arnaud Clement work straight out of the bible according to Fernand Point: foie gras and smoked duck terrine; black pudding stuffed with Toulouse sausage; turbot bourguignon; sea trout meuniere. It's a pretty room above the Sky and the Ground pub, and set menus are excellent value. (Kevin Carley & Arnaud Clement, 112 South Main Street, Wexford ☎ 053-912 4877 ✉ letirebouchon@eircom.net 🖱 www.letirebouchon.com Open 6pm-9pm Sun-Thu, 6pm-10pm Fri & Sat)

Townhouse

● McMenamin's Townhouse

Some people know just how to push the right buttons. Seamus and Kay McMenamin are two of those people. When they opened their B&B they brought to it a lifetime's worth of experience in the hospitality business, and it shows. Other hosts are generous amateurs, but the McMenamins are generous professionals. They can read your mind. They know that you really crave baked lamb's kidneys cooked in sherry for your breakfast, but would be too shy to ask for them. So, they chalk it up on the blackboard, and then Seamus will persuade you that baked lamb's kidneys in sherry is what you really feel like this morning. And you will agree, and that extra special breakfast will linger in your memory for years. Creating that special moment is what Seamus and Kay do, and their cosy, classic house is the perfect backdrop for one of the best B&B experiences in Ireland. (Seamus & Kay McMenamin, 6 Glena Terrace, Spawell Road, Wexford ☎ 053-924 6442 ✉ info@wexford-bedandbreakfast.com 🖱 www.wexford-bedandbreakfast.com)

Farmers' Market

● Wexford Farmers' Market

See you at the Cornmarket on Friday morning – early, mind – to get all the good stuff at the Wexford market. (Mailin Street Car Park, Cornmarket, Wexford 🖱 www.wexfordfarmersmarkets.com – Open 9am-2pm, Fri)

Yoletown

Food Producer

● Stable Diet Foods

Stable Diet? Staple Diet is more like it, for once the excellent breakfast cereals, oat bars, cakes and dips from this inspiring company get into your life, they quickly become staples that you cannot live without. You simply can't do better, for example, than send your kids off to school with a couple of Stable Diet bars to help them negotiate through the drowsy sections of the day, and after they have had some Stable Diet cereal with fruit to get them started. Mind you, it's not a bad idea to copy that practice yourself. Healthful and delicious, and there is a fine café in town to enjoy all the products and many more delightful, happy dishes. (Katherine Carroll & Vincent Power, Yoletown, Broadway ☎ 053-913 1287 Café & Patisserie, 100 South Main Street, Wexford ☎ 053-914 9012 katherine@stablediet.com www.stablediet.com – Café and patisserie open 9am-6pm Mon-Sat)

local knowledge

Ireland's Mills

Ireland rivers are consistently inhabited by the remains of ancient mills and swift running mill streams, races and ponds, ruins that show a history where water was used to power the resonant wheels that are now often silent, or have been restored simply for the purpose of decoration. These wheels powered saw mills for timber, woollen mills to make wool and blankets, and they processed oats, corn and wheat for making flour. Often the same mill converted from one to the other, depending on market requirements.

With the introduction of the leavening agent bicarbonate of soda, in the early nineteenth century, together with the availability of wheat flour from these mills, along with buttermilk and the simple fireside equipment to make a fast-rising domestic bread, one of Ireland's greatest foods emerged. Wheaten soda bread, sometimes called brown cake, was traditionally made with a cross dug deep into it – symbolic of Ireland's religious faith – though the cross also created the ideal shape for even baking.

County Wicklow

Arklow

Farmers' Market

Arklow Farmers' Market

Abbey Lane is the destination on Friday mornings for the good Wicklow gear from some of the best growers and cheesemakers in the county and the country. (Abbey Lane, Arklow, Friday 10am-1pm)

Spit-Roast Pigs

The Goode Life

Stephen and Celine have become staples of many of the best markets on the east coast, from Dublin's Temple Bar down to Waterford, in addition to roasting their pigs for parties and celebrations. Once you get a whiff of that aroma, then all resistance is futile, and you will need a plate of spit-roasted pork with all the trimmings. You want crackling? Of course you want crackling! Fantastic. For the good life, you need the Goode Life. (Celien & Stephen Goode, Seabank Lodge, Arklow ☎ 087-266 9620 supremeone@eircom.net www.thegoodelifefoodcompany.ie)

Bakery

Nubo

"You've got to love it!", Conor Spacey says about the act – the art! – of getting up at 4am to start the baking each day for Nubo. Mr Spacey is using the beautiful Uncle Aidan's flour from Enniscorthy for his soda breads, so they are even more packed with flavour and goodness, and indeed Nubo has been bringing its sourcing ever closer as time goes by: the fruit for their jams is grown ten miles away, their own chickens will be providing the eggs, so everything at this admirable bakery and traiteur is coming home to roost in the best, tastiest, most wholesome way possible. (Conor Spacey, 17 Main Street, Arklow ☎ 0402-32712 – Open 9am-5.30pm Mon-Sat)

Traditional Pork Breeds

Stone Age Pigs

James Burke breeds and sells Irish Grazer, Saddleback and Black pigs at Shelton. You can buy a whole pig or buy shares in the pig to share with friends and family, and you can even adopt a pig and trace it through its life. James is also producing air-dried Hibernian hams, which can be bought whole or in weights ranging between one kilo and 100 grammes. (James Burke, Shelton ☎ 086-089 5097 www.adopt-a-pig.com)

Farmhouse Cheese

Wicklow Farmhouse Cheese

John and Bernie have moved fast ever since creating Wicklow Blue back in 2005. The Blue was quickly joined by the Wicklow Baun, and there is also St Kevin, a brie-style cheese made for the catering industry, and Wicklow Gold, which is a cheddar-style cheese and which is available plain and in flavoured varieties. Two goat's cheeses, made with local milk, are also produced, and there is a splendid buttermilk. The Hempenstalls are dynamic farmers, dynamic cheesemakers, and a dynamic dynasty. (John & Bernie Hempenstall, Curranstown, Arklow ☎ 0402-91713 wfcheese@eircom.net www.wicklowfarmhousecheeseltd.ie)

Wicklow

Ashford

Country House & Cookery School

Ballyknocken House

'I'm a real Wicklow woman', Catherine Fulvio told the writer Pól O Conghaile. Indeed she is. The married name may be Italian, but her maiden name is Catherine Byrne and what she does in Ballyknocken is simply continuing the family business, running a B&B and restaurant – and a cookery school – which dates back to 1969, when her mum first took in guests. We have known Mrs Fulvio since long before she took over at Ballyknocken and, aside from her work ethic, her skills and her astounding efficiency, she has always impressed us as a person who knows, first and foremost, who she is: she is a real Wicklow woman. Her cooking shows this: it's gutsy food that she likes to cook, and there is both purity and simplicity in it, along with the generosity that is an integral, defining, part of her work. Breakfasts are as delicious as dinner, with all the meals bringing the true tastes of Wicklow to the table. (Catherine Fulvio, Glenealy, Ashford ☎ 0404-44627 ✉ info@ballyknocken.com 🖱 www.ballyknocken.com)

Wine Shop

● Caprani Off Licence

The Caprani family run a good wine shop and off licence. (The Caprani family, Chester Beatty Inn, Main Street, Ashford ☎ 0404-40682 🖱 www.personalisedwines.ie – Open noon-10pm Mon-Sun)

Cafe and Gardens

● Mount Usher Avoca Garden Café

A typically beautiful Avoca Café in the midst of some of Ireland's most beautiful gardens: what a duo! What a day out! So, after we have browsed the gardens, time to browse a menu: Gold River Farm salad for me, and then a wild Wicklow game casserole; for you, perhaps the ground lamb with hummus, then the Avoca fish pie, and didn't we have a lovely day, the day we went to Mount Usher! (Simon Pratt, Ashford, ☎ 0404-40116 🖱 www.mountushergardens.ie – Open 9.30am-4.30pm Mon-Fri, 10am-5pm Sat & Sun)

Aughrim

Farmers' Market

● Aughrim Farmers' Market

What could be nicer, on a Saturday morning in pretty Aughrim, than an hour or so spent shopping at the Farmers' Market? Delightful. (The Pavilion, Aughrim, Saturday 11am-2pm)

Organic Farm

● Gold River Farm

Organics with Aesthetics could be the byline of Alan and Mark's revolutionary Gold River Farm. It's not just that their organic produce is so healthful, so delicious, so much the first choice of all the good chefs. It's also the fact that it is so beautiful: we walked into The Brook Lodge Inn one afternoon to find that their centrepiece table in the lobby had nothing but a Gold River Farm cabbage in the centre of it. A big, beautiful, organic cabbage, and it was a stunning centrepiece, and it made everyone who saw it feel very, very good indeed. That's what Gold River Farm does: their produce makes you feel good when you see it, and makes you feel even better when you eat it. (Alan Pierce & Mark Winterbotham, The Sycamores, Tinakilly, Aughrim ☎ 0402-36426 ✉ goldriver@eircom.net)

Baltinglass

Baking

● Ballyhubbock Home Foods

Olive Finlay makes delicious domestic delights, beautiful staples that taste real and ruddy. So, seek out her wonderful Ballyhubbock apple tarts, her fruity sweet jams, her delicious baking, in good shops in the county. (Olive Finlay, Stratford-on-Slaney, Baltinglass ☎ 045-404706 ✉ olivefinlay@yahoo.ie)

made in Wicklow

Avoca

Wicklow

Blessington

Ice Cream

● Goldenhill Farmhouse Ice Cream

Damien and Aoife have become stalwart ice cream purveyors at Electric Picnic over the last few years, their beautiful retro ice cream van a welcome and colourful sight in the midst of all the EP hoo-haa. Their ices have also begun to appear on the menus of many good restaurants, so they are stealthily conquering the world with good ice cream. The secret, of course, is the excellence of their own milk from their own herd, and to this canvas they add sparky, delicious flavours. So, join the queue and it's make up your mind time: vanilla, again? Chocolate chip, hmmm... (Damien & Aoife Clarke, Goldenhill Farm, Golden Hill, Manor Kilbride, Blessington ☎ 01-458 2017/086-364 0135 ✉ info@goldenhill.ie 🖱 www.goldenhill.ie)

Café

Grangecon Café

Richard and Jenny Street's café is one of the very best cafés in Ireland, with a meticulous, dedicated care showing proudly in everything they cook and bake. These guys pour body and soul into everything they do, everything they cook and bake and prepare and serve, and so it is worth the drive to Blessington just to enjoy the sausage rolls. And the shepherd's pie. And the potato and courgette soup, the rhubarb tart, the chocolate cake, the marmalade cake. Inspiring people, inspiring place. (Richard & Jenny Street, Kilbride Road, Blessington ☎ 045-857892 grangeconcafe@eircom.net – Open 9am-4pm Mon-Sat)

Health Food Store

Harvest Fare Health Food Shop

Deirdre Mallitte's shop is a beauty, one of those wholefood paradises that has a zeitgeist all its own, a place where you always discover something new with each visit. Lots of the best local foods make their way here, joining with interesting and essential staples to give you the healthiest diet. (Deirdre Mallitte, Main Street, Blessington ☎ 045-891636 harvestfare@eircom.net www.harvestfarehealthshop.com – Open 10am-6pm Mon-Sat, 'till 5pm Sat)

Bray

Farmers' Market

Bray Farmers' Market

See you on Saturday morning in Bray to get all the good stuff at the market. (Bray Heritage Centre, Main Street, Bray – Open 11am-3pm Sat)

Traiteur

The Butler's Pantry

The Butler's Pantry is like Noma. On their first day in business, the BP sold 12 meals, Now they sell 1,600 a day, aside from their terrific breads and desserts. Noma, a year before it was voted best restaurant in the world, served eight people. A year later, the waiting list for Saturday night dinner was 1,000 people. Everything changes, nothing changes, except for the scale. The BP continue to strive, to improve, to satisfy their customers, and head chef Niall Hill has brought a key dynamic to the company in recent times, increasing their profile, increasing their creative drive. The Butler's Pantry has come a long way, and yet it's exactly where it has always been. (Eileen Bergin, 16-18 Southern Cross Business Par, Boghall Road, Bray ☎ 01-276 1431 www.thebutlerspantry.ie)

Restaurant

Campo de Fiori

Marco and Laura's restaurant has won not one but two *Food & Wine* magazine readers' awards, so it is the people's choice, and how! They have moved since our last edition, and the old restaurant is now their Risto Market. The restaurant and wine bar exude that casual competence you find in Italian establishments in Italy, and indeed you would find CdeF cooking in Italy, for Marco's food is the real deal and not the standard pastiche we find in Ireland. The cooking is generous and richly flavoured – pappardelle with wild boar sauce; beef tagliata with porcini; selection of grilled fish – and is very classically grounded. Put the food, the room, the service and the vibe together and you have the people's choice. (Marco & Laura Roccasalvo, Strand Road, Bray Seafront ☎ 01-276 4257 www.campodefiori.ie – Open 11am-9pm Tue-Thur, 11am-10pm Fri, 10am-10pm Sat, 10am-9pm Sun)

Wicklow

Restaurant

Campo de Fiori Risto Market

The original Campo de Fiori restaurant is now a neat, charismatic shop, deli and wine shop, with a fish counter and their signature pizzas. (Marco & Laura Roccasalvo, 1 Albert Avenue, Bray ☎ 01-276 4257 www.campodefiori.ie)

Coffee and Tea Merchant

Clive McCabe & Co

The story of McCabe's is like the Hewlett-Packard caravan, or Jobs and Woz and the Homebrew Computer Club. It is 1995, and Clive McCabe starts roasting some coffee beans in the garage of his house, out in the Wicklow Mountains. He also sources gourmet teas, and begins to sell them locally. Fast forward to 2012 and Stephen McCabe notes that on a single day he has roasted enough beans for 25,200 lattes. And yet, the character of the company hasn't changed a jot since those days back in the garage: the scale is bigger, but the commitment to quality is as unflinching and expert as ever it was back in the garagista days. Simply terrific, and these coffees and teas improve your life. (Stephen & Clive McCabe, Unit 56, Newtownmountkennedy Business Enterprise Centre ☎ 01-287-5835 🖱 www.mccabecoffee.com)

local knowledge

Organics

Wicklow is known as the Garden of Ireland, but it is more accurately one of the birthplaces of Organic agriculture. The organic pioneers here are also commercial masters, and have pioneered farmers' markets and farmshops ahead of everyone else in Ireland.

Bar & Off Licence

● Holland's Fine Wines & Champagne House

Great wines, great beers from Ireland and the rest of the world, nice cheeses from Sheridan's and good chocolates, and staff who know what it's all about: that's the c.v. for Holland's of Bray. Good CV. (78-80 Main Street, Bray ☎ 01-286 7995 ✉ contact@hollandsofbray.com 🖱 www.hollandsofbray.com)

Tea Rooms and Garden

● Killruddery House & Gardens

The beautiful Kilruddery House and gardens is a hive of activities these days, as Fionnuala and Anthony orchestrate farmers' markets, dance and yoga classes, a kitchen garden, a tea room, a supper club and lots, lots more. "We have lots on", says Fionnuala, which is an understatement if ever there was one. The farmers' market started perfectly, quickly adding in exciting new stalls to a list that included Carrignamuc Cottage vegetables, Kilruddery lamb, Crepe Box, Kingfisher tea, Wild Irish pâtés and others. There's a whirlwind happening here: jump on. (Anthony & Fionnuala Ardee, Bray ☎ 01-286 3405 ✉ info@killruddery.com 🖱 www.killruddery.com)

Yogurts and Soft Cheeses

Old MacDonnell's Farm

Brian and Wendy make lovely yogurts and fresh cheeses, and some very good hummus, and they do it today the way they did it when we first met over twenty years ago: on the farm, with the family, no messing about, just pure and simple and good and healthy. The simple life! (The McDonnell family, Glen of the Downs, Bray ☎ 01-282 8992 📫 sales@oldmacdonnellsfarm.ie 🖱 www.oldmacdonnellsfarm.ie)

Delgany

Butcher

Farrelly's Butchers

The Farrelly brothers are superb butchers, men whose vision and holistic approach to their trade gladdens the heart, before gladdening the appetite. Their meats are peerlessly sourced, and beautifully aged and prepared by traditional, hands-on methods. The shop has been open since 1958 and little has changed in that time, save that they have gotten better and better. Pure class. (Anthony & Padraig Farrelly, Main Street, Delgany ☎ 01-287 4211 – Open 9am-6pm Mon-Sat)

Donard

Wicklow

Organic Vegetables and Herbs

Castleruddery Organic Farm

Dominic and Hilda started their organic farming the same year we began writing guide books – 1989. Their success over the years has been a particular delight, and not just for us, but for everyone lucky to be able to source and cook with their vegetables and salads, bought at the farm shop or at the Naas Farmers' Market on Saturday. They are amongst that aristocratic band of Wicklow organic pioneers who set out their seeds in the 1980's, a bunch of people distinguished by their appetite for hard work, their holistic vision of working, and their fundamental modesty. Eating Castleruddery foods takes you straight to the zeitgeist. (Hilda Crampton & Dominic Quinn, Donard ☎ 045-404925 📫 casorg@eircom.net – Farmshop open 9am-6pm Thur & Fri)

Enniskerry

Café

Avoca Powerscourt Terrace Café

Take lunch on the terrace at Powerscourt and you will feel like an actor in a movie set. Except no actors are fortunate enough to have Avoca doing the catering, so lucky you. (Simon Pratt, Powerscourt House, Enniskerry ☎ 01-204 6066 info@avoca.ie www.avoca.ie – Open 9.30am-5.30pm Mon-Fri, 10am-6pm Sat & Sun)

Café

Kennedy's of Enniskerry

There is a smashing story behind Santina and Andrew's food shop. When he lost his job, she had to fast-forward a dreamy plan for a food store selling delicious things. Desperation made them do it and, despite some tough times, they made it work. Santina became a baker and businesswoman, Andrew became a barista, and a barista so accomplished that writers and others are apt to tell you his flat white is the best they know of. Bretzel breads, Fothergills desserts, Santina's buns, fresh soups and ace coffee show two people who changed course and mastered their new direction. And, to cap it all, a lady from Wichita, Kansas, even wrote a letter to *The Irish Times* telling how Santina's hospitality had transformed her Irish vacation: spread the love! (Santina & Andrew Kennedy, Church Hill, Enniskerry kennedysofenniskerry@gmail.com www.kennedysofenniskerry.com – Open 9am-6pm Mon-Sat, 10am-3pm Sun)

Café & Country Store

Waterfall Farm Shop

Waterfall is the sort of shop that makes strangers contact you, out of the blue, saying, "I've just been to this amazing shop, and you've got to see it. It's amazing!". Indeed it is: Hannah and Michael have culled all the best stuff – Ballymore Farm milk and butter; Kilbeggan oats; Thibault Peigne's breads; Hick's pork; Burke's farm ice cream; Highbank syrup; their own Leyn Wicklow lamb. Hannah and Michael will soon be famous farmers, with the most famous farm shop. (Enniskerry ☎ 087-264 9537 waterfallfarmshop@gmail.com www.waterfallfarm.ie – Open 10am-4pm Sat & Sun)

Glenealy

Organic Store

OOOOBY Store

OOOOBY is a community food store run by Mike and Suzy as part of their organic farm and their Carraig Dúlra skills centre. An incredible amount of activity happens here, from courses of all manner to open days to vegetable box deliveries and whathaveyou. Inspiring. (Mike & Suzy Cahn, Glenealy Landscape Centre, Glenealy ☎ 0404-69570 www.dulra.org/ooooby – Open 10am-5pm Tue-Thu, 11.20am-3.30pm Sat)

Greystones

Traiteur

Butler's Pantry

Greystones outpost of the mighty Irish traiteur and baker. (Eileen Bergin, Burnaby Buildings, Church Road, Greystones ☎ 01-201 0022 www.thebutlerspantry.ie)

Fish Shop, Delicatessen & Café

A Caviston

Amy Caviston and Shane Willis are a team who are as smart as all-get-out, and you can see their intelligence, their judiciousness, in every aspect of A. Caviston. They sell great fish, they sell great artisan foods, and they complete the circle by cooking their superb fish superbly. Like Caviston's of Glasthule, where Ms Caviston learnt her craft, A. Caviston is a place prized by the local community, prized as a shop, prized as a place to eat, prized as an exemplar of all that is good about smart, discriminating food service. The place will be filled with surfers, grannies, business folk, mums and kids, all enjoying magnificent fish cookery, whether you choose pristine turbot or magnificently cooked whiting. And take a tip from us: put the work to one side, get in the car and drive to Greystones, have a walk – or a surf! – and then have lunch in A. Caviston. You will feel reborn. These guys are ahead of the curve. (Amy Caviston, Shane & Ronan Willis, No 1 Westview, Church Road, Greystones, ☎ 01-287 7637 info@acaviston.ie www.acaviston.ie – Cafe open 10am-5pm Mon, 9am-5pm Tue-Sat, Deli open 10am-5pm Mon, 10am-6pm Tue-Sat)

Restaurant

Chakra by Jaipur

A stylish, colourful first-floor room has been home to this branch of the much-respected Jaipur chain of five restaurants, which also includes the ground-breaking Ananda in Dundrum. Chakra offers the modernist Indian cooking that has proven so popular over the decade since they opened, and the execution of the dishes is precise and colourful, and it makes for delicious eating in a lovely room. (Dinesh Chander, 1st Floor, Meridian Point, Church Road, Greystones ☎ 01-201 7222 info@jaipur.ie www.jaipur.ie – Open 5.30pm-11pm Mon-Sat, 1pm-11pm Sun)

Grocery Shop

Donnybrook Fair

The Greystones branch of Joe Doyle's ground-breaking grocery store is an essential address. Donnybrook Fair is the sort of store that makes you feel good from the second you walk through the door. Smart, hip, engaged staff retail the very best foods and wines you can find, and improve your life no end. (Joe Doyle, Grattan Court, Greystones ☎ 01-287 6346 info@donnybrookfair.ie www.donnybrookfair.ie – Open 7am-8pm Sun-Wed, 7am-9pm Thur-Sat)

Pizza Van

Gaillot & Gray

How cool is Gaillot & Gray?! A classic Citroen HY van in shiny silver; a blackboard menu of their wood-fired pizzas – there are 5, with a special to supplement that quintet; they are made with Emmental rather than mozzarella; they are sold in a car park and if it's chilly you can ask to borrow a picnic blanket, and that's us in the queue: two Number 4s please, Gilles, and a Number 1, and some juices and let's watch the sun set over Greystones harbour. How cool? Super cool! (Emma Gray & Gilles Gaillot, Old Watson and Johnson carpark, Mill Road, Greystones ☎ 083-432 6441 gaillotandgray@gmail.com – Open 5pm-9pm Wed-Sun)

Cafe & Deli

The Happy Pear

Phew! Just watched Steve and Dave talking about figs on their Facebook film. Can a Facebook video get an

R-rating? But, let's face it, you could give these twin brothers some kohlrabi to extol, and they would convince you of its inherent sexiness. That's the thing about what the boys do: everything here is up for it, life-affirming, life-improving, culture gathering, from their lovely food market to the smart soups, salads and hip cooking in the café. The spirit of '68 lives on! (Stephen & Dave Flynn, Westview House, Main Street, Greystones ☎ 01-287 3655 www.thehappypear.ie – Cafe & Shop open 9am-6pm Mon-Sat, Cafe only open 10.30am-6pm Sun)

Restaurant and Wine Bar Bistro

● The Hungry Monk

There aren't a whole lot of restaurants in this book that pre-date our first Food Guide, published in 1989, but The Hungry Monk is one of them, for Pat and Sylvia Keown opened their doors in July 1988. Almost a quarter century later, and the 'Monk is doing the good thing, and Julian Keown has just opened the new downstairs bistro as we write in mid-2012, so there is dynamism and determination in this much-loved restaurant and bistro. So, let's share an antipasti platter to start, and some of their superb wines, and let the evening get under way... (Julian, Pat & Sylvia Keown, Church Road, Greystones ☎ 01-287 5759 hungrymonk@eircom.net www.thehungrymonk.ie – Restaurant open 5.30pm-11pm Thur-Sat, noon-7.30pm Sun, Wine Bar open 5pm-11pm Mon-Sat, 12.30pm-9pm Sun)

Food To Go

● Indian Spice Co.

Ronan Fleming has a real love for the zing and zest of Indian street food, and his dishes always have the sharpness and precision of well understoof ethnic cooking. (Ronan Fleming, 19a Church Road, Greystones ☎ 01-201 0868 www.indianspiceco.com – Open 5pm-9.30pm Mon-Thur, 4pm-10.30pm Fri & Sat, 4pm-9.30pm Sun)

Wholefood Shop

● Nature's Gold

What a visionary thing it was for Brod Kearon to open Nature's Gold, way, way back in the day: 1977 to be precise. There wasn't an awful lot going on in Irish retailing at that time, and Greystones was a sleepy village, not the culinary destination it has become today. So, hats off to Mr Kearon for recognising that people want to find good wholefoods and natural products, and want helpful advice when they buy them. Nature's Gold has been doing that ever since 1977, steadily adding in exciting new things all the time, so you can find the dazzling Natasha's Living Foods, for example, and you can also buy a bottle of their own cold-pressed olive oil from a farm they own south of Barcelona. We love the homey feel of the shop, too, its innocent and unpretentious air. (Brod Kearon, Killincarrig Road, Greystones ☎ 01-287 6301 natgold@iol.ie www.naturesgold.ie (shop) www.naturesgoldoliveoil.com – Open 9am-6pm Mon-Sat)

Butcher's Shop

● The Steak Shop

A colourful awning and a nice old vintage bike will alert you to Barry King's shop to begin, but it is the quality and treatment of the meat from his own farm that will have you coming back to this dedicated, respected butcher's shop. Staff could not be more helpful, and The Steak Shop is a key address in town. (Barry King, Trafalgar Road, Greystones ☎ 01-255 7737 – Open 8am-6pm Mon-Sat)

Café

● The Three Q's

The Quinn brothers have notched up six years in business, making the people of gourmet Greystones happy ever since April 2006. Their cooking fuses influences as diverse as Moro and Ottolenghi and Paula Wolfert, so your dish of salmon will have sumac and a green tahini dressing, whilst Spanish fish stew will have smoked paprika and toasted sourdough with rouille. And just to show they can bring it all back home, there is a Ballyshonog Farm ribeye with garlic butter and fries, and foraged wild ingredients from Wicklow, including alexanders and wild cabbage. Their vegetarian dishes show real imagination, and what a delightful, friendly neighbourhood restaurant. (Brian, Paul & Colin Quinn, Gweedore, Church Road, Greystones ☎ 01-287 5477 thethreeqs@gmail.com www.thethreeqs.com – Open 9.30am-4pm, 5.30pm-10pm Tue-Thur, 9.30am-4pm, 6pm-10pm Fri, 9am-3pm, 6pm-10pm Sat, 9am-3pm, 5.30pm-9pm Sun)

Kilcoole

Chilli Sauces

Mic's Chilli

You can find Mic's chilli sauces in Harvey Nichols in London. And in Barcelona. And in your local good food store. Proper order, for these fiery relishes are – no contest! – the slickest designed and hippest marketed product to have come out of Ireland in years. Whatever else Michael Wejchert does in the future, he can always earn a crust giving lectures, with his designer Steve Simpson, about how you put out a product that is visually stunning. But, appearances aside, Mic's Chillis are conquering the planet because they are so darned good, not least the newest sweet chilli and chilli barbecue sauces. "Standout products", said *The Irish Times*. "Fantastico" we say. And there's more to come. (Michael Wejchert, Kilcoole info@micschilli.ie www.micschilli.ie)

made in Wicklow

Coolatin Cheddar

Kilmacanogue

Café

Avoca

Wicklow

The most amazing act in Irish speciality food in recent years has been the steady expansion by Simon Pratt of his Avoca empire, most recently the creation of the brand-new Avoca Food Market, with its Salt Café, on the Crescent in Monkstown, in south Dublin. This is the first Avoca to feature only food, and the alliance of players featured here – Gold River Farm; James Whelan Butchers, Poulet Bonne Femme, amongst others – is a radical new departure for Irish food retailing. To preside over such a grand opening during the worst recession in memory shows Simon Pratt's brilliance: Avoca doesn't play by the rules, it makes the rules. These iconic stores and food halls succeed because everything they do is original, creative and colourful – visually colourful, playfully colourful, culturally colourful, intellectually colourful. They are artists of the food world. (Simon Pratt, Kilmacanogue ☎ 01-286 7466 info@avoca.ie www.avoca.ie – Open 9am-6pm Mon-Fri, 9.30am-6pm Sat & Sun)

Chutneys & Relishes

Janet's Country Fayre

Back in the day, Janet Drew of Janet's Country Fayre used to be an art historian at the National Gallery. Think about it: that fits, doesn't it? Because Ms Drew's approach to her work is curatorial: she wants to show everything she works with in its best light, she wants every element to shine, to be foreground, to be luminous. Having that sort of understanding helps you to understand why the Country Fayre range is so fine, so distinctive, so engaging. It's art, in a jar. Of course. (Janet Drew, Copsewood Farm, KIlmacanogue ☎ 01-201 8008 janet@janetscountryfayre.com www.janetscountryfayre.com)

Kiltegan

Artisan Baking

Daisy Cottage Farm

It's always going to be a good market when Larry and Lorraine's baking is present and available. Their baking nestles nicely at that juncture between the professional and the domestic, so there is polish to the execution, but also wholesomeness in the tastes and flavours. Look out at east coast farmers' markets for those good breads and those tasty chicken and leek pies and goat's cheese and black olive pies, and look forward to a good dinner. (Larry & Lorraine, Borklemor, Kiltegan ☎ 086-317 7146)

Organic Farmer

Denis Healy's Organic Delights

Denis Healy is the public face of organic farming in Ireland. You might open your Saturday *Irish Times* to find a big feature on the man and his family in the colour section, all of them smiling away, happy in the heart of the country. But beneath the public surface lies the most amazing amount of sheer hard graft, for Mr Healy is not just a pioneer of organics, but also a pioneer of farmers' markets, and his presence at markets with his organic produce along the east coast has been pivotal to the spread of both causes. That's why he's on the cover of *The Irish Times*. That, and his devilish good looks, of course. (Denis Healy, Talbotstown Lower, Kiltegan ☎ 059-647 3193 info@organicdellights.ie www.organicdelights.ie)

Bio-Dynamic Produce

● Penny & Udo Lange

Penny and Udo's Ballinroan Farm is one of the outstanding Wicklow organic farming pioneers. Their wisdom as thinkers on growing and farming translates into the most heavenly produce, foods that exult in their healthfulness, goodness and naturalness. To taste them for the first time is to experience a taste epiphany: if this is celery/carrots/fennel, you say to yourself, then what is everyone else growing? Mind-blowing foods. (Penny & Udo Lange, Ballinroan House, Kiltegan ☎ 059-647 3278)

Kilternan

Country Market

● Kilternan Country Market

Kilternan is one of the most famous of the traditional country markets, established as long ago as 1964. Its fame rests on a solid core of creative suppliers who bring beautiful things to the Golden Ball each week. It's brilliant and busy, so pregnant women and children should be careful of all those sharp elbows plundering in for the final organic chicken and the last bag of gooseberries. (Golden Ball, Enniskerry Road, Kilternan ☎ 01-282 2182 🖱 www.kilternancountrymarket.com – 9am-2pm, Saturday)

Macreddin

Country Hotel

● The Brook Lodge Inn

After the first Taste Council summer school orchestrated by Evan Doyle at the Brook Lodge, Mr Doyle curated a 'Harvest dinner from the Garden of Ireland'. His faithful producers lined up, offering Wicklow harbour crab from Mark Byrnes, Stephen Kavanagh's smoked oysters, Brian McDonnell's yogurts, Janet Drew's relishes, Ed Hick's puddings, Farrelly brothers' Angus beef, Mick Healy's game, Mick Murphy's salmon, Denis Healy's vegetables, salads and spuds from Mark and Alan's Gold River farm, and oils from Michael and Paul. John Hempenstall had his cheeses, there was beer from brewer Cuilan Loughnane, wines from Dublin from David Llewellyn, coffee from Deirdre and Michele. It was an astonishment of riches, and surely one of the greatest feasts of local foods ever collated in Ireland. And you know what? Doing this is just what Mr Doyle does every day of the week in this extraordinary hotel. His vision of food is of Wicklow as Cockaigne, the land of plenty, of luxury and ease, and this is what he has created. He turns every day into Lughnasadh, with every day a day devoted to the art of eating. (Evan Doyle, Brook Lodge Inn, Macreddin ☎ 0402-36444 brooklodge@macreddin.ie www.brooklodge.com – Restaurant open 7pm-9.30pm Mon-Sat)

Organic Market

● Macreddin Village Organic Market

The jazz band strikes up, the sun shines, the barbie burns, and it can only be Macreddin Market on the first Sunday of the month. This is both a wonderful market, and a wonderful day out. (Evan Doyle, The Brook Lodge, Macreddin Village. www.brooklodge.com – Open 1.30pm-6.30pm on the 1st Sun of each month from Mar-Oct)

local knowledge

Fraughans

Wild bilberries, or Fraughans have been gathered for centuries from the hills and mountains of County Wicklow, and the fruit is associated with a number of ancient festivals, including Fraughan Sunday, on the first Sunday in August.

Wicklow

Organic Bakery, Smoked Foods, Preserves

● The Store Rooms

The breads, preserves and smoked foods of the Store Rooms are a treat, and the best present to bring home to granny to thank her for babysitting the kids whilst you have been chilling in the hotel. (Evan Doyle, The Brook Lodge, Macreddin Village ☎ 0402-36444 info@brooklodge.com www.brooklodge.com)

Organic Italian Restaurant

● La Taverna Armento

Evan Doyle's tribute to Italian ingredients and southern Italian cookery is no pastiche, nor is it the red sauce Italian stuff that blankets so many restaurants in Ireland. Armento takes organic Italian ingredients and Irish organic ingredients and fuses them deliciously: antipasti plate with courgette, mushrooms, ham and anchovies; sea bream with lemon and caper butter and polenta; sausage, goat's cheese and spring onion pizza; pannacotta with local berries. Lovely wines, lovely room. (Evan Doyle, Brook Lodge Inn, Macreddin ☎ 0402-36444 brooklodge@macreddin.ie www.brooklodge.com – Open from 6.30pm, Wed-Mon. Closed Tues)

Newcastle

Country Market

North Wicklow Country Market

The legendary North Wicklow market is more than forty years' young, and it's a powerhouse of local endeavour, creativity and goodness. "Eat Irish, Eat Local, Eat Well" is their slogan, and they make it all real, with bounteous produce, fantastic baking, lovely crafts, and a nice cup of tea. (Newcastle Community Centre, Newcastle, Saturdays 10.30am-12.30pm)

made in Wicklow

Janet's Country Fayre

Wicklow

Farm Shop

Sweetbank Farm

"Farming is ninety per cent graft and ten per cent romance." David Johnston told the writer Ben Webb. Well, maybe, but is there another farm in Ireland so photogenic as Sweetbank? We don't think so, which is why David and Debbie feature every few years in the glossy magazines, with lots of glamorous photos of their beautiful house and farm, the very incarnation of the Agricultural Arcadia. But ths arcadia is founded not just on graft, but on philosophy, so you should buy Sweetbank fruit and lamb and beef because it is local and delicious and organic, and attend a Sweetbank course to learn how to fashion your own arcadia from the smallest beginnings. Sweetbank is beautiful, yes, but also wise, and that's a rare combination in modern agriculture. (David & Debbie Johnston, Tiglin, Newcastle ☎ 086-173 0497 sweetbankfarm@iolfree.ie www.sweetbankfarm.ie)

Newtownmountkennedy

Café

The Buttery Café @ Fishers

The Buttery Café could easily be called The Yummy Café, because yummy is what they do here. The food is gutsy yet delicate, if that's at all possible – chicken, chorizo and chickpea stew, the signature dish of mushrooms with leeks and blue cheese; the good Sunday lunch roasts. But the biggest yum! goes to their sweet baking, which is worth the trip to Fishers and Newtownmountkennedy alone. Great value, great service, really yummy. (Claire O'Brien, Fishers, Newtownmountkennedy ☎ 01-281 2892 www.thebutterycafe.com – Open 10am-5pm Mon-Sat, 11am-5pm Sun)

Rathdrum

Restaurant

Bates

Leslie Williams enjoyed an excellent dinner at Bates: good breads and focaccia with tapenade and tomato pesto dips to start, then a fine big bowl of seafood chowder, and some gnocchi in tomato sauce with mozzarella and basil. Mains were an excellent rib-eye from the char-grill and sweet, creamy lamb chops, cooked to perfection, and then a creme brulée, caramelised with a blow-torch at the table by the waitress. Service is particularly charming, portions are big – bring a hearty appetite to Bates – and this is cooking to please everyone. (Boris Pleva, 3 Market Street, Market Square, Rathdrum ☎ 0404-29988 www.batesrestaurant.com – Open 6pm-9.30pm Tue-Fri, 5.30pm-9.30pm Sat, 12.30pm-3pm, 6pm-9pm Sun)

Butcher

Synnott's

The shop looks unremarkable, but the quality of meat served by the Synnott brothers is truly top-class. Their beef, in particular, is food for the gods, so make that detour into Rathdrum and you'll enjoy the chat and the service, just as much as you will enjoy the beef. (John & Richard Synnott, Rathdrum ☎ 0404-46132 – Open 8.30am-6pm Mon-Sat)

Game Producer

● Wild Irish Game Ltd

We are lucky to be able to buy Michael Healy's wild Irish game in the English Market in Cork city, and sometimes even as far west as Field's in Skibbereen. The game is always beautifully presented and packaged, and packed with those unique feral flavours that no domesticated animal can match. Glorious stuff. (Michael Healy, Glenmalure, Rathdrum ☎ 0404-46773 wigltd@eircom.net www.wildirishgame.ie)

Roundwood

Country Inn

● The Roundwood Inn

Nothing changes in the Roundwood Inn, and that timelessness is exactly the way visitors and locals alike both like their favourite Inn to be. There is fine bar food, and slightly more involved cooking in the restaurant, but whether you are having a midweek bite in the bar and enjoying the open fire – seafood platter; chicken in a basket; salmon salad – or it's a family dinner at the weekend in the restaurant – goulash soup; their version of Irish stew; rack of Wicklow lamb; suckling pig – the cooking is as ageless as the building and the hospitality. The Roundwood Inn always feels rather special. (Jurgen & Aine Schwalm, Roundwood ☎ 01-281 8107 – Bar food served noon-9pm Mon-Sun, Restaurant open 7.30pm-8.45pm Fri & Sat, 1pm-2pm Sun)

Tullow

Farmhouse Cheese

● Coolattin Cheddar Cheese

Tom Burgess's fantastic farmhouse cheese is closest to a territorial cheddar cheese in style, yet Coolattin also has some elements of a Comte-style to it, so it's a true sport of nature. But what is undoubted is the clean alignment of flavours Mr Burgess brings forth, thanks to excellent animal stewardship – he only milks once a day – and expert, patient cheesemaking using his own summer pasture, early-morning raw milk from happy cows. Coolattin offers sweet notes at the top tier of tastes, then a touch of sweet spice, followed by a long, mellow aftertaste that shows the careful maturation of the cheese. A beautiful, elemental farmhouse food. Look for it in particular at Elizabeth Bradley's cheese stall at the Carlow Farmers' Market on Saturday morning. (Tom Burgess, Knockeen House, Tullow ☎ 086-389 4482 tofiburgess@eircom.net www.coolattincheddar.com)

Wicklow

Café

● Halpin's Bridge Café

"Onwards and upwards" says Robert Doyle of the steady march to success of his fine Wicklow café, regarded by one and all as the best place to eat in the town. Mr Doyle understands that God is in the detail, so he gets the details right, and we just offer up hosannahs for lovely food – slow-cooked beef stew; proper spag bol; smoked cod fish pie; roast chicken with baby roast garlic. Hallelujah for Halpin's. (Robert Doyle, Bridge Street, Wicklow ☎ 0404-32677 www.halpinscafe.com – Open 8.30am-6.30pm Mon-Fri, 8am-6pm Sat, 10am-4pm Sun)

Coffee Roasters

● Mojo Coffee

So we ordered some El Aulsol coffee, sourced from El Salvador by Mojo, ground it and made it and tasted it and we wrote: "El Ausol: sensational. Maltiness that gives it body, yet it is terrifically clean. Brilliant, and addictively satisfying" So, we were pretty knocked out by Kevin McLoughlin's coffee roasting, and we also loved the Carmona Pulcal and the La Gloria from Panama and the Gethumbwini from Kenya. These coffees will really get your mojo working. (Kevin McLoughlin, Unit W6, Wicklow Enterprise Centre, The Murrough, Wicklow Town ☎ 0404-66433 info@coffeemojo.ie www.coffeemojo.ie)

Organic Herbs

● OHCo. Organic Herb Company

Paul and Michael's OHCo. produce beautiful salts, rubs, oils and mixes, and the products look every bit as good as they taste, truly glam products.But don't just think of them as gift foods; you need OHCo. at your side in the kitchen, giving a classy acccent to everything you cook. (Michael Martin & Paul Pritchard, 9 The Exchange, Calmount Business Park, Ballymount, D12 ☎ 0404-31028 info@ifbe.ie www.ifbe.ie)

Organic Vegetables and Meat

● An Tairseach

The Dominican sisters practise bio-dynamic farming on their 70 acres, along with their centre for Ecology and Spirituality. Now, why does that seem so right? Bio-dyn, ecology and spirituality, all in one package? Because they belong together, of course. Because farming is contemplative before it becomes action, because ecology is respect for something we have merely borrowed from our children, because spirituality is where you find yourself when you dig a potato or pod a broad bean you have grown. So, visit the shop, and you will get much more than you might have thought possible. (The Dominican Sisters, Dominican Farm & Ecology Centre, Wicklow ☎ 0404-61833 info@ecocentrewicklow.ie www.ecocentrewicklow.ie)

Wine Shop

● Wicklow Wine Co

Michael and Ben run one of the best, most enterprising wine companies in the country. And one of the most amusing, as this entry from their list shows: "Guilhem Dardé is one of the most extraordinary characters in the southern French wine business. Conservationist, activist, Mayor of the village of Octon and owner of one the most sensational moustaches one may ever encounter". Aha, don't forget Guilhem's moustache. This sort of wit and wisdom is simply charming, almost as charming as the stellar wines they source from all over the world of wine, and which they sell with the true passion of hopelessly devoted wine lovers. Oh, and Guilhem makes a wine he calls The Heretic. As you do.(Michael Anderson & Ben Mason, 7 Main Street, Wicklow ☎ 0404-66767 info@wicklowwineco.ie www.wicklowwineco.ie)

Northern Ireland

County Antrim

Belfast

Bistro

● Ace

Go for the Ace strongpoints – pulled pork slider; classic burger; corn dogs with baked beans; pork, fennel and sausage goulash – and this industrial-chic room hits the spot with gas in the tank. It's not all finger lickin', arms-in-the-sink-cookin' however: they make a quinoa salad; they make porridge for brunch. But mainly it's savoury, carnivore heaven. You will either find the design totally rockin', or trying-too-hard. (Samuel Spain, 20-22 Belmont Road, ☎ 028-9047 3333 – No reservations taken. Open 11am-10pm Mon-Fri, 9am-10pm Sat, 9am-9pm Sun)

Chinese Restaurant

● All Seasons

The "Best Chinese Restaurant in Belfast" debate – always an important yardstick in Belfast over the last three decades – is unanimous in awarding Richard Yip's All Seasons the title these days. All Seasons deserves it not just for some smashing cooking, but for also taking a cerebral approach to the history of Chinese cooking in the city. So they reflect the early days and early favourites – the sweet 'n' sour chicken, the beef with peppers and black bean sauce – and also the contemporary dishes that are their signature – steamed Dover sole with spring onion and ginger; salted chilli squid; char siu and monkfish hot pot with mushrooms and pak choi. Lovely cooking and fine value. (Richard Yip, 96 Botanic Avenue, Belfast ☎ 028-9080 8833 – Open noon-2pm, 5pm-11pm Mon-Fri, 5pm-11pm Sat & Sun)

Delicatessen

● The Arcadia

"Since 1933". It says a lot about Arcadia, that this fine shop has been trading for eighty years. But it doesn't say everything, for we could add "And keeping up with the times" because that is what the Lisburn Road stalwart has done over eight decades: Arcadia, like a true arcadia, is traditional but modern, ageless but contemporary. That's a mighty achievement, and it's a great store, a repository of culinary culture. (Willie Brown, 378 Lisburn Road ☎ 028-9038 1779 info@arcadiadeli.co.uk www.arcadiadeli.co.uk – Open 8.30am-6pm Mon-Sat)

Asian Supermarket

● Asia Supermarket

The best Chinese supermarket we know is also one of the most fun places to shop, largely because it feels like a film set all the time. We know the shoppers aren't choreographed and directed – they are just looking for bitter gourds – but it does look and feel that way. Mighty fun, and we're ready for our close-up. (The Pau family, 189 Ormeau Road ☎ 028-9032 6396 – Open 9.30am-6.30pm Mon-Sun)

Café & Home Store

● Avoca

The Belfast outpost of Ireland's leading luxury food brand is as smart, sexy and accomplished as a store can be. Resistance to its colourful, hip seductivness is futile, and no other store can match them. (Simon Pratt, 41 Arthur Street, Belfast ☎ 028-9027 9955 www.avoca.ie – Open 9am-4pm Mon-Fri, 9am-5pm Sat, 12.30pm-5pm Sun)

Bagel Bar

● Bagel Bagel

Bagel Bagel has proven that the bagel boom of a decade ago wasn't a mere fad, and their bagels are consistent, tasty and fun. Look, you just have to love a bagel named "The Serious Caesar". Bring on The Cicero. (Joan & Paul Barr, 60 Donegall Street ☎ 028-9024 2545 www.bagel-bagel.co.uk – Open 8am-3.30pm Mon-Fri, 10am-3pm Sat)

Coffee Roaster

● Bailie's Coffee

Bailie's are demon coffee roasters, expertly presiding over every step of the process from sourcing to roasting to retailing to operating a gullwing kiosk, and their coffees and their baristas win awards with amazing regularity. Skill, and then more skill, explains their success. (Unit 8, Coastal Warehouse, 83 Dargan Road ☎ 028-9077 1535 🖱 www.bailiescoffee.com)

Gastropub

● The Barking Dog

You come across some lovely food in The Barking Dog: salt and pepper scampi with tartare sauce; cauliflower cheesecake with pine nut and chervil dressing; smoked haddock with crushed new potatoes, broccolini and béarnasise; pear tarte tatin. Chef Michael O'Connor has bi-located to Ace as that restaurant gets under way as we write, and everything is just rockin' along here. (Samuel Spain & Michael O'Connor, 33-35 Malone Road ☎ 028-9066 1885 ✉ barkingdogbelfast@googlemail.com 🖱 www.barkingdogbelfast.com – Open noon-10pm Mon-Thu, noon-11pm Fri, noon-11pm Sat, 11am-4pm Sun)

made in Ulster

The Ulster Fry

Bistro

● Beatrice Kennedy

BK is old-school food and style by the current standards of Belfast's post-industrial, retro-chic restaurant design age, but that is a compliment to Jim McCarthy's enduring restaurant, and we salute their ambition to cook and serve classic dishes as well as they can. (Jim McCarthy, 44 University Road ☎ 028-9020 2290 ✉ reception@beatricekennedy.co.uk 🖱 www.beatricekennedy.co.uk – Open 5pm-10.30pm Tue-Sat, 12.30pm-2.30pm, 5pm-8.30pm Sun)

Tea Room & Coffee & Tea Merchant

● SD Bell's

Robert Bell's family-run tea and coffee business pre-dates the coffee-as-lifestyle generation. Four generations of the family have sourced teas and roasted beans and served good brews in the Leaf & Berry bar, and Bell's is as relevant and happening a firm today as it ever was. (Robert Bell, 516 Newtownards Road ☎ 028-9047 1774 ✉ sales@sdbellsteacoffee.com 🖱 www.sdbellsteacoffee.com – Open 8.30am-5pm Mon-Fri, 8.30am-2pm Sat)

Cookery School

● Belfast Cookery School

This purpose-built cookery school does what a good school should do - it empowers. We've known people to re-stock their entire larder in preparation for all that cooking that they are now inspired to do, thanks to good lessons on bread making, healthy eating, fish cookery, or Italian cooking. One gets the feeling that the tutors are also empowered, local experts are brought in as resident teachers, and it's all overseen by the patient and talented Andy Rea, who is certainly someone we could all learn from. (Andy Rea, 53-54 Castle Street, Belfast ☎ 028-9023 4722 www.belfastcookeryschool.com)

Mexican Fast Food

● Boojum

First of all: get to Boojum early, or late, or else be prepared to queue. Secondly, have you noticed how didactic people get with Boojum: have the pork, not the beef; have the beef, not the pork; you don't need cheese; the guacamole is better on Botanic; the guacamole is better in Dublin. Enough already! Just hand me a burrito bowl and let me decide what deliciousness I want today. (73 Botanic Avenue ☎ 028-9031 5334, Chichester Street ☎ 028-9023 0600 www.boojummex.com. Cash only – Open 11.30am-9pm Mon-Fri, noon-9pm Sat)

Café/bar

● Cafe Conor

The Observer called Craig Reid's Big Breakfast the best in Ulster, and *The Guardian* described it as "The Full English and then some...". So, the liberal intelligentsia like Café Conor's classic fry-up, but there's lots more to like here, and Mr Reid has a cosmopolitan touch that is just right: spiced trout with curried potatoes; Moroccan beef tagine; salmon with cracked wheat; bang-bang chicken. Lovely, lovely room, and great art works by Neil Shawcross. (Manus McConn & William Clarke, 11a Stranmillis Road ☎ 028-9066 3266 www.cafeconor.com – Open 9am-10pm Sun & Mon, 9am-11pm Tue-Sat)

Café

● Cafe Nosh

Great service and a sense of humour are what defines Café Nosh, and the service and the sense of fun lift the room out of the ordinary. Phil and Emma do nice stuff – the soda stack; breakfast twist; pie in the sky; the Nosh stew – and it's all done with such charm and dedication that you will find yourself hurrying back. (Phil & Emma Andrews, 64 Comber Road, Dundonald ☎ 028-9048 9199 phil_andrews@tiscali.co.uk www.cafenosh.co.uk – Open 8am-4pm Mon-Wed, 8am-8pm Thur-Fri, 9.30am-4pm Sat)

Café

● Cakes by James

Wow! Up the stairs through the most insignificant entrance and wow! The cakes. A cup of Suki tea and a lemon meringue cupcake. A cup of coffee and a slice of orange almond cake. If these are cakes, then what on earth is everyone else baking? So, up the stairs to James's studio space, and you will discover that you have just ascended to Cake Heaven. Sublime, and joyously surreal. (James, Dawn & Tanya Watson, 2nd Floor, 37 Queen Street ☎ 028-9543 8545 team@cakesbyjames.co.uk www.cakesbyjames.co.uk)

Restaurant

● Cargoes Café and Deli

The venerable Cargoes is now under the care of Stephen Rogan, who manages this great Lisburn Road destination with charm, efficiency and care. Lovely tasty food, and a covetable place for Sunday brunch. (Stephen Rogan, 613 Lisburn Road ☎ 028-9066 5451 9am-7pm Mon-Sat, Sun from 10am. Kitchen closes at 3pm)

Restaurant

● Cayenne

Paul Rankin's career has had the Icarus arc which seems to beset successful people from Northern Ireland: the rapid ascent, the even more rapid descent. But no one can deny that Paul Rankin at his brilliant best gave us a different – and a better – air to breathe. Others may have played a more important role in the food culture of the North, but Rankin was the original star – glimmering; glittering; extravagantly gifted; inspirational. We are certain that there is still a magic that Rankin will somehow show us. (Paul Rankin, 7 Ascot House, Shaftesbury Square ☎ 028-9033 1532 belinda@cayenne-restaurant.com www.cayenne-restaurant.com – Open noon-2.15pm Thur-Sun, 5pm-late Wed-Sun, 6pm-late Sat)

Kitchenware

● The Chef Shop

Lots of good gear for every conceivable cheffing task is waiting for you in the Chef's shop. (Vincent McKenna, Bruce House, 29 Bruce Street ☎ 028-9032 9200 www.thechefshop.net – Open 9am-5.30pm Mon-Thu, 9am-5pm Fri & Sat)

Restaurant

● CoCo

With a brand new restaurant – The Governor Rocks – opened in Donaghadee just as we write, with a menu that is riffing on modern, casual fish cookery – CoCo poses a fashion dilemma. If you dress up big-style to go and eat in CoCo – and you do – can you dress down to go to the 'Governor? "At CoCo on a Saturday night... young and old couples alike are coiffed and preened" Rosemary McCabe wrote in *The Irish Times*. And it's true: CoCo means a big night out, and a fashion statement to match the food statement, which is as hip as they can make it – risotto with poached pears and Gorgonzola; roast salmon with noodle cake and Thai dressing; spring lamb Moroccan style. Jason More is a sure-handed cook, and his crew are excellent. Louboutins, cocktails, off you go...(Jason More & Yvonne Gray, 7-11 Linenhall Street, Belfast ☎ 028-9031 1150 info@cocobelfast-com www.cocobelfast.com – Open noon-3pm Mon-Fri, 5.30pm-late Mon-Sat, noon-9pm Sun)

Butcher

● Coffey's

The twin Coffey's shops are splendid destinations for great beef and lamb and sausages, and the Lisburn Road branch is one of the best sources of game that you will find anywhere. Skill, dedication and expertise are all here waiting for you. (Philip Armstrong, 380 Lisburn Road ☎ 028-9066 6292, 126b Upper Lisburn Road ☎ 028-9061 1982 – Open 8am-5.45pm Mon-Fri, 8am-6pm Sat)

Restaurants and Cafés

● Deanes

Michael Deane is the Van Morrison of the Northern Irish kitchen: brilliant, fully aware of the culture he works in and to which he is devoted, but with a shy truculence, as if he is slightly uncomfortable around people other than in the workings of the kitchen. But his shyness hasn't stopped him building a neat empire of places to eat, and he has always attracted fine young talent into his kitchen, young people who learn well under his tutelage. Like Van Morrison, he is mysterious, and he may even be mysterious to himself. But if you catch the brilliance that comes out of the brooding, it is magic itself, and the food in his restaurants, at whatever level you experience it, is always echt and smart. (Michael Deane, 36-40 Howard Street ☎ 028-9033 1134 ✉ info@michaeldeane.co.uk 🖱 www.michaeldeane.co.uk – Open noon-3pm, 5.30pm-10pm Mon-Sat. Also ● Deane's Seafood Bar, 36-40 Howard Street ☎ 028-9033 1134 Open Mon-Sat noon-late ● Deane's Deli Bistro, 44 Bedford Street ☎ 028-9024 8800 – Open noon-3pm, 5.30pm-10pm Mon-Sat. ● Deane's Deli Vin Cafe, 44 Bedford Street ☎ 028-9024 8800 – Open 8am-10pm Mon-Fri, 9am-10pm Sat. ● Deanes at Queens, 1 College Gardens, Belfast ☎ 028-9038 2111 – Open noon-3pm, 5.30pm-9pm Mon-Tue, 7.50pm-10pm Wed-Sat, 1pm-4pm Sun)

Wine Merchant

● Direct Wine Shipments

The McAlindon brothers run a great show in DWS – great wines, great service, great space, great classes. As in other areas of its food culture – butchers; bakers; restaurants – Northern Irish wine merchants are simply top notch, guys who are on top of their portfolios, and passionate about their profession. Only excellent. (Peter & Neal McAlindon, 5-7 Corporation Square ☎ 028-9050 8000 ✉ shop@directwine.co.uk 🖱 www.directwineshipments.com – Open 9.30am-7pm Mon-Fri, 9.30am-8pm Thu, 9.30am-5.30pm Sat)

Kitchenshop & Café

● Equinox

Kay Gilbert is one of those people who are simply blessed with good taste. From the day they opened their doors – as long ago as 1985 – there has never been an object stocked and sold in Equinox that seemed wrong or incongruous. If Ms Gilbert has chosen it, then you want it: it's that simple. And Ms Gilbert has applied the same logic to the food served in the Equinox café, so whether you are having scrambled eggs and smoked salmon or meatballs with salad and focaccia, or just a cup of coffee with a croissant, it will be just right, the fruit of judgement and discretion. Excellent. (Kay Gilbert, 32 Howard Street ☎ 028-9023 0089 sales@equinoxshop.com www.equinoxshop.com – Shop open 9.30am-5.30pm Mon-Sat, 8.30am-9pm Thur, Cafe open 9.30am-4pm Mon-Fri, 9.30am-4.30pm Sat)

Fishmonger

● Walter Ewing

Walter Ewing is The Man. Well, the Fish Man, to be precise, but it's because of his expertise in the fish business that he has become The Man. If you are enjoying a superb piece of fish in a top-flight restaurant in Belfast and further afield, the chances are that Walter is responsible for its excellence and its quality, He makes the life of chefs much simpler, his fish makes all our lives better. (Walter Ewing, 124 Shankill Road ☎ 028-9032 5534 ewings.seafoods@btconnect.com – Open 9am-5pm Tue-Sat)

Home Bakery

● St George's Saturday Market

Our last visit to the Saturday St George's Market was an early one, but even at 8am the place was buzzing. People were frying crisps, cooking sausages, toasting sodas, you name it. In fact, the cooking side of the market now outweighs the producers side, but the marriage of both is one of the happiest comminglings in the entire country, and the Saturday market is right up there with the best Irish markets. So, if you want to cook, then the produce is superlative – Mullan's Farm; Pheasant's Hill; Atlantic Ocean Delights; Crawford's granola; Hillstown Farm; Silverhill Fish, to name just a few. If you don't want to cook, but just want delicious food, then the choice is almost overwhelming: a bazaar of curries, crêpes, grills, buns, Lebanese foods, Nepalese cooking, you name it. Just mighty. (4-10 Linenhall Street, Belfast ☎ 028-9032 0202 – Open Saturday, 9am-3pm)

Market

● St George's Friday Market

The Friday market adds more bric-a-brac than you will find on Saturday, but it's still great fun and the fish sellers in particular are brilliant. (Linenhall Street, Belfast ☎ 028-9032 0202 – Open 6am-1pm Fri)

Restaurant

Ginger Bistro

Simon McCance is such an earthy cook, and his food has such tactility, that he scarcely seems like a professional cook at all. Sure, he's a pro, all right, and a fine restaurateur, but there is a huge generosity in his food, as if he never counts the cost of any plate, so when you order that belly of pork, you are also going to get fondant potato, black pudding, cabbage, celeriac in a purée and apple sauce, of course, because this is pork, right? So, in Ginger, Simon feeds you, and makes you feel great, because the food is so simple and true. (Simon McCance, 68-72 Great Victoria Street ☎ 028-9024 4421 info@gingerbistro.com www.gingerbistro.com – Open noon-3pm, 5pm-9.30pm Tue-Thur, 5pm-10pm Fri-Sat)

Pizzeria

Greens

Owned and run by the team behind Café Conor, and a valuable resource for echt pizzas for many years now. Mind you, we may be a bit biased about this: Greens do a pizza with black olives, green peppers, tuna and slow-roasted tomatoes and call it the Helen's Bay, which is where the authors and publishers of this guide met each other, all those years ago. Sentiment aside, Greens is a solid-sender. (Manus McConn & William Clarke, 549 Lisburn Road, Belfast ☎ 028-9066 6033 www.greenspizza.com – Open Dinner Mon-Sun, lunch from noon, Fri-Sun)

Restaurant

Hakka Noodle

A lovely tall, spacious room gives Hakka a head-start, and it's the sort of place where everyone returns to eat exactly what they had last time, and what they will have the next time. Beef shin with five spices and star anise for me, then pork with fermented soya noodles. For you, the guotie pork and veg dumpling, then the braised belly pork with preserved vegetables. Again. Why change? (Eddie Fung, 51 Adelaide Street ☎ 028-9031 3270 www.hakkabelfast.co.uk – Open noon-late Mon-Fri, 3pm-late Sat, 1.30pm-9pm Sun)

Restaurant

● Home

Home has proven to be a movable feast; it started on Callendar Street, but has now shifted to Wellington Place and, as William Barry predicted, its fan base has followed this whacky, humorous creation, with its upcycled furniture from ReFound. Andy Rea and Steve Haller just know what to cook and how to serve it – scallop and prawn cakes with red pepper salsa; beef cheek borguignon with creamy mash; a flawless bread and butter pudding; a good cheeseboard. And, if you fall in love with that chair or that mirror, well go right ahead and buy it. (Andy Rea, Steve Haller, Wellington Place, Belfast ☎ 028-9023 4946 🖰 www.homepopup.com – Open coffee, lunch and dinner)

Restaurant

● James Street South

Niall McKenna is a hard-working guy. Behind every plate of food sent out to the table in this most beautiful room, there is an ocean of intelligent consideration, patient application, and painstaking technique. Every cut and fillet is considered, every choice analysed, everything assessed so that it arrives at the table with painterly perfection. But McKenna's brilliance lies in the fact that despite such care, his food always eats true and, indeed, gutsy. With a dish of cod with McSorley leeks and surf clams, it will be the saline hit of the seaweed beurre blanc that will take the whole dish into the stratosphere, like a hidden kiss of flavour that makes you swoon. Mr McKenna's appetite for full-flavoured food – mackerel, Lough Neagh trout, Crossgar pigeon, Lissara chicken – gives his intricate work real oomph! and tactility, so the food eats as beautifully as it looks. With puddings, he shows exhilarating control in specialities like his classic poached rhubarb and strawberry jelly with yellow man and lavender ice cream, or the brilliant salt caramel and chocolate tart. Top of the class. (Niall McKenna, 21 James Street South ☎ 028-9043 4310 ✉ info@jamesstreetsouth.co.uk 🖰 www.jamesstreetsouth.co.uk – Open noon-2.45pm, 5.45pm-10.45pm Mon-Sat, 5.30pm-9pm Sun)

Restaurant

● James Street South Bar + Grill

"A flawless lunch, beautiful room, and great hip staff: Niall McKenna is on a roll", was what John McKenna (no relation) wrote in his notebook after a lunch with his sisters in Bar + Grill. In fact, the meal was perfect, which is a step-up from flawless – crab on toast; duck salad; prawn cocktail to start, then fish pie with green beans; chive and Parmesan risotto; and oxtail with cauliflower, before pitch perfect rice pudding and superb espressos finished the meal. Perfect meals happen rarely, and this was one of them, and we hadn't even ordered anything cooked on their signature Josper grill. That's for the next time, and we can hadly wait for the next time. (Niall McKenna, 21 James Street South ☎ 028-9043 4310 info@jamesstreetsouth.co.uk www.jamesstreetsouth.co.uk – Open noon-2.45pm, 5.45pm-10.45pm Mon-Sat, 5.30pm-9pm Sun)

local knowledge

Retro Sweets

They call them "Retro Sweets" the colourful candies that come in jars. Old-style sweetie shops are once again popping up on our high streets. In Belfast, the demand for candies such as clove rock, cinnamon lozenges, brandy balls, swizzles, chewits never went away. The difference now is these are hip foods, accompanied by Facebook pages, visitor tours and T-shirts.

● **Aunt Sandra's Candy Factory** (60 Castlereagh Road, Belfast ☎ 028-9073 2868 hello@auntsandras.com www.auntsandras.com) ● **W J Shaw & Sons** (Kevin Holland, Unit B3-B4, 17, Heron Road, Belfast ☎ 028-9045 8877)

Fish & Chips

● John Dory's

Whilst our kids like to try out the burgers and sausages in John Dory's, we can't seem to get beyond the fish and chips. That's because the JD fish and chips are such a benchmark demonstration of the art of frying, and of sourcing good fresh fish – the crisps are crunchy and dry, the fish and batter are succulent and clean-tasting. They make it seem easy, but it isn't, and their success in rcent years has been spectacular, as they have expanded to six destinations in and around the city and further afield. (Mark & Stephen Polley, 220-230 Holywood

Road, Belfast ☎ 028-9047 3535. Also at 1a Ballygowan Road, Belfast ☎ 028-9040 1674. Also at Carryduff Shopping Centre, Church Road, Carryduff, Co Antrim ☎ 028-9081 4595. Also at King's Square Shopping Centre, King's Road, Belfast ☎ 028-9079 9914 Also at Hillsborough Road, Lisburn ☎ 028-9266 6225. Also at Ballhackamore ☎ 028-9047 2492 – Open 9am-10pm Mon-Sat, 1pm-9pm Sun www.johndorys.co.uk)

Gastropub

● The John Hewitt

It opened in 1999 and the JH has been going strong ever since. They have always understood the simple truth that good, tasty food will bring people through the doors, again and again. So, you will hear people raving about how good the mash is, how good the sausages are, how good the smoked cod is, how good the fish and chips are. The bar itself is just a sublime place for drinking good Hilden ales. (51 Donegall Street ☎ 028-9023 3768 www.thejohnhewitt.com – Food served noon-2pm Mon-Sat)

Home Bakery

● June's Cake Shop

The Lisburn Road's classic bakery thrives and survives and endures and delights, everytime. Nice food to go at lunchtime. (Loraine Hindley, 376 Lisburn Road ☎ 028-9066 8886 – Open 7.30am-5.30pm Mon-Sat)

Pizza Chain

● Little Wing

The quest for perfect pizza is an obsessive business, which might seem strange given that the end result is a thin tablet of dough with tomato sauce and melted cheese. Ah, but how thin? And what type of tomatoes? And what sort of mozzarella? And what sort of oven? Conall Wolsey attempts to answer these questions in Little Wing, which has quickly multiplied to four branches, so people like the answers he found to the age-old pizza questions. Attention to detail is very sharp, and the branding is as good as it gets. (Conall Wolsey, 10 Anne Street ☎ 028-9024 7000; 201 Upr Newtownards Road ☎ 028-9065 1555; 322 Lisburn Road ☎ 028-9066 6000; 37-39 Main Street, Bangor ☎ 028-9147 1777 www.littlewingpizzeria.com – Open 11am-10pm Mon-Thur till midnight Fri & Sat, 1pm-10pm Sun)

Fish and Chips

● Long's Fish Restaurant

Long's is one of the great chippers, says William Barry, who rates it right up there with Annalong's The Galley or Cork's Jackie Lennox. Praise indeed. (John Copeland, 39 Athol Street, Belfast ☎ 028-9032 1848)

Restaurant

● Love and Death Inc

Chef Stephen Spratt fires out ace food in this super-funky restaurant, bar and club – scallops with white pudding and bee pollen; ham hock and Gruyere sarnie; Dexter skirt steak; foie gras with chocolate and orange. Love & Death Inc is impossibly hip, so you have to surrender to its vibe, and a cocktail or two from Anthony Farrell will help you do just that. (Stephen Spratt, 10a Ann Street, Belfast ☎ 028-9024 7222 www.loveand-deathinc.com – Open noon-midnight Mon-Sun)

Hotel

● Malmaison

Belfast outpost of the UK chain, and always a nice place to stay thanks to small, perfectly-formed, comfortable rooms. We wish the public rooms were brighter, but that's just us getting old. (34-38 Victoria Street, Belfast ☎ 028-9022 0200 www.malmaison.com)

Butcher

● Thomas McCreery's Butchers

McCreery's is a typical butcher's shop, inasmuch as its standards are stellar. Great service, great meats, and very useful prepared foods all add up to a mighty destination. (Nigel McCreery, 439 Ormeau Road ☎ 028-9064 4911 – Open 7.45am-5.45pm Mon-Fri, 6.45am-5.45pm Sat)

Butcher

● Owen McMahon Butchers

McMahons are famous for their sausages, which is really saying something when you consider the standards of sausage making in Belfast and Northern Ireland. Everything else in the shop is just as good. (Owen McMahon, 3-5 Atlantic Avenue ☎ 028-9074 3535 owen@owenmcmahon.com – Open 8.30am-6pm Mon-Sat)

Hotel

The Merchant Hotel

John Paul Leake is head chef in the Merchant's Great Room restaurant, and whilst his cooking attracts most attention in Bill Wolsey's glamorous hotel, there is also good food on offer in Bert's Jazz Bar and in The Cloth Ear. Hayden Lambert is their mixologist in the bar, and this amiable man is the Ferran Adria of the cocktail shaker, a wizard. No visitor to the city should miss one of Mr Lambert's thrilling inventions. (Bill Wolsey, 16 Skipper Street, Belfast ☎ 028-9023 4888 ⌘ www.themerchanthotel.com)

Restaurant

Molly's Yard

"The chunky chips are fit for a king", says William Barry of the mighty Molly's Yard, and it shows the attention to detail they pay to the little things in life. Says William, "If every town had an enterprise like Molly's Yard then Ireland would definitely be a merrier place". Siobhan Scullion and her team do a great job here, so try Ewing's pale smoked haddock on homemade fadge with crisp black pudding and chive hollandaise, the pan-roasted venison, from Finnebrogue Estate, with celeriac and potato dauphinoise, braised red cabbage, cranberry and onion jus. And, of course, their brilliant signature ales from Hilden Brewery, so you should have a Belfast Blonde sitting on your table. (Siobhan Scullion, 1 College Green Mews, Botanic Avenue, Belfast ☎ 028-9032 2600 – Open noon-9pm Mon-Thu, noon-9.30pm Fri & Sat)

Seafood Bar & Fish Shop

Mourne Seafood Bar

Goodness but they have been busy at The Mourne, growing quickly to encompass both the Belfast Cookery School and the Oyster Bar, in addition to their permanent pop-up, Home. Chef Andy Rea and owner Bob McCoubrey have proven themselves to be a forward-looking and dynamic team, able to stay ahead of the swerve. Ally that gift with great cooking, and you have a special place to eat: gurnard with warm lobster vinaigrette; salmon with chorizo and basil mash; hake with wild mushroom risotto cake. Mr Rea's cooking is gutsy and gracious. (Andy Rea, 34-36 Bank Street, Belfast ☎ 028-9024 8544 – Open 1pm-6pm Sun, noon-6pm Mon, noon-9.30pm Tue-Thur, noon-4pm, 5pm-10.30pm Fri & Sat)

Restaurant

● Neill's Hill

So, Alden's dissolves, Neill's Hill emerges, and boss Jonathan Davis and chef Cath Gradwell, one of the greatest teams in Northern Irish cooking, are back working together. Youngsters won't recall just how dazzling a double-act this pair were but, back in the early noughties, Alden's was one of only four restaurants in the north to hold Icon status in our 100 Best Restaurants guide. To suit the lean room, the cooking now is simpler – chicken parmigiana with chips; beef cheeks with garlic mash; endive salad with warm blue cheese dressing; rocky road sundae. A new icon, we reckon. (Jonathan Davis, 229 Upper Newtownards Road ☎ 028-9065 0079 info@neillshill.com www.neillshill.com – Open noon-2.30pm, 6pm-10.30pm Tue-Sat, 'till 11pm Fri & Sat)

Restaurant

● Nick's Warehouse

We have described Nick Price as "the greatest cook in the history of Northern Ireland", and we meant it, and we were right. In the dog days of the North's Troubles, Mr Price was cooking food in Daft Eddy's in Sketrick the like of which people had never seen. He moved to Kilmood and cooked beautifully there, and for more than twenty years he has been cooking delightful food in Hill Street, in Nick's Warehouse, working alongside his wife, Kathy, and an ever-changing, ever-brilliant team. He is a national treasure. (Nick & Kathy Price, 35-39 Hill Street ☎ 028-9043 9690 info@nickswarehouse.co.uk www.nickswarehouse.co.uk – Open noon-3pm, 6pm-10pm Tue-Sat Anix. Upstairs restaurant open noon-3pm)

local knowledge

Moiled Beef

The Tain is an ancient Irish myth, featuring a cattle raid between the two provinces of Ulster and Connacht, and the moiled cattle of today is said to descend from the bronze age strain of beef of this famous saga. Moiled cattle is a small breed that is now being revived throughout Ireland.

Wine Merchant

● Nick's Wines

Nick Price has always been able to spot great wines, and to write about them and sell them in a direct, humorous, unpretentious way. Beautiful bottles, all the way through the price spectrum. (Nick Price, 35-39 Hill Street ☎ 028-9043 9690 ✉ info@nickswarehouse.co.uk 🖱 www.nickswines.co.uk)

Café

● Café Le Petit Ormeau

There's a style and nous to Le Petit Ormeau which is rather winning, and they know what they are good at: salt beef and pickles; pulled pork; croque Monsieur. They even put a bit of style into the standard fry-up, and the result has been a very successful first year – maybe Le Grand Ormeau is next. (274-276 Ormeau Road, Belfast ☎ 028-9064 9245 – Open 9am-4pm Mon-Tue, 9am-5pm Wed-Sat, 10am-3pm Sun)

Oyster Bar

● The Oyster Bar

Order up the sauvignon blanc and then tuck into the small plates of delights such as peel-and-eat langoustines with mayo, or salt and chilli squid with Napa slaw, or ceviche of scallops with focaccia crisps. We will be having the Japanese-style oysters with shredded cucumber and pickled ginger and spiced soy and then half a grilled lobster with lobster cream, fries and salad. Excellent. (Andy Rea, 34-36 Bank Street, Belfast ☎ 028-9024 8544)

Restaurant

● The Potted Hen

The Potted Hen is high in the Belfast restaurant pecking order, says William Barry, and it deserves to be there: the food is presented with style, the room is superb, value for money is top-notch, and the staff know just what they are doing and they do it well. Kick off with the chicken liver parfait with red onion marmalade and a small, perfectly formed, brioche loaf, or maybe salt and chilli squid with garlic aioli and sweet chilli dips. For mains, smart choices include rib-eye steak with homemade chunky chips or roast breast of Antrim chicken with herb and garlic sable potato, whilst the slow-cooked pork belly with Clonakilty black pudding, celeriac purée, spinach and apple sorbet is the star of

the show. Excellent homemade desserts include apple and plum crumble and spiced pear bread and butter pudding, and Irish cheeses include Crozier Blue, Milleens and Gubbeen. (Dermot & Catherine Regan, Edward Street, Belfast ☎ 028-9023 4554 info@thepottedhen.co.uk www.thepottedhen.co.uk – 10.30am-2.45pm, 5pm-9.30pm Mon-Sat, open till 10pm Fri & Sat, noon-9pm Sun)

made in Ulster

Suki Tea

Restaurant

● Il Pirata

Everyone loves Il Pirata. They like the room, with its minimalist chic and open-view styling, they like the very friendly service, they like the modern, Med-accented food from Tony O'Neill, one of the great modern cooks – spinach and goat's cheese ravioli; butternut squash risotto; and cheese salad was what John McKenna and his sisters shared on their visit. And, of course, everyone is very happy to have a destination in this neck of the woods, serving small plates, serving good drinks, and we are too. Tony O'Neill's cooking won an audience from the day they opened their doors, and Il Pirata hasn't slowed down for a moment since. (Sam Spain, 279-281 Upper Newtownards Road, Belfast iLPirataBelfast@gmail.com – No reservations taken. Open noon-10pm Mon-Thu, noon-11pm Fri-Sat, noon-10pm Sun)

Restaurant

● Restaurant Victoria

Raymond McArdle also runs Restaurant 23 at the Balmoral Hotel in Warrenpoint, so David McGain is head chef at Victoria, even though Ray's name is on the title and it's his mug shot outside this big, ornate room. Mr McArdle is a classicist, as anyone who knows his food from Deane's and the Nuremore Hotel can attest. His pairings are always clean and logical: duck confit with spinach; salt and chilli squid with ginger and spring onion; fish pie with cauliflower gratin; sirloin with Caesar salad. On busy nights the room offers great theatre, and good cooking drives home the vibe. (Ray McArdle, 60 Great Victoria Street, Belfast ☎ 028-9033 2121 eat@restaurantvictoria.co.uk www.restaurantvictoria.co.uk – Open noon-2.30pm, 5.30pm-10pm Mon-Sat)

Burger Restaurant

● Rocket & Relish

It started with a burger van at music festivals, and has morphed into a cool Lisburn Road address with wow! burgers. Chris Boyd's R&R offers amazing lunchtime value as well as those comin'-at-ya burgers: bacon and blue for me, feta and tapenade for Sally, aubergine vegetarian for Connie; cheese and onion for Sam and chicken and sweet chilli for PJ. Now, who's got the Headless Dogs? (Chris Boyd, 479-481 Lisburn Road ☎ 028-9066 5655 www.rocketandrelish.com)

Restaurant

● Rhubarb

It's easy to miss Rhubarb, hidden away off Bruce Street, so put on your best culinary detective to find a little place with honest cooking, and some amazing value for money. Somehow, everything they cook adds up to comfort food – French toast with bacon for breakfast; bacon and cabbage or steak and mushroom stroganoff for lunch; Tyrone beef on roast garlic mash for dinner. BYO in the evenings means a bargain big night out. (Norman Green, 2 Little Victoria Street ☎ 028-9020 0158 www.rhubarb-belfast.co.uk)

Delicatessen

● Sawyer's Deli

Belfast's first true deli is as youthful and energised today as it was when John McKenna used to visit when he was a nipper living just up the road. A treasure trove and a delight, and endlessly surprising. (Kieran Sloan, Fountain Centre ☎ 028-9032 2021 sawyersltd@gmail.com www.sawyersbelfast.com – Open 9am-6pm Mon-Sat)

Restaurant

● Shu

Shu is a class act, all the way home. Alan Reid's team, in the kitchen and at front of house, exude a polished professionalism that has kept the restaurant at the head of the Belfast pack for more than a decade, a mighty achievement for any city destination. And as other city restaurateurs have seen their empires boom and then bust, Mr Reid and his chef, Brian McCann, do what they know they do best: they fire out great food in a room with an intoxicating ambience, and they do it every night. So, put on your good rags and come out to enjoy

some hot contemporary cooking from a brilliant talent – pickled calves' tongue salad; spicy braised beef with harissa and potato purée; 24-hour shoulder and breast of lamb with aubergine caviar; Drumbeg tomatoes with macaroni. (Alan Reid, 253 Lisburn Road ☎ 028-9038 1655 eat@shu-restaurant.com www.shu-restaurant.com – Open noon-2.30pm, 5.30pm-10pm Mon-Sat. Two sittings on Fri & Sat, 7pm & 9.30pm)

Kitchenware & Homeware

● Still

Highly desirable kitchen gear nestles alongside lots of lovely homeware in Still. (Maurice & Sharon Rankin, Royston House, 34 Upper Queen Street ☎ 028-9023 0494 info@stillforlife.com www.stillforlife.com – Open 9.30am-5.30pm Mon-Sat, 9.30am-8pm Thur)

Tea Blenders

● Suki Tea

Anne and Oscar's Suki Tea has really risen to prominence since they started back in 2005. It's no mean feat to get people to divert from their stubborn attachment to established tea brands, but these guys have done it thanks to great brews, and inspired, hip marketing. You will, as they say, find Suki teas in all the best places. (Anne Rooney & Oscar Woolley, 155 Northumberland Street ☎ 028-9033 0938)

Restaurant

● Tedfords

Alan Foster has to be the most low-key chef in Ireland. Where others crave attention, he stays in his kitchen and cooks, and he cooks extremely well, which makes Tedford's one of Belfast's best restaurants. Mr Foster likes formality, both in the setting, and in the cooking: he wants you to see the work, but he doesn't lay it on, and the food is very clean and logical: turbot with crab-crushed potatoes and shellfish foam; roast loin of lamb with slow-cooked shoulder and pommes Anna; cod with chorizo, tomato and whitebean casserole. The great American food writer, Colman Andrews, even dropped us a line after eating in Tedfords, to say how much he enjoyed the cooking, and that is praise indeed. (Alan Foster, 5 Donegall Quay ☎ 028-9043 4000 www.tedfordsrestaurant.com – Open noon-2.30pm Thur-Fri, 5pm-late Tue-Sat)

Restaurant

● Café Vaudeville

Feed droves of people with good food, then turn the place into a hot, rockin' nightspot. That should be impossible, but somehow they manage it in Café Vaudeville. Above all, chef Damian Tumilty and his crew manage a level of culinary consistency that is amazing, given the huge numbers of diners, and given that the dishes have a lot of elements – loin of Lough Erne lamb, 18-hour slow-cooked shoulder, shepherd's pie, carrot purée and glazed shallots – is a fairly typical plate. The decor, meantime, is vaudevillian psychedelia, writ large. (Damian Tumilty, 25-39 Arthur Street, Belfast ☎ 028-9043 9160 www.cafevaudeville.com – Open daily for lunch & dinner)

Wine Shop

● The Vineyard

An Aladdin's cave of everything bibulous, Tony McGurran's shop is simply brilliant. The range of wines, spirits, beers, ciders and gear is unrivalled, and the shop is one of Belfast's unsung glories. If you are in the market for something arcane, obscure and delightful, then the Vineyard should be your first port of call: we could while away hours in here... (Tony McGurran, 375-377 Ormeau Road ☎ 028-9064 5774 info@vineyardbelfast.co.uk www.vineyardbelfast.co.uk – Open 9.30am-10pm Mon-Thu, 9.30am-11pm Fri & Sat, 11.30am-9pm Sun)

Delicatessen

● The Yellow Door

Simon Dougan and his team have been feeding the people well for almost two decades now. From the simplest sandwich to the grandest wedding catered by their catering crew, these guys are the business, and it is easy to understand why. Mr Dougan, you see, is a philosopher of food: he thinks very, very deeply about what he cooks and how he cooks it, what he wants it to be and what he wants his food to do. He is a very nourishing cook, he wants to bring goodness to people's lives, and he has wanted to do that right throughout his career. He is one of the most significant chefs in Northern Ireland, and the Yellow Door is a place where the cooking feeds more than your appetite. (Simon Dougan, 427 Lisburn Road ☎ 028-9038 1961 yellowdoorbelfast@hotmail.com www.yellowdoordeli.co.uk – Open 8am-3.30pm Mon-Sat)

County Antrim

Annaghmore

Artisan Cider

● Toby's Cider

Toby's produce two cider varieties – Original and Katy – with Armagh apples and what is notable about Craig and Karen's ciders is that they use the traditional rack-and-cloth press technique and the ciders are bottle-conditioned, with the final fermentation occurring in the bottle, giving a little fizz. You will find them in great wine shops such as The Vineyard in Belfast and Drink-store and Jus De Vine in Dublin, as well as Mulligan's and The Black Sheep. (Craig & Karen, Annaghmore Craig@TobysCider.co.uk www.tobyscider.co.uk)

Ballyclare

Organic Farm Shop

● Ballylagan Organic Farm

Organic farm, organic farm shop and tea room, and guesthouse. Patricia and Tom Gilbert cover all the bases in Ballylagan, and how! Just look at their wraps in the tea room, for instance: gammon (from their own rare breed pigs); egg (from their own hens); salmon (sustainably fished wild Alaskan). The Gilberts are pioneers, and they are pushing the boundaries of what a working organic farm can be, how it can serve a community, and how it can welcome guests for a pastoral idyll. Their vision is holistic, your delight will be bounteous. (Tom & Patricia Gilbert, 12 Ballylagan Road, Straid, Ballyclare ☎ 028-9332 2867 ✉ ballylagan@aol.com 🖱 www.ballylagan.com – Open 10am-5pm Wed-Sat)

Butcher

● Errol Jenkins Butchers

With beef and lamb from their own Ballycairn Farm, servicing a typically meticulous butcher's shop and deli, Jenkin's is one of the top-flight butchers. Preparation and presentation are top notch, the deli foods are great and, should you happen to live away from Ballyclare, there is a delivery service availlable via their site. (Errol Jenkins, 41 Main Street, Ballyclare ☎ 028-9334 1822 info@jenkinsbutchers.co.uk www.jenkinsbutchers.co.uk – Open 8am-6pm Mon-Sat)

made in Ulster

Bushmills Whiskey

Ballymena

Coffee bar

● Ground Espresso Bar

The London *Independent* included Ground amongst its Fifty Best Coffee shops in spring 2012, a tribute to the high standards of this small chain of shops, who have three in-store branches in Belfast – in Next, Waterstones and DV8 – as well as their quartet of stores in the North. The stores are hip, stylish and fun, and comfortable too. (Karen Gardiner, 30-32 Ballymoney Street ☎ 028-2565 0060 www.groundcoffee.net – Open 9am-5.30pm Mon-Sat. Also 25 Kingsgate Street, Coleraine ☎ 028-7032 8664 at 4 High Street, Ballymoney ☎ 028-2766 2625; 52 Main Street, Portrush ☎ 028-7082 5979)

Guesthouse

● Marlagh Lodge

When we were writing the text for the places to stay and eat for *The Irish Times* Great Drives app – you can get it at www.irishtimes.com/mobile – one of the drives created by Bob Montgomery was on the A43, around the Glen of Antrim. Well, that was an easy one to do: if you are up exploring the Glens, then you stay and eat at Marlagh Lodge. It is as simple as that. Starting from a near-ruin, Robert and Rachel Thompson have resurrected, renovated and restored a stunningly beautiful house, with apposite period details in every room. What is equally stunning is Rachel's glorious cooking, with every dish both graceful and flavour-filled, carefully sourced and cooked, enjoyed in the William Morris-style room by candlelight, with a bottle of wine from James Nicholson's wine merchants to add to the pleasure. Could anything be nicer after a day driving through the Glens? No sir. (Rachel & Robert Thompson, 71 Moorfields Road, Ballymena ☎ 028-2563 1505 info@marlaghlodge.com www.marlaghlodge.com – Open all year)

Ballyrobert

Restaurant

● Oregano

Dermot and Catherine Regan have enjoyed great success with The Potted Hen in Belfast city centre, but it is their work in Oregano that first won them attention for honest, imaginative cooking that was unabashedly delicious. The flair of the cooking is matched by confidence across the discipline: they make a good risotto verde with peas, spinach and broccoli, and will even add avocado ice cream to a crab risotto; they have fun with nice ideas like cauliflower pannacotta, and their fish cookery is sure and true – Glenarm salmon with seared foie gras; saffron monkfish with chorizo pilaf and pork belly. Influences are nicely melded and assimilated, and value is excellent. (Dermot & Catherine Regan, 21 Ballyrobert Road, Ballyrobert ☎ 028-9084 0099 ✉ info@oreganorestaurant.co.uk 🖱 www.oreganorestaurant.co.uk – Open noon-2.30pm, 5.30pm-9.30pm Tue-Fri, 6pm-10pm Sat, noon-7pm Sun)

Bushmills

Garden Centre Cafe

● Bushmills Garden Centre

The Creative Gardens centres at Bushmills and Donaghadee were amongst the first centres to recognise the value of serving good, hand-made food so that a trip to get the seed potatoes or to buy a new Weber barbecue could become a good day out with delicious food and lunches. They maintain their standards with enviable consistency in both centres. (Jane Rankin, Ballyclough Road, Bushmills ☎ 028-9188 3603 🖱 www.creativegardens.net – Open 10am-5pm, 12.30pm-5pm Sun)

Hotel & Restaurant

● The Bushmills Inn

Alan Dunlop knows the value of a peat fire. Should you arrive at the Bushmills Inn in the midst of inclement weather – and it's not unknown to be modestly inclement this far north – then you will walk into the hotel and the peat fire will be burning, and you will feel: I'm at home! What's for dinner? Can I have a glass of whiskey? The cooking will bring on the pleasure principle:

Kilhorne Bay crab macaroni; Donegal salmon with a Parmesan crisp; duo of crêpes with a Cashel Blue sauce; sweet chocolate delice. If you are visiting the new Giants Causeway centre, Bushmills is your base. (Alan Dunlop, 9 Dunluce Road, Bushmills ☎ 028-2073 2339 mail@bushmillsinn.com www.bushmillsinn.com – Open noon-5pm Mon-Sat, 12.30pm-2.30pm Sun, 6pm-9.15pm Mon-Sun)

Distillery

● The Old Bushmills Distillery

The distillery tour of the classic Bushmills Distillery is a tourist trip that is very worth your while. The whiskeys taste even better after you have seen where and how they are made, for the ancient process of fashioning the water of life is fascinating and absorbing. The resulting whiskeys, especially the single malt, are as fine as any whiskey made anywhere. (Bushmills ☎ 028-2073 1521 www.bushmills.com)

local knowledge

Yellowman

Yellowman is a honeycomb sweet that was sold in stalls from Irish fairs and festivals of old, poetically remembered in the Auld Lammas Fair in County Antrim.

Galgorm

Restaurant and Resort

● Galgorm Resort & Spa

"The best meal I've had in years. Everything was sensational", was how William Barry summed up Chris Bell's cooking in the River Room at Galgorm. Mr Bell actually began his career here as a 16-year-old, and now he is back and hunting for glory. He will get it, just as you get the glory of vegetable soup with walnut and Leggygowan goat's cheese; seared scallops with a haggis fritter; slow-cooked pork belly with cider fondant and apple; chicken liver and foie gras parfait with brioche; Angus beef with braised beef shin pie; white chocolate mousse with oats and honey, and a fantastic cheese trolley. Service is impeccable, the room is sumptuous and glam. Chris Bell is one of the best cooks. (Yvonne Moore, Galgorm ☎ 028-2588 1001 www.galgorm.com)

Glenarm

Organic Farmed Salmon

● Glenarm Organic Salmon

Glenarm show how you should raise farmed fish: to organic standards, in fast-flowing waters, producing fish of exceptional quality. One of the North's iconic food brands. (John Russell, Glenarm ☎ 028- 2884 1691 info@glenarmorganicsalmon.com www.glenarmorganicsalmon.com)

Glengormley

Butcher

● Thompson's Butchers

David Thompson runs a great shop, his beef magnificently matured, and all his other products are expertly made, and consistently excellent. (David Thompson, 7 Ballyclare Road, Glengormley thompson-butcher@hotmail.com ☎ 028-9083 2507 – Open 8am-5pm Mon, Wed & Sat, 8am-5.30pm Tue, Thu & Fri)

Lisburn

Artisan Cider & Apple Juice

● DJ's Juice & Cider

Davy and Janet Uprichard run the Hollybrook Nursery and also make the four varieties of Tempted? cider, as well as DJ's apple juice. The ciders come as a medium-dry and a medium-sweet, there is a special reserve cider and a strawberry cider, made with strawberry wine which Davy also produces. The excellent apple juices can be found in good shops as well as the garden centre, and hunt down the Tempted? cider in pubs and good wine shops. (Davy & Janet Uprichard, 2 Agars Road, Lisburn ☎ 028-9262 1219 www.temptedcider.co.uk)

made in Ulster

Twisted Hop

Home Bakery

● Country Kitchen Home Bakery

Chris Ferguson and his team – all 25 of them – bake and cook from early in the morning, getting the good breads and cakes and biscuits ready, preparing their breakfasts and popular lunches. They have been at it for nigh on thirty years, so those farls and baps have a lot of history behind them. (Chris & Audrey Ferguson, 57-59 Sloan Street, Lisburn ☎ 028-9267 1730 country_kitchen@btconnect.com www.countrykitchenlisburn.co.uk – Open 8am-5pm Mon-Sat)

Brew Pub

● Hilden Brewing Company & Tap Room

Philip Clasper's cooking in the smartly renovated Tap Room restaurant, at the wonderful Hilden Brewery, is sharp and tasty: Tap Room gravadlax with quail's egg and chocolate stout wheaten bread; wild mushroom gnocchi with Gorgonzola cream; pressed belly of pork with sautéed Comber potatoes; lemon posset with raspberry coulis. In the brewery itself, Owen Scullion brews up a masterly range of beers, both in bottle and on cask, and it is worth noting, at a time when artisan brewing is one of the dynamos of Irish speciality food, that Hilden is the original Irish micro-brewery, established by Seamus Scullion more than thirty years ago. Look out for the beers in good pubs and in their sister restaurant in Belfast, Molly's Yard. A glass of Twisted Hop, a plate of soused herrings, and isn't life at Hilden just great! (Owen Scullion, Grand Street, Lisburn ☎ 028-9266 3863 www.taproomhilden.com – Tap Room Open 12.30pm-2.30pm, 5.30pm-9pm Tue-Sun)

Bistro

● Square Bistro

Stevie and Christina do the good thing in the Square Bistro, on the Square, and they are hard-working guys, starting first thing with breakfast, on through lunch with a good mix of wraps, sandwiches and other dishes, and then into dinner, where Stevie's cooking can open out – scallops with pea purée and chorizo butter; antipasti plate; trio of pork with dauphinoise potatoes and black pudding; Lissara duck with butternut squash purée. (Stephen & Christina Higginson, 18 Lisburn Square, Lisburn ☎ 028-9266 6677 www.squarebistro.co.uk– Open 9.30am-4pm Mon-Tue, 9.30am-late Wed-Sat)

Deli & Patisserie

● The Yellow Door

The Lisburn branch of Simon Dougan's famed bakery and deli is an indispensible part of the town, and a wonderful place to enjoy real cooking. (Simon Dougan, 46-48 Market Square ☎ 028-9260 6890)

Portrush

College Canteen

● The Academy

Students at the respected Portrush catering college cook for the Academy restaurant. (Portrush College, Portrush ☎ 028-7032 3970 www.ulster.ac.uk/portrush/academy)

B&B

● Maddybenny Farmhouse

The White family's Maddybenny is a complex of guest houses – there are six in total – along with B&B which is offered in the main house, and a top-class riding school – their horse Porterhouse Just a Jiff was selected for the Irish Olympic eventing team in 2012. Maddybenny is an institution, and a lovely getaway, whether or not you want to saddle up. (Karen White, 18 Maddybenny Park, Portrush, Coleraine ☎ 028-7082 3394 www.maddybenny.com)

Restaurants and Wine Bars Complex

● Ramore Restaurants

The Ramore complex rings all the bells – Italian food in Coast, Asian food in the Oriental, international dishes in the Wine Bar, whilst there are steaks and grills from the woodburning grill in the Harbour Bistro. The harbour Bar, meantime, is a darling wee pub. As a mix, it's a little like Las Vegas in Portrush. (George McAlpin, ● **Ramore Oriental** ☎ 028-7082 6969 – Open 5.30pm-9.30pm Wed-Thur, 6.30pm-10.30pm Fri & Sat, 5.30pm-9.30pm Sun ● **Coast** ☎ 028-7082 3311 – Open 5pm-9.30pm Wed-Fri, 4.45pm-10.30pm Sat, 3pm-9pm Sun ● **Harbour Bistro** ☎ 028-7082 2430 – Open 5pm-10pm Mon-Fri, 5pm-10.30pm Sat, 5pm-9.30pm Sun ● **Ramore Wine Bar** ☎ 028-7082 4313 – Open lunch & dinner Mon-Sun www.ramorerestaurant.com)

County Armagh

Armagh

Butcher

● A Flanagan & Son

David Flanagan is a member of the Elite Guild of butchers, and his standards of meat preparation and presentation are stellar. There is an excellent deli as well, and don't miss the sausages and the cured gammons. (David Flanagan, 1 Scotch Street, Armagh ☎ 028-3752 2805 davidflanagan2@hotmail.co.uk– Open 9am-5.30pm Mon-Thur, 8.30am-6pm Fri & Sat)

Bistro

● Uluru Bistro

Dean and Sara have been working away steadily at the pretty Uluru for a few years now, but it's been over the last year or two that their profile has really risen, and the awards and accolades are stacking up. Mr Coppard has a few menu elements as a tribute to his Aussie background – kangaroo and so on – but it's when he stays close to home that the sparks fly – crab with green pea soup; scallops with black pudding and a fennel beurre blanc; wood pigeon with winter ratatouille; chicken with colcannon rosti and wild mushrooms. Mr Coppard loves to cook, and folk just love to eat his cooking – recommend Uluru to a friend and you can expect to be getting the tweets from the minute they sit down. Mrs Coppard runs the rooms superbly. (Dean & Sara Coppard, 16 Market Street, Armagh ☎ 028-3751 8051 uluru_bistro@hotmail.co.uk www.ulurubistro.com – Open noon-3pm Tue-Sat, 5pm-late Tue-Sun)

Craigavon

Craft Brewery

● Clanconnel Brewing Company

The re-branding of Clanconnel's McGrath's ales is one of the best pieces of design work we have seen in ages – well done Drinksology. The beers have been rechristened in honour of the celebrated greyhound, Master

McGrath, and there are five brews: No 1 is the red ale, No 2 is the pale ale, No 3 is the white ale, No 4 is the black stout, and no 5 is the blonde ale, destined for release as we write. (Mark Pearson, PO Box 316, Craigavon ☎ 028-7711 626770 info@clanconnelbrewing.com www.clanconnelbrewing.com)

Country House

● Newforge House

John and Lou have brought great, youthful energy to the beautiful Newforge House, with a lot of that energy finding its way into Mr Mather's fine cooking – garden beetroot with grilled goat's cheese and walnuts; Armagh beef with garlic butter; halibut with watercress; roast rhubarb with yogurt pannacotta. The house itself has been beautifully restored, and the comfort is swaddling. A dynamic destination. (John & Louise Mathers, Magheralin, Craigavon ☎ 028-9261 1255 enquiries@newforgehouse.com www.newforgehouse.com)

Forkhill

Artisan Cider

● Mac's Armagh Cider

Sean McAtee is a true artisan cider maker, and a crusader. His ciders are, he says, in the Health/Medical/Pharmaceutical business, and are the "focal point of the Armagh 'revivalist' cider movement". His trio of ciders are all made in very small batches – Mac's Dry is high in tannins with no added sugar; Mac's Sweet has added sugar and less tannins; and Mac's Lyte has half the alcohol of the others and sweetness thanks to unfermented apple sugar. Mac's Dry is just fascinating, and look for it in the brilliant Vineyard on the Ormeau Road in Belfast and at festivals. (Sean McAtee, Forest Road, Forkhill armaghcider@gmail.com)

Lurgan

Butcher, Deli & Coffee Shop

● John R Dowey & Son

John and Simon's shop is a phenomenon, a place where thousands of customers come every week to buy from a portfolio of almost 1,000 meats and deli goods that have won the team every imaginable award in every imaginable competition. The coffee shop next door provides good coffee and nice things to eat after you have bought all the delicious things you will be cooking for dinner. (John & Simon Dowey, 20 High Street, Lurgan ☎ 028-3832 2547 john@johnrdowey.co.uk wwwjohnrdowey.co.uk – Open 8.30am-5.30pm Mon-Sat)

Portadown

Artisan Cider

● Armagh Cider Company

The Troughton family have been growing apples at Ballinteggart House for four generations, but cider making has only come to the farm in recent years. Today all the cider production is based on the farm, where two brands are fashioned – Madden's Mellow Armagh Cider, and Carson's, the drier of the two blends. There are also apple juices – AJ – and apple cider vinegar, mulled cider and an apple punch. Clean, vivid drinks, and all beautifully packaged. (Philip, Helen and Mark Troughton, Ballinteggart House, 73 Drumnasoo Road, Portadown ☎ 028-3833 4268 info@armaghcider.com www.armaghcider.com)

Apple Juice

● Barnhill Apple Juice

Ken Redmond conjures up a lovely series of mixes from his many varieties of apples, fashioning single-varietal juices and a series of apple juices mixed with other fruits – apple and elderflower; apple and blackberry; apple and cinnamon, and so on. The Barnhill juices are stocked by many good shops, and can be bought from the farm. You will also find them at the St George's Market, and at many fairs and agricultural shows. The juices are pure and refreshing, agrestic and natural. (Ken Redmond, Barnhill, Portadown ☎ 028-3885 1190)

Butcher

● Knox's Food Court

Whether you call it a food court or an emporium, what you need to know about Knox's is that everything you could possibly need is all here, sold with skill and politeness, expertise and culture. Butcher, baker, greengrocer, deli and caterer, Knox's do it all, and do it all as well as it can be done. (Barry Knox, 388 West Street, Portadown ☎ 028-3835 3713 knoxfoodcourt@mail.com www.tknoxfoodcourt.co.uk – Open 8.30am-6pm Mon-Sat)

Artisan Cider Company

● MacIvor's Cider Co

"With cider making, it felt like I had finally come home", Greg MacNeice told John Wilson in *The Irish Times*. Mr MacNeice is a patient man: coming home took four years, in order to get that recipe right for MacIvor's cider, the right balance between dessert apples, Bramleys and cider apples to balance fruit with tannins. The ciders come in two styles: medium, and traditional dry. Medium is sweeter, and a more popular style than the more complex, earthy traditional dry. Look out for the fox in the orchard! (Greg MacNeice, Ardress East, Portadown ☎ 028-3885 1381 sales@macivors.com www.macivors.com)

Delicatessen

● The Yellow Door Deli & Patisserie

Portadown is where the iconic Yellow Door began its journey into the culinary consciousness of Northern Ireland. Simon Dougan has not put a foot wrong since the YD opened, and the company's development has been built on hard work and an implicit understanding of the pleasures of food. Whether you want a creamy bun or a wedding for 200 guests, you just need to open the Yellow Door. (Simon Dougan, 74 Woodhouse Street, Portadown ☎ 028-3835 3528 info@yellowdoordeli.co.uk www.yellowdoordeli.co.uk – Open 9am-5pm Mon-Sat)

Tandragee

Traditional Breeds Farm Shop

● Forthill Farm

"At Forthill, we have returned to the traditionl breeds of both cattle and pigs, namely Belted Galloway and Longhorn cattle, and Gloucester Old Spots and British Saddleback pigs. It is our belief that the older traditional breeds produce meat of superior quality". And so say all of us! Hooray for Ken and Jennifer Gracery and their retro-innovation, giving us back the animals and the tastes and textures that belong in Ireland. We should all be quite clear about the fact that pasture-reared meat from traditional breeds is a health food, one to be consumed with enjoyment in the knowledge that it is doing us good. So, get these fabulous foods into your diet by buying from the farm shop, or ordering online, and look out for the meat in good restaurants who appreciate and respect its flavour and savour. (Kenny & Jennifer Gracey, 80 Ballymore Road, Tandragee ☎ 028-3884 0818 ✉ info@forthillfarm.co.uk 🖱 www.forthillfarm.co.uk – Open 9am-5pm Tue-Sat, late opening till 8.30pm Thur)

Oats

● White's

What Flahavan's are to the Republic, White's are to the North: millers of oats, providers of breakfast. Like Flahavan's, their history extends back over 170 years, to when oats were a vitally important crop, and they have kept the faith, whilst expanding the range to cater for modern tastes and lifestyles. White's is the way to start your day. (23 Scarva Road, Tandragee ☎ 028-3884 0592 ✉ whites@whiteoats.co.uk 🖱 www.whitesoats.co.uk)

local knowledge

Craft Cider

There is a strong tradition of both making and drinking cider in Ireland. Latterly, the two principal apple regions in Ireland were Tipperary and Armagh. But good orchards were widespread in Ireland dating back centuries, and communal presses were common.

Then cider fell out of favour and many of the orchards were destroyed. Ale and beer and whiskey became better known as indigenous Irish drinks.

All that is changing again now, with a burst of producers blossoming throughout the country. Recently, Bramley apples from Armagh have been awarded protected geographical indication status. Meanwhile, real cider vinegar and apple juice are enjoying a corresponding revival.

County Down

Annalong

Fish and Chip Shop

● Galley Fish and Chip Shop

You can enjoy The Galley's legendary fish and chips – and all the other things they make – in their café, but we suspect that for many devotees of Joey and Aileen Chamber's iconic fish and chip shop, the way to eat your supper is to buy from the Carry Out, then head back to your car, and enjoy your fish supper whilst looking out at the sea. There are, of course, many other things to eat on the menu, but the battered haddock, cod, whiting or hake, with their peerless chips, is a dinner to savour, the art of the fryer at its zenith. (Aileen & Joey Chambers, 43 Kilkeel Rd, Annalong ☎ 028-4376 7253 www.thegalleyannalong.co.uk – Open 9am-9pm Mon-Sun)

Ardglass

Restaurant & Bar

● Curran's Seafood & Steak Restaurant

Paula Mahon's inn stands at the junction of five country roads, and in the jumble of rooms you will find swaddling comfort and tasty food for all the family: Dundrum Bay mussels; seafood chowder; ciabatta garlic bread; haddock with mushy peas; steakburger; sirloin with tobacco onions. Great staff offer genuine, warm service in a welcoming place. (Paula Mahon, 83 Strangford Road, Chapeltown, Ardglass ☎ 028-4484 1332 info@curransbar.net www.curransbar.net – Bar open 11.30am-11.30pm. Restaurant open 12.30pm-9pm Mon-Sun, last orders 8.50pm. Sunday carvery 12.30pm-4pm)

Fishmonger

● S&P Milligan

Milligan's operate a fleet of fish vans which sell fresh fish at different locations around the province. (Seamus Milligan, 20 Downpatrick Road, Ardglass ☎ 028-4484 1595 sales@sp-milligan.co.uk www.sp-milligan.co.uk)

Ballynahinch

Fish and Chip Café

● Ginesi's

Gillian and Romano are the third generation of the family to run this venerable institution, which opened originally in Lisburn before moving to Ballynahinch in 1964. It's a place where you fill up with classic fish and chips or an Ulster fry after a big hike in the Mournes. They operate a delivery service for folk in the zone. (Gillian & Romano Ginesi, 34 Main Street, Ballynahinch ☎ 028-9756 2653 – Open 9am-8pm Mon-Tue, 9am-8.30pm Wed, 9am-9pm Thu-Sat, 2.30pm-9pm Sun)

Banbridge

Butcher

● MA Quail

Quail's is a wonderful butcher's shop, deli and café, one of those traditional destination addresses that is the backbone of a town like Banbridge. The original butcher's shop has developed to add the deli and café, and also a second café outlet at the F.E. McWilliam gallery on the Newry Road, wher you can enjoy both Quail's excellent cookery and also the wonderful sculptures of F.E. The shop is famous for hams and limousin beef, aged for a month, but in truth everything here is as good as everything else, and the service culture is wholly exceptional. (Joseph Quail, 13-15 Newry Street, Banbridge ☎ 028-4066 2604 ✉ jquail@quailsfinefoods.co.uk 🖰 www.quailsfinefoods.co.uk – Open 8.30am-5.30pm Mon-Sat)

Coffee Roaster

● Ristretto

There are encouraging signs that the coffee culture that has swept through Dublin in recent years is taking hold in Northern Ireland, and Gregg Radcliffe and Mark Anderson and their crew are doing their best to spread the message and the delights of great, fresh, expertly roasted, expertly served coffee. They supply the best restaurants, and getting Ristretto into your life will improve it no end. (Gregg Radcliffe, Mark Anderson, Unit 49 Banbridge Enterprise Centre, Scarva Road, Banbridge ☎ 028-4062 3242 🖰 www.ristrettocoffee.com)

Home Bakery

● Windsor Bakery

Gordon Scott has a simple ambition in The Windsor: cook tasty food, and serve it with a smile. That's a good, modest formula, and it has worked in The Windsor for fifty five years, for they opened their doors in 1957. The baking is top notch in the way only Northern Irish bakeries do it: precise, yet comforting; skilled, yet unassuming; tasty, and served with a smile. It's a great destination for breads and cakes, and for good comfort cooking in the café. Fifty five more years begin today. (Gordon Scott, 36-38 Newry Street, Banbridge ☎ 028-4062 3666 – Open 7.30am-5.30pm Mon-Sat. Also at 30 Bridge Street, Banbridge ☎ 028-4062 5177 Café open 8am-4.30pm, bread counter open 7.30am-5.30pm 🖃 winbake@btconnect.com)

Bangor

Butcher

● David Burns Butchers

Do you know what amazes us about David Burns Butchers? It's not just the superb quality of the meat – we take that for granted – nor the charm and efficiency of the service – we take that for granted, too. No, it's how phenomenally busy this shop is, from the moment they open their doors at 7am in the morning. And, of course, at holiday times and especially at Xmas, the place goes ballistic. Nothing nicer than waiting in line in Burns's, knowing that George and Brian always do their best, and that everything will be superb. And, of course, don't miss the legendary pork sausages. (Brian & George Burns, 112 Abbey Street, Bangor ☎ 028-9127 0073 🖃 www.burnsbutchers.co.uk– Open 7am-5pm Tue-Thur, 6am-7pm Fri, 6am-5pm Sat)

Restaurant

● The Boat House

"The Boat House is a special place", says Catherine Cleary in *The Irish Times*. With Joery Castell in the kitchen and his brother, Jasper, out front, the interplay between the pair is as sinuous as the best Dutch Total Football. Joery has that great modern gift of being able to use a palette of ingredients, yet never losing his focus on any part of the dish – his crab dish has a buttermilk and lemon grass pannacotta, coriander shoots, pineapple crisps and pearls, and borage flowers, and every part counts, and every part fits. Like his fellow countryman cooking down at the foot of the country, Martin Kajuiter, Mr Castell is alive to colour and scents as well as tastes, so the eyes and nose are as delighted as the mouth, where the various parts of the dishes ping pong around with intense pleasure. His signature dish of turbot with Strangford Lough samphire is a beauty, but even when he introduces Asian notes, as in his dishes such as duck breast and rump of Dexter beef, his cultural and culinary confidence is sure and informed. Fantastic value, excellent service, and The Boathouse is where you want to be in Bangor. (Joery & Jasper Castel, The Boat House, Seacliff Road, Bangor ☎ 028-9146 9253 www.theboathouseni.co.uk Open noon-2.30pm, 5pm-9.30pm Wed-Sat, 1pm-8pm Sun)

Yogurt

● Clandeboye Estate Yoghurt

The Clandeboye yogurt was one of the first sirens of the North's new dairy culture. Using milk from their Jersey and Holstein herd, it is a beautiful dairy product, richly, compactly flavoured, with a nice edge of acidity. It's become widely available in shops and supermarkets, which is good news for the other dairy products now coming in its wake, and shaking up the once moribund dairy culture. (Bryan Boggs, Clandeboye Estate, Bangor ☎ 028-9181 5194 bryan@clandeboye.co.uk www.clandeboye.co.uk)

Gastropub

● Coyle's

Coyle's offers food in the bar and evening meals in the restaurant upstairs. It's a lively, characterful music pub, and the cooking is consistent and tasty. (Kyle Marshall, Mark Coyle, 44 High Street, Bangor ☎ 028-9127 0362 coylesbar@gmail.com www.coylesbistro.co.uk – Food served in bar noon-3pm, Mon-Fri, noon-9pm Sat, 12.30pm-8pm Sun. Restaurant opens 5pm-9pm Mon-Sat, 5pm-8pm Sun)

Home Bakery

● The Heatherlea

The Heatherlea is a legend. A top-class bakery, a deli, a café, it's the real deal – "No part-baked, frozen, prepared bread here!" – they will tell you, and it's true, just hard-working bakers and a hard-working team who always do their best. Paul and Patricia innovate constantly, so the Heatherlea gets better and better, year by year. Excellent. (Paul & Patricia Getty, 94 Main Street, Bangor ☎ 028-9145 3157 ✉ paulgetty@btconnect.com 🖱 www.theheatherlea.com – Open 8.30am-5pm Mon-Sat)

Fishmonger

● McKeown's Fish Shop

McKeown's is an institution in Bangor, and it's here you go for fresh fish, including their own smoked fish. Sean and his team are proud of what they do, and they do it as well as they can, every day. (Sean McKeown, 14 High Street, Bangor ☎ 028-9127 1141 – Open 8.30am-5.30pm Tue-Fri, 8.30am-5pm Sat)

Preserves

● The Offbeat Bottling Company

The Offbeat Bottling crew were present and correct at the St George's Saturday market in Belfast last time we called by. We mention this simply because we were there at the crack of dawn, and so were they. After almost two decades making some of the most imaginative, creative preserves and chutneys, these guys are still up for it, and it is a mark of their distinctiveness that their jars make it all the way down to Cork to landmark stores such as URRU, amongst many other top-flight shops. Top class. (Laura Beattie, Unit 73 Enterprise House, 2/4 Balloo Avenue, Bangor ☎ 028-9127 1525 ✉ neil@offbeatbottling.co.uk)

Butcher and delicatessen

● Primacy Food Village

The Bowman family's food village is a genuinely visionary venture, a place where the foods of their farm are joined by the produce of the best Northern Irish producers in one happy compact. The beef has come no further than from their farm in the Craigantlet hills, and is then slowly dry-aged. The vegetables are local, the take-away meals are made in their own kitchens, and their baking is supplemented by the work of other local craft bakeries. There is both a coffee shop, for simple, tasty eating, and a gift shop. Primacy is actually a one-stop solution for whatever culinary needs, desires and demands you could possibly have. Excellent. (Nicola Bowman, 26A Primacy Road, Bangor ☎ 028-9127 0083 🖱 www.primacymeatsfoodvillage.co.uk – Open 8am-5.30pm Mon-Fri, 8am-5pm Sat, Coffee shop open 9.30am-4.30pm Mon-Sat)

Garden Centre Café

● Rambling Rose Restaurant

Careful sourcing of good ingredients and careful cooking explain the success of the Rambling Rose, at Dickson's garden centre just off the main Belfast-Bangor road. A lot of care is shown here to the simplest things, so you will eat well. (David Perkes, Dickson's Garden Centre, 79 Cootehall Road, Bangor ☎ 028-9185 3001 🖱 www.dicksonsgardencentre.co.uk – Open 9.30am-5pm Mon-Sat, Traditional high tea 4.30pm-6.30pm Fri & Sat, 12.30pm-5pm Sun)

made in Ulster

Clandeboye Estate Yoghurt

Comber

Restaurant with rooms

● The Old Schoolhouse

Will Brown has succeeded his parents, Terry and Avril, in The Old Schoolhouse, and he is a chef with a serious c.v., including a couple of years with the brilliant Philip Howard in The Square. People who worked with Mr Howard always impress with a deep-seated, holistic view of cooking, and Will Brown is no exception. His cooking is colourful and complicated, yet it's neither flashy nor up itself: it has something of the modesty of Andoni Luis Aduriz about it, and the same sense of ambition. Mr Brown even radicalises Sunday lunch: Walter's smoked salmon with potato pancake and pickled heritage beetroot; 12-hour sirloin of Dexter beef; pot-roasted turbot with scallop mousse. But dinner shows the real radicalism: wild sea bass with textures of cauliflower and ras el hanout caramel; venison Scotch egg with a tasting of celeriac, apple and hazelnut; cod with langoustine ravioli and shellfish emulsion. Tremendously exciting work. (Will Brown, 100 Ballydrain Road, 028-9754 1182 ✉ info@theoldschoolhouseinn.com 🖱 www.theoldschoolhouseinn.com – Open 6.30pm-10.30pm Wed-Sat, 12.30pm-4pm Sun)

Vegetable producers

● Mash Direct

Martin and Tracy's Mash Direct is, realistically, too big a company to feature in a Guide dedicted to artisans. But we can't help but admire how this company has been built and has grown over the last decade, from a simple, logical idea – cook the vegetables grown on the farm – into a national brand. They got it right where everyone before them got it wrong. Fair play! as they say down in Cork. (Martin & Tracy Hamilton, 81 Ballyrainey Road, Comber ☎ 028-9187 8316 ✉ info@mashdirect.com 🖰 www.mashdirect.com)

Crossgar

Wine Merchant

● James Nicholson Wine Merchants

In his 2012 catalogue, which marked his 35th year as wine merchant, Jim Nicholson noted three principal areas of development that had occurred during his tenure: "incredible improvements in winemaking, the appearance of new exciting wine making countries and regions, and the amount of brilliant wine making...". He, of course, elided the fourth improvement, which is that brilliant wine merchants have made these three seismic changes apparent to, and available for, wine lovers. And no one has acted as that conduit, as that guide to the culture of wine, better than James Nicholson Wines. Nicholsons are stars in every orbit of the wine world – their selection of global wines; the aesthetic of their shop through which they sell the wines; the excellence of the staff at every part of the organisation; and their ability to offer not just bottles of wine, but the passion and culture that lies within every bottle. Superlatives aren't enough to describe their achievement. (Jim Nicholson, Killyleagh Street, Crossgar ☎ 028-4483 0091 ✉ shop@jnwine.com 🖰 www.jnwine.com – Open 10am-7pm Mon-Sat)

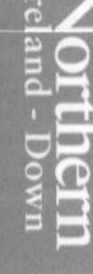

Donaghadee

Garden Centre Café

● Donaghadee Garden Centre

The Donaghadee centre is a twin to the Bushmills garden centre, and both have been trailblazers when it comes to offering real cooking – as opposed to catering – in the garden centres. Excellent baking, and good, moreish savoury foods hit the spot, whether you are interested in gardening or not. (Jane Rankin, 34 Stockbridge Road, Donaghadee ☎ 028-9188 3237 ✉ ddgc@creativegardens.net 🖰 www.creativegardens.net – Open 9.30am-5pm Mon-Tue, 9.30am-8pm Wed-Fri, 9.30am-5pm Sat, 12.30am-5pm Sun)

Restaurant

● The Governor Rocks

A new venture from the team at CoCo in Belfast, and it's a modern riff on seafood classics – salt and pepper squid with lemon mayo; smoked haddock chowder; scallop risotto; fish cake with salsa rossa. Don't feel bad if you want to order the steak: it's from Noel Angus's shop in Greyabbey, so it's top notch. (Jason More, 27 The Parade ✉ 028-9188 4816 🖰 www.thegovernorrocks.com)

made in Ulster

Belfast Black

Gastropub & Accommodation

● Pier 36

"We see an award as a challenge and an honour to live up to". If you know Pier 36 and you know the Waterworth family, you will be able to hear them saying this modest statement, which features on their website. We have known Margaret and Denis – and latterly Jody and Lewis – ever since our first book, back in the late 1980's. We have never known them to be anything other than dedicted to service, devoted to their calling, appositely absorbed by the necessity to do everything they do as well as it can be done. Of course, they have won numerous awards, not least being described by *The Guardian* as one of the six best places to eat seafood in the U.K. But that sort of thing doesn't change them: it encourages them. So take yourself down to Donaghadee for the night, book a room, enjoy dinner in the restaurant, and you will understand what a family business is all about. (The Waterworth family, 36 The Parade, Donaghadee ☎ 028-9188 4466 ✉ info@pier36.co.uk 🖰 www.pier36.co.uk – Open 11.30am-10pm Mon-Sun)

Downpatrick

Venison

● Finnebrogue Venison

Consider this: as we write, that most brilliant chef, Derek Creagh, is working with Finnebrogue, developing and testing recipes. Now, what potential an alliance like that promises, the superb quality of Finnebrogue venison and pork with the imagination and verve of one of the great modern cooks. In the meantime, Denis Lynn continues to live by his maxim: Never Stop. He makes wonderful products for high-end retailers and brand names and he gets their business for that very reason: he doesn't stop. And we suspect he isn't going to anytime soon. (Denis Lynn, Finnebrogue Estate, Downpatrick ☎ 028-4461 7525 ✉ sales@finnebrogue.com 🖱 www.finnebrogue.com)

Bakery & Café

● Oakley Fayre Café & Bakery

"Hard work and dedication" is Darren Kearney's mantra in the family business that is the Oakley Fayre café and bakery. Like a typical young man returning home, he has brought new energy and vision to a business that has been trading for nigh on thirty five years, doing his best, working hard, getting it right. (Darren Kearney, 52 Market Street, Downpatrick ☎ 028-4461 2500 – Open 8am-5pm Mon-Wed, 8am-5.30pm Thur, 8am-8pm Fri & Sat)

Farm Shop

● Pheasant's Hill Farm

To see Janis and Alan working hard early in the morning at the St George's Market, setting up their stall like everyone else all around them, you might not imagine that they are amongst the most significant artisans in the history of Northern Ireland. But they are just that: they are philosophers of food, who specialise in the rare breeds of animals that are native to their part of the agricultural world, but which were almost forgotten when farming became intensified. It was from Alan that we first learnt, many years ago now, of the Irish Moiled cow, the cow that was native to Ulster, but which was almost allowed to disappear completely. They rear Tamworth and Gloucester Old Spots, they offer excellent poultry, as well as wild venison from County Down, and

they prepare everything beautifully. You can buy online, and you can also find these extraordinary foods at their Killyleagh farm shop, and at the Belfast Market, where you will see the philosophers, working away, as if they were just ordinary folk. Ordinary they ain't. (Janis & Alan Bailey, 37 Killyleagh Road, Downpatrick ☎ 028-4461 7246 www.pheasantshill.com)

local knowledge

Comber Potatoes

Comber Earlies are the spuds that grow in the fields around the inlet of Strangford Lough. The soil of this region is red sandstone and gravel. It's a free-draining soil, and good draining protects it from frost and allows the spuds to come on earlier than in other counties. The spuds are credited with a nutty flavour and soft smooth skin.

Dromara

● Abernethy Butter Co

Northern Ireland's specialist dairy culture is emerging from the shadows, and suddenly there are handmade cheeses, farmhouse ice creams and, vitally, there is Will and Alison Abernethy's butter. "Ingredients: cream and a pinch of salt" it wittily says on the label, and this is a beautifully packaged, beautiful butter: hand-churned, clean, not too salty – always a problem with Northern Irish butters – with a long, sinuous taste. It's wonderful that so many good stores have picked up on the butter – and their butter fudge – and we expect them to become one of the key artisan brands in double-quick time. (Will & Alison Abernethy, Beechtree Farm, Ballynahinch Road www.abernethybuttercompany.com)

Dromore

● Boozeberries

Barbara and Stuart make three varieties of Boozeberries – Zesty Blackcurrant; Wild Blueberry and Wild Cranberry. The fruits are placed in the bottle, a grain sprit is poured over and, over the next four months, the alchemy happens. Barbara mentions that a favourite way to enjoy the drinks is to pour some Blueberry Boozeberry into a flute, then top up with cold Prosecco – yum! Others like to do the same with the Wild Cranberry. The drinks are steadily becoming more widely available, not just nationally, but internationally also.(Barbara & Stuart Hughes, 62 The Belfry, Dromore ☎ 077 8011 7737 ✉ info@boozeberries.com 🖱 www.boozeberries.com)

made in Ulster

Abernethy Butter

Dundrum

Restaurant

● The Buck's Head Inn

Michael and Alison are one of the best him 'n' her teams working anywhere in Ireland. She cooks beautifully, he manages the rooms beautifully, and together they are as in sync as Fred and Ginger. Part of what makes them so interesting is that they sit happily outside of any food fashions – they just do their thing, their way. And everyone loves it, especially the generous-hearted cooking at lunch, high-tea and dinner: tempura oysters with chilli, sesame and soy; the best scampi and chips you have ever eaten; monkfish with citrus butter and vegetable tagliatelle. Do note that the Buck's Head is the people's favourite as well as the critic's favourite, so get there early for a table in the summer season. (Michael & Alison Crothers, 77 Main Street, Dundrum ☎ 028-4375 1868 – Open noon-2.30pm, 5pm-9.30pm Mon-Sun)

Guesthouse

● The Carriage House

The jewel of hospitality, to match the jewel-like nature of the area around Dundrum, is Maureen Griffith's Carriage House. Ms Griffith has an aesthete's eye, and a perfectionist's rigour, so the house, the garden and the cooking are all, equally, of a superb standard. Add in the mix of places to eat in the village, and Dundrum offers all you need for a superlative base to explore this glorious region. (Maureen Griffith, 71 Main Street, Dundrum ☎ 028-4375 1635 ✉ inbox@carriagehousedundrum.com 🖱 www.carriagehousedundrum.com)

Seafood Bar

● Mourne Seafood Bar

It's not just the superb shellfish from their own beds that singles out the Mourne Seafood Bars as special places. It's their ability know what is good, and how to use it. So, it's Abernethy butter with your bread; it's the soft egg with smoked haddock; it's the fine linguini with scallops; it's the tarragon mayo in the lobster salad. At each point, the right call is made, the right judgement is shown, the right drink – oyster stout! – is proffered. They make it look easy in the Mourne, but we all know that it isn't easy. (Bob McCoubrey, 10 Main Street, Dundrum ☎ 028-4375 1377 www.mourneseafood.com – Open noon-late Mon-Sat, noon-7.30pm Sun)

Greyabbey

Butcher

● Angus Farm Shop

Noel Angus has just opened the second butchery counter of his stellar farm store, at the Harrison's nursery centre – see below. The Angus is the real boutique butcher's store, which is to say that nothing is sold unless it is, firstly, of the right standard and, secondly, that it is at its peak. Mr Angus is a philosopher of retail, keeping his air miles short – his farm is two miles from the shop – keeping his products natural and health-giving. Superb beef, rare-breed pork, Comber spuds, Abernethy butter, the impish creativity of beef and Ballyblack stout sausages (made with Ards' finest brew) and lots of sage advice. Perfect. (Noel Angus, 42 Main Street, Greyabbey ☎ 028-4278 8695 www.angusfarmshop.com – Open 8.30am-5.30pm Mon-Sat)

Nursery & Farm Shop

● Harrison's of Greyabbey

The Harrison's Nursery also offers a farm shop and a restaurant, and features a butchery counter from the fantastic Noel Angus. So, once you have the car loaded up with all that the garden needs as well as a couple of hanging baskets, it's time for some Ballyblack ale sausages with champ and onion gravy in the bistro before a tour of the farm shop. (Helen Harrison, Ballybryan Road ☎ 028-4278 8088 info@harrisonsofgreyabbey.co.uk www.harrisonsofgreyabbey.co.uk)

Groomsport

Wine Merchant

● Nouveau Wines

Robert Neill of Nouveau Wines is one of the great wine culture figures in Northern Ireland, and it's fantastic to see him back in Groomsport, selling the wines he loves and is passionate, knowledgeable and articulate about. We saw Mr Neill, at the second Inishfoods Festival, briefing the staff on the RN wines they would be serving during the Chef's Homecoming dinner: it was a master-class in description, information, history and wine culture. And it took him all of five minutes. Brilliant. (Robert Neill, 49 Main Street ☎ 028-9146 0408 ✉ info@nouveauwines.co.uk 🖱 www.nouveauwines.co.uk

Bistro

● Strudel Bistro

Sharon and Fritz earned a great reputation when they ran the tiny Strudel in Bangor, but the move to Groomsport has given them more space in a bright new room. Mr Machala cooks confidently and cleanly: braised steak and mushroom pie with puff pastry topping; cod bonne femme with champ; peanut chilli chicken with stir-fry vegetables are typical lunch dishes and they are deftly delivered. His evening menus at the weekends are lovely: sweet-cured herring with pickled cucumber and rye bread; chicken fillet with haggis and barley jus; duo of pork with sauerkraut and thyme velouté; apple strudel with fresh cream. Lovely. (Fritz & Sharon Machala, ☎ 028-9125 6758 ✉ info@strudelbistro.com 🖱 www.strudelbistro.com – Open 10am-4pm Tue-Sat, till 5pm Sat, 6.30pm-11pm Fri-Sat, 10am-3pm Sun)

Helen's Bay

Organic Farm

● Helen's Bay Organic Farm

Northern Ireland - Down

John McCormick is one of the great philosophers and practitioners of organics, and a man who seems to get younger looking every time we see him, so he knows something, alright. You tell us this man has been given his bus pass! We don't believe it! His visibility, via the Root And Branch Organics delivery system and market stall at the St George's Market and at other markets, has thankfully brought his great food and his great common sense to more and more people. And what about those excellent Root and Branch coffees! Jackrabbit Java for us man, for we need good drinks whilst we save the planet. (John McCormick, Coastguard Avenue, Helen's Bay ☎ 028-9185 3122 tastyfood@rootandbranchorganic.com www.rootandbranchorganic.com Office: 13 Seaview Terrace, Holywood)

Hillsborough

Gastropub

● The Parson's Nose

Ronan and Jenny Sweeney do great rooms, and the Parson's Nose is a delight. But, even better is in store as you eat in this inspired gastropub, a sister to the deservedly acclaimed Balloo House in Killinchy, for the cooking is precise, poised, delicious and earthy: potted Lissara duck with Oatland's farm rhubarb chutney; lamb kidneys with wholegrain mustard and scallion soda bread; Dexter beef and Belfast stout pie; hake with Comber potatoes and lemon oil; sticky toffee pudding with Bushmills butterscotch sauce. The rooms are wonderfully comfortable, and you will simply not want to leave this stylish gem. (Ronan & Jennie Sweeney & Danny Millar, 48 Lisburn Street, Hillsborough ☎ 028-9268 3009 www.ballooinns.com – Food served noon-9pm Mon-Sun, till 10pm Fri & Sat)

Gastropub

● The Plough Inn

Derek Patterson's Plough Inn is just one address from a trio of businesses - he also runs The Pheasant at Annahilt and The Tannery Steakhouse, just outside Moira. The Plough has been a staple of pretty Hillsborough for over two decades, and it's a most atmospheric pub, where food is served at lunchtime and on Sunday – lasagne with sea salt focaccia; prawn open sandwich on wheaten bread; Kilkeel scampi with chunky chips. The restaurant opens for lunch, and for dinner at the weekends, and game birds from local estates are a feture of the menu – pheasant Wellington; Caledon estate venison and game birds. (Derek Patterson, 3 The Square ☎ 028-9268 2985 www.theploughhillsborough.co.uk – Open noon-2.30pm Mon-Sat, 5pm-9pm Mon-Thur -9.30pm Fri-Sat, noon-8pm Sun)

Holywood

Café

● The Bay Tree

It's a crazy night in The Bay Tree – more than one hundred covers! – but despite the pressure the Bay Tree breads are amazing and the olives are great, so the juices are flowing from the off. The Silverhill duck with chilli and apricot – they love using fruits here in unexpected ways – is sublime, the poulet grandmere is just as granny would have made it had she been Julia Child, and the cornmeal pancakes with chilli beef, soured cream and guacamole would have had Diego Rivera and Frida Kahlo admiring its painterly beauty, before they scoffed it, of course. It's such happy food they cook here, cooked with love, served with patient care, and it all makes for a zinging resturant, which is why they sometimes have to do 100 covers in these tiny rooms. Unorthodox, inspired, unique, nothing else like it. (Sue & William Farmer, 118 High Street, Holywood ☎ 028-9042 1419 ✉ info@baytreeholywood.co.uk 🖱 www.baytreeholywood.co.uk – Open 8am-5pm Mon-Thur, 8am-9.30pm Fri-Sat, 10am-3pm Sun)

Organic Shop & Bakery

● Camphill Organic Farm Shop & Bakery

Camphill is brill! They cook beautiful soups – curried carrot and lentil; cream of broccoli; corn chowder – bake lovely quiches – roasted pepper; red onion and Stilton – they sell the most amazing vegetables and staples, they bake delicious breads and cakes, and everything they do is done ethically and sustainably. A model shop and bakery: Camphill is brill! (Rob van Duin, Shore Road, Holywood ☎ 028-9042 3203 ✉ camphillholywood@btconnect.com 🖱 www.camphillholywood.co.uk – Shop open 9am-5.30pm Tue-Sat. Cafe open 9am-4.30pm Tue-Sat)

Restaurant

● Fontana

"Respect to Colleen Bennett", writes Connie McKenna, who had an ace lunch on her last visit up the stairs to this "perky little restaurant": scallops in a cream sauce; Glenarm organic salmon with new potatoes and asparagus, then chocolate fondant with raspberries and blueberries, "a cute little mountain of chocolate".

Connie also liked the "urban slick" style of the room. So a good time, all round. (Colleen Bennett, 61a High Street, Holywood ☎ 028-9080 9908 – Open noon-2.30pm, 5pm-9.30pm Tue-Fri, 6.30pm-10pm Sat, 11am-3pm Sun)

Indian Restaurant

● Ganges Holywood

The ever-reliable Joris Minne, writing in *The Belfast Telegraph*, wasn't mincing his words: "Ganges is the best Indian restaurant this side of the Cinnamon Club in Great Smith Street, London, and Kalam Abdul is quite possibly the most talented curry chef this island has ever entertained". Well! There might be some Dublin ethnic restaurants that would beg to disagree, but what an encomium for the modest Ganges. The restaurant has been in Holywood since forever, but Mr Abdul has only recently taken control and begun to cook his food and fashion the room in his style. Both Mr Abdul and Mr Islam are trying for the authentic ethnic cooking that has blossomed in London and Dublin, and Ganges represents the first attempt at a true regional Indian cuisine in Northern Ireland. So, as old backpackers we are delighted to see such fine naan breads and such simple staples as spiced tomato and onion salad, and let's have their lovely samosas, railway shobji, a one-pot hot pot lamb curry and a lovely thali selection. (Fokrul Islam & Kalam Abdul, 47 High Street, Holywood ☎ 028-9042 1217 ✉ ganges-holywood@hotmail.co.uk – Open 5pm-11pm Sun-Thur, 5pm-midnight Fri-Sat)

Restaurant

● Koi

A look at the Koi offer of "urban Asian" food might worry you at first, because the food they propose seems to wander indiscriminately all over the countries of South East Asia. But their secret is simple: what they do, they do well, and they know what they are doing, and people who live in and around Holywood come back to Koi time and time and time again. In fact, the menu may be prolix, but the staff are quite strict about what goes with what successfully, and they know their stuff and you should take their advice in order to maximise the fun. Stylish, simple room, good service, and good value. (10-12 Shore Road, Holywood ☎ 028-9042 4238 – Open noon-11pm Mon-Sat, 2pm-10.30pm Sun)

Butcher & Deli

● Orr's

Orr's is ageless, and looks like someplace transplanted from an Italian hill village. It's the place to come for good cooked meats, fresh fish, excellent deli goods. Proper food, proper place. (Gerry Orr, 56 High Street, Holywood ☎ 028-9042 2288 – Open 8am-5.30pm Mon-Sat)

made in Ulster

Finnebrogue Venison

Restaurant

● Rayanne House

It's the toughest gig in Holywood: what are you going to choose for breakfast from amongst the five starter courses and thirteen main courses prepared by Conor McClelland in Rayanne House. Prune soufflé on a purée of fresh green figs? Chilled porridge with raspberry purée? Croc-pot of ham and eggs with Italian tomato sauce and toast fingers? Scrambled eggs with crab meat, cream cheese and chives? Pork and prune sausages with potato waffles? Mr McClelland relishes a challenge, such as creating the last menu of the Titanic – which he serves for private parties – or reinventing breakfast as we know it. The house itself has ten rooms, all immaculately maintained. Now: make your mind up! (Bernie & Conor McClelland, 60 Demesne Road ☎ 028-9042 5859 info@rayannehouse.com www.rayannehouse.com)

Restaurant

● The Yard

The Yard is the most enigmatic, intelligent mix of gallery and eating space you will find. It's fun, and witty, and arty, and colourful, as if Avoca had been re-thought by a bunch of Situationists. Breakfasts, sandwiches, salads, panini and toasties with good drinks and nice puds cover every angle of your appetite, and just consider this: they have HP sauce to go with your sausage and bacon toastie or your omelette: art or what? (J & M Beattie, 102-104 High Street, Holywood ☎ 028-9042 7210 info@coffeeyard.com www.yardgallery.com – Open 8am-5pm Mon-Sat)

Kearney

Farmhouse Cheese

● Kearney Blue

Paul McClean finished working on his recipe for Northern Ireland's first artisan blue cheese in April 2011. Three months later, with only his second commercial production, Kearney Blue scoops the prize for Best Irish Cheese at the Nantwich Cheese Festival. By any standards, that is an extraordinary achievement. By the standards of cheesemaking in Northern Ireland, it is unbelievable. Dairy policies in the past meant there were no farm cheeses in the 'North, so for the first Northern cheese to take a major international prize is historic. And there's more: Paul followed this up with a bronze medal in the blue cheese category at the World Cheese Awards. Paul uses milk from Fairview Dairies, and production is still very small in scale. But this former civil servant has a clear focus for the future of Kearney Blue: "I want to keep its artisan identity", he says. Hunt it down in shops like Belfast's Arcadia and other good stores, and in local hotels and restaurants. (Paul McClean, Kearney)

Kilkeel

Takeaway

● The Pit Stop

"Quality before Price" is Alan Hanna's motto in The Pit Stop, and this motto brought the team the Northern Ireland prize in the 2012 Fish and Chip Shop Awards. (Alan Hanna, Kilkeel ☎ 028-4176 3999 alan@pitstopfastfood.com www.pitstopfastfood.com)

Brewery

● The Whitewater Brewing Company

How fast great brands are made. It must have seemed slightly crazy when Bernard and Kerry Sloan established Whitewater Brewery back in 1996. The big boys dominated the business, selling pints of Harp lager and Guinness. Sixteen years on, and the iconic beer brands today are Clotworthy Dobbin, or Belfast Black, or Copperhead. And the big boys are in decline, as Whitewater and its companion craft breweries and their beers spread throughout the island, seemingly unstoppably. How did they do it? Simple: with their beers they brought us quality, distinctiveness, cheekiness, decency, fun, camaraderie, deliciousness. Culture versus Mammon. And culture wins. (Bernard & Kerry Sloan, 40 Tullyframe Road, Kilkeel ☎ 028-4176 9449 info@whitewaterbrewery.com www.whitewaterbrewery.com)

made in Ulster

Wee Buns

Killinchy

Restaurant

● Balloo House

The third generation of modern chefs working at the best places in Northern Ireland – Gary Bell, William Farmer, Joery Castell, Will Brown, Chris Bell, Dean Coppard, Sean Farnan, Ian Orr – are following the second generation – Niall McKenna, Brian McCann, Cath Gradwell, Simon Dougan, Tony O'Neill, Andy Rea, Paul Arthurs, Alison Crothers, Simon McCance, Derek Creagh, Danny Millar, Ray McArdle – and the succession makes for a fascinating study of how the post-Roscoff, post-Nick's, post-Deane's culinary template is faring. Unsurprisingly, it has fared very well, and credit must go to those culinary masters who taught so many of these cooks so well, especially Paul Rankin, Nick Price and Michael Deane, teachers who taught them to be ambitious yet unpretentious, and international yet fiercely local. No pupil fits the template better than Danny Millar, a chef whose menus boast of his local riches – Lissara duck, Finnebrogue venison, Strangford fish and shellfish, Rademon estate pigeon, Kilkeel crab – and whose culinary artistry in turning these ingredients into art has defined Balloo House. He has a great touch and sympathy with his food, and his surprises always ring true, with vivid flavours and colours. Both the restaurant and bistro at Balloo are top-notch stuff. (Jennie Sweeney, 1 Comber Road, Killinchy ☎ 028-9754 1210 info@balloohouse.com www.balloohouse.com – Bistro food served noon-9pm Mon-Sun, 'till 8pm Sun. Restaurant open 6pm-9pm Tue-Thu, 6pm-9.30pm Fri & Sat)

Killyleagh

Gastropub

● Dufferin Arms

They serve food in both the bar of the 'Duff and in their Kitchen restaurant, and it's hearty, generous food: seafood chowder; open steak sambo; Hereford burger; lamb shank with mash. (35 High Street, Killyleagh ☎ 028-4482 1182 dufferinarms@hotmail.co.uk www.dufferinarms.co.uk – Open for bar food noon-8pm Mon-Thur & Sun, noon-9pm Fri & Sat)

Guesthouse

● Dufferin Coaching Inn

Leontine Haines got all the details right before opening her doors in this lovely, early 19th-century coaching house in pretty Killyleagh. Part of the building was formerly a bank but, unlike most Irish banks, Ms Haines knows how to run a business properly and professionally. The rooms and bathrooms are beautifully appointed, the towels are fluffy, the Bircher muesli at breakfast is as scrumptious as all the other home-made ingredients that comprise the feast that starts the day. Many guests choose to eat next door at the friendly Dufferin Arms, where the cooking is good, or at Balloo House where the brilliant Danny Millar cooks up a storm. The Dufferin is another feather in the cap of this lovely village in this lovely region. Wine buffs, by the way, shouldn't miss a visit to Jim Nicholson's stunning wine shop in nearby Crossgar. (Leontine Haines, Killyleagh ☎ 028-4482 1134 info@dufferincoachinginn.com www.dufferincoachinginn.com)

Delicatessen and Café

● Picnic

Kath and John have been doing the good thing for ten years now, charming the living daylights out of everyone who comes to Picnic. Here's how the *Belfast Telegraph* summed it up: "Sitting listening to R&B music in the shadow of a scenic castle, with a cappuccino and focaccia with roast chicken, jalapenos, red peppers and cheese, one could be on holiday abroad". Well, almost, but the illusions created by the pleasure of Picnic are indeed intense. So, step into the pretty lilac palace and have some smoked mackerel salad with poached egg and hollandaise, or maybe warm wild mushroom, cream cheese and herb bruschetta, and then a slice of chocolate and orange cake. Ah! Where are we? (Katherine & John Dougherty, 49 High Street, Killyleagh picnicdelicatessen@hotmail.com ☎ 028-4482 8525 – Open 7am-5pm Mon-Fri, 10am-4pm Sat-Sun)

local knowledge

Home Bakeries

Northern Ireland breads are unique and "home bakeries" flourish, selling the likes of pancakes, farls, wheaten sodas & wee buns.

Kircubbin

Restaurant with Rooms

● Paul Arthurs

Restaurant. Bistro. Bar. Accommodation. Beer garden. Chipper. The only thing missing from Paul Arthurs' portfolio of destinations in Kircubbin would be if he had a traditional-style undertakers, as old Irish publicans used to have. No matter, he has everything else you could need, and Mr Arthurs has always been a chef with a sure touch and an understated style. In fact, everything about Arthurs is modest, and we like this low-key approach. The cooking, in both Bella's Bistro and the restaurant, is deft and delicious. (Paul Arthurs, 66 Main Street, Kircubbin ☎ 028-4273 8192 www.arthurskircubbin.com – Open 9am-late Tue-Sun)

Lisbane

Café & Craft Shop

● The Old Post Office Café

Everything is always pretty, pert and pristine in Alison and Trevor's Old Post Office. Let us sit down in here with afternoon tea – freshly cut sandwiches, tray bakes, fresh scones with cream and jam, cakes and a cup of hot tea – and we are the happiest guys on the planet. It's a lovely complex of rooms, with arts, crafts, gifts and pantry goodies all exuding maximum temptation. (Trevor & Alison Smylie, 191 Killinchy Road, Lisbane, Comber ☎ 028-9754 3335 info@oldpostofficelisbane.co.uk www.oldpostofficelisbane.co.uk – Open 9am-5pm Mon-Sat)

Moira

Butcher

● McCartney's of Moira

7,000 products. 350 judges judging 7,000 products. One supreme champion. And what product won the Great Taste Awards Supreme Award for 2011? McCartney's of Moira corned beef, that's what. Surprised? You shouldn't be. McCartney's of Moira is one of the best stores and butcher's shops in these islands, and the standards set by George and Gordon and Judith and Sarah McCartney apply to every product they make. So, you might think corned beef is a so-what product – that Fray Bentos stuff – but McCartney's elevate everything they produce to stellar standards, meticulously removing the fat, dry-curing the beef, putting it into the traditional presses and cooking it long and slow with natural gelatine. The result is food as art, food as craft, food as culture, food as history. So, cast aside any preconceptions, step into this handsome store, and be prepared to be amazed. (George McCartney, 56-57 Main Street, Moira ☎ 028-9261 1422 ✉ info@mccartneysofmoira.co.uk 🖱 www.mccartneysofmoira.co.uk – Open 8.30am-5.30pm Tue-Thur, 8am-5.30pm Fri & Sat)

Gastropub

● Pretty Mary's

A pretty pub with a traditional bar morphs into some comfortable, modern dining spaces at the rere, and the cooking is the best in town. (86 Main Street, Moira ☎ 028-9261 1318 ✉ prettymarys@hotmail.co.uk 🖱 www.prettymarys.co.uk – Open noon-3pm, 5pm-9.30pm Mon-Fri, noon-9.30pm Sat, 12.30pm-8pm Sun)

Newcastle

Deli & Bistro

● The Cookie Jar Bakery

James Herron's craft bakery produces a very famous wheaten bread. Those in the know will tell you, however, that the fruit soda may be even better than the wheaten bread. Only one way to find out if you agree, so buy both. We'll bet you actually buy a whole lot more from the Cookie Jar. (James Herron, 121 Main Street, Newcastle ☎ 028-4372 2427 ✉ thecookiejar@btconnect.com)

Newry

Home Bakery & Café

● The Corn Dolly Home Bakery

The styles of bread could not be more different, but Northern Ireland actually has a bread culture similar to Germany. As in Germany, specialist bread shops and bakeries like Jim and Anthony's Corn Dolly shops, in Newry and Warrenpoint, are at the centre of the culinary culture. They preserve local styles of bread, they innovate to stay up-to-date with demand, they provide a backbone for the food culture, whilst also making wicked Swiss Rolls so you can enjoy a proper, sinful treat. You simply can't overestimate the importance of the Corn Dolly. (Jim & Anthony O'Keeffe, 12 Marcus Square, Newry ☎ 028-3026 0524 ✉ info@corndollyfoods.com 🖱 www.corndollyfoods.com – Open 8.30am-5.30pm Mon-Sat. Also at 28 Church Street, Warrenpoint ☎ 028-4275 3596)

Restaurant

● Graduate Restaurant

It's such a brilliant idea: the culinary students at the Southern Regional College have to cook lunch, and dinner – on Tuesday evening – as part of their culinary studies. This is the point when you find out whether you can actually stand the heat of the kitchen, and it's an inspired plan to get students to be familiar with the stresses and demands of both cookery and service in real time, for real people, in a real restaurant. (Caroline Fegan, Southern Regional College, Patrick Street, Newry ☎ 028-3026 1071/028-3025 9611 🖱 www.src.ac.uk – Open for lunch, 12.30pm, Mon-Fri and Tue evening, 7pm, for dinner during term time)

Newtownards

Craft Brewery

● Ards Brewing Co

Charles Ballantyne is an architect by training, and has switched his skills to the production of Ballyblack Stout, Pig Island Pale Ale and Ards Rockin' Goose. "Flavour is what counts with me", says Mr Ballntyne, and amen to that. Interestingly, Mr Ballantyne uses seaweed finings to clarify his beers, an ancient practice that has almost died out. The beers are bottle conditioned, and show good hop aromas. Look out for these handsomely labelled beers in good pubs in Belfast and elsewhere. (Charles Ballantyne, 34b Carrowdore Road, Newtownards ✉ ardsbrewing@blackwood34.plus.com)

Ice Cream

● Glastry Farm Luxury Ice Cream

When future Ph.D students come to write that thesis about the modern history of the Northern Irish dairy industry, Will Taylor will find himself besieged by earnest and well-meaning young men and women who will want to take up an unconscionable amount of his time in order to get an explanation as to how an industry that was mono-cultural suddenly became multi-cultural. And Glastry Farm ice cream will be their answer. Mr Taylor's move to turn the milk of his herd into smartly branded ice creams that found an ever-increasing audience is one of the key actions in the transformation, and he is a visionary farmer, and a very fine ice cream maker. The Glastry ices are real luxury – natural, hip, fun, delicious. We expect them to conquer the world. (Will Taylor, 43 Manse Road, Kircubbin, Newtownards ☎ 028-4273 8671 ✉ glastryfarm@btconnect.com 🖱 www.glastryfarm.com)

Greengrocer

● Homegrown

Homegrown is a homegrown local star, a treasure of great local vegetables gathered from the region by Trevor and Margaret, and sold in a classic traditional shop. (Trevor & Margaret White, 66b East Street, Newtownards ☎ 028-9181 8318 – Open 9am-5.30pm Mon-Thur, 8am-5.30pm Fri & Sat)

Home Bakery & Coffee Shop

● Knott's Cake & Coffee Shop

Michael Knott's bakery has established two new branches in addition to its Newtownards base – on Belfast's Lisburn Road, and in Holywood. At a time when other specialist bakeries are hurting, this is a hugely significant expansion, but it's all based on quality: quality baking, quality cooking, quality service. Their Newtownards café has been a key destination in the town for almost thirty five years, and it's a place where the self-service queue never seems to dissipate during the day. Grab a tray and enjoy the quality. (Michael Knott, 45 High Street, Newtownards ☎ 028-9181 9098 www.knottsbakery.co.uk – Open 7.30am-5pm Mon-Sat)

Country Store & Restaurant

● McKee's Farm Shop

Way, way up in the Belfast hills, Colin McKee's farm shop and restaurant is nothing less than a phenomenon. John McKenna called in to get some Abernethy butter and some fresh vegetables and good meats from the meat counter and good pies from the deli counter, and the sheer volume of people in the shop and café was astonishing. "It's quiet today" another shopper told him. Well, if this is quiet, then what is busy like? And the answer is that busy is like a human tsunami, queueing for the restaurant, queueing for the foods in the shop. We don't know anywhere else like McKee's. It is the most brilliant venture of its type. (Colin McKee, 28 Holywood Road, Newtownards ☎ 028-9181 1304 orders@mckeesproduce.co.uk www.mckeesproduce.co.uk – Open 8.30am-5.30pm Mon-Sat)

Portaferry

Hotel & Restaurant

● The Portaferry Hotel

Gary Bell's cooking has been knockin' 'em dead in the Portaferry Hotel, and Mr Bell and his namesake – Chris, from Galgorm Manor – are re-writing the book on what it means to eat in an hotel. He's a Wexford man, and cooked with Kevin Thornton before heading to this glorious coaching inn, one of the jewels of the North. He has an intuitive way with his ingredients, and he has superb ingredients to hand – Marlfield chicken; Glenarm beef; Dundrum shellfish. He navigates through the potential of his ingredients with rare skill – his rabbit plate has loin of rabbit, spring roll confit, crisp belly, rabbit beignet, and chocolate sauce, for example. But he also understands how to make a killer bowl of chowder, or Dundrum mussels with saffron butter, and he makes an amazing fish skin poppadom for organic salmon. William Barry found the service to be as well-judged as the cooking, and the value for money for such stellar cooking is amazing. Get there soon. (Bill Wolsey, The Strand, Portaferry ☎ 028-4272 8231 www.portaferryhotel.com)

Saintfield

Blue Goat's Cheese & Goat's Milk Soap

● Leggygowan Farm

Artisan cheeses are like Dublin buses: you wait for ever for one to come, then two come along together. Leggygowan goat's milk blue cheese has joined Kearney blue cheese in the new firmament of artisan cheesemaking in Northern Ireland. What is especially interesting about Leggygowan, however, is that the cheese is made by Adam Kelly and his brothers, Ryan and Jason, using the milk of their own herd of goats, so it is truly artisanal. They run 100 goats on a 20-acre holding, and make a fresh white goat's cheese in addition to the Leggygowan blue. The family also breed Hampshire Down sheep, and make goat's milk soaps, so it's a hive of activity, and a hugely significant new venture. (Adam, Ryan & Jason Kelly, Leggygowan Farm, 94 Crossgar Road, Saintfield ☎ +44-78 5538 2780 info@leggygowanfarm.co.uk www.leggygowanfarm.co.uk)

Real Ale Pub

● The White Horse Inn

The White Horse is owned by the brewers of the brilliant Whitewater Brewery at Kilkeel, and showcases their wonderful beers in the company of some good cooking. The bar feels just right – it feels like a bar should feel – and the unpretentiousness of the setting is matched by the straight-ahead style of the food, tasty and moreish, and great with beers: fritto misto; burger with caramelised onion; pork fillet with apple and brandy cream sauce; rump steak with bacon mash and buttered greens. Very fine indeed. (Bernard & Kerry Sloan, 49 Main Street, Saintfield ☎ 048-9751 1143 info@whitehorsesaintfield.com www.whitehorsesaintfield.com – Bistro open 11.30am-8pm Mon-Thur, 11.30am-9pm Fri-Sat, noon-8pm Sun)

Strangford

Guest Inn & Restaurant

● The Cuan Guest Inn

We aren't quite certain of all the elements that are involved in an inspection by the Taste of Ulster panel, but it is more than worth noting that in 2010, Peter and Caroline's The Cuan got 98%. The next year, they went up a point. And in 2012? Yep: 100%. The Perfect Ten. The Nadia Comaneci. It's a terrific achievement, and richly deserved by a modest, hard-working and characterful destination. So, get down to The Square, book a room for the night, and enjoy Peter's deft seafood cookery: their signature Gun's Island crab claws; surf clam and chorizo chowder; salmon carpaccio with lime, capers and balsamic; steamed smoked seabass; monkfish wrapped in bacon with sweet potato purée; Glenariff rainbow trout with shallots, peas and bacon lardons bonne femme. (Peter & Caroline McErlean, The Square, Strangford ☎ 028-4488 1222 www.thecuan.com – Open noon-8.30pm Sun-Thu, noon-9.30pm Fri & Sat)

Warrenpoint

Home Bakery & Café

● The Corn Dolly Home Bakery

Sister branch of the indispensible Newry bakery, and a key destination for great baking. (Jim & Anthony O'Keeffe, 28 Church Street, Warrenpoint ☎ 028-4175 3596 info@corndollyfoods.com www.corndollyfoods.com – Open 8.30am-6pm Mon-Sat)

Restaurant

● Restaurant 23

The stylish Balmoral Hotel is home to Ray McArdle's Restaurant 23, and enjoys Ray's signature style of beautifully executed, technically precise modern cooking – crisp pork with black pudding bon bons; Lissara duck breast with Asian greens; Dexter beef cheeseburger with skinny fries; sea scallops florentine with whipped celeriac gratin. Nice room, and value for money is very keen. (Raymond McArdle, The Balmoral Hotel, 13 Seaview, Warrenpoint ☎ 028-4175 3222 www.restaurant23.com – Open 12.30pm-2.30pm, 5.30pm-9.30pm Mon-Sat, 12.30pm-8.30pm Sun)

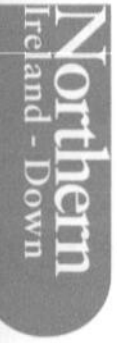

County Fermanagh

Derrygonnelly

Craft Brewery

● Inishmacsaint Brewing Company

Gordon Fallis has a simple mission in Inishmacsaint Brewery: "Make and sell tasty beer. Secure world peace. Discover cure for baldness." No bother, as they say in Fermanagh. Whilst peace and baldness cures are ever elusive, Gordon's brews are getting closer to us, as he has a new brewery installed in the old dairy, so beer is the new milk! He also has a wonderful theory, which is that the monks of Inishmacsaint, in their wanderings in Europe, actually taught the Germans how to make wheat beer, all those centuries ago. So, using Hallertau and Saaz hops from Europe is just reclaiming what is rightfully ours, and Gordon is just bringing it all back home with Fermanagh Beer. (Gordon Fallis, Derrygonnelly ☎ 028-6864 1031)

made in Ulster

Kettyle Beef

Derrylin

Wine Merchant

● The Crushed Grape

Sam Brannigan has some serious bottles in stock in little Derrylin, but having pricey gear doesn't mean he takes himself all serious. He has written, for example, of Pinot Gris: "Fancy a glass of beige? That's Pinot Gris at its worst". And if you buy cheap Chenin Blanc? "Just save yourself the money and go lick a rusty bar dipped in car battery acid." And the derided Merlot? "If cab sauv is Bogey, Merlot is Bacall. Merlot is flamboyant, fleshy, sexy and flirty...". Fantastic. Give this man a television series. (Sam Brannigan, The Market Place, Derrylin ☎ 028-6774 8550 info@thecrushedgrape.co.uk www.thecrushedgrape.co.uk)

Enniskillen

Home Bakery

● Leslie's Bakery

The legendary Fermanagh fruit loaf brings the punters to Leslie Wilkin's bakery, and everything else is equally fine. (Leslie Wilkin, 10 Church Street, Enniskillen ☎ 028-6632 4902 ✉ wilkinsbakeryltd@btinternet.com – Open 8am-5.30pm Mon-Sat)

Butcher

● O'Doherty's

Pat O'Doherty is a maverick. He works like an artist-inventor, yet he would tell you himself that what he does with his meat products is only what people did years ago. He is celebrated for his legendary Fermanagh Black Bacon, but everything he turns his hand to – his black and white puddings; his Angus beef; his sausages – all show the trademark of an ingenious man with an impish sense for creating definitive products, but who is also a guy with an holistic sense of food and nature. He is one of the great contemporary food figures, a gentle soul, lost in his work. Brilliant. (Pat O'Doherty, Belmore Street, Enniskillen ☎ 028-6632 2152 ✉ sales@blackbacon.com 🖱 www.blackbacon.com – Open 8am-6pm Mon-Sat)

Bar, Bistro, Restaurant

● Blakes of the Hollow, Café Merlot & No 6

Blakes is one of the legendary Irish pubs, and no visitor to Enniskillen should miss it. But if food, rather than drink, is what is required, there is a stylish bistro – Café Merlot – downstairs, serving tasty, modern food. Upstairs the smart restaurant, No 6, opens at weekends. Gerry and John also run the popular Russell & Donnelly deli on Darling Street. (Gerry Russell & John Donnelly, Blakes of the Hollow, 6 Church Street ☎ 028-6632 0918 ✉ russellanddonnelly@gmail.com – Cafe Merlot opens noon-3pm, 5.30pm-9pm Mon-Sun, 'till 9.30pm Sat. Restaurant No 6 opens 5.30pm-9.30pm Fri & Sat and for special bookings during the week)

Deli, Wine Shop & Café

● Russell & Donnelly

John and Gerry's deli and wine shop is the place to grab a good cup of Ristretto coffee, grab a bite of lunch, or hunt for that good bottle for dinner whilst you fill a basket with good European and Irish deli foods. (John Donnelly & Gerry Russell, 28 Darling Street, Enniskillen ☎ 028-6632 0111 russellanddonnelly@gmail.com www.russellanddonnelly.com– Open 10am-7pm Mon-Wed, 10am-9pm Thu, 10am-10pm Fri & Sat)

made in Ulster

Tickety-Moo Ice Cream

Irvinestown

Ice Cream

● Tickety-Moo Ice Cream

At Tickety-Moo, they love their Jersey cows. They have a couple of automatic brushes for the girls, so they can get a nice tickle and a scratch when ever they feel like it. And they have installed robotic milkers so the cows can give up their milk whenever it suits them best, without having to wait in line for the other girls to finish. True love, or what? And then all that lovely Jersey milk gets made by Steve and Marcus into Tickety-Moo's 18 gee-whiz! flavours of ice cream – liquorice and black-currant! lemon curd! stracciatella! French macaroon! And, at night, the cows have mattresses to lie down on when they sleep. Bet they say "Night, night" to each other, just like The Waltons. Cow Heaven. (Steve Gillies & Gareth Grey, Moo HQ, Oghill Farm, Kiladeas, Irvinestown ☎ 028-6862 8779 www.tickety-moo.com – Shop open noon-6pm Mon-Sun during summer)

Lisbellaw

Cookery School

● Belle Isle Cookery School

Corrie Cadden has taken on the culinary mantle at Belle Isle from Liz Moore, and she brings with her an impressive background as a tutor at the Ballymaloe Cookery School. Ms Cadden is a Fermanagh girl herself, and is a Slow Food supporter who says, sagely, that cooking "is fun, and accessible, and it's something that you never stop learning about." (Corrie Cadden, Lisbellaw ☎ 028-6638 7231 info@belleisle.com www.irishcookeryschool.com)

Lisnaskea

Specialist Beef

● Kettyle Irish Foods

We all know by now, since we have been reading about and writing about Maurice Kettyle's beef since 2004, that what Maurice Kettyle doesn't know about beef isn't worth knowing. His dry-aged beef is, happily, one of the defining products of our age, beef so fine that it fair takes your breath away. But, it turns out that Mr Kettyle also knows about poultry, and his Fermanagh chickens are superb and have won awards for their quality. And so is his Lough Erne lamb, drawn from the grasslands and islands of the lough, and so is his Fermanagh bacon, and so is his royal rosé veal. He is the master, there is no doubt about it, and these foods, which are now widely available, improve the quality of your life. (Maurice Kettyle, Manderwood Business Park, Drumhaw, Lisnaskea ☎ 028-6772 3777 maurice@kettyleirishfoods.com www.kettyleirishfoods.com)

Restaurant with Rooms

● The Watermill Restaurant

Owner Pascal Brissaud and head chef Fabien Cancre managed to create a celebrated dish as soon as they opened the doors of the thatched Watermill, a restaurant with rooms on the shore of Lough Erne. Their 36-hour roast beef for Sunday lunch led Catherine Cleary, in *The Irish Times*, to speculate that "four out of five people" were having the beef when she paid a visit. M. Brissaud is a keen fisherman who has lived in Ireland for many years with his partner, Valerie Smyth, who manages front of house. They have created a beautiful oasis in The Watermill. The menus are ambitious – pave of seabass in sesame crust with gnocchi; confit venison belly with lasagne and spinach mousse; lobster, root vegetable and citrus salad. There are handsome rooms for staying over. (Pascal Brissaud & Valerie Smyth, Kilmore Quay Club ☎ 028-6772 4369 www.kilmorequayclub.com)

County Londonderry

Ballykelly

Bakery & Café

● Hunter's at the Oven Door

Sean Hunter's bakery and cafés are standard bearers for great Ulster baking and tasty, traditional cooking. (Sean Hunter, 34 Main Street ☎ 028-7776 6228 huntersbakery@aol.com – Open 8.30am-5.30pm Mon-Sat)

Castledawson

Home Bakery & Café

● Ditty's Home Bakery

Can you believe that Ditty's oatcakes, from little Castledawson, are now sold in Japan, Australia, the United States and the Middle East? Slowly, surely, Robert Ditty's baking is conquering the world, and the world should be grateful. Success for his bakeries and for his bakery products hasn't changed Mr Ditty, however. He told *The Irish Times* that if he wasn't a baker – at work at 6am every morning – then he "would like to do aid work in Africa." Not only that, but he described the best thing he had eaten as "barbecued goat served up on a plate of leaves on the ground by a Masai tribesman with a sharpened twig for a fork". Mr Ditty may be famous, his work may be famous, but he hasn't forgotten what really counts. That's the wisdom that great bakers have. (Robert Ditty, 44 Main Street, Castledawson ☎ 028-7946 8243 dittyscafecastledawson@gmail.com www.dittysbakery.com – Open 9am-5.30pm Mon-Sat)

Claudy

Butcher

● O'Kane Meats

The O'Kane brothers are mighty players in Northern Ireland's feverishly competitive butchering trade. They have won every award going for every conceivable product they produce, but they don't rest on their laurels for a second, and they are forever testing, competing, improving. Lucky customers, who get the benefit of this driven ambition. Of course, Michael and Kieran remain as affable and approachable as ever. They are just guys who take excellence as their starting point. (Michael & Kieran O'Kane, Main Street, Claudy ☎ 028-7133 8944 ✉ mail@okanemeats.com 🖱 www.okanemeats.com – Open 7.45am-5.45pm Mon-Sat)

made in Ulster

Ditty's Oatcakes

Coleraine

Home Bakery & Café

● Hunter's at Kitty's of Coleraine

Part of Sean Hunter's trio of excellent bakeries and cafés. See the entry for Limavady. (Sean Hunter, 3 Church Lane, Coleraine ☎ 028-7034 2347 ✉ huntersbakery@aol.com– Open 9am-5.30pm Mon-Sat)

Restaurant

● The Watermargin

A big colourful room above the Boat House and directly overlooking the River Bann, the Boathouse is a venerable destination for classic Chinese cooking. (Tony Cheuk, The Boathouse, Hanover Place, Coleraine ☎ 028-7034 2222 – Open 12.30pm-2.30pm, 5pm-10.30pm Mon-Sun)

Delicatessen and Cafe

● Willow Garden Tea Room

The Willow is a good stop for lunch when you are touring the north Coast. A bowl of mushroom soup, some good breads, a piece of traybake and a cup of tea, and there you go. (James Currie, Pretty Crafty Design Studio, 5 Springhank Road, Castlerock, Coleraine ☎ 028-7084 8146 ✉ prettycraftydesignstudio@yahoo.co.uk 🖱 www.prettycraftydesignstudio.com – Open 10am-5pm Mon-Sat, 11am-5pm. Limited hours off season)

Desertmartin

Farm Shop & Charcuterie

● Moss Brook Farm Shoppe

Trevor and Irene's success as pork producers and manufacturers and marketeers over the last thirteen years has been one of the brightest food stories in Northern Ireland. To see Mr Barclay at work at his huge stall in the St George's Market on Saturday morning is to see a man who is master of his universe, with devoted customers, with an epicurean's firm grasp of everything he makes. Utterly inspiring, in every way. (Trevor & Irene Barclay, 6 Durnascallon Lane, Desertmartin ☎ 028-7963 3454 ✉ mossbrookbaconboys@btinternet.com – Open by arrangement)

Limavady

Artisan rapeseed Oil

● Broighter Gold

Leona and Richard Kane's rapeseed oils are fabulous products. The oil glints golden, and pours like a balm, and their goodness blesses everything you cook. Mrs Kane speaks of the "purity" of the oil, and that is its very essence. The rapeseed is grown, harvested and cold-pressed on the farm, and you really can't get a more healthful oil to work with. A beautiful product, beautifully packaged. We expect it to conquer the world. (Leona & Richard Kane, Broighter Road ☎ 028-7772 2586 ✉ leona@broightergold 🖱 www.broightergold.co.uk)

Home Bakery & Café

● Hunter's at the Oven Door

Sean Hunter's bakeries and cafés are repositories of the culture of baking and hospitality. His three shops bear witness to the great tradition of Northern Irish baking, the pancakes and muffins, the farls and fadge, the batches and wheatens. (Sean Hunter, 5-9 Market Street, Limavady ☎ 028-7772 2411 ✉ huntersbakery@aol.com – Open 8.30am-5.30pm Mon-Sat)

Butcher & Deli

● Norman Hunter & Son

Ian Hunter is a butcher who is comfortable quoting great thinkers like John Ruskin in his shop, and anyone who values the wisdom of Ruskin is our sort of butcher. Hunter's is a great store, with good foods everywhichway and superlative meats. (Ian Hunter, 53-55 Main Street ☎ 028-7776 2665 ✉ normanhunterandson@yahoo.co.uk – Open 9am-5.30pm Mon-Sat)

Farm Shop

● Keady Mountain Farm

The Mullan family's farm has been operating for two decades now, and they are major players at the St George's market on Saturdays when their organic chickens, lamb and eggs are fantastically popular, drawing a devoted queue of food lovers who are here to get those great Limavady flavours into their cooking. The family produce beautiful foods, true tasting, even tempered, satisfying to cook with and delicious to eat and to savour. Brilliant. (Michael Mullan, Limavady ☎ 028-7776 4157 ✉ info@mullansorganicfarm.com 🖱 www.mullansorganicfarm.com)

Restaurant

● The Lime Tree

We need more cooks like Stanley Matthews. Cooks who cook with their heart, who don't jump on the latest culinary bandwagon that pulls into town, cooks who respect and understand the tradition and culture of cooking and serving good food and making customers happy. Stanley and Maria know how to do these things, and they have done them successfully and happily for many years. So, settle in for goat's cheese and caramelised onion tart, and cod with a potato and roast garlic crust, or Stanley's signature cocido, and then have pears in cider jelly, and some nice wines, and you will agree that we need more teams like Stanley and Maria. (Stanley & Maria Matthews, 60 Catherine Street, Limavady ☎ 028-7776 4300 ✉ info@limetreerest.com 🖱 www.limetreerest.com – Open from 6pm Tue-Sat)

Fish & Chips

● McNulty's Fish & Chips

There is something formidably fastidious about McNulty's. Their sense of precision, their obsessive care, makes them the Apple Computers of fish'n'chips, which means, of course, that Brian McNulty is the Steve Jobs of the world of fish'n'chips. This is no idle comparison: Mr McNulty and his team are chasing perfection – their chips must be perfect, so they must have the correct potatoes with the correct level of dry matter. Their fish must be as fresh as can be. When you get those things right, then you can chase perfection, and it's a perfection that means people drive for miles and miles to get a takeaway from the little shop. Like Steve Jobs, Brian McNulty is a tweaker, always finding ways to make things better, improving bit by bit, all the better to be the Apple of your eye. (Brian McNulty, 84 Main Street, Limavady ☎ 028-7776 2148 🖱 www.mcnultysfishandchips.com – Open 9am-11pm Mon-Sat, 4.30pm-11pm Sun)

Londonderry

Hotel

● Beech Hill Country House Hotel

Patsey O'Kane is to Northern hospitality what Myrtle Allen is to Southern hospitality: an original, a person of true conviction, a shining, modest star. What makes the Beech Hill Hotel special is simple, and utterly fundamental: everyone in the hotel over-delivers, everyone is always trying to do their best, to make sure that every detail is done right, done as well as it can be. That is the art of hotel keeping, and it is the very essence of the art we look for in the *McKennas' Guides*, and Ms O'Kane is mistress of that art and practices that art every day in her work in this beautiful, early 18th-century house. Beech Hill is two miles from Derry but, truthfully, it is a place unto itself, a palace of hospitality. Somebody should give this woman a peerage. (Patsey O'Kane, Londonderry ☎ 028-7134 9279 📪 info@beech-hill.com 🖱 www.beech-hill.com)

Brasserie

● Brown's

Ian Orr is a great chef who is fast learning how to be a great restaurateur. He has been endlessly tweaking his offer ever since he opened up in Bonds Hill, most recently adding a barbecue selection on Friday nights which has seen the punters piling in. Like the best chefs, he has judgement and taste, and he knows what works – confit belly of pork with poached rhubarb and shaved fennel; quail with creamed shallots and toasted hazelnuts; veal with saffron risotto; Lough Erne lamb with smoked champ potatoes. And even when he does push the boat out a little – as with that smoked champ, for instance, or with his original take on surf'n'turf where he puts char-grilled hake with sirloin and shaved fennel and an orange salad – it always tastes and eats just right. (Ian Orr, 1 Bonds Hill ☎ 028-7134 5180 eat@brownsrestaurant.com www.brownsrestaurant.com – Open noon-3pm, 5.30pm-late Tue-Fri & Son, Open dinner only Sat)

Café

● Café Blooms

Blooms is situated on Derry's historic walls, and in addition to nice, straight-ahead food, manager Peter McKenzie offers interesting books and music. The cooking includes a tasty breakfast offer, and then stews, soups, hot wraps, salads and even an all-day omelette. Good place. (Peter McKenzie, Verbal Arts Centre, Derry ☎ 028-7128 2720 dohertyrc@btinternet.com – Open 8am-5pm Mon-Sat)

Café

● Café del Mondo

CDM moved to the Craft Village from its original home on Shipquay Place, and offers an excellent mix of daytime café and evening restaurant, with smart cooking: potted crab and brown shrimp with chilli bread; sea trout tartare with rocket salad; duck breast with carrot purée and fondant potato; banana caramel meringues. Nice simple early bird menus are amazing value. Part of their profits go to the Seeds charity which aims to eliminate racial discriminatiom. (Eddie Kerr, The Craft Village ☎ 028-7136 6877 www.cafedelmondo.org)

Restaurant

● Custom House Restaurant

This gorgeous restaurant and wine bar looks like something straight out of central Manhattan, and its restoration has been beautifully and painstakingly achieved. Christoper Moran's menus offer an extensive tableau of dishes, sourcing fish from Greencastle, 21-day aged steaks from Antrim, and chicken from Armagh, and there are lots of tasty things: crispy hen's egg with streaky bacon and homemade brown sauce; chef's lamb plate with aubergine caviar; cod with spinach and fennel potato; Greencastle fish plate. Very stylish, very promising. (Sukhpal Kular & Christopher Moran, Custom House St, Queens Quay, Derry ☎ 028-7137 3366 www.customhouserestaurant.com)

Farm Shop

● The Full Hog Farm Shop

Joe McDermott is known locally as a producer of rare-breed pork – his meat is used in Watts & Co by Kevin Pyke – and his farm shop has artisan foods everywhere. Look out for the rare-breed sausage, made with bacon and cabbage and known as the Danny Boy. Lovely baking, great vegetables, local heroes such as Broighter Gold, and excellent service. Fab. (Joe McDermott, 114 Spencer Road, Londonderry ☎ 077-5366 1118)

Town House Accommodation

● The Merchant's House, Saddler's House

Joan Pyne is a woman in search of an authenticity, in search of an aesthetic. Her restoration work on two major Derry properties – The Saddler's House and The Merchant's House – has been followed by the restoration of the Pump House into rental apartments, and there are also the self-catering properties, Cathedral Cottage and Darcus Cottage, and a 1950's apartment block flat in the Crawford Apartment. This is valuable and important work, especially in a Province that is often fixated on the historical past, but careless about its architectural heritage. And, the breakfasts are terrific. (Joan Pyne, Saddler's House, 36 Gt James Street, Derry; Merchant House, 16 Queen Street, Derry ☎ 028-7126 9691 saddlershouse@btinternet.com www.thesaddlershouse.com)

Restaurant

● Watts & Co

Kevin Pyke is really doing something interesting here in Watts. Mr Pyke likes to coax all of the flavour he can from his ingredients, he is an earthy, rustic cook, so some dishes – ham hock crostini; smoked salmon in a jar with lemon balm mayo; scallop with foie gras and belly pork and beetroot cannelloni; organic lamb with pickled spring vegetables; 24-hour pork shoulder – have flavours that shoot down to your toes and up to the top of your head. He sources superbly, and you can sense the chef's excitement at working with great ingredients and fashioning great dishes. Watch this guy run!
(Kevin Pyke, 167 Spencer Road, Waterside, Londonderry ☎ 028-7134 6040 www.wattsandcorestaurant.com – Open noon-2.30pm Tue-Fri 5pm-9.30pm Tue-Sat)

Maghera

Butcher

● McKee's Butchers

Two handsome shops in Maghera give customers a double opportunity to source the superlative beef that comes to the shops direct from George McKee's own farm. The beef is world-class, but so are the charcuterie and deli skills evident in every aspect of Mr McKee's fastidious operation. (George McKee, 26 & 78 Main Street, Maghera ☎ 028-7964 2559 ✉ mckeespies@btopenworld.com – Open 8am-6pm Mon-Sat)

Magherafelt

Home Bakery & Café

● Ditty's Home Bakery

See the entry for Ditty's Bakery in Castledawson. (33 Rainey Street, Magherafelt ☎ 028-7963 3944 – Open 8am-5.30pm Mon-Sat)

Brasserie

● Gardiner's G2

Sean Gardiner is one of the great personalities of Northern Irish cooking, an ebullient, amusing guy with oodles of energy. He likes big tasting, generous food, and likes to roam around the culinary world, so his menus will offer Pad Thai alongside centre-cut fillet steak with Bushmills sauce and champ. Value for money is terrific, so bring a gang and have a big night out. (Sean Owens, 7 Garden Street, Magherafelt ☎ 028-7930 0333 ✉ gardiners2000@hotmail.com 🖱 www.gardiners.net – Open 5pm-9pm Wed, Thur & Sun, 5pm-10pm Fri, 5pm-10.30pm Sat, noon-3pm Sun)

Supermarket

● JC Stewart

JC Stewart's food hall is one of the best, most inspiring places to shop in Ireland. The meticulous style, design and aesthetic of the store is matched by levels of service and skill that few others can compete with. A haven for local foods from all over Ulster, they have everything that is good, from everyone who is good. If you can imagine Ardkeen from Waterford crossed with Scally's of Clonakilty with a touch of Avoca Handweavers and a bit of Fallon & Byrne, then you have JC Stewart. A true classic. (Paul Stewart, 1 Union Road, Magherafelt ☎ 028-7930 2930 ✉ www.jcstewart.co.uk – Open 8am-7pm Mon-Wed, 8am-9pm Thur & Fri, 8am-6pm Sat)

made in Ulster

Broighter Gold Rapeseed Oil

Portstewart

Bakery & Coffee Shop

● McLaughlin's

McLaughlin's is a stylish, relaxed bakery and coffee shop, a place to enjoy a coffee and a nice sweet bun, and to get some good breads and farls to take away with you. (Stewart & Robert McLaughlin, 91 The Promenade, Portstewart ☎ 028-7083 4460 ✉ stewartmclaughlin@hotmail.co.uk – Open 9.30am-5.30pm Mon-Sun)

Butcher

● JE Toms & Sons

Alan Toms is a first-class butcher, whose particular USP is his fabulous range of meats prepared for the barbecue. Alongside the barbie specialities, everything else is good. (Alan Toms, 46 The Promenade ☎ 028-7083 2869 – Open 8am-5.30pm Mon-Sat, from 7.30am Sat)

County Tyrone

Donaghmore

Gastropub

● The Brewer's House

Ciaran and Vicki are really trying something new in The Brewer's House. They are planning a microbrewery and already stock a great selection of craft beers and ciders, they have wine and food evenings with wine luminaries like Jane Boyce, and they bagged the award for best gastropub in their first year of business. Chef David Kenny is pushing the envelope for food served in an Irish bar – textures of rabbit with celeriac truffle mash; roast gurnard with risotto cake; apricot and Stilton quail Scotch egg; caramelised apple with toffee sauce and puff pastry wrappers. Tyrone has seen nothing like The Brewer's House. (Ciaran & Vicki McCausland, Donaghmore ☎ 028-8776 1932 www.thebrewershouse.com)

Dungannon

Farm Shop

● Cloughbane Farm Shop

My goodness but Cloughbane is a farm shop dynamo. When you consider how the Richardson family have built their farm shop and retail business, and you consider that it was only a decade ago that they began, their success has been phenomenal. Their beef and lamb is of exceptional quality, but it has been their ingenuity in creating a range of pies and cooked food meals, soups and salads that has been the rocket driving the business. They have won every award going, and deserve every one of them. A pioneering farm. (Lorna & Richard Robinson, 160 Tandragee Road, Dungannon ☎ 028-8775 8246 info@cloughbanefarm.com www.cloughbanefarm.com – Open 8am-6pm Mon-Fri, 8am-5pm Sat)

Guesthouse & Cookery School

● Grange Lodge

Nora Brown is a legendary figure in Northern Irish

food, and conducts cookery classes in the beautiful Grange Lodge. There is also accommodation in five rooms for guests staying overnight and having dinner, and the house can be booked for functions. (Norah & Ralph Brown, Grange Road, Dungannon ☎ 028-8778 4212 ✉ stay@grangelodgecountryhouse.com 🖱 www.grangelodgecountryhouse.com)

Farmer's Market

● Tyrone Farmers' Market

Check out the Tyrone marketeers on the first and third Saturday of each month, in the supermarket car park.

Fivemiletown

Creamery Cheese

● Fivemiletown Creamery

Fivemiletown's steady growth and development is unusual amongst Irish cheeses, in that it has on occasion expanded by taking over other cheesemaking operations – the most recent is the Causeway Cheese Company, and in the past they brought in Boilie. This technique has given them a large portfolio of cheeses, from the well-known Ballybrie, Ballyoak and Ballyblue to the O'Neill's goat's cheeses and a range of Fivemiletown cheddars. (Mervyn McCaughey, 14 Ballylurgan Road, Fivemiletown ☎ 028-8952 1209 🖱 www.fivemiletown.com)

Moygashel

Café

● Deli on the Green

The Deli has been serving tasty modern food for almost a decade now, and it's a good address for informal, friendly cooking. The Bistro is open for breakfast and lunch, and serves dinner at the weekend, when there is some thoughtful cooking from James Devine, a chef with a mighty c.v. and his own confident style – chicken supreme with bacon and leek pie; tasting plate of lamb; scallops with pork belly. (Claire Murray, 30 The Linen Green, Moygashel ☎ 028-8775 1775 ✉ delionthegreen@btconnect.com 🖱 www.delionthegreen.com – Open 8.30am-6pm Mon-Wed, 8.30am-9.30pm Thur-Sat)

Farm Shop

● Linen Green Farm Shop

Fred Bolton's beautiful, spacious store has a great selection of locally made foods, and is a vital address for Cloughbane Farm beef and lamb from Pomeroy. (Fred Bolton, 27A Linen Green, Moygashel)

Café

● The Loft

The café in The Loft is a great spot to grab something good to eat from their buffet lunch after a bout of shopping, especially a lavish cup cake or an ice cream for the kids. (Claire Murray, 10A Linen Green, Moygashel ☎ 028- 8772 9929 – Open 9.15am-5pm Mon-Sat)

Omagh

Butcher's Shop

● Mr Eatwells

Joe McMahon is a member of the Elite Guild of butchers and runs a top-class butcher's shop, with a particular specialisation in sausage making. (Joe McMahon, 16 Campsie Road ☎ 028-8224 1104 – Open 8.30am-6pm Mon-Sat)

Strabane

Restaurant

● Oysters

It's fantastic that the Oysters team bring their produce – relishes, jams, truffles, breads, vegetables and so on – to local markets and fairs, getting the word out about their creativity. Back at base chef Niall Gorham is working hard to make a reputation with food that is well-sourced, with a lot of flair and a strong eye for colour. Very promising. (Niall Gorham, 37 Patrick Street, Strabane ☎ 028-7138 2690 www.oystersrestaurant.co.uk – Open noon-5pm Mon-Sat, 5pm-7pm Mon-Fri, 5pm-9.30pm Sat, noon-4pm Sun)

Farmers' Market

● Strabane Farmers' Market

Look out for Seskinore Farm Meats and other local foods. (Last Sat of the month, Score Centre, Dock Rd – Open 9am-1.30pm)

Abbeyleix 424
Abbey Organic Cheese Co. 425
Abbot's Ale House 54
Abernethy Butter Co, 647, 648
Academy, The 632
Accommodation
- Ariel House 259
- Brook's Hotel 180
- Cliff Townhouse Hotel 186
- Pembroke Townhouse 267

Ace 606
Achill Cliff House Hotel 466
Achill Island Lamb 467
Achill Island Turbot 466
Adare 435
Adare Farm Foods 435
Adare Farm Shop 446
Adrigole 108
Against the Grain 172
Aghada 95
Ahakista 108
Ahern, Dan, Organic Chicken 99
Aherne's 106
Aillwee Cave 32
Aine Handmade Chocolates 30
Albatross Enterprise 118
Aldridge Lodge 571
Alexis Bar & Grill 296
Allenwood 395
Allo's 388
All Seasons 606
Alternative Bread Company 61
Ananda 287
Anchor Bar, The 459
An Cupan Caife 51
An Cupan Tae 375
Anderson's 243
Anderson's Creperie 243
An Dún 336
An Fear Gorta 32
Angel Foods 117
Angel Park Eatery 172
Angler's Return 357
Angus Farm Shop 649
Aniar 315
Annacotty 436
Annagassan 456
Annaghmore 626
Annahilt 638
Annalong 638
Annascaul 360
Anne Lloyd's Market Kitchen 447
Annie's Roasts 106
An Port Mor 476
Anseo 172
An Tairseach 604
An Tobairin 131
Antonio's 109
Anton's 316
Apple Bettys Café 148
Apple Farm, The 517
Approach Trade 518
Aqua 247
Aran Island Potatoes 337
Aran Islands 336
Arbutus Bread 54, 78
Arbutus Hotel 381
Arcadia, The 606
Arch Bistro 287
Arco, L' 34
Ardara 155
Ard Bia 316
Ardee 456
Ardglass 638
Ardgroom 108
Ardkeen Producers' Market 554
Ardkeen Stores 553
Ardmore 539
Ardrahan Cheese 87

Index

Ardsallagh Goat's Cheese 96, 97
Ards Brewing Co 660
Argentine
Bondiola Argentina 178
Ariel House 259
Ariosa Coffee Roasting Boutique 483, 492
Arklow Farmers' Market 583
Armagh 633
Armagh Cider Company 635
Aroma Coffee Shop 159
Arthurs, Paul 658
Arthurstown 569
Artisan 317
Aruna Sauces 456, 461
Arún Bakery 238
Ashbourne 483
Ashe's Black Pudding 360
Ashford 584
Ashlee Lodge 79
Asia Market 173
Asian Junction 129
Asian Tea House Restaurant 317
Asia Supermarket 607
Athboy 485
Athboy Stables Farmers' Market 485
Athenaeum Hotel 549
Athenry 338
Athlone (Roscommon) 504
Athlone (Westmeath) 562
Athlone Farmers' Market 562
Athy Farmers' Market 395
Atlantic Sea Kayaking 141
Atlantic Seaweed 161
Atmosphere, L' 554
Aubergine Gallery Café 453
Aughnacliffe 453
Aughrim Farmers' Market 585
Auntie May's 120
Avoca 173, 301, 304, 351, 568, 596, 607
Avoca, Belfast 607
Avoca Powerscourt Terrace Café 591
Azzurro at The Ship 547
Baccaro, Il 173
Bacus 366
Badger & Dodo 86
Bagel Bagel 607
Bagenalstown 21
Baggot Street Wines 174
Bailey's Hotel 519
Bailie's Coffee 607
Bakehouse, The 174
Baking Emporium, The 139
Bald Barista, The 174, 215
Baldwin's Ice Cream 550
Ballacolla 425
Ballickmoyler 425
Ballina (Clare) 31
Ballina (Mayo) 468
Ballinadee 125
Ballinafad 339
Ballinahown 498
Ballinasloe 340
Ballincollig 76
Ballincurrig 95
Ballineen 126
Ballingarry 437
Ballinhassig 126
Ballinkeele House 571
Ballinskelligs 360
Ballinspittle 126
Ballinterry House 93
Ballintubber Farm 97
Ballinwillin House 91
Ballivor 485
Ballon Free Range Eggs 22
Balloo House 656
Ballsbridge 259

Ballybay Farmers' Market 495
Ballybrado 517
Ballybunion 361
Ballycastle 471
Ballyclare 626
Ballyconneely 341
Ballycoolin 246
Ballycotton 95
Ballycotton Free-range Poultry 95
Ballycotton Potatoes 96
Ballycotton Seafood 61
Ballycross Apple Farm 569
Ballydehob 109
Ballyduff 540
Ballyfin 425
Ballygarvan 77
Ballyherkin 128
Ballyhoura Mountain Mushrooms 83
Ballyhubbock Home Foods 586
Ballykelly 669
Ballyknocken House 584
Ballylagan Organic Farm 626
Ballymacarbry (Tipperary) 516
Ballymacarbry (Waterford) 540
Ballymaloe Cookery School 103
Ballymaloe House 104
Ballymaloe Relish 103
Ballymaloe Shop 104
Ballymena 627
Ballyminane Mills 571
Ballymore Eustace 396
Ballymore Farm 396
Ballymore Inn 397
Ballymote 508
Ballynacally 31
Ballynahinch 639
Ballynahinch Castle 339
Ballyogan House 409
Ballypheane 77
Ballyrobert 628
Ballysax Organic Chicken 397
Ballyvaughan Farmers' Market 32
Ballyvolane House 85
Ballyvourney 83
Baltimore 128
Baltinglass 586
Banagher 498
Banbridge 639
Bandon 129
Bandon Farmers' Market 130
Bangor 640
Bang Restaurant 174
Bantry 110
Bantry Cookware Company 110
Bantry Friday Market 110
Bar 8 317
Bar Italia 175
Barking Dog, The 608
Barm Brack 526
Barnhill Apple Juice 635
Bar Pintxo 175
Barron's Bakery 541
Barry's Tea 55
Base 259, 269
Basilico 354
Batch Loaves 455
Bates 601
Bay Lough Farmhouse Cheese 521
Bay Tree Fine Food Co 395
Bay Tree, The 652
Beaches Restaurant 578
Beach House Bar & Restaurant 156
Béal Lodge Dairy Farm 388
Bear 175

Index

Beara 108
Bearna 341
Beatrice Kennedy 608
Beckett & Bull 269
Beech Hill Country House Hotel 673
Beechlawn Organic Farm 340
Beechlawn Organics 334
Beehive, The 466
Beer Club, The 288
Befani's Mediterranean Restaurant 522
Béile le Chéile 368
Belfast 606
Belfast Black 645
Belfast Cookery School 609
Belgooly 132
Bellagio 270
Belle Isle Cookery School 667
Bellingham Blue 460, 463
Bellinter House 489
Bells, SD 608
Belturbet 27
Belvelly Smokehouse 98
Bennettsbridge 406
Benoit Lorge 362
Berfranks 555
Bernard Shaw, The 176, 242, 264
Bervie 467
Beshoff's The Market 247
Bia Blasta 457
Bianconi's 259
Bibis 282
Bier Haus 55
Big Red Kitchen 493
Bijou 270
Bin No 9 300
Birr 498
Bistro One 289
Bite 176
Bite of Life 282
Blaa 541
Blackberry Café 420
Blackboard Bistro 177
Blackfield 467
Blacklion 27
Black Pig, The 260
Blackrock 78, 292, 457
Blackrock Village Farmers' Market 78
Black Sheep, The 177
Blackwater 362
Blair's Cove 119
Blair's Inn 79
Blakes of the Hollow 666
Blarney 79, 83
Blarney Woollen Mills 83
Blazing Salads Food Company 177
Blessington 586
Blindgate House 143
Bloom Brasserie 177
Bluebell Falls Goat's Cheese 31
Blueberry Tearoom 160
Blue Geranium, The 140
Boathouse, The (Kerry) 374
Boat House, The 640
Bóbós 178
Bóbós Burritos & Blues 264
Bodega! 555
Bodega, La 275
Boheme, La 556
Bombay Pantry 270
Bonane 362
Bon Appetit 253
Bon Appetit Creperie 446
Bon Crubeen, Le 178
Bondiola Argentina 178, 198
Boojum 179, 609
Boolies Farm Canteen 487
Boozeberries 647
Borris 23

Borrisokane 516
Borzalino Restaurant 460
Botanic Gardens 225
Botticelli 179
Boulabán Ice Cream 534
Boulangerie Francaise, La 257
Box Tree, The 289
Boxty 30, 431
Boxty Bakers 430
Boyle Farmers' Market 504
Boyne Valley Blue 491, 493
Bradley's 56
Brasserie Le Pont 179
Brawn and White Meat 452
Bray Farmers' Market 587
Breadcrumb, The 375
Brennan & Co 56
Bresnan and Son 56
Bresnan, Liam 81
Bretzel Bakery, The 282
Brew 56
Brewer's House, The 678
Bric Farm 368
Bricin 381
Bric's Brew Pub 368
Bridge Bar, The 389
Bridgend 155
Bridgestown 569
Bridie's General Store 411
Brigit's Garden 356
Broadway 569
Brocka-on-the-Water 528
Brogan's Butchers 485
Broighter Gold 671, 677
Brook Lane Hotel 375
Brook Lodge Inn 598
Brook's Hotel 180
Brother Hubbard 180
Brown Bear, The 402
Brown Envelope Seeds 139, 148
Browne's Deli and Café 259
Browne's Soups 538
Brown's 673
Brudair's Bakery 438
Bubble Brothers 57
Buchetto, Er 272
Buck's Head, The 648
Builin Blasta 359
Bull & Castle, The 181, 242
Bulman, The 146
Bunclody 570
Buncrana 156
Bunratty Cookery School 34
Buns Cup Cakes 238
Burdocks, Leo 207, 264
Burgundy Direct 292
Burke's Family Butchers 452
Burke's Farm Ice Cream 490, 493
Burns Butchers 390
Burns, David, Butchers 640
Burren Beef and Lamb 46
Burren Fine Food & Wine 33
Burren Free Range Pork 44
Burren Perfumery, The 35, 36
Burren Smokehouse 38, 50
Burritos & Blues 181
Burtonport 157
Bushmills 628
Bushmills Distillery, The Old 629
Bushmills Garden Centre 628
Bushmills Inn, The 628
Bushmills Whiskey 627
Butcher Grill, The 271
Butler's Pantry 260, 587, 592
Butlerstown 541
Butter 402
Buttermarket Cafe 47
Buttery Café @ Fishers 601
Buttervant 84
Byrne, Michael 261

Index

Byrne, Phelim 575
Cabot & Co 477
Cáca Milis 552
Café Anraith 61
Café Bar H 181
Cafe Conor 609
Cafe Blooms 674
Cafe del Mundo 674
Café Fresh 182
Café Gusto 57
Café Hans 519
Café Lazio 446
Cafe Le Petit Ormeau 621
Café Merlot 666
Café Mocha 415
Café Noir 440
Cafe Nosh 609, 610
Café Nutshell 577
Café Paradiso 57
Café Rua 472
Café Sol 411
Cafe Vaudeville 625
Caffe Banba 166
Caffe Cagliostro 182
Caffe di Napoli 182
Caherbeg Free-Range Pork 147
Caherdaniel Market 362
Cahermore 116
Cahersiveen Market 363
Cahir 517
Cahir Farmers' Market 517
Cajun
  Tante Zoe's 226
Cake Café, The 183
Cakes & Co 292
Cakes by James 610
Cake Stand, The 304
Callaghan's Butchers and Deli 456
Callan 406
Callan's Wine Shop 463
Calvey's Butchers 468
Calvey's Restaurant 468
Camden Kitchen 183
Campagne 411
Camphill Organic Farm Shop & Bakery 652
Campo de Fiori 588
Cappoquin 541
Caprani Off Licence 585
Carbury 397
Carey's Butchers 130
Cargoes Café and Deli 610
Carlingford Peninsula 457
Carlow 23
Carrigtwohill 96
Castlemaine 367
Carlow Brewing Company 21
Carlow Cheese 25
Carlow Farmers' Market 23
Carlow Foods Limited 25
Carnaross 485
Carndonagh 158
Carne 570
Carraig Fhada Seaweed 509, 512
Carraig na Breac Smoke house 432
Carriage House, The 648
Carrickmacross 495
Carrick-on-Shannon 430
Carrick-on-Suir 518
Carrick-on-Suir Farmers' Market 519
Carrie's Cakes 39
Carrigaholt 35
Carrigaline 79
Carrigaline Country Market 79
Carrigaline Farmhouse Cheese 79
Carrigbyrne Farmhouse Cheese 572
Carron 35

Carrowholly Cheese 477
Casa Diego 122
Cases 318
Casey's Natural Produce 565
Casey's Smokehouse 105
Cashel 519
Cashel Blue 528
Cashel Blue Cheese 527
Cassidy's 391
Castlebaldwin 508
Castlebar 471
Castlebellingham 460
Castlecomer 406
Castlecove 366
Castledawson 669
Castledermot 398
Castlefarm Shop 396
Castlegregory 366
Castlelyons 85
Castlemaine 367
Castlemartyr 97
Castlemary Farm 97
Castlemine 504
Castlemine Farm 504
Castle Murray House 163
Castle Restaurant, The 78
Castleruddery Organic Farm 590
Castletownbere 117
Castletownroche 85
Castletownshend 132
Castlewood House 369
Cava 318
Cavan 28
Cavan Farmers' Market 28
Caveau, Le 412
Caviston, A 592
Caviston's Food Emporium 299
Cayenne 610
Cellar Bar, The 184
Cellar Restaurant 184, 277
Celtic Whiskey Shop 184
Central Fish Market 110
Chakra by Jaipur 593
Chalet, The 468
Chamberlain, John 121
Chameleon 185
Chapter 40 381
Chapter One 185
Charleville 85
Chart House, The 369
Cheese Etc 431
Cheese Pantry, The 243
Chef's Shop, The 611
Cherry Tree, The 31
Cherry Blossom Bakery 471
Chez Emily 258, 483
Chez Hans 519
Chez Max 185
Chez Pierre 412
Chi 319
Chia Bia 552
China Sichuan 290
Chocolate Garden 26
Chocolate Here 39
Chocolate Shop, The 58
ChocOneill 453
Chop House, O'Brien's 549, 551
Chop House, The 242, 261
Chuck Wagon 198
Chuck Wagon, The 258
Churchtown 287
Ciao Bella Roma 186
Cill Rialaig Art Café 360
Cinnamon Alley Café 529
Cinnamon Café 238, 271
Cinnamon Cottage 82
Claire's Tearooms 343
Claire The Bakers 158
Clanconnel Brewing 633
Clandeboy Estate Yoghurt 641, 643
Clane 398
Clanwood Farm 500

Index

Claregalway 343
Claregalway Farmers' Market 343
Clare Jam Company, The 36
Claremorris 473
Clarence, The 227
Clarinbridge 343
Clarke's Fruit Farm 492
Clarke's Salmon Smokery 468
Clarke's Seafood Delicatessen 478
Claudy 669
Cleggan 344
Cleggan Seaweed Company 344
Clifden 344
Cliff House Hotel 539, 549
Cliff Townhouse Hotel, The 186
Cloghan 500
Clogheen 521
Clonakilty 133
Clonee 486
Clonegal 24
Clones 496
Clonmany 159
Clonmel Farmers' Market 522
Clonmore Goat's Cheese 85
Clontarf 233
Clontibret 496
Cloon Keen Atelier 328
Cloudberry Bakery 367
Cloughbane Farm Shop 678
Cloughjordan Community Farm 525
Cloughjordan House 525
Cloughjordan Bakery 526
Cloverhill 29
Coal Quay Market 58
Coastguard Seafoods 456
Cobblers 187
Cobh Farmers' Market 98
CoCo 610, 611
Cocoa Atelier 187
Cocoa Bean Artisan Chocolates 360
Coddle 252
Coffee Angel 187, 215
Coffee Central 59
Coffee Shop, The 154
Coffey's 611
Coleraine 670
Colinstown 563
Colleran, John E & Sons 320
Collier, Ray 247
Collooney 508
Comber 643
Comber Potatoes 647
Comeragh Mountain Lamb 550
Cong 473
Connemara Abalone 348, 356
Connemara Coast Hotel 347
Connemara Hamper, The 344
Connemara Hill Lamb 315
Connemara Smokehouse 327, 341
Connolly's Fish Company 245
Connonagh 137
Conor Cafe Bar 609
Cookie Jar, The 522
Cookie Jar Bakery 659
Cooks Academy 187
Coolanowle Country House 425
Coolattin Cheddar Cheese 602
Coolea 86
Coolea Cheese 86, 94
Cooleeney Cheese 530, 535
Coolepump Dairy 407

Coolfin Gardens Organic Bakery 498
Coolnagrower 501
Coopershill 510
Cootehill 29
Copper Hen, The 548
Copper Kettle 117
Copper & Spice 436, 440
Coppinger Row 188
Cork Butter Museum 63
Cork City Centre 54
Cork City suburbs 76
Cork Coffee Roasters 59
Corkscrew, The 188
Corleggy Farmhouse Cheese 27
Corn Dolly Home Bakery 660, 664
Corner Bakery, The 272
Cornstore 441
Cornucopia 189
Corrandulla 347
Corrylane Smoked Foods 568
Corry's Food Hall & Café 352
Corte del Caffè, La 189, 215
Cosgrove's 510
Costelloe's Malthouse 133
Cosy Cafe, The 426
Cottage, The 433
Coturnix Quail 139
Coughlan, P 61
Country Choice 446, 529
Country Kitchen Home Bakery 631
Country Market, The 248
Country Store 543
Courthouse Restaurant 495
Courthouse,The 433
Courtyard, The 122
Cowan, Cathal 455, 488
Coyle's 641
Crackbird 189
Crackpots 143
Craft Cider 637
Craigavon 633
Cramer's Grove 407
Cramer's Grove Ice Cream 407
Cratloe 36
Cratloe Hills Sheep's Cheese 36
Crawford Gallery Café 60
Crinnaghtaun Apple Juice 542
Croagh Patrick Seafoods 475
Cromane 368
Cromleach Lodge 508
Cronin's Pub & Mad Fish Restaurant 80
Crookhaven 137
Crookhaven Inn 137
Crossgar 644
Crosshaven 80
Crosshaven Farmers' Market 81
Crossogue Preserves 536
Crowe, Barry John 28
Crowe's Farm 526
Crowley's Craft Butchers 100
Crozier Blue 522
Crozier Dairy Products 520
Crumlin 282
Crunch 189, 198, 215
Crushed Grape, The 665
Cuan Guest Inn, The 663
Cucina Italiana 382
Cucina, La 441
Cuffesgrange 407
Cuinneog 472
Cuinneog Country Butter 472
Culdaff 158
Cullinan's 37

Index

Cupàn Caifè, An 51
Cupan Tae 319
Cupcake Bakery, The 319
Cupcakes By Dee 391
Curious Wines 60
Curragower Bar, The 442
Curran's Seafood & Steak Restaurant 638
Curraun Blue Trout Farm 475
Cusack, Rene 41, 442
Custom House Restaurant 674
Daisy Cottage Farm 597
Dalkey Farmers' Market 293
Dalkey Food Company 294
Da Roberta Pizzeria 357
Da Tang Noodle House 320
Da Tommaso 233
Dave's Wood-fired Pizza Co 190
Dax 190
Deane, Restaurant Michael 611
Deasy's Harbour Bar 133
Deep 248
Delgany 590
Delhi O'Deli 191
Delicious 80
Delight 321
Deli on the Green 679
Delphi Lodge 350
Denis Healy's Organic Delights 597
Derek Molloy 40
Derg Inn, The 535
Derreenaclaurig Farmhouse Cheese 390
Derrycama Farm 460
Derrygonnelly 665
Derrylin 665
Derryvilla Farm 501
Desertmartin 671
Devon Dell 321
Devour Bakery 468
Devoy's Organic Farm 147
Dexter Beef 389
Diep le Shaker 191
Dillinger's 272, 277
Dillon's Restaurant 153
Dingle 368
Dingle Brewing Company 370
Dingle Dexter Beef 370
Dingle Local Produce and Craft Market 370
Dingle Peninsula Cheese 366
Dingle Pies 363
Dingle Reel Fish & Chip Shop 370
Direct Wine Shipments 612
Ditty's Home Bakery 669, 676
Diva Boutique Bakery 126
Diva Café 127
Divilly, Martin 321
DJ's Juice & Cider 630
Doherty's Café 155
Doherty, Thomas 487
Dolce Vita, La 579
Dolphin Beach 345
Dom Mimi 233
Donaghadee Garden Centre 644
Donaghmore 678
Donard 590
Donegal 159
Donegal Farmers' Market 160
Donegal Rapeseed Oil 158, 167
Donnybrook 259
Donnybrook Fair 261, 593
Dooley's Fish and Chips 553
Doolin 36
Doonbeg 38

Doonbeg Lodge 38
Doran's on the Pier 248
Douglas 81
Douglas Farmers' Market 81
Douglas Village Foods 81
Dovinia 371
Dowey, John R, & Son 634
Downe's Bar 556
Downey, John & Son 274
Downpatrick 646
Drimoleague 138
Drimoleague Chipper 138
Drink Store 238
Drisheen 59
Drogheda 460
Dromahair 431
Dromara 647
Drombeg 154
Dromod Homemade Boxty 432
Dromore 647
Dromquinna Manor 376
Drumcollogher 438
Drumcondra 243
Drumcreehy House 33
Drummully Boxty 30
Drumshanbo 432
Duane's Fish Shop 345
Dublin 172
Dublin Cookery School, The 292
Dublin Food Co-Op 283
Dublin South 259
Dublin Wine Rooms 191
Dublin Wine School 192
Ducartes at the Hunt Museum 443
Dufferin Arms 657
Dufferin Coaching Inn 657
Dufferin Coaching Inn 657
Duinin Seafoods 391
Dunany Flour 460
Dunbrody Country House 569
Duncannon 571
Dundalk Farmers' Market 463
Dundrum 287, 526, 647, 648
Dunfanaghy 162
Dungannon 678
Dungarvan Brewing Company 543
Dungarvan Farmers' Market 544
Dungarvan Stout 555
Dunhill Castle Sparkling Spirit 546
Dunkineely 163
Dun Laoghaire Farmers' Market 296
Dunleer 465
Dunmanus Seafoods Ltd 121
Dunmanway 139
Dunmore East 547
Dunne & Crescenzi 192, 215
Dunne's of Donnybrook 262
Durcan, Tom 60
Durrus Farmhouse Cheese 118, 119
Dursey Deli 121
D'Vine 461
Eastern Seaboard Bar & Grill 461
Eatery 120 273
Eatwells, Mr 680
Écrivain, L' 193
Eddie Walsh & Sons 161
Eden 193
Egan's Ocean Fresh 256
Eight Degrees Brewing 91
Electric 61
Ella Wine Bar 249
Ely Bar & Brasserie 194
Ely Gastropub 194
Ely Wine Bar 195
Emlagh House 371

Index

Emly 527
Emma's Cafe & Deli 498
Emyvale 496
English Market 55, 58, 59, 61, 62, 66, 71, 72, 73, 74
Enjoy 352
Ennis 39
Ennis Butchers 283
Enniscorthy 571
Enniscorthy Farmers' Market 572
Ennis Farmers' Market 39
Ennis Gourmet Store 39
Enniskeane 140
Enniskerry 591
Enniskillen 666
Ennistymon Farmers' Market 42
Enoteca d'Asti 243
Enoteca delle Langhe 195
Epicurean Food Mall 195
Equinox 612
Ernie's Fish Stores 322
Errol Jenkins Butchers 626
Espresso 556
Europe Hotel, The 382
Evergreen 196
Eve's Chocolate Shop 62
Ewe Gallery 125
Ewing, Walter 613
Exchange Toffee Works 62
Exchequer, The 196, 242, 277
Eyeries 120
Fabiola's Patisserie & Café 37
Fade Street, No. 3 196, 277
Fahan 163
Fairview 233
Fairways Bar, The 530
Fairyhouse Food & Wine School 490
Fallon & Byrne 197, 198, 215
Fallon's of Kilcullen 398
Fanore 43
Farmer Brown's 197
Farmer's Gate, The 502
Farm Factory Direct 502
Farmgate, The 101
Farmgate Café 59, 62
Farmhouse Cheddar
Hegarty's Farmhouse Cheddar 94
Farmleigh House 283
Farm Shop, The 167
Farrelly's Butchers 590
Fast Al's 63
Fatted Calf, The 564
Featherbed Farm Foods 572
Feeney's Fish 288
Feirm Ur 132
Fenagh 25
Fenelon's Craft Butchers 305
Fenor 548
Fergus View 47
Fermoy 86
Fermoy Natural Cheeses 87
Ferns 573
Ferrybank 549
Fethard 527
Field and Vine 273
Field's SuperValu Supermarket 149
Filligan's Preserves 164
Fine Wines 443
Finglas 244
Finnebrogue Venison 646, 654
Finnerty, Roger & Sons 355
Firehouse, The 149
Fish at The Marina 371
Fish Cart, The 462
Fisherman, The 322
Fish Kitchen, The 111
Fish Station, The 150
Fishy Fishy Café 143
Fishy Fishy Shop 144

Fitzpatrick's Bar & Restaurant 457
Fitzsimons, JL Fish Shop 284
Fivemiletown Creamery 679
Flahavan's 549
Flahavan's Oats 543
Flanagan, A, & Son 633
Flavin, Jim 443
Flemings Fine Foods 288
Flying Cheese Brigade 447
Flynn's Kitchen 147
Foley's Bar 510
Folláin 83
Fontana 652
Food For Thought 322, 458
Food Game 262
Food Heaven 40
Food Room, The 233
Foods of Athenry 338, 355
Food Store, The 473
Foodware Store 198, 253
Foodworks 412
Forage & Find 127
Forge Craft & Coffee Shop 22
Forge, The 485
Forkhill 634
Fornaio, Il 198, 236
Forthill Farm 636
Fortview House 141
Fothergill's 273
Foxrock 289
Franciscan Well Brew Pub 63
Fraughans 599
Freddy's Bistro 443
French Paradox, The 262
French Quarter Café 538
French Table, The 444
Fresh The Good Food Market 199
Friendly Farmer, The 339
Fruit Boost 61
Fruit Hill Farm 111
Fruit'n'Nut Place 427
Fuchsia House 457
Full Hog Farm Shop 675
Full of Beans 556
Furama 263
Furbo 347
FXB 302
Gaby's 382
Gaillot & Gray 593
Galgorm Resort & Spa 629
Gallery 29 566
Gallery Cafe 348
Galley Fish and Chip Shop 638
Gallic Kitchen, The 424
Galway Bay Seafoods 332
Galway Cakery Café 353
Galway City 315
Galway City Museum 330
Galway Hooker 506
Galway Saturday Market 323
Ganges Holywood 653
Gannet Fish Pantry 323
Garden Café 371
Garden Works 253, 486
Gardiner's G2 676
Garinish 121
Garnish House 64
Garrett's Speciality Butchers 444
Gateway, The 120
Gathabawn Farmhouse Ice Cream 408
Geoff's Café Bar 557
George's Pastisserie and Delicatessen 491
German Butcher, The 383
Get Fresh 288
Ghan House 458
G Hotel 322
Gibney's Fine Wines 254
Ginesi's 639
Ginger Bistro 614

Index

Gingergirl 445
Giovanelli's 386
Glandore 141
Glasha Farmhouse 540
Glasnevin 243, 244
Glasraí & Goodies 409
Glasson 564
Glasthule 299
Glastry Farm Luxury Ice Cream 660, 661
Gleann Gabhra Goat's Cheese 494
Glebe Brethan 459, 465
Glebe Country House 125
Glebe Gardens 128
Gleeson's Artisan Food & Wine Shop 505
Gleeson's Townhouse & Manse Restaurant 506
Glenarm Organic Salmon 630
Glenealy 592
Glengormley 630
Glen House 159
Glenilen Dairy 138
Glenisk Organic Dairy 501, 503
Glenmar Shellfish 154
Glenmore Organics 540
Glen, The 142
Glenties 164
Glenveagh Tearooms 164
Global Village 371
Glór Foods 383
Glorious Sushi 557
Goatsbridge Premium Irish Trout 420
Goatstown 300
Goat Street Café 372
Golden 527
Golden Bean 105
Goldenhill Farmhouse Ice Cream 586
Gold River Farm 585
Goleen 141
Good Earth 164
Goode Life, The 583
Good Food Gallery, The 399
Good Things Café & Cookery School 119
Good World Chinese Restaurant 199, 264
Gorey Farmers' Market 574
Gorman's Clifftop House 372
Gort Farmers' Market 348
Gortnadiha Lodge 544
Gort na Nain 128
Gougane Barra Hotel 142
Gourmandises, Les 65
Gourmet Burger Bistro 64
Gourmet Burger Co 273
Gourmet Food Company 258
Gourmet Food Parlour 297
Gourmey, Le 106
Gourmet Parlour 511
Gourmet Store 413
Gourmet Tart Company 324, 359
Governor Rocks, The 645
Govindas 199
Gowran 409
Goya's 324
Graduate Restaurant 660
Graiguenamanagh 409
Granary @ Waterford Treasures Museum 557
Grange 509
Grangecon Café 587
Grange Lodge 678
Gravediggers, The 242, 244
Gravitas 46
Green 19 200
Greenacres 580
Green Acres 447

Green Apron, The 437, 447
Green Bean 463
Greencastle 165
Green Earth Organics 347
Greene's 64
Green Hen, The 200
Greenhouse, The 201
Green Man, The 162
Greenmount House 372
Greens 614
Green Saffron 98, 105, 447
Green Spot Whiskey 281
Gregan's Castle Hotel 33
Greyabbey 649
Greystones 592
Griffin's Bakery 325
Grogan's of Glasson 564
Groomsport 650
Ground Expresso Bar 627
Grove House 122
G's Gourmet Jams 424
Gubbeen Bacon 128
Gubbeen Farmhouse Cheese 123, 140
Gubbeen Smokehouse 123
Gueueleton, L' 201
Guilbaud, Restaurant Patrick 219
Gulpd @ Triskel Arts Centre 75
Gur Cake 246
Hackett's 530
Hackett's Bar 123
Hadji Bey 398, 405
Hakka Noodle 614
Hall's Market Garden 389
Halpin's Bridge Café 603
Hampton's 445
Hand-Crafted Knives 111
Hanlon's 502, 530
Hanna's Artisan Baking 576
Hanora's Cottage 540
Happy Pear, The 593
Hargadon's 511
Hargadon's Wine Shop 512
Harney's Bakery 417
Harold's Cross 282
Harrington's Bakery 376
Harrington's Post Office 108
Harrison's of Greyabbey 649
Harry's 202
Harry's Restaurant 156
Harte's Bar & Grill 400
Hart's Coffee Shop 134
Harty's Pepper Jellies 392
Harvest Fare Health Food Shop 587
Harvest Kitchen 402
Havana 202
Hawthorn House 376
Hayes' Bar 141
Healing Harvest 349
Healy's, Denis, Organic Delights 597
Healy's of Waterford 546
Heatherlea, The 641
Heaton's Guest House 373
Heaven Preserved 85
Heaven's Cake 65
Hederman, Frank 61
Heffernan's Fine Foods 469
Hegarty's Farmhouse Cheddar 94
Helen's Bay Organic Farm 650
Hellfire Pigs 306
Hemmingway's 234
Hennessy's Fine Food Store 23
Herb Garden, The 254
Herbstreet 203
Heritage, The 426
Heron Gallery and Café 108
Heron's Rest 325
Herterich's Butchers 454
Hickey's Bakery 557

Index

Hickey's Bakery & Café 523
Hick & Sons, J 298
Hick's Sausages 183, 316
Highbank Orchard Syrup 423
Highbank Organic Orchards 407
Hilden Brewing Company & Tap Room 631
Hillsborough 651
Hillside Farm 504
Hilton Park 496
Hole in the Wall 239
Holland's Fine Wines & Champagne House 589
Holywood 652
Home 615
Homegrown 661
Honest2Goodness Market 244
Honest to Goodness 198, 203
Honeypot, The 523
Hooker Brewery, The 506
Hop House, The 206
Hopsack, The 274
Hospital 439
House Café 65
House Hotel, The 325
House, The 249
Howling Gale Ale 93
Howth 247
Howth Farmer's Market 250
Hudson's 109
Hudson's Pantry 474
Hugh Maguire 483
Hugo's 203
Hungry Monk, The 594
Hunter, Norman 671
Hunter's at Kitty's of Coleraine 670
Hunter's at the Oven Door 669, 671
Huntsman Inn, The 326
Hyland's Traditional Fish & Chips 489
Iago 65
Ice House, The 470
Ice Plant, The 297
Idaho Café 66
Idlewilde Café 294
Il Pirata 622
Il Vicoletto 230
Inagh Farmhouse Cheeses 43
In A Nutshell 577
Inch House 536
Inchydoney Island Lodge & Spa 134
Indian Spice Company 594
Inishannon 142
Inish Beg 129
Inishmacsaint Brewing Company 665
Inis Meáin Restaurant and Suites 336
Inis Mór 336
Inis Oirr 337
Inistioge 410
Inn @ Ballilogue Clochán 410
Interval Bistro 306
Ireland's Mills 582
Ireland's Traditional Foods 455, 488
Irish Atlantic Sea Salt 115
Irish butter 402
Irish Farmhouse Cheese 488
Irish Organic Meats 30
Irish Piemontese Beef 428, 536
Irish Seed Savers 44
Irish Village Markets 263
Irish whiskey 100
Irvinestown 667
Isaac's 66
Iskeroon 363
Island Cottage 150

Issie's Handmade Chocolate Shop 117
Italee Caffe Italiano 67
Itsa4 263
Itsabagel 297
Ivan's of Caherdavin 445
Ivan's Oyster Bar & Grill 250
Ivyleigh House 427
Jackie Lennox Restaurant 68
Jack McCarthy 88
Jack's 386
Jack's Coastguard Restaurant 368
Jacques 67
Jaipur 204
Jam 376, 383
James Street South 615
Jamestown 433
James Whelan Butchers 524
Jam @ Hanley's 67
Jane Russell's Original Irish Sausages 400, 401
Janet's Country Fayre 597, 600
Jarrow Café 406
Jasmine Palace 446
Java Republic 246
Jay Bees 558
Jerry Kennedy 373
Jinny's Bakery 432
Jo'burger 264, 274
John David Power 545
John Dory's 616
John Hewitt, The 617
John Kavanagh 242, 244
John R's 389
June's Cake Shop 617
Juniors 264, 277
Juno's Café 198, 239, 277
Jus de Vine 255
Just Food 99
Just Nuts 67
Kai 329
Kalbo's Café 150
Kanturk 87
Kanum 204, 264
Kappa-Ya 326
Karoo Farm Shop 576
Karwig's Wines 80
Kate's Farm Shop 580
Kate's Kitchen 512
Kate's Place 354
Katie's Real Chocolate 130
Kavanagh's, WJ 205, 242
Kay O'Connell 71
KC Peaches 205, 215, 277
KC's Fish & Son & Sons 82
Keady Mountain Farm 672
Kealy's Seafood Bar 165
Kearney Blue 655
Kearney's, Tom, Family Butchers 558
Keem Bay Fish Products 468
Kells Farmers' Market 487
Kelly Kettle 482
Kelly, Michael, Shellfish 349
Kelly's Butchers 476
Kelly's Resort Hotel & Beaches Restaurant 578
Kenmare 374
Kenmare Ice Cream 377
Kenmare Select 377
Kennedy, Beatrice 609
Kennedy's 234
Kennedy's of Enniskerry 591
Keogh's Crisps 248, 255
Keogh's Model Bakery 406
Kerlogue 575
Kerry Black Puddings 377
Kerry Cow, The 394
Keshk Café 264
Kettle of Fish 326, 348
Kettyle Irish Foods 667, 668
Kilavullen Farmers' Market 88
Kilbeg Dairy Delights 487

Index

Kilbeggan 565
Kilbeggan Organic Oats 565, 567
Kilbrittain 142
Kilcolgan 349
Kilcolman Rectory 140
Kilcoole 596
Kilcornan 439
Kilcullen 398
Kilcullen's Hot Sea Water Baths 509
Kildare 400
Kilfenora 44
Kilgarvan Quay 528
Kilgraney House 21
Kilkee 44
Kilkeel 655
Kilkenny 411
Kilkenny Design Centre 414
Kilkenny Farmers' Market 414
Kilkenny Free Range 419
Kilkenny Ormonde Hotel 414
Kilkishen 46
Killaloe 46
Killaloe Farmers' Market 47
Killarney 380
Killarney Park Hotel 383
Killbeg Dairy Delights 494
Killeen Farmhouse Cheese 340
Killeigh 501
Killenard 426
Killeshandra 30
Killinchy 656
Killiney 300
Killinick 576
Killonan 440
Killorglin 385
Killowen Yogurts 573, 577
Killruddery House & Gardens 589
Killyleagh 657
Kilmacanogue 596
Kilmacow 417
Kilmacthomas 549
Kilmore Quay 576
Kilmurvey House 336
Kilnaboy 47
Kilrush 47
Kilrush Farmers' Market 48
Kilshanny Cheese 48
Kiltegan 597
Kilternan Country Market 598
Kimchi 242
Kimchi@The Hop House 206
Kinara 234
Kinara Kitchen 275
Kingdom Food & Wine 392
Kingfisher Bistro 459
Kingfisher Tea 300
Kingfisher, The 427
King Sitric 250
Kinlough 433
Kinnegar Brewing 168
Kinsale 143
Kinsale Farmers' Market 144
Kinvara 349
Kinvara Friday Market 350
Kinvara Smoked Salmon 349, 351
Kircubbin 658
Kish Fish 239
Kitchen Complements 206
Kitchen in the Castle 251
Knife Craft 111
Knockalara Cheese 542
Knockanore Cheese 550
Knockara Pates 527
Knockatee Dairy 393
Knockatullera Farm 92
Knockdrinna Farmhouse Cheese 419

Knockdrinna Farm Shop 419
Knockdrinna Kilree Goat's Cheese 407
Knockeven House 99
Knocknarea Honey 509
Knockranny House Hotel 478
Knott's Cake & Coffee Shop 661
Knox's Food Court 635
Koh 206
Koi 653
Konkan 284
Kooky Dough 240
Korean
Kimchi@The Hop House 206
Krawczyk's West Cork Charcuterie 124
Kylemore Acres 340
Kylemore Acres Herb Mixes 324
Kylemore Farm produce 421
Ladysbridge 99
Lahinch 48
La Marine 579
Lancaster Lodge 68
Landon, Stephen 61
Lange, Penny & Udo 598
L'Arco 34
Larkin's Bar & Restaurant 531
L'Atmosphere 554
L'Attitude 51 54
Lavistown Farmhouse 417
Lavistown Farmhouse Cheese 419
Lawlor's Butchers 275
Laytown 489
Le Caveau 412
L'Écrivain 193
Leenane 350
Left Bank Bistro 562
Leggygowan Farm 663
Leighlinbridge 25
Le Levain 207
Lemon Leaf Café, The 144
Lemon Tree, The 547
Lemybrien 551
Lennon's @ VISUAL 24
Lennox Café 206, 277
Lennox, C.F. 77
Leo Burdocks 207
Leopardstown Farmers' Market 301
Leslie's Bakery 666
Leslie's Diner 151
Le Tire Bouchon 580
Lettercollum Kitchen Project Shop 134
Letterfrack 351
Letterkenny 165
Levain, Le 207
Le Voyage 152
L'Gueuleton 201
Liberties 282
Liberty Grill 68
Lilliput Loaf Company 566
Lilliput Stores 240
Lily Mai's Café 527
Limavady 671
Limerick City 440
Limerick Milk Market 446
Lime Tree, The 672
Linen Green Farm Shop 680
Linnalla Ice Cream 52
Linsfort Castle 157
Lisanley Honey 98
Lisbane 658
Lisbellaw 667
Lisburn 630
Liscannor 49
Lisdoonvarna 50
Lisloughrey Lodge 473
Lismore 550
Lisnaskea 668

Index

Liss Ard Estate 151
Liston's 207
Listowel 389
Listowel Farmers' Market 389
Little Apple Co, The 418
Little Cheese Shop, The 373
Little Jerusalem 264, 276
Little Wing 617
Llewellyn's Orchard Produce 237, 252
Lobster Pot Seafood Bar 570
Lobster Pot, The 265
Locks Brasserie 284
L'Officina 400
Loft, The 680
Lolly & Cooks 208
Londonderry 673
Long Dock, The 35
Longford 453
Longford Farmers' Market 454
Long Room at Doonbeg Lodge 38
Long's Fish Restaurant 618
Longueville House 89
Long Walk Market 316
Loop de Loop 117
Lordan's Family Butcher 127
Lorragh 529
Lorum Old Rectory 22
L'Osteria da Roberta 358
Lotide Fine Foods 479
Lotide Sausages 481
Lough Bishop House 563
Lough Boora Farm 500
Lough Derg Chocolates 531
Lough Inagh Lodge 356
Lough Owel Organic Farm 566
Loughrea 352
Louie's 208
Louis Albrouze 265
Louisburgh 474
Lou Lou Bakery 265
Love and Death Inc 618
Love Fish 96
Lovely Food Company 276, 277
Lovin' Catering 285
Luceys The Good Food Shop 90
Lurgan 634
Lusk 252
Lyon's Café 512
MacIvor's Cider Co 636
Mackesy's, Billy 81
MacNean Restaurant 27
Macreddin 598
Macreddin Village Organic Market 599
Macroom 89
Macroom Oatmeal 89
Mac's Armagh Cider 634
Maddybenny Farmhouse 632
Mad Fish Restaurant 80
Mad Hatter Cafe 398
Madina Desi Curry Co 209
Maghera 676
Magherafelt 676
Magnetti Pasta 343
Mag's Home Baking 532
Maguire, Hugh 483
Maher's Coffee 69, 72
Mahon Point Farmers' Market 69
Maison, La 209
M & L 209
Malahide Farmers' Market 254
Malin Head 166
Mallow 89
Malmaison 618
Malone Fruit Farm 22
Maloney's Meat Centre 130
Malt House, The 327

Malton, The 384
Man Friday 145
Manifesto 276
Manning's Emporium 112
Man of Aran Fudge 485
Mantraa 210
Marble City Bar & Tea Rooms 415
Marine, La 579
Market Butcher, The 305
Market Kithcen 470
Markets, The 384
Market Street Restaurant 553
Market Yard Farmers' Market 430
Marlagh Lodge 627
Marlene's Chocolate Haven 479
Maughnasily Organic Farm 112
Martine's Quay Street Wine Bar 329
Martin, William 61
Mary Ann's 132
Mary-Kathryn's Deli 401
Mary's Bakery 470
Mash Direct 644
Massimo 327
Matz at the G 322
Max's Wine Bar 145
Maxwell's Restaurant 329
Mayfield & Mayfield @ Union Square 277
Maynooth 401
McAteer's The Food Hall 464
McCabe, Cllive, & Co 588
McCabe's Wines 292
McCambridge's 330
McCarthy, Jack 88
McCarthy's Bar 118
McCarthy's Black Pudding 92
McCartney's of Moira 659
McCormack, Kate & Sons 479
McCreery's, Thomas, Butchers 618
McDonagh's Seafood House 330
McEvoy's Farm Shop 465
McGeough's Butchers 355
McGeough's Smoked Sausages 330
McGettigan's Butchers 160
McGettigan's Sausages 166
McGrath, Michael 550
McGrory's 158
McHugh's Off Licence 237
McHugh's Wine & Dine 237
McKee's Butchers 676
McKee's Farm Shop 662
McKeown's Fish Shop 642
McLaughlin's 677
McMahon, Owen, Butchers 618
McMenamin's Townhouse 581
McNally Family Farm 254
McNulty's Fish & Chips 672
M&D Bakery 559
Meadowsweet Apiaries & Farm Shop 498
Mealagulla Orchard 93
Meat Centre, The 61
Mella's Fudge 135, 136
Merchant Hotel 619
Merchant's House, The 675
Mere Zou, La 210
Merrion Hotel, The 211
Merrion Inn, The 242, 266
Messrs Maguire 211
Metalman Brewing 558
Metalman Pale Ale 544
Michael's Food & Wine 303
Michie Sushi 277

Index

Mic's Chilli 596
Midleton 99
Midleton Farmers' Market 101
Mileeven 418
Milk Market 446
Mill Cove Gallery 117
Milleens Farmhouse Cheese 120, 133
Milligan, S&P 638
Mill Restaurant, The 162
Milltown Organic Market 389
Milltown Organic Store 390
Mill Wine Cellar 401
Miss Courtney's 382
Miss Katie's Tea Rooms 84
Miss Marples Tea Rooms 447
Missy Moo's Ice Cream 403, 404
Mitchel House 537
Mitchell's 345
Mitchell & Son 211
Mitchelstown 91
M&L 209
Moiled Beef 620
Moira 659
Mojo Coffee 603
Molloy, Derek 40
Molloy's Bakery 507
Molloy's of Donnybrook 266
Molloy & Son, Jack 559
Molly's Yard 619
Moloughney's 235
Monart 573
Monkstown 301
Monty's of Kathmandu 212
Moorfield Lodge 167
Moorings, The 390
Moran's Oyster Cottage 349
Morgan, Johnny 464
Morrissey's Pub 38
Mortell's 448
Morton's 198, 278
Morton's of Galway 358
Moss Brook Farm Shoppe 671
Mosse's Apple Juice 408
Mossfield Organic Farm 499, 502
Mount Callan Cheddar 42
Mountcharles 166
Mount Juliet 421
Mount Merrion 303
Mountrath 426
Mount Shannon 51
Mount Usher Avoca Garden Café 585
Mount Vernon 52
Mourne Seafood Bar 619, 649
Moville 167
Moycullen 352
Moycullen Farmers' Market 353
Moygashel 679
Moy House 48
Mr Bell's 55
Mr Eatwells 680
Mulberry Garden 266
Mulberry Meadow Farm 496
Mullicháin Café 26
Mulligan, L Grocer 240, 242
Mullingar 565
Mullingar Farmers' Market 566
Mulranny Park Hotel 474
Multyfarnham 568
Murphy, Billy 559
Murphy Blacks 44
Murphy, Frank 101
Murphy, Laz 26
Murphy's Ice Cream 373, 383, 384
Murrevagh Honey 479
Musashi 212

Mushroom Man, The 447
Mustard Seed, The 438
Naas 402
Naas Farmers' Market 403
Nadura Organic Breads 363
Nancy's Bar 155
Nash 19 70
Natasha's Living Foods 192, 241
Natural Foods Bakery 70, 78
Nature's Bounty 439
Nature's Gold 594
Naul 254
Navan 489
Nectar Wines 290
Neill's Hill 620
Nelly's 285
Nenagh 529
Nenagh Farmers' Market 532
Neon Asian Street Food 212
Newbarn Farm 484
Newbridge 405
Newcastle 304, 659
Newcastle West 452
Newcastle, Wicklow 600
Newforge House 632, 633, 634
Newmarket 92
New Millennium 213
Newport 475
Newport House 476
New Quay 52
New Ross Farmers' Market 577
Newry 660
Newtownards 660
Newtown House 107
Newtownmountkennedy 601
Nicholson, James, Wine Merchants 644
Nick's Fish 405, 484
Nick's Restaurant 387
Nick's Warehouse 620
Nick's Wines 621
Nicky Mosse Pottery 406
Nicky's Plaice 251
Nimmo's 316
No 6 Restaurant 666
No. 32 464
No. 35 378
Nóirín's Bakehouse 573
Nolan's 235, 399
Nook, The 338
Noonan, K Pork & Bacon 61
Normandy Ireland 124
North Cork 83
North Cork Milk 84
North Dublin 233
Northern Ireland 606
North Strand 233
North Wicklow Country Market 600
Nosh 277
Nourish 415
Nouveau Wines 650
Nubo 583
Nude Food 544
No 6 Restaurant 666
Number Five Bistro 364
Number FortyOne 198
Nuremore Hotel 495
Oakley Fayre Café & Bakery 646
Oak Room, The 28
Oar House, The 251
Oarsman, The 430
Oats 561
O'Brien Chop House 549, 551
O'Brien's Chop House 549
O'Brien's Farm Shop 518
O'Brien's, M 268
O'Callaghan's 92
O'Callaghan-Walshe 148
Ocean Path 252
Ochos 278

Index

O'Conaill Chocolates 70
O'Connell, Aaron 392
O'Connell, Rory 96
O'Connell's 267
O'Connell's Butchers 448
O'Connell's Ducks and Poultry 361
O'Connor's, Pat, Butchers 448
O'Connor's Seafood Restaurant 112
O Crualaoi Butchers 87
O'Crualaoi, Michael 76
O'Doherty's 666
O'Donnells Crisps 523
O'Donoghue's Bakery 503
O'Dowd's Seafood Bar & Restaurant 357
O'Driscoll's Fish 124
O'Dwyer, Una Fine Foods 520
Offbeat Bottling Company 642
Officina, L' 289, 400
Off The Square 346
O'Flynn's 71
O'Flynn's Butcher's 559
O'Flynn's Gourmet Sausage Grill 72
O'Grady's on the Pier 341
O'Hara's Stout 22, 34, 38, 72, 91, 577, 586
O'Hare's, PJ 459
OH Co Organic Herb Company 603
O'Kane Meats 669
O'Keeffe's Artisan Food Store 72
Old Barracks, The 338
Old Convent, The 521
Olde Castle Bar & Restaurant 160
Olde Post Inn 29
Old Farm Pork 529, 533
Old Ground Hotel, The 41
Old MacDonnell's Farm 590
Old Millbank Smokehouse 84
Old Mill Stores 137
Old Post Office Café 658
Old Schoolhouse, The 643
Oldtown 255
Oldtown Hill Farmhouse Bakery 422
O'Leary's 29
Olio & Farina 330, 448
Olive 256
Olive Branch, The 135
Olive Grove, The 562
O'Lochlainn's Bar 34
O'Loughlin, Michael 449
Omagh 680
O'Mahony's Butchers 71
Omega Beef Direct 516
O'Neill Foods 574
O'Neill's Bar 364
101 Talbot 213
161 Café & Bistro 279
One Pery Square 449
One Pico 213
On the Grapevine 294
On The Pig's Back 73, 82
On The Wild Side 367
OOOOBY Store 592
Open Sesame 41
Oranmore Farmers' Market 354
Orchard Cottage Dairy 126
Orchard Restaurant 530
Oregano 628
O'Reilly, A & Sons 73
O'Reilly & Sons 59
Organic Centre, The 434
Organic College & Market 438
Organic Garden & Paradise Garden 74

Organic Herb Company, The 603
Organico 113
Organico Café 113
Organic Store, The 499
Organic Supermarket, The 293
Orr's 654
Oscar's 331, 566
Oslo 358
Oslo Bay Ale 340
Ósta Café & Wine Bar 513
O'Sullivan, Deirdre and Norman 397
O'Sullivan's Bar 137
O'Sullivan's Sneem Black Pudding 391
O'Toole's Butchers 280
Oughterard 355
Out of the Blue 245, 374
Ouzos 294
Ovens 93
Oyster Bar, The 621
Oystercatcher Bistro, The 459
Oysters 680
Pablo Picante 214
Packies 378
Paddy's O'Granola 427
Palma, La, on the Mall 559
Pandora Bell 440
Panem 214
Panorama, Il Café 250
Pantry and Corkscrew 480
Pantry Shop & Bakery 45
Pantry, The 102, 532
Pantry, The 378
Paradise Creperie 124
Paris Bakery 214
Park Hotel, The 378
Park Lodge Café 560
Parson's Nose, The 651
Partridge's 574
Patisserie Régale Cookies of Character 139
Pat Mulcahy Knives 111
Paulie's Pizza 264
Pavilion, The 77
Pawle, Mary, Wines 379
Pay As You Please Restaurant 385
Pearl Brasserie 215
Peg's Shop 108
Pembroke Town House 267
Peploe's 216
Peppermill, The 532
Peppermint Farm 114
Pepper Pot, The 216
Petit Delice, Le (Galway) 331
Petit Delice (Kerry) 364
Pheasant's Hill Guesthouse 646, 647
Phelim Byrne 575
Philip Dreaper 501
Phoenix Café 286
Phoenix, The 367
Pichet 216
Pickled In Dingle 392
Picnic 657
Piemontese Beef 428
Pier 36 645
Pier House 145
Pig & Heifer 198, 217
Pig's Ear, The 217
Pigs on the Green 503
Piltown 418
Pine Grove Farm 541
Pink Ginger 267
Pinocchio 279
Pins Bakery, The 342
Piog Pies 374, 447
Pit Stop, The 655
Pizza Base 114
Pizza da Piero 279, 305
Pizza Dozzina 342
Pizzeria, La 462

Index

Plan B 241
Plough Inn, The 651
Poacher's Inn, The 130
Point Seafood Bar, The 364
Polke's 471
Polonia Food Market 447
Ponaire Coffee 436, 437, 447
Porcetto, Il 352
Pork and Bacon 531
Portadown 635
Portaferry 662
Portarlington 501
Porterhouse Brewing Co 218, 231
Port House, The 218
Portlaoise 427
Portlaw 552
Portmagee 389
Portmarnock 255
Portabello 282
Portrush 632
Portstewart 677
Potted Hen, The 621
Potter's Hand, The 48
Power, John David 545
Powersfield House 545
Pretty Mary's 659
Primacy Food Village 642
Probus Wines 355
Providence Market Kitchen 331, 344
Prue & Simon's 499
Purty Kitchen, The 302
Punjab Balti 280
Purple Heather, The 379
QC's 365
Quail, MA 639
Quality Sea Vegetables 157, 161
Quarrymount Free-Range Meats 501
Quay Co-Op 74
Quay Cottage 480
Quay Food Co 146
Quay House 346
Quealy's Café Bar 545
Queen of Tarts 219
Quigley's 533
Quilty 53
Quinlan's Kerry Fish 365
Quinlan's Seafood Bar 385
Quintessential Wines 464
Rachel's Garden Café 25
Ragazzi 294
Raheny 236
Rambling Rose Restaurant 643
Ramelton 167
Ramore Restaurants 632
Ranelagh 269
Rapeseed Oil 409
Raphoe 167
Rasam 299
Rathcoole 304
Rathcormac 93
Rathdowney 428
Rathdrum 601
Rathfarnham 287
Rathgar 269
Rathlee 509
Rathmines 269
Rathmullan House 168
Rathowen 568
Ratoath 490
Rayanne House 654
Ray's Pizza 219
Real Gourmet Burger 298
Real Italian Foodies 442
Real Olive Co 447
Real Olive Company 74
Recess 356
Red Bank House 256
Red Door, The 163
Red Island Wines 257
Redmond's of Ranelagh 280
Red Nose Wine 524

Red Stables Food Market 235
René Cusack 41, 442, 447
Renvyle House Hotel 351
Restaurant 23 664
Restaurant Ten Fourteen 236
Restaurant Victoria 622
Rhubarb 623
Rialto 282
Richmond House 542
Richy's Bar & Bistro 135
Rigby's Deli 268
Rigney's Farmhouse Bed and Breakfast 439
Ring of Kerry Quality Lamb 365
Rinuccini 415
Ristretto 639
River Bistro, The 449
River House, The 518
River Lane Café 126
Riverside Café 151
Riverstick 147
Riverstown 510
Roadford House 37
Roadside Tavern 50
Roaring Water Wholefood Shop 125
Robinson, Eddie & Caroline 131
Rochestown 82
Rocket & Relish 623
Roger Finnerty & Sons 355
Rohu's Country Market 142
Rolf's Country House 129
Roly's Bistro 268
Rory Conner Knives 111
Roscahill 356
Roscommon 505
Roscommon Lamb 505
Roscrea 534
Rose Cottage Farm 447
Rosie's Farmshop 524
Rosleague Manor 352
Rossaveal 356
Rosscarbery 147
Rossinver 434
Rosslare 578
Rossmore Farmhouse Ice Cream 428
Ross, The 385
Rotana Cafe 220
Rothar Bicycle Café 232
Roundstone 357
Roundwood 602
Roundwood House 426
Roundwood Inn, The 602
Rowe, Tim 113
Rowe, Tim, Rose Hives 114
Royal Villa 354, 358
Rua 472
Rupert's Farm 98
Russell & Donnelly 666
Russell Gallery 53
Rustic Stone 220
Ryan's Bar 490
Ryan's Farm 488
Ryeland House 408
Saba 221
Sabai 560
Sabores de Mexico 221
Saddler's House, The 675
Sadlier, John 450
Sagaar 264
Sage 102, 480
Sage Café, The 450
Saintfield 663
Sallymills Artisan Cakes & Desserts 447, 450
Salthill 357
Salt House 332
Saltmills 579
Sandwich Stall, The 61
Sandyford 289
Sandymount 259
San Lorenzo's 221

Index

Saoirse Goat's Cheese 115
Savoy Hotel, The 450
Sawyer's Deli 623
Scally's Supervalu 136
Scannell, Willie 96
Scattery Island 40
Scholars Townhouse Hotel 462
Schull 108, 122
Schull Market 125
Scullery, The 534
SD Bells 608
Seafood Centre @ Galway Bay Seafoods 332
Seagrass 222
Sea Lyons Seafood Sales 35
Sea Mist House 346
Sean MacD's 286
Seapoint Fish & Grill 302
Searson's 303
Seasons Bistro 428
Sea View House Hotel 114
Second Nature Oils 423
Secret Garden, The 92
Select Stores 295
7 Cross Street 320
777 222
Seven Social 241
Sexton, Regina 455, 488
Seymour, Michael 516
Seymour's of Cork 131
Shanagarry 103
Shanahan's 223
Sha Roe Bistro 24
Sheedy's 51
Sheep's Head 108
Shelburne Lodge 379
Shells 515
Shellumsrath 419
Sheridan's Cheesemongers 223, 333, 486
Sheridan's Winebar 332
Shop Easi 286
Shortis Wong 416
Shu 623
Sichuan House 223, 264
Silk Road Café 224
Silver Apple, The 513
Silver Fox, The 576
Silverhill Ducks 496
Silver Hill Foods 496
Simon's Place 198, 224
Simple Simon Natural Foods 161
64 Wine 300
Skeaghanore Ducks 109, 112
Skelligs Chocolate Company 361, 367
Skerries 256
Skibbereen 148
Skibbereen Saturday Market 151
Skinflint 225
Slane 491
Slane Food Circle 491
Slice of Heaven 416
Sligo 510
Sligo Farmers' Market 514
Slipway, The 129
Smithfield 238
Smokehouse, The 385
Sneem 390
Snug, The 115
Sober Lane 74
Sody Farls 614
Solaris Botanicals 333
Sol Bistro 421
Sol Oriens 426
Sol Rio 481
Sol y Sombra 387
Sonairte National Ecology Centre 489
Soup Dragon 225
Source 514
South Aran Guesthouse & Restaurant 337

South County Dublin 292
Sowan's Organic 429
Spanish Point Sea Vegetables 53
Spa Seafoods 393
Speak Easy Cafe Bar 190
Spearman, The 520
Spiced Beef 73
Spiddal 359
Spillane's Seafood 386
Spinnaker Bar, The 548
Springfort Hall 90
Square Bistro 631
Stable Diet Foods 576, 581
Stamullen 492
Star Anise 75
Starfish Café and Bistro 162
Steak Shop, The 595
Steam 347
Stella Maris (Mayo)471
Stella Maris (Clare) 45
Stepaside 289
Step House Hotel 23
Stewarts, JC 676
St George's Market 613
Still 624
Stillorgan 305
St Mullins 26
Stockwell Artisan Foods 462
Stone Age Pigs 584
Stonewell Cider 146
Stoneybatter 238
Stoneyford 419
Stoop Your Head 242, 257
Store Rooms, The 599
Strabane 680
Strabane Farmers' Market 680
Stradbally 428
Stradbally Country Market 429
Stradone 30
Strandhill 515
Strand Hotel, The 451
Strand, The (Clare) 45
Strangford 663
Strawberry Field, The 362
Strudel Bistro 650
Stuffed Olive, The 115
Sugar and Spice 570
Suki Tea 624
Sullivan's Traditional Irish Ginger Beer 24
Summerhouse, The 551
Sundaes Ice Cream Parlour 361
Sunflower Bakery 46
Superfruit 61
Supervalu Mount Merrion 303
Sushi King 226
Sussex, The 268
Sweaty Betty 318
Sweeney's Wine Merchants 246
Sweetbank Farm 600
Sweet Creations 502
Sweetie Pies 333
Swords 257
Synnott's 601
Tallaght 306
Tandragee 636
Tankardstown House 492
Tannery, The 545, 549
Tannery Townhouse & Cookery School 546
Tante Zoe's 226
Tap Room 631
Tara 493
Taste 118
Taste A Memory 94
Tastefully Yours 547
Taste of Days Gone By 475
Taste of Emilia 215, 226
Tasty Treats 518
Tattie Hoaker 507

Index

Taverna Armento, La 599
Tea Room, The 227
Ted Browne's Crab Meat 362, 369
Tedfords 624
Temple Bar Market 215, 227
Temple House 508
Templemore 534
Ten Thousand 228
Terenure 269
Termonfeckin 465
Terra Madre 228
Terroirs 269
Terryglass 535
Thai House 295
Third Floor Espresso 215, 228
Thomas's Delicatessen 291
Thomastown 420
Thomas Walshe Butchers 152
Thompson's Butchers 630
Thornhill Ducks 28
Thornton's 229
Three Q's, The 595
Thurles 535
Thurles Farmers' Market 537
Thyme 563
Thyme Out 295
Tickety-Moo Ice Cream 667
Tide Full Inn, The 350
Timoleague 153
Tinnock Farm Produce 577
Tipperary Apples 537
Tipperary Kitchen, The 538
Tipperary Town 538
Tire Bouchon, Le 580
Tir na nOg 514
Toby's Cider 626
Toddies @ The Bulman 146
Toffoli 229
Toirtin @ River Lane Café 126
Toms, JE, & Sons 677
Toonsbridge Dairy 89
Toonsbridge Mozzarella 91
Torc Café and Food Hall 454
Tormey, CR & Sons 333, 567
Tormey's Butchers 503
Tormey & Sons, CR 567
Town Hall Café, The 41
Trader's Coffee House 490
Traders Coffee House 462
Trail Kilkenny 418
Tralee 390
Tralee Farmers' Market 393
Tramore 552
Treat Deli & Gift Shop 242
Tribeca 280
Triskel Farmhouse Cheeses 552
Triskel Arts Centre 75
Trouble Brewing 395
Truffle Fairy 422
Truffle Pig Fine Foods 380
Tuamgraney 53
Tullamore 502
Tullaroan 422
Tullow 26, 602
Tulsi 334
Tuosist 393
Twelve, The 342
Twisted Hop 630
Twisted Pepper 228
Twomey, Edward 136
Twomey's Bakery 439
Tyrone Farmers' Market 679
Tyrrell & Co 404
UL Market 451
Uluru Bistro 633
Ummera Smokehouse 153
Una O'Dwyer 520
Úna's Pies 77
Unglert's Bakery 42
Union Hall 154
Urban Picnic 230

Urlingford 423
URRU 132
Valentia 394
Valentia Island Farmhouse Dairy 393, 394
Valentino, Il 230
Vanilla Grape 380
Vanilla Pod Restaurant 488
Vasco 43
Vaughan Lodge 49
Vaughan's Anchor Inn 49
VDC@home 404
Vie de Chateaux, La 403
Vicoletto, Il 230
Vicolo, Il 334
Viewmount House 454
Village Food Fare, The 508
Village Greengrocer & Foodhall 97
Village Grocer & The Gateway 120
Village Tavern, The 166
Vina Mara 335
Vineyard, The 625
Vintry, The 281
VISUAL 24
Voilà 231
Volcano Pizzas 95
Voyage, Le 152
Wa Café 335
Wall & Keogh 231
Walsh, Eddie & Sons 161
Walshe, Thomas Butchers 152
Ward, The 258
Warrenpoint 664
Waterfall Farm Shop 591
Waterford 553
Waterford Blaa 541
Waterford Castle 560
Waterford Crystal Visitors Centre 561
Waterford Treasures 557
Watergrasshill 94
Watermargin, The 670
Watatermill Restaurant 668
Watts & Co 675
Waterside 410
Weafer & Cooper 300
Wee Buns 656
Weir's Bar & Restaurant 568
Well & Good 102
West Clare Artisan Bread 45
West Cork Gourmet Store 110
West Cork Hotel 152
West Cork Sea Urchins 121
Westcove Farmhouse Shop 366
West End Café 155
Westport 476
Westport Country Market 481
Westport Food & Craft Market 481
Westport Plaza Hotel 482
West Waterford Weekend 549
Wexford 579
Wexford Farmers' Market 581
Wharton's 380
Whelan, James, Butchers 524
Whelan, Suzie & Patrick 579
Whitechurch 94
White Gables 353
White Gypsy Brewery 534
White Horse Inn, The 663
White Horses 539
White Pudding 575
White's 637
White Sage 435
White Tea 298
Whitewater Brewing 655
Whole Hoggs, The 492
Wicklow 603

Index

Wicklow Farmhouse Cheese 584
Wicklow Wine Co 604
Wild About 575
Wilde's Chocolates 53
Wild Garlic Bistro 380
Wild Geese, The 436
Wild Goose Grill 281
Wild Honey Inn 51
Wild Irish Game Ltd 602
Wild Onion Bakeshop 451
Wild Orchard 439
Wildside Catering 105
Wildside, The 447
Wildways 75
Willie Pa's 116
Willow Garden Tea Room 670
Wilma's Killorglin Farmhouse Cheese 387
Winding Stair 232
Windsor Bakery 640
Wine Academy Ireland 422
Wine Buff, The 42, 76, 165, 452, 514, 525
Wine Centre,The 416
Wineport Lodge 564
Wines Direct 567
Wine Store, The 404
Wok About 116
Woodberry's, Thomas 335
Woodcock Smokery 133, 153
Woodford, The 76
Woodside Farm 95
Woodstock Café 242
World Wide Wines 561
Wright's of Marino 236
Yard, The 654
Yawl Bay Seafoods 107
Yellow Door Deli & Patisserie 636
Yellow Door, The 625, 632
Yellowman 629
Yoletown 581
Youghal 106
Zanna Cookhouse 569
Zest Café 388, 398
Zuni 417